International acclaim for *Memory o*

"This is an epic book that will destroy your ... ...
Dorfman

"To publish Eduardo Galeano is to publish the enemy: the enemy of lies, indifference, above all, of forgetfulness. Thanks to him our crimes will be remembered. His tenderness is devastating, his truthfulness furious" John Berger

"A masterpiece of artistic collation – original and inspiring, Eduardo Galeano is one of the most interesting of the South American writers" Alan Sillitoe

"To read Genesis . . . is to walk into a blinding mosaic of gold, lust, slavery, more lust, and always the lust for power" *The Guardian*

"The imagery of heaven and hell – of paradise found and lost – courses through Memory of Fire: Genesis . . . a fantastic assemblage of historical data, anthropology, poetry and folklore" *The Sunday Times*

"A dazzling originality is at work in Memory of Fire . . . this is an intriguing and richly absorbing book, put together like pieces of a mosaic to reflect a grand and tragic picture of greed, cruelty conquest and war" *Sunday Telegraph*

"Fascinating, instructive . . . compelling, apparently exhaustively researched . . . lyrical, startling and sometimes enchanting . . . The whole fictional agglomeration . . . is immensely interesting" *The Times*

"Galeano's style is lyrical and smooth . . . his technique is to bring us to the threshold of historical experience evoked in an episode, a scene, a portrait or a dialogue, and hold us there as blinking witness" *New Statesman*

About the Author

The author was born in Montevideo, Uruguay, in 1940. His full
name is Eduardo Hughes Galeano. He entered journalism as a
political caricaturist for the socialist weekly *El Sol*, signing himself
"Gius," the nearest approximation to the Spanish pronunciation of
his paternal surname. Later he was an editor of the weekly
Marcha, and he edited the daily *Epoca* and various Montevideo
weeklies. In 1973 he went into exile in Argentina, where he
founded and edited the magazine *Crisis*. He lived in Spain from
1976 to 1984, but has now returned to Uruguay.

Among his books, *Open Veins of Latin America* (1971), *Days
and Nights of Love and War* (1978), and the first two volumes of
this trilogy: *Genesis* (1982) and *Faces and Masks* (1984), have been
published in English, and both *Days and Nights* and *The Song of
Ourselves* (a novel, 1975) have won the Cuban Casa de las Américas prizes.

About the Translator

Born in London in 1904, Cedric Belfrage came to the U.S. in 1925
and began writing about movies in Hollywood. He was a co-
founder of the *National Guardian* in 1948 and its editor until 1955,
when a brush with McCarthy led to his deportation. He has written
ten books and novels, published in this country, including *Away
from It All*, *Abide with Me*, *My Master Columbus*, and *The American Inquisition, 1945–1960*. He lives with his wife, Mary, in Cuernavaca, Mexico.

MEMORY of FIRE

EDUARDO GALEANO

Translated by Cedric Belfrage

QUARTET BOOKS

First published in Great Britain by
Quartet Books Limited as three volumes in 1985, 1987 and 1989

First published in a single volume in 1995
by Quartet Books

A member of the Namara Group
27 Goodge Street
London W1P 1FD

Translation Copyright © 1985, 1987 & 1988 by Cedric Belfrage

This edition published by arrangement with
Pantheon Books, a division of Random House
Inc. New York

Originally published in Spain
by Siglo Veintiuno de España Editores
S.A. Copyright © by Siglo Veintiuno Editores S.A.;
copyright © 1982, 1984 & 1986 by Eduardo Galeano

A catalogue record for this title is available from the British Library

Text design by Marsha Cohen

Printed and bound in Finland by WSOY

Memory of Fire

A Trilogy

I
Genesis

II
Faces and Masks

III
Century of the Wind

Genesis

Contents

Old New World 61

10 Contents

Preface

I was a wretched history student. History classes were like visits to the waxworks or the Region of the Dead. The past was lifeless, hollow, dumb. They taught us about the past so that we should resign ourselves with drained consciences to the present: not to make history, which was already made, but to accept it. Poor History had stopped breathing: betrayed in academic texts, lied about in classrooms, drowned in dates, they had imprisoned her in museums and buried her, with floral wreaths, beneath statuary bronze and monumental marble.

Perhaps *Memory of Fire* can help give her back breath, liberty, and the word.

Through the centuries, Latin America has been despoiled of gold and silver, nitrates and rubber, copper and oil: its memory has also been usurped. From the outset it has been condemned to amnesia by those who have prevented it from being. Official Latin American history boils down to a military parade of bigwigs in uniforms fresh from the dry-cleaners. I am not a historian. I am a writer who would like to contribute to the rescue of the kidnapped memory of all America, but above all of Latin America, that despised and beloved land: I would like to talk to her, share her secrets, ask her of what difficult clays she was born, from what acts of love and violation she comes.

I don't know to what literary form this voice of voices belongs. *Memory of Fire* is not an anthology, clearly not; but I don't know if it is a novel or essay or epic poem or testament or chronicle or . . . Deciding robs me of no sleep. I do not believe in the frontiers that, according to literature's customs officers, separate the forms.

I did not want to write an objective work—neither wanted to nor could. There is nothing neutral about this historical narration. Unable to distance myself, I take sides: I confess it and am not sorry. However, each fragment of this huge mosaic is based on a solid documentary foundation. What is told here has happened, although I tell it in my style and manner.

This Book

is the first of a trilogy. It is divided into two parts. In one, indigenous creation myths raise the curtain on pre-Columbian America. In the other, the history of America unfolds from the end of the fifteenth century to the year 1700. The second volume of *Memory of Fire* will cover the eighteenth and nineteenth centuries. The third volume will reach up to our times.

The numbers in parentheses at the foot of each text indicate the principal works consulted by the author in search of information and reference points. The documentary sources are listed at the end.

The heading on each historical episode shows the year and place of its occurrence.

Literal transcriptions appear in italics. The author has modernized the spelling of the ancient sources cited.

Acknowledgments

to Jorge Enrique Adoum, Angel Berenguer, Hortensia Campanella, Juan Gelman, Ernesto González Bermejo, Carlos María Gutiérrez, Mercedes López-Baralt, Guy Prim, Fernando Rodríguez, Nicole Rouan, César Salsamendi, Héctor Tizón, José María Valverde, and Federico Vogelius, who read the drafts and made valuable comments and suggestions;

to Federico Alvarez, Ricardo Bada, José Fernando Balbi, Alvaro Barros-Lémez, Borja and José María Calzado, Ernesto Cardenal, Rosa del Olmo, Jorge Ferrer, Eduardo Heras León, Juana Martínez, Augusto Monterroso, Dámaso Murúa, Manuel Pereira, Pedro Saad, Nicole Vaisse, Rosita and Alberto Villagra, Ricardo Willson, and Sheila Wilson-Serfaty, who eased the author's access to the necessary bibliography;

to José Juan Arrom, Ramón Carande, Alvaro Jara, Magnus Mörner, Augusto Roa Bastos, Laurette Sejourné, and Eric R. Wolff, who answered queries;

to the AGKED Foundation of West Germany, which contributed to the realization of this project;

and especially to Helena Villagra, who was its implacable and beloved critic, page by page, as it was realized.

This Book

is dedicated to Grandmother Esther. She knew it before she died.

E. G.

*The dry grass will set fire
to the damp grass*

—African proverb brought
to the Americas by slaves

FIRST VOICES

The Creation

The woman and the man dreamed that God was dreaming about them.

God was singing and clacking his maracas as he dreamed his dream in a cloud of tobacco smoke, feeling happy but shaken by doubt and mystery.

The Makiritare Indians know that if God dreams about eating, he gives fertility and food. If God dreams about life, he is born and gives birth.

In their dream about God's dream, the woman and the man were inside a great shining egg, singing and dancing and kicking up a fuss because they were crazy to be born. In God's dream happiness was stronger than doubt and mystery. So dreaming, God created them with a song:

"I break this egg and the woman is born and the man is born. And together they will live and die. But they will be born again. They will be born and die again and be born again. They will never stop being born, because death is a lie."

(51)*

Time

For the Maya, time was born and had a name when the sky didn't exist and the earth had not yet awakened.

The days set out from the east and started walking.

The first day produced from its entrails the sky and the earth.

The second day made the stairway for the rain to run down.

The cycles of the sea and the land, and the multitude of things, were the work of the third day.

The fourth day willed the earth and the sky to tilt so that they could meet.

The fifth day decided that everyone had to work.

The first light emanated from the sixth day.

In places where there was nothing, the seventh day put soil; the eighth plunged its hands and feet in the soil.

* This number indicates the source consulted by the author, as listed at the end of the book.

The ninth day created the nether worlds; the tenth earmarked for them those who had poison in their souls.

Inside the sun, the eleventh day modeled stone and tree.

It was the twelfth that made the wind. Wind blew, and it was called spirit because there was no death in it.

The thirteenth day moistened the earth and kneaded the mud into a body like ours.

Thus it is remembered in Yucatán.

(208)

The Sun and the Moon

The first sun, the watery sun, was carried off by the flood. All that lived in the world became fish.

The second sun was devoured by tigers.

The third was demolished by a fiery rain that set people ablaze.

The fourth sun, the wind sun, was wiped out by storm. People turned into monkeys and spread throughout the hills.

The gods became thoughtful and got together in Teotihuacán.

"Who will take on the job of dawning?"

The Lord of the Shells, famous for his strength and beauty, stepped forward. "I'll be the sun," he said.

"Who else?"

Silence.

Everybody looked at the Small Syphilitic God, the ugliest and wretchedest of all gods, and said, "You."

The Lord of the Shells and the Small Syphilitic God withdrew to the hills that are now the pyramids of the sun and the moon. There they fasted and meditated.

Afterward the gods piled up firewood, made a bonfire, and called to them.

The Small Syphilitic God ran up and threw himself into the flames. He immediately emerged, incandescent, in the sky.

The Lord of the Shells looked at the bonfire with a frown, moved forward, backward, hesitated, made a couple of turns. As he could not decide, they had to push him. After a long delay he rose into the sky. The gods were furious and beat him about the face with a rabbit, again and again, until they extinguished his glow. Thus, the arrogant Lord of the Shells became the moon. The stains on the moon are the scars from that beating.

But the resplendent sun didn't move. The obsidian hawk flew toward the Small Syphilitic God. "Why don't you get going?"

The despised, purulent, humpbacked, crippled one answered, "Because I need blood and power."

This fifth sun, the sun that moves, gave light to the Toltecs and gives it to the Aztecs. He has claws and feeds on human hearts.

(108)

The Clouds

Cloud let fall a drop of rain on the body of a woman. After nine months, she had twins.

When they grew up, they wanted to know who their father was.

"Tomorrow morning early," she said, "look toward the east. You'll see him there, up in the sky like a tower."

Across earth and sky, the twins went in search of their father.

Cloud was incredulous and demanded, "Show me that you are my children."

One of the twins sent a flash of lightning to the earth. The other, a thunderclap. As Cloud was still doubtful, they crossed a flood and came out safe.

Then Cloud made a place for them by his side, among his many brothers and nephews.

(174)

The Wind

When God made the first of the Wawenock Indians, some bits of clay remained on the earth. With these bits Gluskabe made himself.

From on high, God asked in astonishment, "Well, where did *you* come from?"

"I'm miraculous," said Gluskabe. "Nobody made me."

God stood beside him and reached out his hand toward the universe. "Look at my work," he challenged. "If you're miraculous, show me things you have invented."

"I can make wind, if you like." And Gluskabe blew at the top of his lungs.

The wind was born and immediately died.

"I can make wind," Gluskabe admitted shamefacedly, "but I can't make it stay."

Then God blew, so powerfully that Gluskabe fell down and lost all his hair.

(174)

The Rain

In the region of the great northern lakes, a little girl suddenly discovered she was alive. The wonders of the world opened her eyes and she took off at random.

Following the trail of the Menomenee nation's hunters and woodcutters, she came to a big log cabin. There lived ten brothers, birds of the thunder, who offered her shelter and food.

One bad morning, when she was fetching water from the creek, a hairy snake caught her and carried her into the depths of a rocky mountain. The snakes were about to eat her up when the little girl sang.

From far away, the thunder birds heard the call. They attacked the rocky mountain with lightning, rescued the prisoner, and killed the snakes.

The thunder birds left the little girl in the fork of a tree.

"You'll live here," they told her. "We'll come every time you sing."

Whenever the little green tree frog sings from his tree, the thunderclaps gather and it rains upon the world.

(113)

The Rainbow

The forest dwarfs had caught Yobuënahuaboshka in an ambush and cut off his head.

The head bumped its way back to the land of the Cashinahuas.

Although it had learned to jump and balance gracefully, nobody wanted a head without a body.

"Mother, brothers, countrymen," it said with a sigh, "Why do you reject me? Why are you ashamed of me?"

To stop the complaints and get rid of the head, the mother proposed that it should change itself into something, but the head refused to change into what already existed. The head thought, dreamed, figured. The moon didn't exist. The rainbow didn't exist.

It asked for seven little balls of thread of all colors.

It took aim and threw the balls into the sky one after the other. The balls got hooked up beyond the clouds; the threads gently unraveled toward the earth.

Before going up, the head warned: "Whoever doesn't recognize me will be punished. When you see me up there, say: 'There's the high and handsome Yobuënahuaboshka!' "

Then it plaited the seven hanging threads together and climbed up the rope to the sky.

That night a white gash appeared for the first time among the stars. A girl raised her eyes and asked in astonishment: "What's that?"

Immediately a red parrot swooped upon her, gave a sudden twirl, and pricked her between the legs with his sharp-pointed tail. The girl bled. From that moment, women bleed when the moon says so.

Next morning the cord of seven colors blazed in the sky.

A man pointed his finger at it. "Look, look! How extraordinary!" He said it and fell down.

And that was the first time that someone died.

(59)

Day

The crow, which now dominates the totem of the Haida nation, was the grandson of that great divine chief who made the world.

When the crow wept asking for the moon, which hung from the wall of tree trunks, his grandfather gave it to him. The crow threw it into the sky through the chimney opening and started crying again, wishing for the stars. When he got them he spread them around the moon.

Then he wept and hopped about and screamed until his grandfather gave him the carved wooden box in which he kept daylight. The great divine chief forbade him to take the box out of the house. He had decided that the world should live in the dark.

The crow played with the box, pretending to be satisfied, but out of the corner of his eye he watched the guards who were watching him.

When they weren't looking, he fled with the box in his claw. The point of the claw split passing through the chimney, and his feathers were burned and stayed black from then on.

The crow arrived at some islands off the northern coast. He heard human voices and asked for food. They wouldn't give him any. He threatened to break the wooden box.

"I've got daylight in here," he warned, "and if it escapes, the sky will never put out its light. No one will be able to sleep, nor to keep secrets, and everybody will know who is people, who is bird, and who is beast of the forest."

They laughed. The crow broke open the box, and light burst forth in the universe.

(87)

Night

The sun never stopped shining and the Cashinahua Indians didn't know the sweetness of rest.

Badly in need of peace, exhausted by so much light, they borrowed night from the mouse.

It got dark, but the mouse's night was hardly long enough for a bite of food and a smoke in front of the fire. The people had just settled down in their hammocks when morning came.

So then they tried out the tapir's night. With the tapir's night they could sleep soundly and they enjoyed the long and much-deserved rest. But when they awoke, so much time had passed that undergrowth from the hills had invaded their lands and destroyed their houses.

After a big search they settled for the night of the armadillo. They borrowed it from him and never gave it back.

Deprived of night, the armadillo sleeps during the daytime.

(59)

The Stars

By playing the flute love is declared, or the return of the hunters announced. With the strains of the flute, the Waiwai Indians summon their guests. For the Tukanos, the flute weeps; for the Kalinas it talks, because it's the trumpet that shouts.

On the banks of the Negro River, the flute confirms the power of the men. Flutes are sacred and hidden, and any woman who approaches deserves death.

In very remote times, when the women had the sacred flutes, men toted firewood and water and prepared the cassava bread. As the men tell it, the sun got indignant at the sight of women running the world, so he dropped into the forest and fertilized a virgin by slipping leaf juices between her legs. Thus was born Jurupari.

Jurupari stole the sacred flutes and gave them to the men. He taught the men to hide them and defend them and to celebrate ritual feasts without women. He also told them the secrets they were to transmit to their male children.

When Jurupari's mother found where the sacred flutes were hidden, she condemned him to death; and with the bits that remained of him she made the stars of the sky.

(91 and 112)

The Milky Way

No bigger than a worm, he ate the hearts of birds. His father was the best hunter of the Moseten people.

Soon he was a serpent as big as an arm. He kept asking for more hearts. The hunter spent the whole day in the forest killing for his son.

When the serpent got too big for the shack, the forest had been emptied of birds. The father, an expert bowman, brought him jaguars' hearts.

The serpent devoured them and grew. Then there were no more jaguars in the forest.

"I want human hearts," said the serpent.

The hunter emptied his village and its vicinity of people, until one day in a far-off village he was spotted on a tree branch and killed.

Driven by hunger and nostalgia, the serpent went to look for him.

He coiled his body around the guilty village so that no one could escape. While the men let fly all their arrows against this giant ring that had laid siege to them, the serpent rescued his father's body and grew upward. There he can still be seen undulating, bristling with luminous arrows, across the night sky.

(174)

The Evening Star

The moon, stooping mother, asked her son, "I don't know where your father is. Find him and give him word of me."

The son took off in search of the brightest of all lights. He didn't find him at noontime, when the sun of the Tarascan people drinks his wine and dances with his women to the beat of drums.

He didn't find him on the horizons and in the regions of the dead. The sun wasn't in any of his four houses.

The evening star is still hunting his father across the sky. He always arrives too early or too late.

(55)

Language

The First Father of the Guaranís rose in darkness lit by reflections from his own heart and created flames and thin mist. He created love and had nobody to give it to. He created language and had no one to listen to him.

Then he recommended to the gods that they should construct the world and take charge of fire, mist, rain, and wind. And he turned over to them the music and words of the sacred hymn so that they would give life to women and to men.

So love became communion, language took on life, and the First Father redeemed his solitude. Now he accompanies men and women who sing as they go:

We're walking this earth,
We're walking this shining earth.

(40 and 192)

Fire

The nights were icy because the gods had taken away fire. The cold cut into the flesh and words of men. Shivering, they implored with broken voices; the gods turned a deaf ear.

Once, they gave fire back and the men danced for joy, chanting hymns of gratitude. But soon the gods sent rain and hail and put out the bonfires.

The gods spoke and demanded: to deserve fire, men must cut open their chests with obsidian daggers and surrender their hearts.

The Quiché Indians offered the blood of their prisoners and saved themselves from the cold.

The Cakchiquels didn't accept the bargain. The Cakchiquels, cousins of the Quichés and likewise descended from the Mayas, slipped away on feathered feet through the smoke, stole the fire, and hid it in their mountain caves.

(188)

The Forest

In a dream, the Father of the Uitoto Indians glimpsed a shining mist. The mist was alive with mosses and lichens and resonant with winds, birds, and snakes. The Father could catch the mist, and he held it with the thread of his breath. He pulled it out of the dream and mixed it with earth.

Several times he spat on the misty earth. In the foamy mash the forest rose up, trees unfolded their enormous crowns, fruit and flowers erupted. On the moistened earth the grasshopper, the monkey, the tapir, the wild boar, the armadillo, the deer, the jaguar, and the anteater took shape and voice. Into the air soared the golden eagle, the macaw, the vulture, the hummingbird, the white heron, the duck, and the bat.

The wasp arrived in a great hurry. He left toads and men without tails and then rested.

(174)

The Cedar

The First Father conjured the world to birth with the tip of his wand and covered it with down.

Out of the down rose the cedar, the sacred tree from which flows the word. Then the First Father told the Mby'a-guaranís to hollow out the trunk and listen to what it had in it. He said that whoever could listen to the cedar, the casket of words, would know where to establish his hearth. Whoever couldn't would return to despised dust.

(192)

The Guaiacum Tree

A young woman of the Nivakle people was going in search of water when she came upon a leafy tree, Nasuk, the guaiacum, and felt its call. She embraced its firm trunk, pressing her whole body against it, and dug her nails into its bark. The tree bled.

Leaving it, she said, "How I wish, Nasuk, that you were a man!"

And the guaiacum turned into a man and ran after her. When he found her, he showed her his scratched shoulder and stretched out by her side.

(192)

Colors

White were once the feathers of birds, and white the skin of animals.

Blue now are those that bathed in a lake into which no river emptied and from which none was born. Red, those that dipped in the lake of blood shed by a child of the Kadiueu tribe. Earth-color, those that rolled in the mud, and ashen those that sought warmth in extinguished campfires. Green, those that rubbed their bodies in the foliage, white those that stayed still.

(174)

Love

In the Amazonian jungle, the first woman and the first man looked at each other with curiosity. It was odd what they had between their legs.

"Did they cut yours off?" asked the man.

"No," she said, "I've always been like that."

He examined her close up. He scratched his head. There was an open wound there. He said: "Better not eat any cassava or bananas or any fruit that splits when it ripens. I'll cure you. Get in the hammock and rest."

She obeyed. Patiently she swallowed herb teas and let him rub on pomades and unguents. She had to grit her teeth to keep from laughing when he said to her, "Don't worry."

She enjoyed the game, although she was beginning to tire of fasting in a hammock. The memory of fruit made her mouth water.

One evening the man came running through the glade. He jumped with excitement and cried, "I found it!"

He had just seen the male monkey curing the female monkey in the arm of a tree.

"That's how it's done," said the man, approaching the woman.

When the long embrace ended, a dense aroma of flowers and fruit filled the air. From the bodies lying together came unheard of vapors and glowings, and it was all so beautiful that the suns and the gods died of embarrassment.

(59)

The Rivers and the Sea

There was no water in the forest of the Chocos. God knew that the ant had it and asked her for some. She didn't want to listen. God tightened her waist, making it permanently slim, and the ant exuded the water she kept in her belly.

"Now tell me where you got it."

The ant led God to a tree that had nothing unusual about it.

Frogs and men with axes worked on it for four days and four

nights, but the tree wouldn't fall. A liana kept it from touching the ground.

God ordered the toucan, "Cut it."

The toucan couldn't, and for that was sentenced to eat fruit whole.

The macaw cut the liana with his hard, sharp beak.

When the water tree fell, the sea was born from its trunk and the rivers from its branches.

All of the water was sweet. It was the Devil that kept chucking fistfuls of salt into it.

(174)

The Tides

In olden times, winds blew unremittingly on Vancouver Island. Good weather didn't exist, and there was no low tide.

Men decided to kill the winds. They sent in spies. The winter blackbird failed; so did the sardine. Despite his bad vision and broken arms, it was the sea gull that managed to dodge the hurricanes mounting guard on the house of the winds.

Then men sent in an army of fish led by the sea gull. The fish hurled themselves in a body against the door. The winds, rushing out, trod on them, slipping and falling one after another on the stingray, which pierced them with his tail and devoured them.

The west wind was captured alive. Imprisoned by the men, it promised that it would not blow continuously, that there would be soft air and light breezes, and that the waters would recede a couple of times a day so that shellfish could be gathered at low tide. They spared its life.

The west wind has kept its word.

(114)

Snow

"I want you to fly!" said the master of the house, and the house took off and flew. It moved through the air in the darkness, whistling as it went, until the master ordered, "I want you to stop here!" And the house stopped, suspended in the night and the falling snow.

There was no whale blubber to light the lamps, so the master gathered a fistful of fresh snow, and the snow gave him light.

The house landed in an Iglulik village. Someone came over to greet it, and when he saw the lamp lit with snow, exclaimed, "The snow is burning!" and the lamps went out.

(174)

The Flood

At the foot of the Andes, the heads of communities had a meeting. They smoked and discussed.

The tree of abundance reared its rich crown far above the roof of the world. From below could be seen the high branches bent by the weight of fruit, luxuriant with pineapples, coconuts, papayas, guanábanas, corn, cassava, beans . . .

Mice and birds enjoyed the feast. People, no. The fox went up and down giving himself banquets, sharing with no one. Men who tried to make the climb crashed to the ground.

"What shall we do?"

One of the chiefs conjured up an ax in his sleep. He awoke with a toad in his hand and struck it against the enormous trunk of the tree of abundance, but the little creature merely vomited up its liver.

"That dream was lying."

Another chief, in a dream, begged the Father of all for an ax. The Father warned that the tree would get its own back but sent a red parrot. Grasping the parrot, the chief struck the tree of abundance. A rain of food fell to the ground, and the earth was deafened by the noise. Then the most unusual storm burst from the depths of the rivers. The waters rose, covering the world.

Only one man survived. He swam and swam for days and nights, until he could cling to the top of a palm tree that stuck out of the water.

(174)

The Tortoise

When the Flood receded, the Oaxaca Valley was a quagmire.

A handful of mud took on life and started walking. The tortoise walked very, very slowly. He moved with his head stretched out and his eyes very open, discovering the world that the sun was bringing back to life.

In a place that stank, the tortoise saw the vulture devouring corpses.

"Take me to heaven," he said. "I want to meet God."

The vulture made him keep asking. The corpses were tasty. The tortoise stuck out his head in entreaty, then pulled it back under his shell, unable to stand the stench.

"You who have wings, take me," he begged.

Bored by his persistence, the vulture opened his huge black wings and flew off with the tortoise on his back. They flew through clouds, and the tortoise, his head tucked in, complained, "How disgusting you smell!"

The vulture pretended not to hear.

"What a stink of putrefaction!" the tortoise repeated.

He kept it up until the hideous bird lost patience, leaned over brusquely, and threw him down to earth.

God came down from heaven and put the bits together.

The shell shows where the mends were.

(92)

The Parrot

After the Flood, the forest was green but empty. The survivor shot his arrows through the trees, and the arrows hit nothing but shadows and foliage.

One evening, after much walking and searching, the survivor returned to his refuge and found roast meat and cassava cakes. The same happened the next day, and the next. From desperate hunger and loneliness, he turned to wondering whom he had to thank for his good fortune. In the morning, he hid and waited.

Two parrots appeared out of the sky. No sooner had they alit on the ground than they turned into women. They lit a fire and started cooking.

The only man chose the one with the longest hair and the finest and brightest feathers. The other woman, scorned, flew off.

The Mayna Indians, descendants of this couple, curse their ancestor when their women turn lazy or grouchy. They say it's all his fault because he chose the useless one. The other was mother and father of all the parrots living in the forest.

(191)

The Hummingbird

At dawn he greets the sun. Night falls and he's still at work. He goes buzzing from branch to branch, from flower to flower, quick and necessary like light itself. At times he's doubtful and pauses suspended in the air; at times he flies backward as no one else can. At times he's a little drunk from all the honey he has sucked. As he flies, he emits flashes of color.

He brings messages from the gods, becomes a bolt of lightning to carry out their vengeance, blows prophecies in the ears of the soothsayers. When a Guaraní child dies, he rescues its soul, which lies in the calyx of a flower, and takes it in his long needle beak to the Land Without Evil. He has known the way there since the beginning of time. Before the world was born, he already existed; he freshened the mouth of the First Father with drops of dew and assuaged his hunger with the nectar of flowers.

He led the long pilgrimage of the Toltecs to the sacred city of Tula before bringing the warmth of the sun to the Aztecs.

As captain of the Chontals, he glides over the camps of the enemy, assesses their strength, dive-bombs them, and kills their chief in his sleep. As the sun of the Kekchis, he flies to the moon, takes her by surprise in her chamber, and makes love to her.

His body is the size of an almond. He is born from an egg no bigger than a bean, in a nest that fits inside a nut. He sleeps with a little leaf as covering.

(40, 206, and 210)

The Night Bird (Urutaú)

"I am the daughter of misfortune," said the chief's daughter Ñeambiú, when her father forbade her love for a man of an enemy community.

She said it and fled.

After a while they found her in the Iguazú Mountains. They found a statue. Ñeambiú looked without seeing; her mouth was still and her heart asleep.

The chief sent for the one who deciphers mysteries and heals sicknesses. The whole community came out to witness the resurrection.

The shaman sought advice from maté tea and cassava wine. He went up to Ñeambiú and lied right into her ear:

"The man you love has just died."

Ñeambiú's scream turned all the people into weeping willows. She flew off, turned into a bird.

The screams of the urutaú, which shake the mountains at nighttime, can be heard more than half a league away. It's difficult to see the urutaú, impossible to hunt him. No one can catch up with the phantom bird.

(86)

The Ovenbird

When he reached the age for the three manhood tests, this boy
ran and swam better than anyone and spent nine days without food,
stretched out by leather thongs, without moving or complaining.
During the tests he heard a woman's voice singing to him from far
away, which helped him to endure.

The chief of the community decided that the boy should marry
his daughter, but he took flight and got lost in the woods of the
Paraguay River, searching for the singer.

There you still meet the ovenbird. He flaps his wings powerfully and utters glad sounds when he thinks the sought-after voice
is flying his way. Waiting for the one who doesn't come, he has
built a house of mud, with the door open to the northern breeze,
in a place secure from lightning.

Everyone respects him. He who kills the ovenbird or breaks
his house draws the storm upon himself.

(144)

The Crow

The lakes were dry, the riverbeds empty. The Takelma Indians,
dying of thirst, sent the male and the female crow to look for water.

The male crow got tired right away. He urinated in a bowl
and said that was the water he was bringing from a far place.

The female kept on flying. She returned much later with a
load of fresh water and saved the Takelma people from the drought.

As a punishment the male crow was sentenced to suffer thirst
through the summers. Unable to moisten his throat, he talks in a
very raucous voice while the weather is hot.

(114)

The Condor

Cauillaca was weaving cloth in the shade of a tree, and overhead soared Coniraya, who had turned into a bird. The girl paid absolutely no attention to his warblings and flutterings.

Coniraya knew that other, older, more important gods burned with desire for Cauillaca. However, he sent his seed down to her from up there, in the form of a ripe fruit. When she saw the fleshy fruit at her feet, she picked it up and bit into it. She felt a strange pleasure and became pregnant.

Afterward he turned into a person—a ragged, sad sack of a man—and pursued her all over Peru. Cauillaca fled toward the ocean with her little son on her back, and behind trekked Coniraya, furiously hunting her.

He made inquiries of a skunk. The skunk, noticing his bleeding feet and general distress, answered, "Idiot. Can't you see there's no point in following her?"

So Coniraya cursed him, "You shall wander about by night, leaving a bad smell wherever you go. When you die, no one will pick you up off the ground."

But the condor put spirit into the hunter. "Run!" he called to him. "Run and you'll catch her!"

So Coniraya blessed him, "You shall fly wherever you want. There won't be any place in the sky or on earth where you can't go. No one will get to where you build your nest. You'll never lack for food; and he who kills you will die."

After climbing a lot of mountains, Coniraya reached the coast. He was too late. The girl and her son were already an island, carved in rock, out in midocean.

(100)

The Jaguar

The jaguar was out hunting with bow and arrows when he met a shadow. He tried to catch it and couldn't. He lifted his head. The master of the shadow was young Botoque of the Kayapó tribe, who was near death from hunger on top of a rock.

Botoque had no strength to move and could only just stammer a few words. The jaguar lowered his bow and invited him to a roast meat dinner in his house. Although the lad didn't know what "roast" meant, he accepted and dropped on to the hunter's back.

"You're carrying some stranger's child," said the jaguar's wife.

"He's mine now," said the jaguar.

Botoque saw fire for the first time. He got acquainted with the stone oven and the smell of roast tapir and venison. He learned that fire illuminates and warms. The jaguar gave him a bow and arrows and taught him to defend himself.

One day Botoque fled. He had killed the jaguar's wife.

He ran desperately for a long time and didn't stop till he reached his village. There he told his story and displayed the secrets: the new weapon and the roast meat. The Kayapós decided to appropriate fire, and he led them to the remote house. Nothing was left to the jaguar of the fire except its reflection shining in his eyes.

Ever since then, the jaguar has hated men. For hunting, all he has are his fangs and claws, and he eats the flesh of his victims raw.

(111)

The Bear

The day animals and the night animals got together to decide what they would do about the sun, which then came and went whenever it liked. The animals resolved to leave the problem to fate. The winning group in the game of riddles would decide how long the world would have sunlight in the future.

They were still talking when the sun approached, intrigued by the discussion. The sun came so close that the night animals had to scatter. The bear was a victim of the general flurry. He put his right foot into his left moccasin and his left foot into his right moccasin, and took off on the run as best he could.

According to the Comanches, since then the bear walks with a lurch.

(132)

The Crocodile

The sun of the Macusi people was worried. Every day there were fewer fish in their ponds.

He put the crocodile in charge of security. The ponds got emptier. The crocodile, security guard and thief, invented a good story about invisible assailants, but the sun didn't believe it, took a machete, and left the crocodile's body all crisscrossed with cuts.

To calm him down, the crocodile offered his beautiful daughter in marriage.

"I'll be expecting her," said the sun.

As the crocodile had no daughter, he sculpted a woman in the trunk of a wild plum tree.

"Here she is," he said, and plunged into the water, looking out of the corner of his eye, the way he always looks.

It was the woodpecker who saved his life. Before the sun arrived, the woodpecker pecked at the wooden girl below the belly. Thus she, who was incomplete, was open for the sun to enter.

(112)

The Armadillo

A big fiesta was announced on Lake Titicaca, and the armadillo, who was a very superior creature, wanted to dazzle everybody.

Long beforehand, he set to weaving a cloak of such elegance that it would knock all eyes out.

The fox noticed him at work. "Are you in a bad mood?"

"Don't distract me. I'm busy."

"What's that for?"

The armadillo explained.

"Ah," said the fox, savoring the words, "for the fiesta tonight?"

"What do you mean, tonight?"

The armadillo's heart sank. He had never been more sure of his time calculations. "And me with my cloak only half finished!"

While the fox took off with a smothered laugh, the armadillo finished the cloak in a hurry. As time was flying, he had to use coarser threads, and the weave ended up too big. For this reason the armadillo's shell is tight-warped around the neck and very open at the back.

(174)

The Rabbit

The rabbit wanted to grow.

God promised to increase his size if he would bring him the skins of a tiger, of a monkey, of a lizard, and of a snake.

The rabbit went to visit the tiger. "God has let me into a secret," he said confidentially.

The tiger wanted to know it, and the rabbit announced an impending hurricane. "I'll save myself because I'm small. I'll hide in some hole. But what'll you do? The hurricane won't spare you."

A tear rolled down between the tiger's mustaches.

"I can think of only one way to save you," said the rabbit. "We'll look for a tree with a very strong trunk. I'll tie you to the trunk by the neck and paws, and the hurricane won't carry you off."

The grateful tiger let himself be tied. Then the rabbit killed him with one blow, stripped him, and went on his way into the woods of the Zapotec country.

He stopped under a tree in which a monkey was eating. Taking a knife, the rabbit began striking his own neck with the blunt side of it. With each blow of the knife, a chuckle. After much hitting and chuckling, he left the knife on the ground and hopped away.

He hid among the branches, on the watch. The monkey soon climbed down. He examined the object that made one laugh, and he scratched his head. He seized the knife and at the first blow fell with his throat cut.

Two skins to go. The rabbit invited the lizard to play ball. The ball was of stone. He hit the lizard at the base of the tail and left him dead.

Near the snake, the rabbit pretended to be asleep. Just as the snake was tensing up, before it could jump, the rabbit plunged his claws into its eyes.

He went to the sky with the four skins.

"Now make me grow," he demanded.

And God thought, "The rabbit is so small, yet he did all this. If I make him bigger, what won't he do? If the rabbit were big, maybe I wouldn't be God."

The rabbit waited. God came up softly, stroked his back, and suddenly caught him by the ears, whirled him about, and threw him to the ground.

Since then the rabbit has had big ears, short front feet from having stretching them out to break his fall, and pink eyes from panic.

(92)

The Snake

God said to him, "Three canoes will pass down the river. In two of them, death will be traveling. If you guess which one is without death, I'll liberate you from the shortness of life."

The snake let pass the first canoe, which was laden with baskets of putrid meat. Nor did he pay attention to the second, which was full of people. The third looked empty, but when it arrived, he welcomed it.

For this reason the snake is immortal in the region of the Shipaiás.

Every time he begins to get old, God presents him with a new skin.

(111)

The Frog

From a cave in Haiti came the first Taino Indians.

The sun had no mercy on them. Suddenly, without warning, he would kidnap and transform them. He turned the one who mounted guard by night into a stone; of the fisherman he made trees, and the one who went out for herbs he caught on the road and turned into a bird that sings in the morning.

One of the men fled from the sun. When he took off, he took all the women with him.

There is no laughter in the song of the little frogs in the Caribbean islands. They are the Taino children of those days. They say, "Toa, toa," which is their way of calling to their mothers.

(126 and 168)

The Bat

When time was yet in the cradle, there was no uglier creature in the world than the bat.

The bat went up to heaven to look for God. He didn't say, "I'm bored with being hideous. Give me colored feathers." No. He said, "Please give me feathers, I'm dying of cold."

But God had not a single feather left over.

"Each bird will give you a feather," he decided.

Thus the bat got the white feather of the dove and the green one of the parrot, the iridescent one of the hummingbird, the pink one of the flamingo, the red of the cardinal's tuft and the blue of the kingfisher's back, the clayey one of the eagle's wing, and the sun feather that burns in the breast of the toucan.

The bat, luxuriant with colors and softness, moved between earth and clouds. Wherever he went, the air became pleasant and the birds dumb with admiration. According to the Zapotec peoples, the rainbow was born of the echo of his flight.

Vanity puffed out his chest. He acquired a disdainful look and made insulting remarks.

The birds called a meeting. Together they flew up to God.

"The bat makes fun of us," they complained. "And what's more, we feel cold for lack of the feathers he took."

Next day, when the bat shook his feathers in full flight, he suddenly became naked. A rain of feathers fell to earth.

He is still searching for them. Blind and ugly, enemy of the light, he lives hidden in caves. He goes out in pursuit of the lost feathers after night has fallen and flies very fast, never stopping because it shames him to be seen.

(92)

Mosquitos

There were many dead in the Nooktas village. In each dead body there was a hole through which blood had been stolen.

The murderer, a child who was already killing before he learned to walk, received his sentence roaring with laughter. They pierced him with lances and he laughingly picked them out of his body like thorns.

"I'll teach you to kill me," said the child.

He suggested to his executioners that they should light a big bonfire and throw him into it.

His ashes scattered through the air, anxious to do harm, and thus the first mosquitos started to fly.

(174)

Honey

Honey was in flight from his two sisters-in-law. They had thrown him out of the hammock several times.

They came after him night and day. They saw him and it made their mouths water. Only in dreams did they succeed in touching him, licking him, eating him.

Their spite kept growing. One morning when the sisters-in-law were bathing, they came upon Honey on the riverbank. They ran and splashed him. Once wet, Honey dissolved.

In the Gulf of Paria it's not easy to find the lost honey. You have to climb the trees, ax in hand, open up the trunks, and do a lot of rummaging. The rare honey is eaten with pleasure and with fear, because sometimes it kills.

(112)

Seeds

Pachacamac, who was a son of the sun, made a man and a woman in the dunes of Lurín.

There was nothing to eat, and the man died of hunger.

When the woman was bent over searching for roots, the sun entered her and made a child.

Jealous, Pachacamac caught the newborn baby and chopped it to pieces. But suddenly he repented, or was scared of the anger of his father, the sun, and scattered about the world the pieces of his murdered brother.

From the teeth of the dead baby, corn grew; from the ribs and bones, cassava. The blood made the land fertile, and fruit trees and shade trees rose from the sown flesh.

Thus the women and men born on these shores, where it never rains, find food.

(57)

Corn

The gods made the first Maya-Quichés out of clay. Few survived. They were soft, lacking strength; they fell apart before they could walk.

Then the gods tried wood. The wooden dolls talked and walked but were dry; they had no blood nor substance, no memory and no purpose. They didn't know how to talk to the gods, or couldn't think of anything to say to them.

Then the gods made mothers and fathers out of corn. They molded their flesh with yellow corn and white corn.

The women and men of corn saw as much as the gods. Their glance ranged over the whole world.

The gods breathed on them and left their eyes forever clouded, because they didn't want people to see over the horizon.

(188)

Tobacco

The Cariri Indians had implored the Grandfather to let them try the flesh of wild pigs, which didn't yet exist. The Grandfather, architect of the Universe, kidnapped the little children of the Carirís and turned them into wild pigs. He created a big tree so that they could escape into the sky.

The people pursued the pigs up the tree from branch to branch and managed to kill a few. The Grandfather ordered the ants to bring down the tree. When it fell, the people suffered broken bones. Ever since that great fall, we all have divided bones and so are able to bend our fingers and legs or tilt our bodies.

With the dead boars a great banquet was made in the village.

The people besought the Grandfather to come down from the sky, where he was minding the children saved from the hunt, but he preferred to stay up there.

The Grandfather sent tobacco to take his place among men. Smoking, the people talked with God.

(111)

Maté

The moon was simply dying to tread the earth. She wanted to sample the fruit and to bathe in some river.

Thanks to the clouds, she was able to come down. From sunset until dawn, clouds covered the sky so that no one could see the moon was missing.

Nighttime on the earth was marvelous. The moon strolled through the forest of the high Paraná, caught mysterious aromas and flavors, and had a long swim in the river. Twice an old peasant rescued her. When the jaguar was about to sink his teeth into the moon's neck, the old man cut the beast's throat with his knife; and when the moon got hungry, he took her to his house. "We offer you our poverty," said the peasant's wife, and gave her some corn tortillas.

On the next night the moon looked down from the sky at her friends' house. The old peasant had built his hut in a forest clearing very far from the villages. He lived there like an exile with his wife and daughter.

The moon found that the house had nothing left in it to eat. The last corn tortillas had been for her. Then she turned on her brightest light and asked the clouds to shed a very special drizzle around the hut.

In the morning some unknown trees had sprung up there. Amid their dark green leaves appeared white flowers.

The old peasant's daughter never died. She is the queen of the maté and goes about the world offering it to others. The tea of the maté awakens sleepers, activates the lazy, and makes brothers and sisters of people who don't know each other.

(86 and 144)

Cassava

No man had touched her, but a boy-child grew in the belly of the chief's daughter.

They called him Mani. A few days after birth he was already running and talking. From the forest's farthest corners people came to meet the prodigious Mani.

Mani caught no disease, but on reaching the age of one, he said, "I'm going to die," and he died.

A little time passed, and on Mani's grave sprouted a plant never before seen, which the mother watered every morning. The plant grew, flowered, and gave fruit. The birds that picked at it flew strangely, fluttering in mad spirals and singing like crazy.

One day the ground where Mani lay split open. The chief thrust his hand in and pulled out a big, fleshy root. He grated it with a stone, made a dough, wrung it out, and with the warmth of the fire cooked bread for everyone.

They called the root *mani oca*, "house of Mani," and manioc is its name in the Amazon basin and other places.

(174)

The Potato

A chief on Chiloé Island, a place populated by sea gulls, wanted to make love like the gods.

When pairs of gods embraced, the earth shook and tidal waves were set moving. That much was known, but no one had seen them.

Anxious to surprise them, the chief swam out to the forbidden isle. All he got to see was a giant lizard, with its mouth wide open and full of foam and an outsized tongue that gave off fire at the tip.

The gods buried the indiscreet chief in the ground and condemned him to be eaten by the others. As punishment for his curiosity, they covered his body with blind eyes.

(178)

The Kitchen

In the center of the wood, a woman of the Tillamook people came upon a cabin that was throwing out smoke. Curious, she approached and went in.

Fire burned amid stones in the center of the cabin. From the ceiling hung a number of salmons. One fell on her head. The woman picked it up and hung it back in place. Once again the fish fell and hit her on the head. Again she hung it back up, and again it fell.

The woman threw on the fire the roots she had gathered to eat. The fire burned them up in a flash. Furious, she struck the fire several times with the poker, so violently that the fire was almost out when the master of the house arrived and stayed her arm.

The mysterious man revived the flames, sat down beside the woman, and explained to her, "You didn't understand."

By striking the flames and dispersing the embers she had been on the point of blinding the fire, and that was a punishment it didn't deserve. The fire had eaten up the roots because it thought the woman was offering them to it. And before that, it was the fire that had caused the salmon to fall several times on the woman's head, not to hurt her but to tell her that she could cook it.

"Cook it? What's that?"

So the master of the house taught the woman how to talk to the fire, to roast the fish on the embers, and eat it with relish.

(114)

Music

While the spirit Bopé-joku whistled a melody, corn rose out of the ground, unstoppable, luminous, and offered giant ears swollen with grains.

A woman was picking them and doing it wrong. Tugging hard at an ear, she injured it. The ear took revenge by wounding her hand. The woman insulted Bopé-joku and cursed his whistling.

When Bopé-joku closed his lips, the corn withered and dried up. The happy whistlings that made the cornfields bloom and gave them vigor and beauty were heard no more. From then on the Bororo people cultivated corn with pain and effort and reaped wretched crops.

Spirits express themselves by whistling. When the stars come out at night, that's how the spirits greet them. Each star responds to a note, which is its name.

(112)

Death

The first of the Modoc Indians, Kumokums, built a village on the banks of a river. Although it left the bears plenty of room to curl up and sleep, the deer complained that it was very cold and there wasn't enough grass.

Kumokums built another village far from there and decided to spend half of every year in each. For this he divided the year into two parts, six moons of summer and six of winter, and the remaining moon was dedicated to moving.

Life between the two villages was as happy as could be, and births multiplied amazingly; but people who died refused to get out, and the population got so big that there was no way to feed it.

Then Kumokums decided to throw out the dead people. He knew that the chief of the land of the dead was a great man and didn't mistreat anybody.

Soon afterward Kumokums's small daughter died. She died and left the country of the Modocs, as her father had ordered.

In despair, Kumokums consulted the porcupine.

"You made the decision," said the porcupine, "and now you must take the consequences like anyone else."

But Kumokums journeyed to the far-off land of the dead and claimed his daughter.

"Now your daughter is my daughter," said the big skeleton in charge there. "She has no flesh or blood. What can she do in your country?"

"I want her anyway," said Kumokums.

The chief of the land of the dead thought for a long time.

"Take her," he yielded, and warned, "She'll walk behind you. On approaching the country of the living, flesh will return to cover her bones. But you may not turn around till you arrive. Understand? I give you this chance."

Kumokums set out. The daughter walked behind him.

Several times he touched her hand, which was more fleshy and warm each time, and still he didn't look back. But when the green woods appeared on the horizon he couldn't stand the strain and turned his head. A handful of bones crumbled before his eyes.

(132)

Resurrection

After five days it was the custom for the dead to return to Peru. They drank a glass of chicha and said, "Now I'm eternal."

There were too many people in the world. Crops were sown at the bottom of precipices and on the edge of abysses, but even so, the food wouldn't go around.

Then a man died in Huarochirí.

The whole community gathered on the fifth day to receive him. They waited for him from morning till well after nightfall. The hot dishes got cold, and sleep began closing eyelids. The dead man didn't come.

He came the next day. Everyone was furious. The one who boiled most with indignation was his wife, who yelled, "You good-for-nothing! Always the same good-for-nothing! All the dead are punctual except you!"

The resurrected one stammered some excuse, but the woman threw a corncob at his head and left him stretched out on the floor. Then the soul left the body and flew off, a quick, buzzing insect, never to return.

Since that time no dead person has come back to mix with the living and compete for their food.

(14)

Magic

An extremely old Tukuna woman chastised some young girls who had denied her food. During the night she tore the bones out of their legs and devoured the marrow, so the girls could never walk again.

In her infancy, soon after birth, the old woman had received from a frog the powers of healing and vengeance. The frog had taught her to cure and kill, to hear unhearable voices and see unseeable colors. She learned to defend herself before she learned to talk. Before she could walk she already knew how to be where she wasn't, because the shafts of love and hate instantly pierce the densest jungles and deepest rivers.

When the Tukunas cut off her head, the old woman collected her own blood in her hands and blew it toward the sun.

"My soul enters you, too!" she shouted.

Since then anyone who kills receives in his body, without wanting or knowing it, the soul of his victim.

(112)

Laughter

The bat, hanging from a branch by his feet, noticed a Kayapó warrior leaning over the stream.

He wanted to be his friend.

He dropped on the warrior and embraced him. As he didn't know the Kayapó language, he talked to him with his hands. The bat's caresses drew from the man the first laugh. The more he laughed, the weaker he felt. He laughed so much that finally he lost all his strength and fell in a faint.

When the villagers learned about it, they were furious. The warriors burned a heap of dry leaves in the bats' cave and blocked up the entrance.

Afterward they had a discussion. The warriors resolved that laughter should be used only by women and children.

(111)

Fear

These incredible bodies called to them, but the Nivakle men dared not enter. They had seen the women eat: they swallowed the flesh of fish with the upper mouth, but chewed it first with the lower mouth. Between their legs they had teeth.

So the men lit bonfires, called to the women, and sang and danced for them.

The women sat around in a circle with their legs crossed.

The men danced all through the night. They undulated, turned, and flew like smoke and birds. When dawn came they fell fainting to the ground. The women gently lifted them and gave them water to drink.

Where they had been sitting, the ground was all littered with teeth.

(192)

Authority

In remote times women sat in the bow of the canoe and men in the stern. It was the women who hunted and fished. They left the villages and returned when they could or wanted. The men built the huts, prepared the meals, kept the fires burning against the cold, minded the children, and tanned skins for clothes.

Such was life for the Ona and Yagan Indians in Tierra del Fuego, until one day the men killed all the women and put on the masks that the women had invented to scare them.

Only newly born girls were spared extermination. While they grew up, the murderers kept repeating to them that serving men was their destiny. They believed it. Their daughters believed it, too, likewise the daughters of their daughters.

(91 and 178)

Power

In the lands where the Juruá River is born, Old Meanie was lord of the corn. He gave out the grains roasted, so that no one could plant them.

The lizard succeeded in stealing a raw grain from him. Old Meanie caught her and ripped off her jaw and fingers and toes; but she had managed to conceal the grain behind her back molar. The lizard afterward spat out the raw grain on the common land. Her jaw was too big and her fingers and toes too long to be completely torn off.

Old Meanie was also lord of the fire. The parrot sneaked up

close to it and started screeching her lungs out. Old Meanie threw at her everything that was handy, and the little parrot dodged the projectiles until she saw a lighted stick flying her way. Then she picked it up with her beak, which was an enormous as a toucan's, and fled. A trail of sparks followed her. The embers, fanned by the wind, burned her beak, but she had already reached the trees when Old Meanie beat his drum and let loose a rainstorm.

The parrot managed to leave the burning stick in the hollow of a tree under the care of the other birds and flew back into the downpour. The water relieved her burns, but her beak, shortened and curved, still shows a white scar from the fire.

The birds protected the stolen fire with their bodies.

(59)

War

At dawn, the trumpet call announced from the mountain that it was time for crossbows and blowguns.

At nightfall, nothing remained of the village except smoke.

A man lay among the dead without moving. He smeared his body with blood and waited. He was the only survivor of the Palawiyang people.

When the enemy moved off, that man got up. He contemplated his destroyed world. He walked among the people who had shared hunger and food with him. He sought in vain some person or thing that hadn't been wiped out. The terrifying silence dazed him. The smell of fire and blood sickened him. He felt disgusted to be alive, and he threw himself back down among his own.

With the first light came the vultures. There was nothing left in that man except fog and a yearning to sleep and let himself be devoured.

But the condor's daughter opened a path through the circling birds of prey. She beat her wings hard and dived. He grabbed onto her feet, and the condor's daughter took him far away.

(54)

Parties

An Inuit, bow in hand, was out hunting reindeer when an eagle unexpectedly appeared behind him.

"I killed your two brothers," said the eagle. "If you want to save yourself you must give a party in your village so everyone can sing and dance."

"A party? Sing, what's that? What's dance?"

"Come with me."

The eagle showed him a party. There was a lot of good food and drink. The drum beat as hard as the heart of the eagle's old mother, its rhythm guiding her children from her house across the vast expanses of ice and mountain. Wolves, foxes, and other guests danced and sang until sunup.

The hunter returned to his village.

A long time afterward he learned that the eagle's old mother and all the oldsters of the eagle world were strong and handsome and swift. Human beings had finally learned to sing and dance, and had sent them, from afar, from their own parties, gaieties that warmed the blood.

(174)

Conscience

When the waters of the Orinoco lowered, canoes brought the Caribs with their battle-axes.

No one had a chance against the sons of the jaguar. They leveled villages and made flutes from their victims' bones. They feared nobody. The only thing that struck panic into them was a phantom born in their own hearts.

The phantom lay in wait for them behind the trees. He broke their bridges and placed in their paths tangled lianas. He traveled by night. To throw them off the track, he walked backward. He was on the slope from which rocks broke off, in the mud that sank beneath their feet, in the leaf of the poisonous plant, in the touch of the spider. He knocked them down with a breath, injected fever through their ears, and robbed them of shade.

He was not pain, but he hurt. He was not death, but he killed. His name was Kanaima, and he was born among the conquerors to avenge the conquered.

(54)

The Sacred City

Wiracocha, who had fled from the darkness, ordered the sun to send a daughter and a son to earth to light the way for the blind.

The sun's children arrived on the banks of Lake Titicaca and set out through the Andean ravines. They carried a golden staff. Wherever it sank in at the first blow, they would there found a new kingdom. From the throne they would act like their father, who gives light, clarity, and warmth, sheds rain and dew, promotes harvests, multiplies flocks, and never lets a day pass without visiting the world.

They tried everywhere to stick in the golden staff, but the earth bounced it back. They scaled heights and crossed cataracts and plateaus. Whatever their feet touched was transformed; arid ground became fertile, swamps dried, and rivers returned to their beds. At dawn, wild geese escorted them; in the evening, condors.

Finally, beside Mount Wanakauri, the sun's children stuck in the staff. When the earth swallowed it, a rainbow rose in the sky.

Then the first of the Incas said to his sister and wife:

"Let us call the people together."

Between the mountains and the prairie, the valley was covered with scrub. No one had a house. The people lived in holes or in the shelter of rocks, eating roots, and didn't know how to weave cotton or wool to keep out the cold.

Everyone followed the sun's children. Everyone believed in them. Everyone knew, by the brilliance of their words and eyes, that the sun's children were not lying, and accompanied them to the place where the great city of Cuzco, still unborn, awaited them.

(76)

Pilgrims

The Maya-Quichés came from the east.

When they first reached the new lands, carrying their gods on their backs, they were scared that there would be no dawn. They had left happiness back in Tulán and arrived out of breath after a long and painful trek. They waited at the edge of the Izmachí forest, silent, huddled together, without anybody sitting down or stretching out to rest. But time passed and it went on being dark.

At last the morning star appeared in the sky.

The Quichés hugged each other and danced; and afterward, says the sacred book, *the sun rose like a man.*

Since then the Quichés gather at the end of each night to greet the morning star and watch the birth of the sun. When the sun is first about to peep out, they say:

"That's where we come from."

(188)

The Promised Land

Sleepless, naked, and battered, they journeyed night and day for more than two centuries. They went in search of the place where the land extends between canes and sedges.

Several times they got lost, scattered, and joined up again. They were buffeted by the winds and dragged themselves ahead lashed together, bumping and pushing each other. They fell from hunger and got up and fell again and got up again. In the volcanic region where no grass grows, they ate snake meat.

They carried the banner and the cloak of the god who had spoken to the priests in sleep and promised a kingdom of gold and quetzal feathers. *You shall subject all the peoples and cities from sea to sea,* the god had announced, *and not by witchcraft but by valor of the heart and strength of the arm.*

When they approached the luminous lake under the noonday sun, for the first time the Aztecs wept. There was the little island of clay: on the nopal cactus, higher than the rushes and wild grasses, the eagle spread his wings.

Seeing them come, the eagle lowered his head. These outcasts, massed on the edge of the lake, filthy, trembling, were the chosen, those who in remote times had been born out of the mouths of the gods.

Huitzilopochtli welcomed them. *"This is the place of our rest and our greatness,"* his voice resounded. *"I order that the city which will be queen of all others be called Tenochtitlán. This is Mexico!"*

(60 and 210)

Dangers

He who made the sun and the moon warned the Taínos to watch out for the dead.

In the daytime the dead hid themselves and ate guavas, but at night they went out for a stroll and challenged the living. Dead men offered duels and dead women, love. In the duels they vanished at will; and at the climax of love the lover found himself with nothing in his arms. Before accepting a duel with a man or lying down with a woman, one should feel the belly with one's hand, because the dead have no navels.

The lord of the sky also warned the Taínos to watch out even more for people with clothes on.

Chief Cáicihu fasted for a week and was worthy of his words. *Brief shall be the enjoyment of life,* announced the invisible one, he who has a mother but no beginning. *Men wearing clothes shall come, dominate, and kill.*

(51)

The Spider Web

Waterdrinker, priest of the Sioux, dreamed that outlandish creatures were weaving a huge spider web around his people. He awoke knowing that was how it was going to be and said to his people,

*When this happens, you shall live in square gray houses, in a barren
land, and beside those square gray houses you shall starve.*

(152)

The Prophet

Stretched out on his mat, the priest-jaguar of Yucatán listened to
the gods' message. They spoke to him through the roof, sitting
astride of his house, in a language that no one else knew.

Chilam Balam, he who was the mouth of the gods, remembered what had not yet happened:

*"Scattered through the world shall be the women who sing
and the men who sing and all who sing . . . No one will escape,
no one will be saved . . . There will be much misery in the years
of the rule of greed. Men will turn into slaves. Sad will be the face
of the sun . . . The world will be depopulated, it will become small
and humiliated . . ."*

(25)

OLD NEW WORLD

1492: The Ocean Sea

The Sun Route to the Indies

The breezes are sweet and soft, as in spring in Seville, and the sea is like a Guadalquivir river, but the swell no sooner rises than they get seasick and vomit, jammed into their fo'c'sles, the men who in three patched-up little ships cleave the unknown sea, the sea without a frame. Men, little drops in the wind. And if the sea doesn't love them? Night falls on the caravels. Whither will the wind toss them? A dorado, chasing a flying fish, jumps on board and the panic grows. The crew don't appreciate the savory aroma of the slightly choppy sea, nor do they listen to the din of the sea gulls and gannets that come from the west. That horizon: does the abyss begin there? Does the sea end?

Feverish eyes of mariners weatherbeaten in a thousand voyages, burning eyes of jailbirds yanked from Andalusian prisons and embarked by force: these eyes see no prophetic reflections of gold and silver in the foam of the waves, nor in the country and river birds that keep flying over the ships, nor in the green rushes and branches thick with shells that drift in the sargassos. The bottom of the abyss—is that where hell starts to burn? Into what kind of jaws will the trade winds hurl these little men? They gaze at the stars, seeking God, but the sky is as inscrutable as this never-navigated sea. They hear its roar, mother sea, the hoarse voice answering the wind with phrases of eternal condemnation, mysterious drums resounding in the depths. They cross themselves and want to pray and stammer: "Tonight we'll fall off the world, tonight we'll fall off the world."

(52)

1492: Guanahaní

Columbus

He falls on his knees, weeps, kisses the earth. He steps forward, staggering because for more than a month he has hardly slept, and beheads some shrubs with his sword.

Then he raises the flag. On one knee, eyes lifted to heaven, he pronounces three times the names of Isabella and Ferdinand. Beside him the scribe Rodrigo de Escobedo, a man slow of pen, draws up the document.

From today, everything belongs to those remote monarchs: the coral sea, the beaches, the rocks all green with moss, the woods, the parrots, and these laurel-skinned people who don't yet know about clothes, sin, or money and gaze dazedly at the scene.

Luis de Torres translates Christopher Columbus's questions into Hebrew: "Do you know the kingdom of the Great Khan? Where does the gold you have in your noses and ears come from?"

The naked men stare at him with open mouths, and the interpreter tries out his small stock of Chaldean: "Gold? Temples? Palaces? King of kings? Gold?"

Then he tries his Arabic, the little he knows of it: "Japan? China? Gold?"

The interpreter apologizes to Columbus in the language of Castile. Columbus curses in Genovese and throws to the ground his credentials, written in Latin and addressed to the Great Khan. The naked men watch the anger of the intruder with red hair and coarse skin, who wears a velvet cape and very shiny clothes.

Soon the word will run through the islands:

"Come and see the men who arrived from the sky! Bring them food and drink!"

(52)

1493: Barcelona

Day of Glory

The heralds announce him with their trumpets. The bells peal and the drums beat out festive rhythms. The admiral, newly returned from the Indies, mounts the stone steps and advances on the crimson carpet amid the silken dazzle of the applauding royal court. The man who has made the saints' and sages' prophecies come true reaches the platform, kneels, and kisses the hands of the queen and the king.

From the rear come the trophies: gleaming on trays, the bits of gold that Columbus had exchanged for little mirrors and red caps in the remote gardens newly burst from the sea. On branches and dead leaves are paraded the skins of lizards and snakes; and behind them, trembling and weeping, enter the beings never before seen. They are the few who have survived the colds, the measles, and the disgust for the Christians' food and bad smell. Not naked, as they were when they approached the three caravels and were captured, they have been covered up with trousers, shirts, and a few parrots that have been put in their hands and on their heads and shoulders. The parrots, robbed of their feathers by the foul winds of the voyage, look as moribund as the men. Of the captured women and children, none has survived.

Hostile murmurs are heard in the salon. The gold is minimal, and there is not a trace of black pepper, or nutmeg, or cloves, or ginger; and Columbus has not brought in any bearded sirens or men with tails, or the ones with only one eye or foot—and that foot big enough when raised to be protection from the fierce sun.

(44)

1493: Rome

The Testament of Adam

In the dim light of the Vatican, fragrant with oriental perfumes, the pope dictates a new bull.

A short time has passed since Rodrigo Borgia, of Xátiva, Valencia, took the name Alexander VI. Not a year yet since the day he bought for cash the seven votes he was short in the Sacred College, and could change a cardinal's purple for the ermine cape of the supreme pontiff.

Alexander devotes more time to calculating the price of indulgences than to meditating on the mystery of the Holy Trinity. Everyone knows that he prefers very brief Masses, except for the ones his jester Gabriellino celebrates in a mask in his private chambers, and everyone knows that the new pope is capable of rerouting the Corpus Christi procession to pass beneath a pretty woman's balcony.

He is also capable of cutting up the world as if it were a chicken: he raises a hand and traces a frontier, from head to tail of the planet, across the unknown sea. God's agent concedes in perpetuity all that has been or is being discovered, to the west of that line, to Isabella of Castile and Ferdinand of Aragon and their heirs on the Spanish throne. He entrusts them to send good, God-fearing, erudite, wise, expert men to the islands and mainlands discovered or to be discovered, to instruct the natives in the Catholic faith

and teach them good customs. Whatever is discovered to the east
will belong to the Portuguese crown.

Anguish and euphoria of sails unfurled: in Andalusia Columbus
is already preparing a second voyage to the regions where gold
grows in bunches on the vines and precious stones await in the
craniums of dragons.

(180)

1493: Huexotzingo

Where Is the Truth? Where Are the Roots?

This is the city of music, not of war: Huexotzingo, in the valley of
Tlaxcala. In a flash the Aztecs attack and damage it, and take prisoners to sacrifice to their gods.

On this evening, Tecayehuatzin, king of Huexotzingo, has
assembled the poets from other areas. In the palace gardens, the
poets chat about the flowers and songs that come down to earth,
a region of the fleeting moment, from within the sky, and that only
last up there in the house of the Giver of life. The poets talk and
doubt:

Can it be that men are real?
Will our song
Still be real tomorrow?

The voices follow one another. When night falls, the king of
Huexotzingo thanks them and says good-bye:

We know something that is real
The hearts of our friends.

(108)

1493: Pasto

Everybody Pays Taxes

Even these remote heights far to the north are reached by the Inca
Empire's tax collector.

The Quillacinga people have nothing to give, but in this vast kingdom all communities pay tribute, in kind or in labor time. No one, however far off and however poor, can forget who is in charge.

At the foot of the volcano, the chief of the Quillacingas steps forward and places a bamboo cylinder in the hands of the envoy from Cuzco. The cylinder is full of live lice.

(57 and 150)

1493: Santa Cruz Island

An Experience of Miquele de Cuneo from Savona

The shadow of the sails spreads across the sea. Gulfweed and jellyfish, moved by the waves, drift over the surface toward the coast.

From the quarterdeck of one of the caravels, Columbus contemplates the white beaches where he has again planted the cross and the gallows. This is his second voyage. How long it will last he doesn't know; but his heart tells him that all will come out well, and why wouldn't the admiral believe it? Doesn't he have the habit of measuring the ship's speed with his hand against his chest, counting the heartbeats?

Belowdecks in another caravel, in the captain's cabin, a young girl shows her teeth. Miquele de Cuneo reaches for her breasts, and she scratches and kicks him and screams. Miquele received her a while ago. She is a gift from Columbus.

He lashes her with a rope. He beats her hard on the head and stomach and legs. Her screams become moans, the moans become wails. Finally all that can be heard are the comings and goings of sea gulls and the creak of rocked timbers. From time to time waves send a spray through the porthole.

Miquele hurls himself upon the bleeding body and thrusts, gasps, wrestles. The air smells of tar, of saltpeter, of sweat. Then the girl, who seems to have fainted or died, suddenly fastens her nails in Miquele's back, knots herself around his legs, and rolls him over in a fierce embrace.

After some time, when Miquele comes to, he doesn't know where he is or what has happened. Livid, he detaches himself from her and knocks her away with his fist.

He staggers up on deck. Mouth open, he takes a deep breath of sea breeze. In a loud voice, as if announcing an eternal truth, he says, "These Indian woman are all whores."

(181)

1495: Salamanca
The First Word from America

Elio Antonio de Nebrija, language scholar, publishes here his "Spanish-Latin Vocabulary." The dictionary includes the first Americanism of the Castilian language:

Canoa: Boat made from a single timber.

The new word comes from the Antilles.

These boats without sails, made of the trunk of a ceiba tree, welcomed Christopher Columbus. Out from the islands, paddling canoes, came the men with long black hair and bodies tattooed with vermilion symbols. They approached the caravels, offered fresh water, and exchanged gold for the kind of little tin bells that sell for a copper in Castile.

(52 and 154)

1495: La Isabela
Caonabó

Detached, aloof, the prisoner sits at the entrance of Christopher Columbus's house, He has iron shackles on his ankles, and hand-cuffs trap his wrists.

Caonabó was the one who burned to ashes the Navidad fort that the admiral had built when he discovered this island of Haiti. He burned the fort and killed its occupants. And not only them: In these two long years he has castigated with arrows any Spaniards he came across in Cibao, his mountain territory, for their hunting of gold and people.

Alonso de Ojeda, veteran of the wars against the Moors, paid him a visit on the pretext of peace. He invited him to mount his horse, and put on him these handcuffs of burnished metal that tie his hands, saying that they were jewels worn by the monarchs of Castile in their balls and festivities.

Now Chief Caonabó spends the days sitting beside the door, his eyes fixed on the tongue of light that invades the earth floor at dawn and slowly retreats in the evening. He doesn't move an eyelash when Columbus comes around. On the other hand, when Ojeda appears, he manages to stand up and salute with a bow the only man who has defeated him.

(103 and 158)

1496: La Concepción

Sacrilege

Bartholomew Columbus, Christopher's brother and lieutenant, attends an incineration of human flesh.

Six men play the leads in the grand opening of Haiti's incinerator. The smoke makes everyone cough. The six are burning as a punishment and as a lesson: They have buried the images of Christ and the Virgin that Fray Ramón Pané left with them for protection and consolation. Fray Ramón taught them to pray on their knees, to say the Ave Maria and Paternoster and to invoke the name of Jesus in the face of temptation, injury, and death.

No one has asked them why they buried the images. They were hoping that the new gods would fertilize their fields of corn, cassava, boniato, and beans.

The fire adds warmth to the humid, sticky heat that foreshadows heavy rain.

(103)

1498: Santo Domingo

Earthly Paradise

In the evening, beside the Ozama River, Christopher Columbus writes a letter. His body creaks with rheumatism, but his heart jumps for joy. The discoverer explains to Their Catholic Majesties *that which is plainly evident:* Earthly Paradise is on the nipple of a woman's breast.

He realized it two months ago, when his caravels entered the

Gulf of Paria. *There ships start rising gently toward the sky* . . .
Navigating upstream to where the air has no weight, Columbus
has reached the farthest limit of the Orient. *In these the world's
most beautiful lands*, the men show cleverness, ingenuity, and
valor, and the extremely beautiful women wear only their long hair
and necklaces of many pearls wound around their bodies. The
water, sweet and clear, awakens thirst. Winter does not punish
nor summer burn, and the breeze caresses what it touches. The
trees offer fresh shade and, within arm's reach, fruits of great
delectability that arouse hunger.

But beyond *this greenness and this loveliness* no ship can go.
This is the frontier of the Orient. Here waters, lands, and islands
end. Very high and far away, the Tree of Life spreads its enormous
crown and the source of the four sacred rivers bubbles up. One of
them is the Orinoco, *which I doubt if such a great and deep river
is known in the world*.

The world is not round. The world is a woman's tit. The nipple
begins in the Gulf of Paria and rises to a point very close to the
heavens. The tip, where the juices of Paradise flow, will never be
reached by any man.

(53)

The Language of Paradise

The Guaraos, who live in the suburbs of Earthly Paradise, call the
rainbow *snake of necklaces* and the firmament *overhead sea*. Lightning is *glow of the rain*. One's friend, *my other heart*. The soul,
sun of the breast. The owl, *lord of the dark night*. A walking cane
is a *permanent grandson;* and for "I forgive," they say *I forget*.

(17)

1499: Granada

Who Are Spaniards?

The mosques remain open in Granada, seven years after the surrender of this last redoubt of the Moors in Spain. The advance of
the cross behind the victory of the sword is slow. Archbishop Cisneros decides that Christ cannot wait.

"Moors" is the Christian Spaniards' name for Spaniards of Islamic culture, who have been here for eight centuries. Thousands and thousands of Spaniards of Jewish culture have been condemned to exile. The Moors will likewise get the choice between baptism and exile; and for false converts burn the fires of the Inquisition. The unity of Spain, this Spain that has discovered America, will not result from the sum of its parts.

By Archbishop Cisneros's order the Muslim sages of Granada troop off to prison. Lofty flames devour Islamic books—religion and poetry, philosophy and science—the only copies guarding the words of a culture that has irrigated these lands and flourished in them.

From on high, the carved palaces of the Alhambra are mute witnesses of the enslavement, while its fountains continue giving water to the gardens.

(64, 218, and 223)

1500: Florence

Leonardo

He is just back from the market with various cages on his back. He puts them on the balcony, opens the little doors, and the birds make off. He watches the birds lose themselves in the sky, fluttering joyously, then sits down to work.

The noon sunshine warms his hand. On a wide board Leonardo da Vinci draws the world. And in the world that Leonardo draws appear the lands that Columbus has found toward the sunset. The artist invents them, as previously he has invented the airplane, the tank, the parachute, and the submarine, and he gives them form as previously he has incarnated the mystery of virgins and the passion of saints: He imagines the body of America, which still doesn't have that name, and sketches it as new land and not as part of Asia.

Columbus, seeking the Levant, has found the West. Leonardo guesses that the world has grown.

(209)

1506: Valladolid

The Fifth Voyage

Last night he dictated his last testament. This morning he asked if the king's messenger had arrived. Afterward, he slept. Nonsense mutterings and groans. He still breathes, but stertorously, as if battling against the air.

At court, no one has listened to his entreaties. He returned from the third voyage in chains, and on the fourth there was no one to pay attention to his titles and dignities.

Christopher Columbus is going out knowing that there is no passion or glory that does not lead to pain. On the other hand, he does not know that within a few years the banner that he stuck for the first time into the sands of the Caribbean will be waving over the empire of the Aztecs, in lands yet unknown, and over the kingdom of the Incas, under the unknown skies of the Southern Cross. He does not know that with all his lies, promises, and ravings, he has still fallen short. The supreme admiral of the ocean sea still believes he has reached Asia from the rear.

The ocean will not be called the Sea of Columbus; nor will the new world bear his name, but that of his Florentine friend Amerigo Vespucci, navigator and pilot master. But it was Columbus who found dazzling color that didn't exist in the European rainbow. Blind, he dies without seeing it.

(12 and 166)

1506: Tenochtitlán

The Universal God

Moctezuma has conquered in Teuctepec.

Fire rages in the temples. The drums beat. One after another, prisoners mount the steps toward the round, sacrificial stone. The priest plunges the obsidian dagger into each breast, lifts up the heart, and shows it to the sun, which rises above the blue volcanoes.

To what god is the blood offered? The sun demands it, to be born each day and travel from one horizon to the other. But the ostentatious death ceremonies also serve another god who does not appear in the codices nor in the chants.

If that god did not reign over the world, there would be no slaves nor masters nor vassals nor colonies. The Aztec merchants could not wrest a diamond for a bean from the defeated peoples, nor an emerald for a grain of corn, nor gold for sweetmeats, nor cacao for stones. The carriers would not be crossing the immensity of the empire in long lines with tons of tribute on their backs. The common people would dare to put on cotton tunics and would drink chocolate and audaciously wear the forbidden quetzal feathers and gold bracelets and magnolias and orchids reserved for the nobility. Then the masks hiding the warrior chiefs' faces would fall, the eagle's beak, the tiger's jaws, the plumes that wave and sparkle in the air.

The steps of the great temple are stained with blood, and skulls accumulate in the center of the plaza. Not only so that the sun should move, no; also so that that secret god should decide instead of man. In homage to that god, across the sea inquisitors fry heretics on bonfires or twist them in the torture chambers. It is the God of Fear. The God of Fear, who has rat's teeth and vulture's wings.

(60)

1511: Guauravo River

Agüeynaba

Three years ago, Captain Ponce de León arrived at this island of Puerto Rico in a caravel. Chief Agüeynaba opened his home to him, offered him food and drink and the choice of one of his daughters, and showed him the rivers from which gold was taken. He also gave him his name. Juan Ponce de León started calling himself Agüeynaba, and Agüeynaba received in exchange the name of the conquistador.

Three days ago the soldier Salcedo came alone to the banks of the Guauravo River. The Indians offered their backs for him to cross on. When they reached midstream, they let him fall and held him down against the river bottom until he stopped kicking. Afterward they laid him out on the grass.

Salcedo is now a glob of purple contorted flesh squeezed into a suit of armor, attacked by insects and quickly putrefying in the sun. The Indians look at it, holding their noses. Night and day they have been begging the stranger's pardon, for the benefit of the doubt. No point in it now. The drums broadcast the good news: *The invaders are not immortal.*

Tomorrow will come the rising. Agüeynaba will head it. The chief of the rebels will go back to his old name. He will recover his name, which has been used to humiliate his people.

"*Co-qui, co-qui,*" cry the little frogs. The drums calling for struggle drown out their crystal-counterpoint singsong.

(1)

1511: Aymaco

Becerrillo

The insurrection of chiefs Agüeynaba and Mabodamaca has been put down and all the prisoners have gone to their deaths.

Captain Diego de Salazar comes upon the old woman hidden in the underbrush and does not run his sword through her. "Here," he says to her, "take this letter to the governor, who is in Caparra."

The old woman opens her eyes slightly. Trembling, she holds out her fingers.

And she sets off. She walks like a small child, with a baby-bear lurch, carrying the envelope like a standard or a flag.

While the old woman is still within crossbow range, the captain releases Becerrillo. Governor Ponce de León has ordered that Becerrillo should receive twice the pay of a crossbowman, as an expert flusher-out of ambushes and hunter of Indians. The Indians of Puerto Rico have no worse enemy.

The first arrow knocks the old woman over. Becerrillo, his ears perked up, his eyes bulging, would devour her in one bite.

"Mr. Dog," she entreats him, "I'm taking this letter to the governor."

Becerrillo doesn't know the local language, but the old woman shows him the empty envelope.

"Don't do me harm, Mr. Dog."

Becerrillo sniffs at the envelope. He circles a few times the trembling bag of bones that whines words, lifts a paw, and pees on her.

(166)

1511: Yara

Hatuey

In these islands, in these Calvaries, those who choose death by hanging themselves or drinking poison along with their children are many. The invaders cannot avoid this vengeance, but know how to explain it: the Indians, *so savage that they think everything is in common*, as Oviedo will say, *are people by nature idle and vicious, doing little work. For a pastime many killed themselves with venom so as not to work, and others hanged themselves with their own hands.*

Hatuey, Indian chief of the Guahaba region, has not killed himself. He fled with his people from Haiti in a canoe and took refuge in the caves and mountains of eastern Cuba.

There he pointed to a basketful of gold and said: "This is the god of the Christians. For him they pursue us. For him our fathers and our brothers have died. Let us dance for him. If our dance pleases him, this god will order them not to mistreat us."

They catch him three months later.

They tie him to a stake.

Before lighting the fire that will reduce him to charcoal and ash, the priest promises him glory and eternal rest if he agrees to be baptized. Hatuey asks:

"Are there Christians in that heaven?"

"Yes."

Hatuey chooses hell, and the firewood begins to crackle.

(102,103, and 166)

1511: Santo Domingo

The First Protest

In the log-walled, palm-roofed church, Antonio de Montesinos, Dominican friar, hurls thunder from the pulpit. He denounces the extermination:

"By what right and by what justice do you hold the Indians in such cruel and horrible bondage? Aren't they dying, or better said, aren't you killing them, to get gold every day? Are you not

obliged to love them as yourselves? Don't you understand this, don't you feel it?"

Then Montesinos, head high, makes his way through the astounded multitude.

A murmur of fury swells up. They didn't bargain for this, these peasants from Estremadura and shepherds from Andalusia who have repudiated their names and histories and, with rusty arquebuses slung over their shoulders, left at random in search of the mountains of gold and the nude princesses on this side of the ocean. A Mass of pardon and consolation was what was needed by these adventurers bought with promises on the steps of Seville Cathedral, these flea-bitten captains, veterans of no battle, and condemned prisoners who had to choose between America and jail or gallows.

"We'll denounce you to King Ferdinand! You'll be deported!"

One bewildered man remains silent. He came to these lands nine years ago. Owner of Indians, gold mines, and plantations, he has made a small fortune. His name is Bartolomé de las Casas, and he will soon be the first priest ordained in the New World.

(103)

1513: Cuareca

Leoncico

Their muscles almost burst through the skin. Their yellow eyes never stop flashing. They pant. They snap their jaws and bite holes in the air. No chain can hold them when they get the command to attack.

Tonight, by order of Captain Balboa, the dogs will sink their teeth into the naked flesh of fifty Indians of Panama. They will disembowel and devour fifty who were guilty of the abominable sin of sodomy, *who only lacked tits and wombs to be women*. The spectacle will take place in this mountain clearing, among the trees that the storm uprooted a few days ago. By torchlight the soldiers quarrel and jockey for the best places.

Vasco Núñez de Balboa chairs the ceremony. His dog Leoncico heads up God's avengers. Leoncico, son of Becerrillo, has a body crisscrossed with scars. He is a past master of capturings and quarterings. He gets a sublieutenant's pay and a share of each gold or slave booty.

In two days' time Balboa will discover the Pacific Ocean.

(81 and 166)

1513: Gulf of San Miguel

Balboa

With water up to his waist, he raises his sword and yells to the four winds.

His men carve an immense cross in the sand. The scribe Valderrábano registers the names of those who have just discovered the new ocean, and Father Andrés intones the *Te Deum Laudamus*.

Balboa discards his fifteen kilos of armor, throws his sword far away, and jumps in.

He splashes about and lets himself be dragged by the waves, dizzy with a joy he won't feel again. The sea opens for him, embraces him, rocks him. Balboa would like to drink it dry.

(141)

1514: Sinú River

The Summons

They have crossed much water and time and are fed up with heat, jungles, and mosquitos. They carry out, however, the king's instructions: not to attack the natives without first summoning them to surrender. St. Augustine authorizes war against those who abuse their liberty, because their liberty would make them dangerous if they were not tamed; but as St. Isidore well says, no war is just without a previous declaration.

Before they start the rush for the gold, for nuggets possibly as big as eggs, lawyer Martín Fernández de Enciso reads, complete with periods and commas, the ultimatum that the interpreter translates painfully by fits and starts.

Enciso speaks in the name of King Ferdinand and Queen Juana, his daughter, tamers of barbarous peoples. He makes it known to the Indians of the Sinú that God came to the world and left St. Peter as his representative, that St. Peter's successor is the holy father and that the holy father, lord of the universe, has awarded to the king of Castile all the lands of the Indies and of this peninsula.

The soldiers bake in their armor. Enciso slowly and meticulously summons the Indians to leave these lands since they don't belong to them, and if they want to stay to pay their highnesses tribute in gold in token of obedience. The interpreter does his best.

The two chiefs listen, sitting down and without blinking, to the odd character who announces to them that in case of refusal or delay he will make war on them, turn them into slaves along with their women and children, and sell and dispose of them as such and that the deaths and damages of that just war will not be the Spaniards' responsibility.

The chiefs reply, without a glance at Enciso, that the holy father has indeed been generous with others' property but must have been drunk to dispose of what was not his and that the king of Castile is impertinent to come threatening folk he doesn't know.

Then the blood flows.

Subsequently the long speech will be read at dead of night, without an interpreter and half a league away from villages that will be taken by surprise. The natives, asleep, won't hear the words that declare them guilty of the crime committed against them.

(78, 81, and 166)

1514: Santa María del Darién

For Love of Fruit

Gonzalo Fernández de Oviedo, a new arrival, tries out the fruit of the New World.

The guava seems to him much superior to the apple.

The guanábana is pretty to look at and offers a white, watery pulp of very mild flavor, which, however much you eat of it, causes neither harm nor indigestion.

The mamey has a finger-licking flavor and smells very good. *Nothing better exists*, he finds.

But he bites into a medlar, and an aroma unequaled even by musk invades his head. *The medlar is the best fruit*, he corrects himself, *and nothing comparable can be found*.

Then he peels a pineapple. The golden pine smells as peaches would like to and is able to give an appetite to people who have forgotten the joys of eating. Oviedo knows no words worthy of describing its virtues. It delights his eyes, his nose, his fingers, his tongue. *This outdoes them all, as the feathers of the peacock outshine those of any bird*.

(166)

1515: Antwerp

Utopia

The New World adventures bring the taverns of this Flemish port to the boil. One summer night, on the waterfront, Thomas More meets or invents Rafael Hithloday, a sailor from Amerigo Vespucci's fleet, who says he has discovered the isle of Utopia off some coast of America.

The sailor relates that in Utopia neither money nor private property exists. There, scorn for gold and for superfluous consumption is encouraged, and no one dresses ostentatiously. Everybody gives the fruits of his work to the public stores and freely collects what he needs. The economy is planned. There is no hoarding, which is the son of fear, nor is hunger known. The people choose their prince and the people can depose him; they also elect the priests. The inhabitants of Utopia loathe war and its honors, although they fiercely defend their frontiers. They have a religion that does not offend reason and rejects useless mortifications and forcible conversions. The laws permit divorce but severely punish conjugal betrayals and oblige everyone to work six hours a day. Work and rest are shared; the table is shared. The community takes charge of children while their parents are busy. Sick people get privileged treatment; euthanasia avoids long, painful agonies. Gardens and orchards occupy most of the space, and music is heard wherever one goes.

(146)

1519: Frankfurt

Charles V

A half century has passed since Gutenberg's death, and printeries multiply all over Europe; they publish the Bible in Gothic letters, and gold and silver price quotations in Gothic numerals. The monarch devours men, and men shit gold coins in Hieronymus Bosch's garden of delights; and Michaelangelo, while painting and sculpting his athletic saints and prophets, writes: *The blood of Christ is sold by the spoonful*. Everything has its price: the pope's throne and the monarch's crown, the cardinal's cape and the bishop's miter. Indulgences, excommunications, and titles of nobility are bought. The Church deems lending at interest a sin, but the holy father mortgages Vatican lands to the bankers; and on the banks of the Rhine, the crown of the Holy Empire is offered to the highest bidder.

Three candidates dispute the heritage of Charlemagne. The electors swear by the purity of their votes and cleanliness of their hands and pronounce their verdict at noon, the hour of the Angelus: they sell the crown of Europe to the king of Spain, Charles I, son of the seducer and the madwoman and grandson of the Catholic monarchs, for 850,000 florins, which Germany's bankers Függer and Welser plunk down on the table.

Charles I turns himself into Charles V, emperor of Spain, Germany, Austria, Naples, Sicily, the Low Countries, and the immense New World, defender of the Catholic faith, and God's warrior vicar on earth.

Meanwhile, the Muslims threaten the frontiers, and Martin Luther nails up his defiant heresies on the door of a Wittemberg church. A prince must have war as his sole objective and thought, Macchiavelli has written. At age nineteen, the new monarch is the most powerful man in history. On his knees, he kisses the sword.

(116, 209, and 218)

1519: Acla

Pedrarias

Noise of sea and drums. Night has fallen, but there is light from the moon. Around the plaza, fish and dried ears of corn hang from the straw roofs.

Enter Balboa, chained, hands bound behind his back. They untie him. Balboa smokes his last cigar. Without saying a word, he places his neck on the block. The executioner raises the ax.

From his house, Pedro Arias de Avila peers furtively through the cane wall. He is sitting on the coffin that he brought from Spain. He uses the coffin as a chair or a table, and once a year,

year after year, covers it with candles, during the requiem that celebrates his resurrection. They call him Pedrarias the Buried ever since he got up out of this coffin, wrapped in a shroud, as nuns sang the office of the dead and relatives sobbed uncontrollably. Previously they had called him Pedrarias the Gallant, because of his invincibility in tournaments, battles, and gallantries; and now, although he is nearing eighty, he deserves the name of Fury of the Lord. When Pedrarias wakes up shaking his white mane because he lost a hundred Indians at dice the night before, his glance is better avoided.

Ever since he landed on these beaches, Pedrarias has distrusted Balboa. Balboa being his son-in-law, he doesn't kill him without a trial. There are not too many lawyers around here, so the judge is also counsel and prosecutor; the trial, long.

Balboa's head rolls on the sand.

It was Balboa who had founded this town of Acla, among trees twisted by the winds. On the day Acla was born, a black bird of prey dived from above the clouds, seized the steel helmet from Balboa's head, and took off, cawing.

Here Balboa was building, piece by piece, the brigantines that would be launched to explore the new sea he had discovered.

The job will be completed by the executioner. He will found an enterprise of conquest, and Pedrarias will be his partner. The executioner, who came with Columbus on his last voyage, will be a marquis with twenty thousand vassals in the mysterious kingdoms to the south. His name is Francisco Pizarro.

(81 and 141)

1519: Tenochtitlán

Portents of Fire, Water, Earth, and Air

One day long ago, the soothsayers flew to the cave of the mother of the god of war. The witch, who had not washed for eight centuries, did not smile or greet them. Without thanking them, she accepted their gifts—cloth, skins, feathers—and listened sourly to their news. *Mexico*, the soothsayers told her, *is mistress and queen, and all cities are under her orders*. The old woman grunted her sole comment: *The Aztecs have defeated the others*, she said, *and others will come who will defeat the Aztecs*.

Time passed.

For the past ten years, portents have been piling up.

A bonfire leaked flames from the middle of the sky for a whole night.

A sudden three-tongued fire came up from the horizon and flew to meet the sun.

The house of the god of war committed suicide, setting fire to itself. Buckets of water were thrown on it, and the water enlivened the flames.

Another temple was burned by a flash of lightning one evening when there was no storm.

The lake in which the city is situated turning into a boiling cauldron. The waters rose, white-hot, towering with fury, carrying away houses, even tearing up foundations.

Fishermen's nets brought up an ash-colored bird along with the fish. On the bird's head there was a round mirror. In the mirror, Emperor Moctezuma saw advancing an army of soldiers who ran on the legs of deer, and he heard their war cries. Then the soothsayers who could neither read the mirror nor had eyes to see the two-headed monsters that implacably haunted Moctezuma's sleeping and waking hours were punished. The emperor shut them up in cages and condemned them to die of hunger.

Every night the cries of an unseen woman startle all who sleep in Tenochtitlán and in Tlatelolco. *My little children,* she cries, *now we have to go far from here!* There is no wall that the woman's cry does not pierce: *Where shall we go, my little children?*

(60 and 210)

1519: Cempoala

Cortés

Twilight of soaring flames on the coast of Veracruz. Eleven ships are burning up; burning, too, the rebel soldiers who hang from the yardarm of the flagship. While the sea opens its jaws to devour the bonfires, Hernán Cortés, standing on the beach, presses on the pommel of his sword and uncovers his head.

Not only the ships and the hanged have met their end; now there is no going back, no more life than what is born tomorrow, either gold and glory or the vulture of defeat. On the Veracruz beach have been sunk the dreams of those who would have liked to return to Cuba to sleep the colonial siesta in net hammocks, wrapped in women's hair and cigar smoke: the sea leads to the past and the land to danger. Those who could afford it will go forward on horseback, the others on foot: seven hundred men into Mexico, toward the mountains and the volcanos and the mystery of Moctezuma.

Cortés adjusts his feathered headpiece and turns his back on the flames. In one gallop he makes it to the native village of Cempoala, while night is still falling. He says nothing to the men. They will find out as they go.

He drinks wine alone in his tent. Perhaps he thinks about the men he has killed without confession or the women he has bedded without marriage since those student days in Salamanca that seem so far off, or his lost years as a bureaucrat in the Antilles during the waiting time. Perhaps he thinks about Governor Diego Velázquez, who will soon be quivering with rage in Santiago de Cuba. Certainly he smiles if he thinks about that soporific fool, whose orders he will never again obey; or about the surprise that awaits the soldiers whom he hears laughing and cursing at games of dice and cards.

Something of this runs in his head, or maybe the fascination and panic of the days to come; then he looks up, sees her at the door, recognizes her against the light. Her name was Malinali or Malinche when the chief of Tabasco made her a gift to him. She has been known as Marina for a week.

Cortés speaks a few words while she waits, perfectly still. Then in a single movement the girl loosens her hair and clothing. A cascade of colored cloths falls between her bare feet, and the glow of her body silences him.

A few paces away by the light of the moon, the soldier Bernal Díaz del Castillo records the day's events. He uses a drum as a table.

(56 and 62)

1519: Tenochtitlán

Moctezuma

Great mountains have arrived, moving over the sea, off the coasts of Yucatán. The god Quetzalcóatl has come back. The people kiss the bows of the ships.

Emperor Moctezuma mistrusts his own shadow.

"What shall I do? Where will I hide?"

Moctezuma would like to turn into a stone or a stick. The court jesters cannot distract him. Quetzalcóatl, the bearded god, he who loaned the land and the beautiful songs, has come to demand what is his.

In olden times, Quetzalcóatl had departed for the east after burning his house of gold and his house of coral. The handsomest birds flew to open the way for him. He put out to sea on a raft of snakes and was lost to sight sailing into the dawn. Now he has returned. The bearded god, the plumed serpent has returned hungry.

The earth shakes. In the stewpots the birds dance as they boil. *No one will remain*, the poet had said. *No one, no one, truly no one alive on the earth.*

Moctezuma has sent great offerings of gold to the god Quetzalcóatl, helmets filled with gold dust, golden ducks, golden dogs, golden tigers, golden necklaces, and wands and bows and arrows, but the more gold the god eats, the more he wants; and he is advancing toward Tenochtitlán, dissatisfied. He marches between the great volcanos, and behind him come other bearded gods. The hands of the invaders send forth thunder that stuns and fire that kills.

"What shall I do? Where will I hide?"

Moctezuma lives with his head buried in his hands.

Two years ago, when there were already omens aplenty of the god's return and vengeance, Moctezuma sent his soothsayers to the cave of Huémac, king of the dead. The soothsayers descended into the depths of Chapultepec with a retinue of dwarfs and hunchbacks and delivered to Huémac on the emperor's behalf an offering of skins of recently flayed prisoners. Huémac sent word back to Moctezuma:

"Don't fool yourself. Here there's no rest or joy."

And he told him to fast and to sleep without a woman.

Moctezuma obeyed. He made a long penitence. The eunuchs shut tight the quarters of his wives; the cooks forgot about his favorite dishes. But things got worse. The black crows of distress came in flocks. Moctezuma lost the protection of Tlazoltéotl, the goddess of love, also the goddess of shit, she who eats our nastiness so that love is possible; and thus the soul of the solitary emperor was drowned in garbage and blackness. He sent more messengers to Huémac on several occasions with entreaties and gifts, until finally the king of the dead gave him an appointment.

On the night arranged, Moctezuma went to meet him. His boat headed for Chapultepec. The emperor stood in the bow, and the mist over the lake opened up for his flamingo plume.

Shortly before reaching the foot of the mountain, Moctezuma heard the sound of oars. A canoe appeared, moving rapidly, and somebody shone out for an instant in the black mist, naked and alone, his paddle raised like a lance.

"Is that you, Huémac?"

Whoever it was kept moving nearer until he almost grazed the emperor. He looked into the emperor's eyes as no man can look. "Coward!" he said to him and disappeared.

(60, 200, and 210)

1519: Tenochtitlán

The Capital of the Aztecs

Dumbfounded by the beauty of it, the conquistadors ride down the causeway. Tenochtitlán seems to have been torn from the pages of Amadís, *things never heard of, never seen, nor even dreamed* . . . The sun rises behind the volcanos, enters the lake, and breaks the floating mist into shreds. The city—streets, canals, high-towered temples—glitters before them. A multitude comes out to greet the invaders, silent and unhurried, while innumerable canoes open furrows in the cobalt waters.

Moctezuma arrives on a litter, seated on a soft jaguar skin, beneath a canopy of gold, pearls, and green feathers. The lords of the kingdom go ahead sweeping the ground he will tread.

He welcomes the god Quetzalcóatl:

"Thou hast come to occupy thy throne," he says. *"Thou hast come amid clouds, amid mists. I am not seeing thee in dreams. I am not dreaming. Unto thy land hast thou come . . ."*

Those who accompany Quetzalcóatl receive garlands of magnolias, necklaces of flowers around their necks, on their arms, on their breasts: the flower of the shield and the flower of the heart, the flowers of fine perfume and of golden hue.

Quetzalcóatl is a native of Estremadura who landed on American shores with his whole wardrobe on his back and a few coins in his purse. He was nineteen when he set foot on the wharf at

Santo Domingo and asked: *Where is the gold?* He is now thirty-four and a captain of great daring. He wears armor of black iron and leads an army of horsemen, lancers, crossbowmen, riflemen, and fierce dogs. He has promised his soldiers: *"I will make you in a very short time the richest men of all who ever came to the Indies."*

Emperor Moctezuma, who opens the gates of Tenochtitlán, will soon be finished. In a short while he will be called *woman of the Spaniards,* and his own people will stone him to death. Young Cuauhtémoc will take his place. *He* will fight.

(60 and 62)

Aztec Song of the Shield

On the shield, the virgin gave birth
to the great warrior.
On the shield, the virgin gave birth
to the great warrior.

On the mountain of the serpent, the conqueror,
amid the mountains,
with war paint
and with eagle shield.

No one, for sure, could face him,
The ground began to spin
when he put on his war paint
and raised his shield.

(77)

1520: Teocalhueyacan

"Night of Sorrow"

Hernán Cortés reviews the few survivors of his army while Malinche sews the torn flags.

Tenochtitlán is behind them. Behind, too, as if bidding them farewell, the column of smoke spewed by the volcano Popocatépetl, which no wind seemed able to bend.

The Aztecs have recovered their city, the roofs bristling with bows and lances, the lake covered with battle canoes. The conquistadors fled in disorder, pursued by a storm of arrows and stones, while war drums, yells, and curses stunned the night.

These wounded, mutilated, dying men left to Cortés saved themselves by using corpses as a bridge: They crossed to the other shore stepping on horses that slipped and drowned and on soldiers killed by arrows and stones or drowned by the weight of the gold-filled sacks that they could not bring themselves to leave behind.

(62 and 200)

1520: Segura de la Frontera

The Distribution of Wealth

Murmurings and scufflings in the Spaniards' camp. The soldiers have no alternative. They must surrender the gold bars saved from the disaster. Anyone hiding something will be hanged.

The bars come from the works of Mexico's goldsmiths and sculptors. Before being turned into booty and melted into ingots, this gold was a serpent about to strike, a tiger about to jump, an eagle about to soar, or a dagger that snaked and flowed like a river in the air.

Cortés explains that this gold is mere bubbles compared with what awaits them. He takes out the fifth part for the king, another fifth for himself, plus the shares due to his father and the horse that died under him, and gives almost all the rest to the captains. Little or nothing remains for the soldiers who have licked this gold, bitten it, weighed it in their hands, slept with their heads pillowed on it, told it their dreams of revenge.

Meanwhile, branding irons mark the faces of Indian slaves newly captured in Tepeaca and Huaquechula.

The air smells of burned flesh.

(62 and 205)

1520: Brussels

Dürer

These things must be emanations from the sun, like the men and women who made them in the remote land they inhabit: helmets and girdles, feather fans, dresses, cloaks, hunting gear, a gold sun and a silver moon, a blowgun, and other weapons of such beauty that they seem made to revive their victims.

The greatest draftsman of all the ages does not tire of staring at them. This is part of the booty that Cortés seized from Moctezuma: the only pieces that were not melted into ingots. King Charles, newly seated on the Holy Empire's throne, is exhibiting to the public the trophies from his new bits of world.

Albrecht Dürer doesn't know the Mexican poem that explains that the true artist finds pleasure in his work and talks with his heart, because he has one that isn't dead and eaten by ants. But seeing what he sees, Dürer hears those words and finds that he is experiencing the greatest happiness of his half century of life.

(108)

1520: Tlaxcala

Toward the Reconquest
of Tenochtitlán

The year is close to its end. As soon as the sun comes out, Cortés will give the order to march. His troops, pulverized by the Aztecs, have been rehabilitated in a few months under the protection of their Indian allies of Tlaxcala, Huexotzingo, and Texcoco. An army of fifty thousand natives is under his orders, and new soldiers have come from Spain, Santo Domingo, and Cuba, well provided with horses, arquebuses, crossbows, and cannon. To fight on the water when they reach the lake, Cortés will have sails, iron fittings, and masts to equip three brigantines. The Huexotzingo Indians will lay down the timbers.

The first light throws the volcanic skyline into relief. Beyond, rising out of the prodigious waters, Tenochtitlán awaits defiantly.

(56)

1521: *Tlatelolco*

Sword of Fire

Blood flows like water; the drinking water is acid with blood. To eat, only earth remains. They fight house by house, over the ruins and over the dead, day and night. Almost three months of battle without letup. Only dust and the stink of corpses to breathe; but still drums beat in the last towers, bells tinkle on the ankles of the last warriors. The strength-giving battle cries and chants continue. The last women take up battle-axes from the fallen and until they collapse keep hammering on shields.

Emperor Cuauhtémoc summons the best of his captains. He puts on the long-feathered owl headpiece and takes up the sword of fire. With this sword in his fist, the god of war had emerged from his mother's belly, back in the most remote of times. With this serpent of sunbeams, Huitzilopochtli had decapitated his sister the moon and had cut to pieces his four hundred brothers, the stars, because they didn't want to let him be born.

Cuauhtémoc orders: *"Let our enemies look on it and be struck with terror."*

The sword of fire opens up an avenue. The chosen captain advances, alone, through the smoke and debris.

They fell him with a single shot from an arquebus.

(60, 107, and 200)

1521: *Tenochtitlán*

The World Is Silenced in the Rain

Suddenly, all at once, the cries and the drums cease. Gods and men have been defeated. With the gods' death, time has died. With the men's death, the city has died. This warrior city, she of the white willows and white rushes, has died fighting as she lived. No more will conquered princes of all the regions come in boats through the mist to pay her tribute.

A stunning silence reigns. And the rain begins to fall. Thunder and lightning fill the sky, and it rains all through the night.

The gold is piled into huge baskets. Gold of shields and insignia of war, gold of the masks of gods, lip and ear pendants, ornaments, lockets. The gold is weighed and the prisoners priced. *One of these wretches is hardly worth two handfuls of corn* . . . The soldiers gather to play dice and cards.

Fire burns the soles of Emperor Cuauhtémoc's feet, anointed with oil, while the world is silent, and it rains.

[60, 107, and 200)

1521: Florida
Ponce de León

He was old, or felt he was. There wouldn't be enough time, nor would the weary heart hold out. Juan Ponce de León wanted to discover and win the unconquered world that the Florida islands had announced. He wanted to dwarf the memory of Christopher Columbus by the grandeur of his feats.

Here he landed, following the magic river that crosses the garden of delights. Instead of the fountain of youth, he has met this arrow that penetrates his breast. He will never bathe in the waters that restore energy to the muscles and shine to the eyes without erasing the experience of the mature spirit.

The soldiers carry him in their arms toward the ship. The conquered captain murmurs complaints like a newborn baby, but his years remain many and he is still aging. The men carrying him confirm without astonishment that here a new defeat has occurred in the continuous struggle between the alwayses and the nevers.

(166)

1522: Highways of Santo Domingo
Feet

The rebellion, the first by black slaves in America, has been smashed. It had broken out in the sugar mills of Diego Columbus, son of the discoverer. Fire had spread through the mills and plantations of the whole island. The blacks had risen up with the few surviving Indians, armed with sticks and stones and sugar-cane lances that broke against armor in futile fury.

Now from gallows scattered along the highways hang women and men, the young and the old. At the traveler's eye level dangle feet by which he can guess what the victims were before death came. Among these leathery limbs, gashed by toil and tread, are frisky feet and formal feet; prisoner feet and feet that still dance, loving the earth and calling for war.

(166)

1522: Seville

The Longest Voyage Ever Made

No one thought they were still alive, but last night they arrived. They dropped anchor and fired all their guns. They didn't land right away, nor let themselves be seen. In the morning they appeared on the wharf. Shaking and in rags, they entered Seville carrying lighted torches. The crowd opened up, amazed, for this procession of scarecrows headed by Juan Sebastián de Elcano. They stumbled ahead, leaning on each other for support, from church to church, fulfilling pledges, always pursued by the crowd. They chanted as they went.

They had left three years ago, down the river in five elegant ships that headed west, a bunch of adventurers who had come together to seek the passage between the oceans, and fortune and glory. All fugitives, they put to sea in flight from poverty, love, jail, or the gallows.

Now the survivors talk of storms, crimes, and marvels. They have seen seas and lands without map or name; six times they have crossed the zone where the world boils, without ever getting burned. To the south they have encountered blue snow and in the sky, four stars forming a cross. They have seen the sun and the moon moving backward and fish flying. They have heard of women whom the wind impregnates and met some black birds like crows that rush into the open jaws of whales and devour their hearts. On one very remote island, they report, live little people half a meter tall, with ears that reach down to their feet. So long are their ears that when they go to bed, one serves as pillow and the other as blanket. They also report that when the Molucca Indians saw the small boats launched from the ships, they thought those boats were small daughters of the ships, that the ships gave them birth and suckled them.

The survivors say that in the South of the South, where the lands open up and the oceans embrace, the Indians light huge bonfires night and day to keep from dying of cold. Those Indians are such giants, they say, that our heads hardly reached their waists. Magellan, who headed the expedition, caught two of them by putting iron fetters on their ankles and wrists as adornments; but later one died of scurvy and the other of heat.

They say that they had no alternative to drinking stagnant water, holding their noses, and that they ate sawdust, hides, and the rats that showed up to dispute with them the last wormy biscuits. Anyone who died of hunger they threw overboard, and as they had no stones to sink them, the corpses remained floating on the water: Europeans with faces to heaven and Indians face down. When they got to the Moluccas, one sailor traded the Indians a playing card, the king of diamonds, for six fowls, but couldn't even take a bite of them, so swollen were his gums.

They have seen Magellan weep—tears in the eyes of the tough Portuguese navigator when the ships entered the ocean never before crossed by a European. And they have known his terrible tempers, when he had two rebellious captains beheaded and quartered and left other rebels in the desert. Magellan is now carrion, a trophy in the hands of Filipino natives who shot a poisoned arrow into his leg.

Of the 237 sailors and soldiers who left Seville three years ago, 18 have returned. They arrived in one creaky ship with a worm-eaten keel that leaks on all four sides.

The survivors. These men dead of hunger who have just sailed around the world for the first time.

(20 and 78)

1523: Cuzco

Huaina Cápac

Before the rising sun he throws himself down and touches his forehead to the ground. He grasps the first rays in his hands, brings them to his mouth, and drinks the light. Then he rises, stands, and looks straight at the sun, without blinking.

Behind Huaina Cápac his many women wait with bowed heads. Waiting, too, in silence, the many princes. The Inca is looking at the sun, he looks at it equal to equal, and a murmur of scandal grows among the priests.

Many years have passed since the day when Huaina Cápac, son of the resplendent father, came to the throne with the title of young-and-potent-chief-rich-in-virtues. He has extended the empire far beyond the frontiers of his ancestors. Eager for power, Huaina Cápac, discoverer, conqueror, has led his armies from the Amazon jungle to the heights of Quito and from the Chaco to the coasts of Chile. With flying arrow and deadly battle-ax, he has made himself the master of new mountains, plains, and sandy deserts. There is no one who does not dream about him and fear him in this kingdom that is now bigger than Europe. On Huaina Cápac depend pastures, water, and people. His will has moved mountains and men. In this empire that does not know the wheel, he has had buildings constructed in Quito with stones from Cuzco *so that in the future his greatness may be known and his word believed by men*.

The Inca looks fixedly at the sun. Not defiantly, as the priests fear, but out of pity. Huaina Cápac feels sorry for the sun, because, being his father and father of all the Incas since the most ancient of days, the sun has no right to fatigue or boredom. The sun never rests, plays, or forgets. He may not miss his daily appointment and runs today the same course across the sky as yesterday and to-morrow.

While he contemplates the sun, Huaina Cápac decides: "Soon I'll be dying."

(50 and 76)

1523: Cuauhcapolca

The Chief's Questions

He delivers food and gold and accepts baptism. But he asks Gil González de Avila to explain how Jesus can be man and god; and Mary, virgin and mother. He asks where souls go when they leave the body and whether the holy father in Rome is immune to death.

He asks who elected the king of Castile. Chief Nicaragua was elected by the elders of the communities, assembled at the foot of a ceiba tree. Was the king elected by the elders of his communities?

The chief also asks the conquistador to tell him for what purpose so few men want so much gold. Will their bodies be big enough for so much adornment?

Later he asks if it is true, as a prophet said, that the sun, stars, and moon will lose their light and the sky will fall.

Chief Nicaragua does not ask why no children will be born in these parts. No prophet has told him that within a few years the women will refuse to give birth to slaves.

(81 and 103)

1523: Painala

Malinche

By Cortés she had a child and for Cortés she opened the gates of an empire. She has been his shadow and watchman, interpreter, counselor, go-between, and mistress all through the conquest of Mexico and continues to ride beside him.

She passes through Painala dressed as a Spanish woman, fine woolens, silks, satins, and at first no one recognizes the distinguished lady who comes with the new masters. From the back of a chestnut steed, Malinche surveys the banks of the river, takes a deep breath of the sweet air, and seeks in vain the leafy nooks where she discovered magic and fear more than twenty years ago. She has known many rains and suns and sufferings and sorrows since her mother sold her as a slave and she was dragged from Mexican soil to serve the Maya lords of Yucatán.

When her mother learns who has come to visit her in Painala, she throws herself at her feet and bathes them in tears imploring forgiveness. Malinche restrains her with a gesture, raises her by the shoulders, embraces her, and hangs around her neck the necklaces she is wearing. Then she remounts her horse and continues on her way with the Spaniards.

She does not need to hate her mother. Ever since the lords of Yucatán made a present of her to Hernán Cortés four years before, Malinche has had time to avenge herself. The debt is paid: Mexicans bow and tremble at her approach. One glance from her black eyes is enough for a prince to hang on the gallows. Long after her death, her shadow will hover over the great Tenochtitlán that she did so much to defeat and humiliate, and her ghost with

the long loose hair and billowing robe will continue striking fear
for ever and ever, from the woods and caves of Chapultepec.

(29 and 62)

1524: Quetzaltenango
The Poet Will Tell Children the Story of This Battle

The poet will speak of Pedro de Alvarado and of those who came
with him to teach fear.

He will relate that when the native troops had been destroyed,
and when Guatemala was a slaughterhouse, Captain Tecum Umán
rose into the air and flew with wings, and feathers sprouted from
his body. He flew and fell upon Alvarado and with one fierce blow
severed the head of his horse. But Alvarado and the horse divided
into two and stayed that way: the conquistador detached himself
from the decapitated horse and stood up. Captain Tecum flew off
again and rose higher, all aglow. When he dived down from the
clouds, Alvarado dodged and ran him through with this lance. The
dogs dashed up to tear Tecum Umán apart, and Alvarado's sword
held them back. For a long time Alvarado contemplated his beaten
enemy, his body slashed open, the quetzal feathers sprouting from
his arms and legs, the wings broken, the triple crown of pearls,
diamonds, and emeralds. Alvarado called to his soldiers. "Look,"
he said to them, and made them remove their helmets.

The children, seated in a circle around the poet, will ask: "And
all this you saw? You heard?"

"Yes."

"You were here?" the children will ask.

"No. None of our people who were here survived."

The poet will point to the moving clouds and the sway of the
treetops.

"See the lances?" he will ask. "See the horses' hooves? The
rain of arrows? The smoke? Listen," he will say, and put his ear
against the ground, filled with explosions.

And he will teach them to smell history in the wind, to touch
it in stones polished by the river, and to recognize its taste by
chewing certain herbs, without hurry, as one chews on sadness.

(8 and 107)

1524: Utatlán

The Vengeance of the Vanquished

The Indian chiefs are a handful of bones, black as soot, which lie amid the rubble of the city. Today in the capital of the Quichés there is nothing that does not smell of burning.

Almost a century ago, a prophet had spoken. It was a chief of the Cakchiqueles who said, when the Quichés were about to tear out his heart: *Know that certain men, armed and clothed from head to feet and not naked like us, will destroy these buildings and reduce you to living in the caves of owls and wildcats and all this grandeur will vanish.*

He spoke while they killed him, here, in this city of ravines that Pedro de Alvarado's soldiers have just turned into a bonfire. The vanquished chief cursed the Quichés, and even then it had already been a long time that the Quichés had dominated Guatemala's other peoples.

(8 and 188)

1524: Scorpion Islands

Communion Ceremony

The sea swallowed them, vomited them out, gobbled them up again, and dashed them against the rocks. Dolphins and manatees flew through the air, and the sky was all foam. When the little ship fell to pieces, the men did their best to embrace the crags. All night long the waves fought to tear them off, blow by blow; many were dislodged, smashed against the stones, and devoured.

At dawn the storm let up and the tide receded. Those who were saved left their destination to fate and set themselves adrift in a ramshackle canoe. For five days they drifted among the reefs, finding no drinking water nor any fruit to put in their mouths.

This morning they landed on one of the islets.

They crawl forward on all fours beneath a sun that fries the stones. None has the strength to drag anyone who is left behind. Naked, badly wounded, they curse the captain, lawyer Alonso Zuazo, a good litigant and a bad navigator, and curse the mother who bore him, and the king, the pope, and God.

This little slope is the highest mountain in the world. The men keep climbing and console themselves counting the hours that remain before death.

And suddenly they rub their eyes. They can't believe it. Five giant turtles await them on the beach. Five of those turtles that in the sea look like rocky islands and that make love unperturbed as ships graze against them.

The men rush for them, grab their shells, howling with hunger and fury, and shove until the turtles turn over and lie pawing the air. They stick in their knives, open the turtles' bellies with slashes and fists, and bury their heads in the gushing blood.

And they fall asleep, submerged to their necks in these barrels of good wine, while the sun continues its slow march to the center of the sky.

No one listens to lawyer Alonso Zuazo. His mouth smeared with blood, he kneels in the sand, raises his hands, and offers the turtles to the five wounds of Our Redeemer.

(166)

1525: Tuxkahá

Cuauhtémoc

From the branch of an old ceiba tree, hung by the ankles, swings the body of the last king of the Aztecs.

Cortés has cut off his head.

He had arrived in the world in a cradle surrounded by shields and spears, and these were the first sounds he heard: *"Your real home is elsewhere. You are promised to another land. Your proper place is the battlefield. Your task is to give the blood of your enemy to the sun to drink and the body of your enemy to the earth to eat."*

Twenty-nine years ago, the soothsayers poured water over his head and pronounced the ritual words: *"Where are you hiding, misfortune? In which limb do you conceal yourself? Away from this child!"*

They called him Cuauhtémoc, *eagle that falls*. His father had extended the empire from sea to sea. When the prince took over the throne, the invaders had already come and conquered. Cuauh-

témoc rose up and resisted. Four years after the defeat of Tenochtitlán, the songs that call for the warrior's return still resound
from the depths of the forest.

Who now rocks his mutilated body? The wind, or the ceiba
tree? Isn't it the ceiba from its enormous crown? Does it not accept
this broken branch as one more arm of the thousand that spring
from its majestic trunk? Will red flowers sprout from it?

Life goes on. Life and death go on.

(212)

1526: Toledo

The American Tiger

Around the Alcázar of Toledo the tamer parades the tiger that the
king has received from the New World. The tamer, a Lombard
with a broad smile and pointed mustachio, leads him by a leash
like a little dog as the jaguar slips over the gravel with padded
steps.

Gonzalo Fernández de Oviedo's blood freezes. From afar he
yells to the keeper not to be so trusting, not to be chummy with
this wild beast, that such animals are not for people.

The tamer laughs, turns the jaguar loose, and strokes its back.
Oviedo hears its deep purr. He well knows that that clenched-
teeth growl means prayer to the devil and threat. One day not far
off, he is sure the tamer will fall into the trap. He will stretch out
his hand to scratch the tiger and be gobbled up after one quick
lash of a paw. Does this poor fellow believe God has given the
jaguar claws and teeth so that a tamer may serve him his meals at
regular hours? None of his lineage has ever sat down to dinner at
the sound of a bell, nor known any manners but devouring. Oviedo
looks at the smiling Lombard and sees a heap of minced meat
between four candles.

"Cut his nails!" he advises, turning away. "Pull his nails out
by the roots, and all his teeth and fangs!"

(166)

To Loosen the Purse Strings

The cold filters through the cracks and freezes the ink in the ink-pots.

Charles V owes every saint a candle. With money from the Welsers, the Augsburg bankers, he has bought his imperial crown, paid for his wedding, and financed a good part of the wars that have enabled him to humiliate Rome, suppress the Flemish rebellion, and scatter half of France's warrior nobles on the fields of Pavia.

The emperor's teeth ache as he signs the decree conceding to the Welsers the exploration, exploitation, and government of Venezuela.

For many long years Venezuela will have German governors. The first, Ambrosio Alfinger, will leave no Indian not branded and sold in the markets of Santa Marta, Jamaica, and Santo Domingo and will die with his throat pierced by an arrow.

(41, 103, and 165)

Day of Surprises

The southern sea expedition finally comes upon a coast free of mangrove swamps and mosquitos. Francisco Pizarro, who has word of a village nearby, orders a soldier and an African slave to start walking.

The white and the black reach Tumbes across lands that are planted and well watered by irrigation ditches, sowings such as they had never seen in America; in Tumbes, people who neither go naked nor sleep outdoors surround the newcomers and welcome them with gifts. Alonso de Molina's eyes are not big enough to measure the gold and silver covering the walls of the temple.

The people of Tumbes are dazzled by so many things from another world. They pull Alonso de Molina's beard and touch his clothing and iron ax. They gesture to ask about this captured monster with the red crest that shrieks in a cage: What does it want? Alonso points to it, says "rooster," and they learn their first word in the language of Castile.

The African accompanying the soldier is not doing so well. He defends himself by slapping the Indians, who want to rub his skin with dry corncobs. Water is boiling in a huge pot. They want to put him in it to soak out the color.

(166 and 185)

1528: Bad Luck Island

"People Very Generous with What They Have . . ."

Of the ships that sailed for Florida from San Lúcar de Barrameda, one was hurled by a storm onto the treetops of Cuba, and the sea devoured the others in successive shipwrecks. No better fate awaited the ships that Narváez's and Cabeza de Vaca's men improvised with shirts for sails and horses' manes for rigging.

The shipwrecked men, naked specters, tremble with cold and weep among the rocks of Mal Hado Island. Some Indians turn up to bring them water and fish and roots and seeing them weep, weep with them. The Indians shed rivers of tears, and the longer the lamentations continue, the sorrier the Spaniards feel for themselves.

The Indians lead them to their village. So that the sailors won't die from the cold, they keep lighting fires at rest stops along the way. Between bonfire and bonfire they carry them on litters, without letting their feet touch ground.

The Spaniards imagine that the Indians will cut them into pieces and throw them in the stewpot, but in the village they continue sharing with them the little food they have. As Álvar Núñez Cabeza de Vaca will tell it, the Indians are horrified and hot with anger when they learn that, while on the beach, five Christians *ate one another until only one remained, who being alone had no one to eat him*.

(39)

1531: Orinoco River
Diego de Ordaz

The wind remains recalcitrant, and launches tow the ship upstream. The sun flagellates the water.

The captain's coat of arms features the cone of the volcano Popocatépetl, because he was the first Spaniard to tread the snow of its summit. On that day he was at such an altitude that through the whirlwinds of volcanic ash he saw the backs of eagles as well as the city of Tenochtitlán shimmering in the lake; but he had to make a fast getaway because the volcano thundered with fury and threatened him with a rain of fire and stones and black smoke.

Today Diego de Ordaz, drenched to the bone, wonders if this Orinoco River will lead him to where the gold waits. The Indians of the villages keep gesturing, farther on, farther on, while the captain chases mosquitos and eases the crudely patched hull of the ship creakily forward. The monkeys protest and invisible parrots scream *getoutahere, getoutahere,* and many nameless birds flutter between the shores singing *youwontgetme, youwontgetme, youwontgetme.*

(175)

Piaroa People's Song About the White Man

The water of the river is bad.
The fish take shelter
high in the ravines
red with mud.
The man with the beard passes,
the white man.
The man with the beard passes
in the big canoe
with creaking oars
that the snakes bite.

(17)

1531: Mexico City

The Virgin of Guadelupe

That light, does it rise from the earth or fall from the sky? Is it lightning bug or bright star? It doesn't want to leave the slopes of Tepeyac and in dead of night persists, shining on the stones and entangling itself in the branches. Hallucinating, inspired, the naked Indian Juan Diego sees it: The light of lights opens up for him, breaks into golden and ruby pieces, and in its glowing heart appears that most luminous of Mexican women, she who says to him in the Náhuatl language: "I am the mother of God."

Bishop Zumárraga listens and doubts. The bishop is the Indians' official protector, appointed by the emperor, and also guardian of the branding iron that stamps on the Indians' faces the names of their proprietors. He threw the Aztec codices into the fire, papers painted by the hand of Satan, and destroyed five hundred temples and twenty thousand idols. Bishop Zumárraga well knows that the goddess of earth, Tonantzin, had her sanctuary high on the slopes of Tepeyac and that the Indians used to make pilgrimages there to worship *our mother*, as they called that woman clad in snakes and hearts and hands.

The bishop is doubtful and decides that the Indian Juan Diego has seen the Virgin of Guadelupe. The Virgin born in Estremadura, darkened by the suns of Spain, has come to the valley of the Aztecs to be the mother of the vanquished.

(60 and 79)

1531: Santo Domingo

A Letter

He presses his temples as he follows the words that advance and retreat: *Do not consider my lowly estate and roughness of expression*, he entreats, *but the goodwill that moves me to say it*.

Fray Bartolomé de las Casas is writing to the Council of the Indies. It would have been better for the Indians, he maintains, *to go to hell with their heresies, their procrastination and their isolation*, than to be saved by the Christians. *The cries of so much spilled human blood reach all the way to heaven: those burned alive, roasted on grills, thrown to wild dogs . . .*

He gets up, walks. His white habit flaps amid clouds of dust.

Later he sits on the edge of the studded chair. He scratches his nose with the quill pen. The bony hand writes. For the Indians in America to be saved and for God's law to be fulfilled, Fray Bartolomé proposes that the cross should rule over the sword. The garrisons should submit to the bishops; and colonists should be sent to cultivate the soil under protection of strong fortresses. The colonists, he says, *could bring black or Moorish or some kind of slaves to serve them, or live by their own labor or in some other way not prejudicial to the Indians . . .*

(27)

1531: Serrana Island

The Castaway and the Other

A wind of salt and sun mortifies Pedro Serrano, who wanders naked along the clifftop. Sea gulls flutter in pursuit of him. Shaded by an uplraised hand, his eyes are fixed on enemy territory.

He descends into the cove and walks on the sand. Reaching the frontier line, he pees. He does not cross the line but knows that if the other is watching from some hideaway, he will appear at one bound to settle accounts for such a provocation.

He pees and waits. The birds scream and fly off. Where has the man stuck himself? The sky is a dazzling white, a light of lime, and the island is a burning stone; white rocks, white shadows, foam over the white sand: a small world of sand and lime. Where can that bastard be hiding?

Much time has passed since Pedro's ship broke up on that stormy night, and his hair and beard already reached his chest when the other appeared, riding a board that the furious tide threw onto the shore. Pedro wrung the water from his lungs, gave him food and drink, and taught him how not to die on this desert island, where only rocks grow. He taught him to turn over turtles and finish them off with one slash, to cut the meat in strips to dry in the sun, and to collect rainwater in their shells. He taught him to pray for rain and to dig for clams under the sand, showed him the crabs' and shrimps' hideouts and offered him turtle eggs and oysters that the sea brought in attached to mangrove branches. The other knew from Pedro that it was necessary to collect everything that the sea delivered to the reefs so that the bonfire would burn night and day, fed by dry algae, seaweed, stray branches, starfish, and fish bones. Pedro helped him put up a roof of turtle shells, a bit of shade against the sun, for lack of trees.

The first war was the water war. Pedro suspected that the other was stealing while he slept, and the other accused him of drinking like a beast. When the water gave out and the last drops disputed with fists were spilt, they had no alternative but to drink their own urine and the blood they got from the only turtle that was to be seen. Then they stretched out to die in the shade and had only enough saliva left for muted insults.

Finally rain saved them. The other thought that Pedro could well reduce by half the roof of his house now that turtle shells were so scarce: "Your house is a turtle-shell palace," he said, "and in mine I spend the day all twisted up."

"I shit on God," said Pedro, "and on the mother that calved you. If you don't like my island, get lost!" And he pointed a finger at the vast sea.

They decided to divide the water. From then on, there was a rain deposit on each end of the island.

The fire war came second. They took turns tending the bonfire, in case some ship passed in the distance. One night, when the other was on guard, the fire went out. Pedro cursed and shook him awake.

"If the island is yours, you do it, you swine," said the other and showed his teeth.

They rolled in the sand. When they tired of hitting each other, they resolved that each would light his own fire. Pedro's knife lashed a stone until it produced a few sparks; and since then there is a bonfire at each end of the island.

The knife war came third. The other had nothing to cut with, and Pedro demanded payment in fresh shrimp each time he lent the knife.

Then the food war and the shell-necklace war broke out.

When the latter war ended in an exchange of stones, they signed an armistice and a border treaty. There was no document, since in this desolation not even a cupay leaf can be found on which to scribble anything, and furthermore neither can sign his name; but they marked off a frontier and swore by God and king to respect it. They tossed a fish into the air. Pedro drew the half of the island that faces Cartagena; the other, the half facing Santiago de Cuba.

Now, standing at the frontier, Pedro bites his nails, looks upward as if seeking rain, and thinks: "He must be hiding in some cranny. I can smell him. Mangy. In midocean and he never bathes. He'd rather fry in his own grease. There he goes, yes, on the dodge as ever."

"Hey, asshole!" he yells.

For answer, the thunder of surf, the racket of gulls, the voices of the wind.

"Ingrate!" he shouts, "Son-of-a-bitch!" and shouts until his throat bursts, and runs from one end of the island to the other, backward and forward, alone and naked on the sand without anybody.

(76)

1532: Cajamarca

Pizarro

A thousand men sweep the path of the Inca into the great square where the Spaniards wait in hiding. The multitude trembles at the passage of the Beloved Father, the One, the Only, lord of labors and fiestas; the singers fall silent, and the dancers freeze up. In the half light, last light of the day, the crowns and vestments of Atahualpa and his cortege of nobles of the realm gleam with gold and silver.

Where are the gods brought by the wind? The Inca reaches the center of the square and gives the order to wait. A few days ago, a spy penetrated the camp of the invaders, tugged at their beards, and returned to report that they were no more than a handful of crooks from the sea. That blasphemy cost his life. Where are the sons of Wirachocha, who wear stars on their heels and send forth thunders that provoke stupor, stampede, and death?

The priest Vicente de Valverde emerges from the shadows and goes to meet Atahualpa. He raises the Bible in one hand and a crucifix in the other, as if exorcising a storm on the high seas, and cries that here is God, the true one, and that all the rest is nonsense. The interpreter translates and Atahualpa, at the head of the throng, asks: "Who told you that?"

"The Bible says it, the sacred book."

"Give it here so it can tell me."

A few paces away, Pizarro unsheathes his sword.

Atahualpa looks at the Bible, turns it over in his hand, shakes it to make it talk, and presses it against his ear: "It says nothing. It's empty."

And he drops it to the ground.

Pizarro has been awaiting this moment ever since the day he knelt before Emperor Charles V, described the empire as big as Europe that he had discovered and proposed to conquer, and promised him the most splendid treasure in human history. And even earlier: since the day when his sword drew a line in the sand and a few soldiers dying of hunger, bent with disease, swore to follow him to the end. And earlier yet, much earlier: Pizarro has awaited this moment since he was dumped at the door of an Estremadura church fifty-four years ago and drank sow's milk for lack of anyone to suckle him.

Pizarro yells and pounces. At the signal, the trap is sprung. From the ambush trumpets blare, arquebuses roar, and the cavalry charges the stunned and unarmed crowd.

(76, 96, and 221)

1533: Cajamarca

The Ransom

To buy the life of Atahualpa, silver and gold pour in. Like a swarm of ants down the empire's four highways come long lines of llamas, and people with shoulders bent under their loads. The most splendid booty comes from Cuzco: an entire garden, trees and flowers of solid gold, and uncut precious stones, and birds and animals of pure silver and turquoise and lapis lazuli.

The oven receives gods and adornments and vomits bars of gold and silver. Officers and soldiers shout to have it divided. For six years they have had no pay.

Of each five ingots, Francisco Pizarro sets one apart for the king. Then he crosses himself. He asks the help of God, who knows all, to see justice done and asks the help of Hernando de Soto, who knows how to read, to keep an eye on the scribe.

He assigns one part to the church and another to the military vicar. He handsomely rewards his brothers and the other captains.

Each soldier of the line gets more than Prince Philip makes in a year, and Pizarro becomes the richest man in the world. The hunter of Atahualpa assigns to himself twice as much as the court of Charles V, with its six hundred servants, spends in a year—without counting the Incas' litter, eighty-three kilos of solid gold, which is his trophy as general.

(76 and 184)

1533: Cajamarca

Atahualpa

A black rainbow crossed the sky. The Inca Atahualpa didn't want to believe it.

In the days of the fiesta of the sun, a condor fell lifeless in the Plaza of Happiness. Atahualpa didn't want to believe it.

He put to death messengers who brought bad news and with one ax blow decapitated the old prophet who announced misfortune. He had the oracle's house burned down and witnesses of the prophecy cut to pieces.

Atahualpa had the eighty sons of his brother Huáscar bound to posts on the roads, and the vultures gorged themselves with that meat. Huáscar's wives tinted the waters of the Adamarca River with blood. Huáscar, Atahualpa's prisoner, ate human shit and sheep's piss and had a dressed-up stone for a wife. Later Huáscar said and was the last to say: *Soon they will kill him as he kills me*. And Atahualpa didn't want to believe it.

When his palace turned into his jail, he didn't want to believe it. Atahualpa, Pizarro's prisoner, said: *I am the greatest of all princes on earth*. The ransom filled one room with gold and two rooms with silver. The invaders melted down even the golden cradle in which Atahualpa heard his first song.

Seated on Atahualpa's throne, Pizarro told him he had decided to confirm his death sentence. Atahualpa replied: *"Don't tell me those jokes."* Nor does he want to believe it now, as step by step he mounts the stairs, dragging his chains, in the milky light of dawn.

Soon the news will be spread among the countless children of the earth who owe obedience and tribute to the son of the sun. In Quito they will mourn the death of the Shadow That Protects:

puzzled, lost, memory denied, alone. In Cuzco there will be joy and drunken sprees.

Atahualpa is bound by the hands, feet, and neck, but still thinks: *What did I do to deserve death?*

At the foot of the gallows, he refuses to believe that he has been defeated by man. Only gods could have done it. His father, the sun, has betrayed him.

Before the iron tourniquet breaks his neck, he weeps, kisses the cross, and accepts baptism with another name. Giving his name as Francisco, which is his conqueror's name, he beats on the doors of the Paradise of the Europeans, where no place is reserved for him.

(57, 76, and 221)

1533: Xaquixaguana

The Secret

Pizarro marches on Cuzco. Now he heads a great army. Manco Cápac, the Incas' new king, has added thousands of Indians to the side of the handful of conquistadors. But Atahualpa's generals harry the advance. In the valley of Xaquixaguana, Pizarro captures a messenger of his enemies.

Fire licks the soles of the prisoner's feet.

"What does this message say?"

The Chasqui is a man experienced in endless trottings through the icy winds of the plain and the scorching heat of the desert. The job has accustomed him to pain and fatigue. He moans but won't talk.

After very long torment his tongue loosens: "That the horses won't be able to climb the mountains."

"What else?"

"That there's nothing to fear. That horses are scary but do no harm."

"And what else?"

They make him tread on the fire.

"And what else?"

He has lost his feet. Before losing his life, he says: "That you people die, too."

(81 and 185)

1533: Cuzco

The Conquerors Enter
the Sacred City

In the noon radiance, the soldiers make their way through the cloud of smoke. A whiff of damp leather mixes with the smell of burning, while the clatter of horses' hooves and cannon wheels is heard.

An altar rises in the plaza. Silk banners embroidered with eagles escort the new god, who has his arms open and wears a beard like his sons. Isn't the new god seeing his sons, battle-axes in hand, pounce upon the gold of the temples and tombs?

Amid the stones of Cuzco, blackened by fire, the old and the paralytic dumbly await the days to come.

(50 and 76)

1533: Riobamba

Alvarado

Half a year before, the ships anchored in Puerto Viejo. Inspired by promises of a virgin kingdom, Pedro de Alvarado had sailed from Guatemala. With him went five hundred Spaniards and two thousand Indian and Negro slaves. Messengers had reported to him: "The power that awaits you makes what you have seem like dirt. To the north of Tumbes you will multiply your fame and wealth. To the south, Pizarro and Almagro have now become the masters, but the fabulous kingdom of Quito belongs to no one."

In the coastal villages they found gold, silver, and emeralds. Loaded with quick fortunes, they set off for the mountains. They faced jungles, swamps, fevers that kill in a day or leave one mad, and terrifying rains of volcanic ash. In the Andean foothills, snowstorms and winds that cut like knives broke the bodies of the slaves, who had never known cold, and many Spaniards left their bones in the mountains. Soldiers dismounting to tighten their horses' girths remained permanently frozen. The booty was thrown to the bottom of ravines: Alvarado offered gold, and the soldiers clamored for food and shelter. His eyes burned by the blinding snow, Alvarado kept charging up the trail to cut off with one sword-blow the heads of slaves who fell and of soldiers who wished they hadn't come.

More dead than alive, with muscles iced and blood frozen, the toughest ones managed to reach the plateau. Finally today they have hit the royal highway of the Incas, the one that leads to Quito, to paradise. No sooner do they arrive than they find in the mud fresh hoofprints. Captain Benalcázar has beaten them to it.

(81 and 97)

1533: Quito

This City Kills Itself

Benalcázar's men break in, unstoppable. Thousands of Indian allies, enemies of the Incas, are spying and fighting for them. After three battles, the die is cast. Already beating a retreat, General Rumiñahui sets fire to Quito. The invaders won't enjoy it alive or find any treasures except those they can dig from graves. The city of Quito, cradle and throne of Atahualpa, is a giant bonfire between two volcanos.

Rumiñahui, who has never been wounded in the back, turns away from the soaring flames. There are tears in his eyes, from the smoke.

(158 and 214)

1533: Barcelona

The Holy Wars

From America come the heralds of good tidings. The emperor closes his eyes and sees sails approaching and savors the smell of tar and salt. The emperor breathes like the ocean, high tide, low tide; and he blows to speed the ships swollen with treasure.

Fate has just awarded him a new kingdom, *where gold and silver abound like iron in Vizcaya*. The astounding booty is on its way. With it he will finally be able to calm down the bankers who are strangling him and pay his soldiers—Swiss pikemen, German mercenaries, Spanish infantry—who never see a coin even in dreams. The Atahualpa ransom will finance the holy wars against the Islamic half moon, which has reached the very gates of Vienna, and against the heretics who follow Luther in Germany. The emperor will fit out a great fleet to sweep Sultan Suliman and the old pirate Redbeard off the Mediterranean.

The mirror reflects the image of the god of war: damascene armor with chiseled insertions at the edge of the gorget and breastplate, feathered helmet, face illumined by the sun of glory—bristling eyebrows over melancholy eyes, bearded chin thrust out. The emperor dreams of Algiers and hears the call of Constantinople. Tunis, fallen into infidel hands, also awaits the general of Jesus Christ.

(41 and 50)

1533: Seville

The Treasure of the Incas

From the first of the ships, gold and silver are tossed onto the docks of Seville. Oxen drag the loaded vats in carts to the Chamber of Commerce. Murmurs of wonder arise from the crowd assembled to witness the unloading. There is talk of mysteries and of the conquered monarch across the ocean.

Two men, two drunks, emerge arm-in-arm from the tavern that faces the docks. They join the crowd and ask shrilly where the notary is. They are not celebrating the treasure of the Incas. They are flushed and glowing from a session of good wine and because they have made a very cordial pact. They have agreed to exchange wives, you take mine, who is a jewel, I take yours, although she isn't worth much, and they are looking for the notary to make it official.

They pay no mind to the gold and silver of Peru; and the dazzled crowd pays none to the castaway who has arrived along with the treasure. The ship, drawn by a bonfire, has rescued him from a Caribbean islet. His name is Pedro Serrano, and nine years before he had swum to safety from a shipwreck. He uses his hair to sit on, his beard as an apron, has leathery skin, and hasn't stopped talking since they took him aboard. Now he keeps on telling his story amid the uproar. No one listens.

(41 and 76)

1534: Riobamba

Inflation

When news of Atahualpa's gold reached Santo Domingo, everyone went looking for a ship. Alonso Hernández, dealer in Indians, was among the first to take off in a hurry. He embarked in Panama and on arrival at Tumbes bought himself a horse. In Tumbes the horse cost seven times more than in Panama and thirty times more than in Santo Domingo.

The climb into the mountains has put Hernández back on foot. To complete the journey to Quito, he buys another horse. He pays ninety times the Santo Domingo price. For 350 pesos he also buys a black slave. In Riobamba a·horse costs eight times more than a man.

All is for sale in this realm, even the flags smeared with mud and blood, and everything is priced sky-high. A bar of gold is charged for two sheets of paper.

The merchants, newly arrived, defeat the conquistadors without drawing a sword.

(81, 166, and 184)

1535: Cuzco

The Brass Throne

On the knees of the little king, vassal to another king, lies no gold scepter but a stick shining with bits of colored glass. Manco Inca wears the scarlet tassel on his head, but the triple gold necklace is missing from his breast, where the sun does not gleam, nor do the resplendent discs hang from his ears. The cloak of gold and silver threads and vicuña wool is missing from the back of Atahualpa's brother and enemy and inheritor. From the banners beaten by the wind the falcons have disappeared, replaced by the eagles of the emperor of Europe.

No one kneels at the feet of the Inca crowned by Pizarro.

(57)

1536: Mexico City

Motolinía

Fray Toribio de Motolinía walks barefoot up the hill. He carries a heavy sack on his back.

Motolinía is the local word for someone poor and afflicted. He still wears the patched, ragged habit that gave him his name years ago, when he arrived walking barefoot, as now, from the port of Veracruz.

He stops at the top of the slope. At his feet extends the enormous lake and in it gleams the city of Mexico. Motolinía passes a hand over his forehead, breathes deeply, and drives into the ground, one after the other, ten crude crosses, branches tied with rope. As he drives them in, he dedicates them:

"This cross, my God, is for the diseases that were not known here and that rage so terribly among the natives."

"This one is for war, and this for hunger, which have killed as many Indians as there are drops in the sea and grains in the sand."

"This is for the tribute collectors, drones who eat the honey of the Indians; and this one for the tribute, which the Indians must sell their children and their lands to pay."

"This one is for the gold mines, which stink so of death that one can't go within a league of them."

"This is for the great city of Mexico, reared on the ruins of Tenochtitlán, and for those who brought beams and stones on their backs to build it, singing and crying out night and day, until they died of exhaustion or were crushed by landslides."

"This is for the slaves who have been dragged here from all directions like herds of beasts, branded on the face; and this one for those who fall by the wayside carrying the enormous loads to maintain the mines."

"And this one, Lord, for the perpetual conflicts and skirmishes of us Spaniards, which always end with the torture and murder of Indians."

Kneeling before the crosses, Motolinía prays: "Forgive them, Lord. I entreat you to forgive them. I know too well that they continue worshiping bloody idols and that if before they had a hundred gods, with you they have a hundred and one. They can't distinguish the Host from a grain of corn. But if they deserve the punishment of your firm hand, they also deserve the pity of your generous heart."

Then Motolinía crosses himself, shakes his habit, and starts back down the hill. A little before Ave Maria time, he reaches the monastery. Alone in his cell, he stretches out on his pallet and slowly munches a tortilla.

(60 and 213)

1536: Machu Picchu
Manco Inca

Sick of being a king treated like a dog, Manco Inca rises against the men with hairy faces. On the empty throne Pizarro installs Paullo, brother of Manco Inca and of Atahualpa and of Huáscar.

On horseback at the head of a large army, Manco Inca lays siege to Cuzco. Bonfires blaze around the city and arrows of burning tinder fall in a steady rain, but hunger strikes the besiegers harder than the besieged, and Manco Inca's troops withdraw after half a year amid war cries that split the earth.

The Inca crosses the Urubamba River valley and emerges among the high, fogbound peaks. Stone steps lead him to the secret mountaintop hideaway. Protected by parapets and fortified towers, the fortress of Machu Picchu wields supremacy beyond the world.

(57 and 76)

1536: Valley of Ulúa
Gonzalo Guerrero

Victorious, Alonso de Avila's horsemen withdraw. On the battlefield, among the losers, lies an Indian with a beard. His nude body is an arabesque of ink and blood. Golden symbols hang from his nose, lips, and ears. An arquebus shot has split his forehead.

His name was Gonzalo Guerrero. In his first life he had been a sailor from the port of Palos. His second life began a quarter century ago when he was shipwrecked on the Yucatán coast. Since then he has lived among the Indians. He was a chief in peacetime and a captain in war. He had three children by a Maya woman.

In 1519, Hernán Cortés sent for him.

"*No,*" said Gonzalo to the messenger, "*look at my kids, how pretty they are. Just leave me some of those green beads you're carrying. I'll give them to my kids and tell them: 'My brothers sent you these toys, from my country.'*"

Long afterward, Gonzalo Guerrero has fallen defending another country, fighting beside other brothers, the brothers he chose. He is the first conquistador conquered by the Indians.

(62 and 119)

1536: Culiacán

Cabeza de Vaca

Eight years have passed since Cabeza de Vaca was shipwrecked on Mal Hado Island. Of the six hundred men who sailed from Andalusia, a few deserted along the way and the sea swallowed many; others died of hunger, cold, or Indians, and four, just four, now reach Culiacán.

Álvar Núñez Cabeza de Vaca, Alonso del Castillo, Andrés Dorantes, and Estebanico, black Arab, have crossed all America on foot from Florida to the shores of the Pacific. Naked, shedding their skin like snakes, they have eaten wild grasses and roots, worms and lizards, and anything they could find alive until the Indians gave them blankets and prickly pears and ears of corn in exchange for their miracles and cures. Cabeza de Vaca has brought more than one dead Indian back to life with his Paternosters and Ave Marias and healed many sick ones making the sign of the cross and blowing on the place where they hurt. From league to league grew the fame of these miracle workers; multitudes came out to greet them on the roads, and villages sent them on their way with dance and song.

In Sinaloa, as they made their way south, appeared the first traces of Christians. Cabeza de Vaca and his companions found buckles, horseshoe nails, hitching posts. They also found fear: abandoned fields, Indians who had fled into the mountains.

"We're getting warm," said Cabeza de Vaca. "After such a long walk, we're close to our people."

"*They aren't like you,*" the Indians said. "*You come from where*

the sun rises and they from where it sets. You heal the sick and
they kill the healthy. You go naked and barefoot. You aren't greedy
for anything."

(39)

1537: Rome
The Pope Says They Are Like Us

Pope Paul III stamps his name with the leaden seal, which carries
the likenesses of St. Peter and St. Paul, and ties it to the parchment.
A new bull issues from the Vatican. It is called *Sublimis Deus* and
reveals that Indians are human beings, endowed with soul and
reason.

(103)

1538: Santo Domingo
The Mirror

The noonday sun makes the stones smoke and metals flash. Uproar
in the port. Galleons have brought heavy artillery from Seville for
the Santo Domingo fortress.

The mayor, Fernández de Oviedo, supervises the transpor-
tation of culverins and cannons. Under the lash, blacks haul the
cargo at top speed. The carts creak under their load of iron and
bronze, and other slaves come and go through the turmoil, throwing buckets of water on the flames that spurt from overheated axles.

Amid the bustle and pandemonium, an Indian girl is searching
for her master. Her skin is covered with blisters, each step a triumph
as her scanty clothing tortures her skin. Throughout the night and
half the day, from one scream to the next, this girl has endured
the burns of acid. She herself roasted the *guao* tree roots and
rubbed them between her hands to make a paste, then anointed
her whole body, from the roots of her hair to the soles of her feet,
because *guao* burns the skin and removes its color, thus turning
Indian and black women into white ladies of Castile.

"Don't you recognize me, sir?"

Oviedo shoves her away; but the girl insists in her thin voice,
sticking to her master like a shadow, as Oviedo runs shouting orders
to the foremen.

"Don't you know who I am?"

The girl falls to the ground and from the ground keeps asking: "Sir, sir, I bet you don't know who I am?"

(166)

1538: Valley of Bogotá

Blackbeard, Redbeard, Whitebeard

A year ago Gonzalo Jiménez de Quesada, black beard, black eyes, went in search of the springs of gold at the source of the Magdalena River. Half the population of Santa Marta went after him.

They crossed swamps and lands that steamed in the sun. When they reached the banks of the river, not one of the thousands of naked Indians who were brought along to carry the guns and bread and salt remained alive. As there were no longer any slaves to hunt down and catch, they threw the dogs into vats of boiling water. Then the horses, too, were cut into bits. The hunger was worse than the crocodiles, snakes, and mosquitos. They ate roots and leather straps. They quarreled over the flesh of any man who fell, before the priest had even finished giving him passage to Paradise.

They continued up the river, stung by rains and with no wind in the sails, until Quesada decided to change course. El Dorado must be on the other side of the mountains, he had concluded, not at the river's source. So they walked across the mountains.

After much climbing, Quesada now approaches the green valleys of the Chibcha nation. In the presence of seventy scarecrows eaten up with fever, he raises his sword, takes possession, and proclaims that he will never again obey his governor's orders.

Three and a half years ago, Nicolás de Federmann, red beard, blue eyes, left Coro in search of the earth's golden center, on a pilgrimage through mountains and plains. His Indians and blacks were the first to die.

When Federmann reaches the peaks where they tangle with the clouds, he sees the verdant valleys of the Chibcha nation. One hundred and seventy soldiers have survived, ghosts dragging themselves along wrapped in deerskins. Federmann kisses his sword, takes possession, and proclaims that he will never again obey his governor's orders.

Three long years ago Sebastián de Benalcázar, gray eyes, white beard either from age or from road dust, sallied forth in search of the treasures that the city of Quito, emptied and burned, had denied him. Of the multitude that followed him, one hundred and sixty exhausted Europeans and not one Indian remain. Leveler of cities, founder of cities, Benalcázar has left behind him a trail of ashes and blood and new worlds born from the point of his sword: surrounding the gallows, the plaza; around the plaza, church, houses, ramparts.

The conquistador's helmet gleams on the crest of the cordillera. Benalcázar takes possession of the green valleys of the Chibcha nation and proclaims that he will never again obey the orders of his governor.

From the north has come Quesada. From the east, Federmann. From the south, Benalcázar. Cross and arquebus, sky and soil: After so many crazy wanderings, the three rebel captains descend the cordillera slopes and meet on the plain of Bogotá.

Benalcázar knows that the chiefs of this place travel on golden litters. Federmann hears the sweet melodies that breezes play on the sheets of gold hanging from temples and palaces. Quesada kneels at the shore of the lake where native priests covered with gold dust immerse themselves.

Who will end up with El Dorado? Quesada, the Granadan, who says he got here first? Federmann, the German from Ulm, who conquers in the name of the banker Welser? Benalcázar, the Cordoban?

The three armies, ulcerated skin and bones in rags, size up each other and wait.

Then the German bursts out laughing, doubles up with mirth, and the Andalusians catch the contagion until the three captains collapse, floored by laughter and hunger and what brought them all there, that which is without being and arrived without coming: the realization that El Dorado won't be anybody's.

(13)

1538: Masaya Volcano

Vulcan, God of Money

From the mouth of the volcano Masaya came in other times a naked old woman, wise in many secrets, who gave good advice about corn and war. Since the Christians arrived, say the Indians, the old woman refuses to leave the burning mountain.

Many Christians think the Masaya is a mouth of hell and that its flare-ups and everlasting fiery smoke announce eternal chastisements. Others assert that this incandescent smoke cloud, visible for fifty leagues, is produced by gold and silver being melted and purified, seething in the belly of the mountain. The more the fire blazes, the purer they become.

The expedition has been in preparation for a year. Father Blas del Castillo rises very early and hears the confessions of Pedro Ruiz, Benito Dávila, and Juan Sánchez. The four implore forgiveness with tears in their eyes and begin the march at daybreak.

The priest is the first to go down. He climbs into a basket, helmet on head, stole on chest, and cross in hand, and reaches the huge esplanade that surrounds the mouth of fire.

"It isn't hell but paradise!" he proclaims, black with ashes, as he sticks the cross among the stones. Immediately his companions follow him down. From above, the Indians also send down pulley, chains, cauldrons, beams, bolts . . .

They submerge the iron cauldron. From the depths come neither gold nor silver, nothing but sulphur slag. When they dip the cauldron in deeper, the volcano eats it up.

(203)

1541: Santiago de Chile
Inés Suárez

Some months ago Pedro de Valdivia discovered this hill and this valley. The Araucanians, who had discovered the hill thousands of years earlier, called it Huelén, which means *pain*. Valdivia baptized it Santa Lucía.

From the crest of the hill Valdivia saw the green earth between arms of the river and decided that the world contained no better place to dedicate a city to the apostle Santiago, who accompanies the conquistadors and fights for them. He cut the air with his sword to the four cardinal points of the compass and so was born Santiago of the New Frontier. Now it is enjoying its first summer: a few houses of mud and sticks, roofed with straw, a plaza at the center, stockade all around.

A mere fifty men have remained in Santiago. Valdivia stays with them on the banks of the Cachapoal River. At break of day, the sentry sounds the alarm from the top of the stockade. Squadrons of natives are approaching from all four sides. The Spaniards hear the war cries, and immediately a downpour of arrows falls on them.

By noon some houses are nothing but ashes, and the stockade has fallen. They are fighting body to body in the plaza. Then Inés runs to the hut that serves as prison. There, the guard is standing watch over seven Araucanian chiefs whom the Spaniards captured some time ago. She suggests, implores, orders him to cut their heads off.

"What?"

"Their heads!"

"What?"

"Like this!"

Inés seizes his sword, and seven heads fly through the air. Those heads turn the besieged into pursuers. Taking the offensive, the Spaniards invoke not the apostle Santiago but Our Lady of Good Help.

Inés Suárez, the woman from Malaga, had been the first to sign up when Valdivia started recruiting at his house in Cuzco. She came to these southern lands at the head of the invading forces, riding alongside Valdivia, sword of stout steel, coat of fine mail, and ever since she marches, fights, and sleeps with Valdivia. Today she has taken his place.

She is the only woman among the men. They say: "She's *macho*" and compare her with Roldán or El Cid, while she rubs oil on the fingers of Captain Francisco de Aguirre. They have stuck to his sword hilt and cannot be prised off although, for today, the war is over.

(67, 85, and 130)

1541: Rock of Nochistlán

Never

They had seized even his mule. Those who now eat off his silver service and tread his carpets had thrown him out of Mexico with fettered feet.

Ten years later they, the officials, summon the warrior back. Alvarado leaves off governing Guatemala and comes to chastise Indians in these ungrateful lands that he conquered along with Cortés. He wants to push on north to the seven golden cities of

Cíbola, but this morning, at the height of the battle, a horse falls on him and throws him down a cliff.

To Mexico Pedro de Alvarado has returned, and in Mexico he lies. His helmet hangs from a branch, and his sword has fallen among the brambles. *Don't sheath me without honor* can still be read on the steel blade.

(81)

1541: Old Guatemala City

Beatriz

Pedro de Alvarado had married Francisca, but Francisca was struck down by the orange-blossom tea that she drank on the road to Veracruz. Then he married Francisca's sister, Beatriz.

Beatriz was waiting for him in Guatemala when she learned she had been two months widowed. She decked her house in black inside and out and nailed up doors and windows so that she could cry her heart out in private.

She weeps looking in the mirror at her nude body, which has dried up from so much waiting and now has nothing left to wait for, a body that no longer sings, and she weeps through her mouth, which can only sob: "Are you there, my darling?"

She weeps for this house that she hates and this land that is not hers and for the years spent between this house and the church, from Mass to Mess and from baptism to burial, surrounded by drunken soldiers and Indian servants who make her sick. She weeps for the food that upsets her and for him who never came, because there was always some war to fight or land to be conquered. She weeps for all the tears she has shed alone in her bed, when a dog's bark or a rooster's crow made her jump and she learned, all alone, to read the darkness and listen to the silence and make drawings in the air. She weeps and weeps, broken up inside.

When she finally emerges from seclusion, she announces: "I am the governor of Guatemala."

She cannot govern for long.

The volcano vomits a cataract of water and stones that drowns the city and kills whatever it touches. The flood keeps advancing toward Beatriz's house, while she runs to the chapel, goes to the altar, and embraces the Virgin. Her eleven maids embrace her feet and each other while Beatriz cries: "Are you there, my darling?"

The torrent destroys the city that Alvarado founded and, as it roars ever louder, Beatriz keeps crying out: "Are you there?"

(81)

1541: Cabo Frío

At Dawn, the Cricket Sang

It had been silent ever since they took it aboard in the port of Cádiz, two and a half months of silence and sadness in its little cage, until today its cry of joy rang out from bow to stern and woke everybody up.

"A miracle! A miracle!"

There was just time for the ship to alter course. The cricket was celebrating the approach of land. Thanks to its alarm, the sailors were not dashed to pieces against the rocks of the Brazilian coast.

Cabeza de Vaca, chief of this expedition to the River Plate, is very knowing about such matters. They call him Alvar the Miracle Worker since he crossed America from coast to coast reviving the dead in Indian villages.

(39)

1542: Quito

El Dorado

For a long time Gonzalo Pizarro's men have been trekking deep into the jungle, in search of the gold-skinned prince and the groves of cinnamon. They have found snakes and bats, armies of mosquitos, swamps and rains that never stop. Night after night lightning flashed the way for this caravan of naked men huddled together by panic.

Skin and bones and sores, they are arriving this afternoon at the outskirts of Quito. Each one recites his name in order to be recognized. Of the expedition's four thousand Indian slaves, none has returned.

Captain Gonzalo Pizarro kneels and kisses the ground. Last night he dreamed of a dragon that jumped on him, tore him apart, and ate his heart. This keeps him from blinking, now, when they tell him the news:

"Your brother Francisco has been assassinated in Lima."

(97)

1542: Conlapayara

The Amazons

The battle wasn't going badly today, St. John's Day. With bursts of arquebus and crossbow, from their brigantines, Francisco de Orellana's men were emptying the white canoes coming from shore. But witches were on the warpath. The warrior women appeared suddenly, scandalously beautiful and ferocious, and then canoes covered the river, and the ships took flight upstream like scared porcupines, bristling with arrows from stem to stern and even in the mainmasts.

These viragos laughed as they fought. They put themselves in front of the men, females of great attractiveness and charm, and there was no more fear in the village of Conlapayara. They fought laughing and dancing and singing, their breasts quivering in the breeze, until the Spaniards got lost beyond the mouth of the Tapajós River, exhausted from so much effort and astonishment.

They had heard tell of such women, and now they believe it. The women live to the south, in dominions without men, where children born male are drowned. When the body hungers, they make war on the coastal tribes and take prisoners. They return them the next morning. After a night of love, he who went as a boy returns an old man.

Orellana and his soldiers will keep sailing down the world's mightiest river and reach the sea without pilot or compass or chart. They sail in the two brigantines that they improvised with strokes of the ax in midjungle, making nails and hinges out of dead horses' shoes and bellows from old shoe leather. They let themselves drift down the Amazon River, through the jungle, without the energy to row, and mumbling prayers: They pray to God to make the next enemies male, however many they may be.

(45)

1542: Iguazú River

In Broad Daylight

Steamy beneath his iron clothing, tormented by bites and wounds, Álvar Núñez Cabeza de Vaca dismounts from his horse and sees God for the first time.

Huge butterflies flutter around him. Cabeza de Vaca kneels before the Iguazú waterfalls. The roaring, foaming waters plunge from the heavens to wash off the blood of all the fallen and redeem all the deserts, torrents that turn loose vapors and rainbows, that drag jungles from the depths of the dry earth; waters that bellow, God's ejaculation, fertilizing the land, eternal first day of Creation.

To come upon this rain of God, Cabeza de Vaca has walked half the world and sailed the other half. To meet it he has endured shipwrecks and sufferings; to see it he was born with eyes in his face. What remains to him of life will be a gift.

(39)

1543: Cubagua

The Pearl Fishers

The city of New Cádiz has fallen, overwhelmed by seaquake and pirates. Previously the whole island had fallen, this island of Cubagua where forty-five years ago Columbus traded the Indians broken dishes for pearls. After so much fishing, the oysters have given out and the pearl divers lie at the sea bottom.

In these waters, Indian slaves were sent down with stones tied to their backs, to reach where the biggest pearls lay, and from sun to sun they swam without a break, gathering the oysters stuck to the rocks and the bottom.

No slave lasted long. Sooner or later their lungs burst: a stream of blood rose to the surface instead of the diver. The men who had caught or bought them said that the sea turned red because, like women, oysters menstruate.

(102 and 103)

1544: Machu Picchu
The Stone Throne

From here Manco Inca has reigned over the lands of Vilcabamba. From here he has waged a long and hard war, a war of burnings and ambushes. The invaders do not know the labyrinths that lead to the secret citadel. No enemy knows them.

Only Captain Diego Méndez could reach the hideaway. He came in flight. On orders from the son of Almagro, his sword had pierced the throat of Francisco Pizarro. Manco Inca gave him asylum. Afterward Diego Méndez stuck a dagger into Manco Inca's back.

Amid the stones of Machu Picchu, where the bright flowers offer honey to whoever fertilizes them, lies the Inca wrapped in beautiful cloths.

(57)

War Song of the Incas

We will drink from the skull of the traitor
And from his teeth a necklace make.
Of his bones we will make flutes,
Of his skin a drum.
Then we will dance.

(202)

1544: Campeche
Las Casas

For some time he has been waiting, here in the port, alone with the heat and mosquitos. He wanders along the wharves, barefoot, listening to the sea's rise and fall and the tap of his staff on the

stones. No one has a word to say to the newly anointed bishop of
Chiapas.

This is the most hated man in America, *the Antichrist* of the
colonial masters, *the scourge of these lands*. He is responsible for
the emperor's promulgation of new laws that deprive the conquistadors' sons of Indian slaves. What will become of them without
the hands that sustain them in mines and plantations? The new
laws take the food from their mouths.

This is the most beloved man in America. Voice of the voiceless, stubborn defender of *those who get worse treatment than the
dung in the plazas*, denouncer of *those who for greed turn Jesus
Christ into the cruelest of gods and the king into a wolf ravening
for human flesh*.

No sooner had he landed in Campeche than Fray Bartolomé
de las Casas announced that no owner of Indians would be absolved
in confession. They answered that here his bishop's credentials
were worthless, as were the new laws, because they had come
printed and not in the royal scribes' handwriting. He threatened
excommunication, and they laughed. They roared with laughter,
because Fray Bartolomé was well known to be deaf.

This evening the messenger has arrived from the royal city of
Chiapas. The town government sends word that there is nothing
in its treasury to pay for the bishop's journey to his diocese and
sends him a few coins from the burial fund.

(27 and 70)

1544: Lima

Carvajal

The dawn light gives form and face to the shadows that hang from
the plaza lanterns. Some early riser recognizes them with a start:
Two conquistadors of early vintage, from among those who captured the Inca Atahualpa in Cajamarca, swing with protuding tongues
and staring eyes.

Roll of drums, clatter of hooves: The city jumps awake. The
town crier shouts at the top of his lungs, and at his side, Francisco
Carvajal dictates and listens. The crier announces that all of Lima's
principal gentry will be hanged like those two and not a house will
be spared from plunder if the council does not accept Gonzalo

Pizarro as governor. General Carvajal, field commander of the rebel troops, gives a noon deadline.

"Carvajal!"

Before the echo dies away, the judges of the royal tribunal and the notables of Lima have flung on some clothes and rushed in disarray to the palace and are signing, without discussion, the decree recognizing Gonzalo Pizarro as sole and absolute authority.

All that is lacking is the signature of lawyer Zárate, who strokes his neck and hesitates while the others wait, dazed, trembling, hearing or thinking they hear the panting of horses and the curses of soldiers who take the field at short rein, eager to attack.

"Get a move on," they implore.

Zárate thinks about the good dowry he is leaving for his un-married daughter, Teresa, and his generous offerings to the Church that have more than paid for another, serener life than this one.

"What is your honor waiting for?"

"Carvajal's patience is short!"

Carvajal: more than thirty years of wars in Europe, ten in America. He fought at Ravenna and at Pavia. He was in on the sack of Rome. He fought with Cortés in Mexico and with Francisco Pizarro in Peru. Six times he has crossed the cordillera.

"The Devil of the Andes!"

He is a giant who has been known to throw off helmet and cuirass in midbattle and offer his breast. He eats and sleeps on his horse.

"Calm, gentlemen, keep calm!"

"Innocent blood will flow!"

"No time to lose!"

The shadow of the gallows looms over newly purchased titles of nobility.

"Sign, sir! Let us avoid further tragedies for Peru!"

Lawyer Zárate dips the goose-quill pen, draws a cross, and beneath, before signing, writes: *I swear by God and this Cross and by the words of the Evangelist Saints that I sign for three reasons: for fear, for fear, and for fear.*

(167)

1545: Royal City of Chiapas

The Bad News Comes
from Valladolid

The Crown has suspended the most important new laws, which set the Indians free. While they lasted, barely three years, who observed them? In reality, even Indians marked *free* on the arm in vivid red continued to be slaves.

"For this they have told me I was right?"

Fray Bartolomé feels abandoned by God, a leaf without a branch, alone and a nobody.

"They said yes to me so that nothing would change. Now not even paper will protect those who have no more shield than their bowels. Did the monarchs receive the New World from the pope for this? Is God a mere pretext? This hangman's shadow, does it come from my body?"

Wrapped in a blanket, he writes a letter to Prince Philip. He announces that he will visit Valladolid without waiting for a reply or permission.

Then Fray Bartolomé kneels on the mat, facing the night, and recites aloud a prayer invented by himself.

(70)

1546: Potosí

The Silver of Potosí

Fifty Indians killed for refusing to work in the excavations. Less than a year since the first vein appeared, and already the slopes of the mountain have been stained with human blood. And a league from here the rocks of the ravine show the dark green spots of the Devil's blood. The Devil shut tight the ravine that leads to Cuzco and crushed Spaniards who passed that way. An archangel hauled the Devil from his cave and dashed him against the rocks. Now the Potosí silver mines have plenty of labor and an open road.

Before the conquest, in the days of the Inca Huaina Cápac,

when the flint pick bit into the mountain's veins of silver, a frightful roar shook the world. Then the voice of the mountain said to the Indians: *"This wealth has other owners."*

(21)

1547: Valparaíso
The Parting

Flies buzz among the remains of the banquet. Neither all that wine nor all this sun puts the guzzlers to sleep. This morning, hearts beat fast. Beneath the arbor, facing the sea, Pedro Valdivia is saying good-bye to those who are about to leave. After so much war and hunger in the wilds of Chile, fifteen of his men are returning to Spain. A tear rolls down Valdivia's cheek as he recalls the shared years, the cities born out of nothing, the Indians subdued by the iron of Spanish lances.

"My only consolation," he says, his speech warming up, *"is the knowledge that you will be resting and enjoying what you so well deserve, and that eases my grief at least a little."*

Not far from the beach, waves rock the ship that will take them to Peru. From there they will sail for Panama; across Panama to the other sea, and then . . . It will be long, but a stretch of the legs makes one feel that one is already walking the wharves of Seville. The baggage, clothing, and gold has been on board since the night before. The scribe Juan Pinel will be taking three thousand pesos in gold from Chile. With his bundle of papers, quill pen, and inkpot, he has followed Valdivia like a shadow, attesting to his every step and giving his every act the force of law. Many times death has scraped against him. This small fortune will more than even up the score for the teenage daughters who await scribe Pinel in far-off Spain.

The soldiers are dreaming out loud when suddenly someone jumps up and shouts: "Valdivia? Where's Valdivia?"

Valdivia is looking smaller by the second. There he goes, rowing the only boat toward the ship loaded with everybody's gold.

On the beach of Valparaíso curses and threats drown out the din of the waves.

The sails swell out and move off in the direction of Peru. Valdivia is off chasing the title of governor of Chile. With the gold that is aboard, and the vigor of his arm, he hopes to convince the top men in Lima.

Sitting on a rock, scribe Juan Pinel clutches his head and cannot stop laughing. His daughters will die as virgins in Spain. Some of the men weep, scarlet with fury; and bugler Alonso de Torres plays an old melody out of tune and then smashes the bugle, which was all he had left.

(67 and 85)

Song of Nostalgia,
from the Spanish Songbook

Lonesome I am for thee,
Country that suckled me.

If luckless I should die,
In the mountains bury me high,
So that my body in the grave
Won't miss the land I crave.
Bury me high as you can bear,
To see if I can see from there
The land for which I shed a tear.

(7)

1548: Xaquixaguana

The Battle of Xaquixaguana
Is Over

Gonzalo Pizarro, the best lancer in America, the man who can split a mosquito in flight with an arquebus or a crossbow, yields his sword to Pedro de La Gasca.

Gonzalo slowly removes his armor of Milanese steel. La Gasca came on a mission to clip his wings, and now the chief of the rebels no longer dreams of crowning himself king of Peru. He only dreams of La Gasca sparing his life.

Pedro de Valdivia enters the tent of the victors. The infantry have fought under his orders.

"The king's honor rested in your hands, Governor," says La Gasca.

This is the first time the king's representative calls him governor, governor of Chile. Valdivia thanks him with a nod. He has other things to ask, but hardly does he open his mouth when the soldiers bring in Gonzalo Pizarro's second-in-command. General Carvajal enters wearing his spectacularly plumed helmet. His captors dare not touch him.

Of all Pizarro's officers, Carvajal is the only one who did not change sides when La Gasca offered the king's pardon to repentant rebels. Many soldiers and captains quickly spurred their horses and galloped across the marsh to the other camp. Carvajal stayed put and fought until they unhorsed him.

"Carvajal," says Diego Centeno, commander of the victorious troops, "you have fallen with honor, Carvajal."

The old man does not even look at him.

"Are you pretending not to know me?" says Centeno and puts out a hand to receive his sword.

Carvajal, who has more than once defeated Centeno and has put him to flight and chased him through half of Peru, stares at him and says: "I only knew you from the back."

And he gives his sword to Pedro de Valdivia.

(67 and 85)

1548: Xaquixaguana
The Executioner

Wrapped in ropes and chains, Carvajal arrives inside an enormous basket hauled by mules. Amid clouds of dust and cries of hatred, the old warrior sings. His hoarse voice pierces the clamor of insults, ignoring the kicks and blows of those who yesterday applauded him and today spit in his face.

What a fable!
A child in a cradle,
Old man in a cradle!
What a fable!

he sings from the basket that bumps him along. When the mules reach the block, the soldiers throw Carvajal out at the executioner's feet. The crowd howls as the executioner slowly unsheaths the sword.

"Brother Juan," asks Carvajal, "since we're both in the same trade, treat me like one tailor to another."

Juan Enríquez is the name of this lad with the kind face. He had another name in Seville, when he wandered the wharves dreaming of being the king's executioner in America. They say he loves the job because it instills fear, and there is no important gentleman or great warrior who does not draw aside on passing him in the street. They also say that he is a lucky avenger. They pay him to kill; and his weapon never rusts, nor does his smile vanish.

> Poor old grandpa!
> Poor old grandpa!

hums Carvajal in a low, sad voice, because he has just thought of his horse Boscanillo, who is also old and defeated, and how well they understood one another.

Juan Enríquez seizes his beard with the left hand and, with the right, slices his neck with one blow.

Beneath the golden sun, applause breaks out.

The executioner holds up the head of Carvajal, who until a moment ago was eighty-four years old and had never forgiven anyone.

(76 and 167)

1548: Xaquixaguana

On Cannibalism in America

Since Francisco Pizarro attended, in mourning dress, the funeral of his victim Atahualpa, several men have succeeded to command and power over the vast kingdom that was the Incas'.

Diego de Almagro, governor of one part of that land, rose against Francisco Pizarro, governor of the other. Both had sworn on the sacred Host that they would share honors, Indians, and lands *without either taking more*, but Pizarro wanted it and won out and Almagro was beheaded.

Almagro's son avenged his father and proclaimed himself governor over the corpse of Pizarro. Then Almagro's son was sent to the scaffold by Cristóbal Vaca de Castro, who passed into history as the only one who escaped gallows, ax, or sword.

Later Gonzalo Pizarro, brother of Francisco, rose in arms against Blasco Núñez Vela, first viceroy of Peru. Núñez Vela fell from his horse badly wounded. His head was cut off and nailed to a pike.

Gonzalo Pizarro was on the point of crowning himself king. Today, Monday, April 9, he ascends the slope that leads to the block. He goes mounted on a mule. They have bound his hands behind his back and thrown over him a black cape, which covers his face and keeps him from seeing the bodiless head of Francisco de Carvajal.

(76 and 81)

1548: Guanajuato

Birth of the Guanajuato Mines

"God's peace be with you, brother."

"So be it, traveler."

Greetings pass between the two muleteers who come from Mexico City and decide to encamp. Night has fallen, and from the shadows those who sleep by day watch them.

"Isn't that the mountain of Cubilete?"

"Of the damned, you might call it."

Maese Pedro and Martín Rodrigo are off to Zacatecas to seek their fortune in its mines, and they bring what they have, a few mules, to sell at a good price. At dawn they will continue on their way.

They lay a few branches on a mattress of dry leaves and encircle it with stones. Flint strikes steel, the spark becomes a flame: facing the fire, the muleteers swap stories, their bad luck, and while they are at it, rags and nostalgia, one of them yells: "They shine!"

"What?"

"The stones!"

Martín Rodrigo leaps into the air, forming a squalid five-pointed star against the moonlit sky, and Maese Pedro breaks his nails on the hot rocks and burns his lips kissing them.

(182)

1549: *La Serena*

The Return

Pedro de Valdivia has just disembarked at the Quintero anchorage, and soon he runs into the acid smell of carrion.

In Peru, Valdivia has carried more than enough weight to avoid traps and surmount doubts and enemies. The vigor of his arm placed at the king's service plus the glitter of the gold he grabbed from his men on the Valparaiso beach have proved highly eloquent to the top men in Lima. After two years, he returns with his title of governor of Chile well signed and sealed. He also takes back the obligation to return that gold to the last gram as well as another obligation, which gnaws at his heart. Given his brand-new title, he must put an end to his affair with Inés Suárez and bring his legal wife here from Spain.

Chile does not receive him with a smile. In this city of La Serena, which he had baptized with the name of his birthplace, the Spaniards are lying about handless and headless among ruins. His fascinating life stories do not interest the vultures.

(67 and 85)

The Last Time

At dawn an undulating streak opens in the black mist and separates earth from sky.

Inés, who has not slept, detaches herself from Valdivia's embrace and leans on her elbow. She is saturated with him, and every little corner of her body feels fiercely alive; she looks at her hand in the misty first light. Her own fingers scare her: they burn. She feels for the dagger. She raises it. Valdivia is asleep and snoring. The dagger hesitates in midair over the nude body.

Centuries pass.

Finally Inés softly plunges the dagger into the pillow beside his face and moves away on tiptoe over the earth floor, leaving the bed woman-free.

1552: Valladolid

He Who Always Took the Orders Now Gives Them

The woman kisses the bar of silver with her lips, with her forehead, with her breasts, while the priest reads aloud the letter from her husband, Juan Prieto, dated in Potosí. The letter and ingot have taken nearly a year to cross the ocean and reach Valladolid.

Juan Prieto writes that while others spend their time at drinking bouts and bullfights, he doesn't hang out in the taverns or the bullring, that in Potosí men put hand to sword on the slightest provocation, and that there are dust storms that ruin the clothing and madden the spirit. That he thinks of nothing but returning to Spain and now sends this big silver bar for the construction of a garden in which his welcome-home banquet will be held.

The garden must have a double iron gate and a stone arch broad enough for the guests invited to the fiesta to pass through in their carriages. It is to be a walled garden, high walls without any openings, full of trees and flowers and rabbits and doves. In the center there must be a big table with viands for the gentry of Valladolid whom he had served years before as a domestic. A carpet should be laid over the grass next to the head of the table, and on the carpet should sit his wife and his daughter Sabina.

He especially stresses to his wife that she must not take her eyes off Sabina nor let even the sun touch her, that it is to get her a good dowry and good marriage that he has spent all these years in the Indies.

(120)

1553: The Banks of the San Pedro River

Miguel

Plenty of his skin has stuck to the cords of the whip. They accused him of slacking off at work or of losing a tool, and the overseer said, "Let him pay with his body." When they were going to tie him up for some more lashes, Miguel grabbed a sword and lost himself in the woods.

Other slaves from the Buría mines fled behind him. A few Indians joined the black runaways. Thus was born the small army that last year attacked the mines and the newborn city of Barquisimeto.

Afterward the rebels moved farther into the mountains and, far away from everything, founded this free kingdom on the riverbanks. The Jirijara Indians painted themselves black from head to foot and, together with the Africans, proclaimed the Negro Miguel king.

Queen Guiomar strolls magnificently among the palms. Her full skirt of brocade rustles. Two pages raise the tip of her silk train.

From his wooden throne, Miguel orders trenches dug and palisades built, names officials and ministers, and appoints the most learned of his men as bishop. At his feet the heir-apparent plays with little stones.

"My kingdom is round and clear-watered," says Miguel as a courtier straightens his lace ruff and another stretches the sleeves of his soldier's jerkin.

In Tocuyo the troop that will kill Miguel and liquidate his kingdom is being readied under the command of Diego de Losada. The Spaniards will come armed with arquebuses and dogs and crossbows. The blacks and Indians who survive will lose their ears or their testicles or the tendons of their feet as an example for all Venezuela.

(2)

A Dream of Pedro de Valdivia

Light from the torches flutters in the fog. Sound of spurs that strike sparks from the paving on a parade ground that is not of Chile nor of anywhere else. In the gallery, a row of court noblemen; long black capes, swords tight at their waists, plumed hats. As Pedro de Valdivia passes, each of the men bows and doffs his hat. When they remove their hats, they remove their heads.

(67 and 85)

1553: Tucapel

Lautaro

The scourge of war has hit every part of Chile.

At the head of the Araucanians waves the red cloak of Caupolicán, the Cyclops who can tear out a tree by the roots.

The Spanish cavalry charges. Caupolicán's army opens up like a fan, lets the cavalry enter, snaps shut, and devours it from the flanks.

Valdivia sends in a second battalion, which shatters against a wall of thousands of men. Then he attacks, followed by his best soldiers. He charges at full speed, shouting, lance in hand, and the Araucanians crumble before his lightning offensive.

Meanwhile, at the head of the Indians who serve the Spanish army, Lautaro waits on a hillside.

"What sort of cowardice is this? What shame for our country?"

Until this moment Lautaro has been Valdivia's page. In a flash of fury the page chooses treason; he chooses loyalty. He blows the horn that hangs on his breast and at full gallop launches the attack. He opens a path with blows to right and left, splitting armor plate and forcing horses to their knees, until he reaches Valdivia, stares him in the face, and brings him down.

He is not yet twenty, this new leader of the Araucanians.

(5)

1553: Tucapel

Valdivia

There is a fiesta around the cinnamon tree.

The vanquished, clad in loincloths, are watching the dances of the victors, who wear helmet and armor. Lautaro sports the clothes of Valdivia, the green doublet embroidered with gold and silver, the shiny cuirass and the gold-visored helmet topped with emeralds and elegant plumes.

Valdivia, naked, is bidding farewell to the world.

No one has blundered. This is the land that Valdivia chose to die in thirteen years ago, when he left Cuzco followed by seven Spaniards on horseback and a thousand Indians on foot. No one blundered except Doña Marina, the wife he left behind in Estremadura, who after twenty years has decided to cross the ocean and is now aboard ship, with a retinue worthy of her rank as governor's wife, silver throne, blue velvet bed, carpets, and all her court of relatives and servants.

The Araucanians open Valdivia's mouth and fill it with dirt. They make him swallow dirt, handful after handful. They swell up his body with Chilean soil as they tell him: *"You want gold? Eat gold. Stuff yourself with gold."*

(5 and 26)

1553: Potosí
Beauty and the Mayor

If Potosí had a hospital and she passed by the door, the sick would be cured. But this city or bunch of houses, born less than six years ago, has no hospital.

The mining camp has grown crazily, now containing twenty thousand souls. Each morning new roofs rear up, raised by adventurers who come from everywhere, elbowing and stabbing each other, in search of an easy fortune. No man takes a chance in its earth streets without a sword and leather doublet, and the women are condemned to live behind shutters. The least ugly run the greatest risk; and among them the Beauty—a spinster on top of everything—has no alternative but to cut herself off from the world. She only emerges at dawn, heavily chaperoned, to attend Mass, because just seeing her makes anyone crave to gobble her up, either in one gulp or in sips, and one-armed people to clap hands.

The lord mayor of the town, Don Diego de Esquivel, has cast an eye upon her. They say that this is why he goes about with a broad grin, and all the world knows that he hasn't smiled since that remote day in his infancy when he hurt his facial muscles trying it.

(167)

To the Strains of the Barrel Organ
a Blind Man Sings to Her
Who Sleeps Alone

Lady,
why do you sleep alone,
When you could sleep with a lad
who has trousers
with polished buttons
and jacket
with silver buttonholes?
Up above
there's a green olive tree.
Down below
there's a green orange tree.
And in between
there's a black bird
that sucks
its lump of sugar.

(196)

1553: Potosí

The Mayor and the Gallant

"Don't sleep alone," says someone, "sleep with that one." And points him out. The girl's favorite is a soldier of fine bearing who has honey in his eyes and voice. Don Diego chews over his despair and decides to await his opportunity.

The opportunity comes one night, in one of Potosí's gambling dens, by the hand of a friar who has gambled away the contents of his begging bowl. A skilled card sharp is picking up the fruits of his efforts when the cleaned-out one lowers an arm, pulls a dagger out from beneath his habit, and nails the man's hand to the table. The gallant, who is there out of pure curiosity, jumps into the fray.

All are taken under arrest.

The mayor, Don Diego, has to decide the matter. He faces the gallant and makes him an offer: "Fine or beating."

"A fine I can't pay. I am poor, but a gentleman of pure blood and honored lineage."

"Twelve lashes for this prince," decides the mayor.

"To a Spanish gentleman!" protests the soldier.

"Tell it to my other ear, this one doesn't believe it," says Don Diego, and sits down to enjoy the beating.

When they unbind him, the beaten lover threatens: "I'll take revenge on those ears of yours, Mr. Mayor. I lend them to you for a year. You can use them for that long, but then they're mine."

(167)

1554: Cuzco

The Mayor and the Ears

Ever since the gallant's threat, Don Diego feels his ears every morning on waking up and measures them in the mirror. He has found that his ears grow when they are happy and that cold and depression make them shrink; that glances and calumnies heat them to bright red and that they flap desperately, like birds in a cage, when they hear the screech of a steel blade being sharpened.

To ensure their safety, Don Diego takes them to Cuzco. Guards and slaves accompany him on the long journey.

One Sunday morning, Don Diego is leaving church after Mass, more parading than walking, followed by the little black boy who carries his velvet hassock. Suddenly a pair of eyes fastens on his ears with sure aim, and a blue cloak flashes through the crowd and disappears, fluttering, in the distance.

His ears feel they have been hurt.

(167)

1554: Lima

The Mayor and the Bill Collector

Before long the cathedral bells will be ringing out midnight. It will mark just a year since that stupid episode that obliged Don Diego to move to Cuzco, and from Cuzco to Lima.

Don Diego confirms for the thousandth time that the doors are bolted and that the people standing guard even on the roof

have not fallen asleep. He has personally inspected the house corner by corner, without forgetting even the woodpile in the kitchen.

Soon he will throw a party. There will be bullfights and masquerades, joustings and fireworks, fowls roasting on spits, and barrels of wine with open spigots. Don Diego will knock Lima's eye
out. At the party he will try out his new damask cloak and his new
steed with the black velvet gold-studded saddle, which goes so
well with the crimson caparison.

He sits down to await the chimes. He counts them. Takes a
deep breath.

A slave raises the candelabrum and lights his carpeted way to
the bedroom. Another slave takes off his doublet and shoes, those
shoes that look like gloves, and his openwork white hose. The slaves
close the door and retire to take up their lookout posts until morning.

Don Diego blows out the candles, buries his head in the big
silk pillow and, for the first time in a year, falls into an unperturbed
sleep.

Much later, the suit of armor that adorns a corner of the
bedroom begins to move. Sword in hand, the armor advances in
the darkness, very slowly, toward the bed.

(167)

1554: Mexico City
Sepúlveda

The city council of Mexico, cream of the colonial nobility, resolves
to send Juan Ginés de Sepúlveda two hundred pesos in gold in
recognition of his services and to encourage him in the future.

Sepúlveda, the humanist, is not only a doctor and archpriest,
chronicler and chaplain to Charles V. He also shines in business,
as witness his growing fortune; and in the courts, he works as an
ardent publicity agent for the owners of America's lands and Indians.

In rebuttal to Bartolomé de Las Casas's assertions, Sepúlveda
maintains that Indians are serfs by nature, according to God's will,
and that the Holy Scriptures contain examples to spare of the
punishment of the unjust. When Las Casas proposes that Spaniards
learn the Indians' languages and Indians the language of Castile,
Sepúlveda replies that the difference between Spaniards and In-

dians is the same as that between male and female and almost the same as that between man and monkeys. For Sepúlveda, what Las Casas calls abuse and crime is a legitimate system of dominion, and he commends the arts of hunting against those who, born to obey, refuse slavery.

The king, who publishes Las Casas's attacks, places a ban on Sepúlveda's treatise on the just causes of the colonial war. Sepúlveda accepts the censure smiling and without protest. In the last analysis, reality is more potent than bad conscience, and he well knows what those in command all know in their hearts: The desire to make money, not to win souls, is what builds empires.

(90 and 118)

1556: Asunción, Paraguay

Conquistadoras

They carried the firewood and the wounded on their backs. The women treated the men like small children: They gave them fresh water and consolation and cobwebs for their bruises. The words of encouragement and of alarm came from their mouths, and likewise the curses that scourged the cowards and pushed the weaklings. They fired the crossbows and guns while the men lay down seeking a bit of shade in which to die. When the survivors of hunger and arrows reached the brigantines, it was the women who hoisted the sails and set the course upriver, rowing and rowing without complaint. Thus it was in Buenos Aires and on the Paraná River.

After twenty years Governor Irala has distributed Indians and lands in Asunción. Bartolomé García, one of those who arrived in brigantines from the South, mumbles his protests. Irala has given him only sixteen Indians: he who still carries an arrowhead in his arm and who fought body-to-body against the pumas that jumped over the Buenos Aires stockade.

"What about me? If you're beefing, what shall *I* say?" cries Doña Isabel de Guevara.

She also had been there from the outset. She came from Spain to found Buenos Aires together with Mendoza and went with Irala up to Asunción. For being a woman, the governor has given her no Indians at all.

(120)

1556: Asunción, Paraguay

"The Paradise of Mahomet"

The dice roll. An Indian woman holds up the candle. Whoever wins her takes her naked, for the one who loses her has wagered her without clothes.

In Paraguay, Indian women are trophies of the wheel, dice, or cards, the booty of expeditions into the jungle, the motives for duels and murders. Although there are many of them, the ugliest is worth as much as a side of bacon or a horse. The conquistadors of Indies and Indians go to Mass followed by flocks of women. In this land sterile of gold and silver, some have eighty or a hundred, who by day grind sugarcane and by night spin thread and let themselves be loved, to provide their masters with honey, clothing, children: They help toward forgetting the dream of wealth that reality denied and the distant girlfriends who grow old waiting in Spain.

"Careful. They go to bed with hatred," warns Domingo Martínez, father of countless mestizos and future monks. He says the Indian women are rancorous and stubborn, always eager to return to the woods where they were captured, and that one can't trust them with even an ounce of cotton because they hide it or burn it or give it away, *that their glory is just to ruin the Christians and destroy whatever there is*. Some have hanged themselves or eaten dirt and there are some who deny the breast to their newly born children. The Indian Juliana killed conquistador Nuño de Cabrera one night and shouted to the others to follow her example.

(73 and 74)

Womanizer Song,
from the Spanish Songbook

If the Moors can use
seven women,
Why should Spaniards refuse
to use as many?

Oh, what joy
that Spain is back
on the Moorish track.
To love one is nothing,
To love two is hypocrisy,
To love three and deceive four,
That's the glory that comes from God!

(196)

1556: La Imperial
Mariño de Lobera

The horse, golden of hide and full of dash, decides direction and pace. If he wants to gallop, he gallops; he seeks open country and romps amid tall grasses, approaches the stream, and backs away; respectfully, without haste, he comes and goes along the dirt streets of the brand-new city.

Riding bareback with a free rein, Pedro Mariño de Lobera parades and celebrates. All the wine there was in La Imperial flows through his veins. From time to time he giggles and makes some remark. The horse turns his head, looks, and approves.

It is four years today since Pedro quit the entourage of the viceroy in Lima and took the long road to Chile.

"I'm four years old," says Don Pedro to the horse. "Four little years. You're older and stupider."

During those years he has seen plenty and fought plenty. He says that these Chilean lands sprout joys and gold the way plants grow elsewhere. And when there is war, as there always is, the Virgin throws out a thick fog to blind the Indians, and the apostle Santiago contributes his lance and white horse to the conquering host. Not far from here nor long ago, when the Araucanian squadrons had their backs to the sea, a giant wave knocked them down and swallowed them up.

Don Pedro remembers and comments, and the horse nods.

Suddenly lightning snakes across the sky and thunder shakes the ground.

"It's raining," Don Pedro observes. "It's raining milk!"

The horse raises his head and drinks.

(130)

1558: *Cañete*

The War Goes On

With a hundred arrows in his breast, Caupolicán meets his end. The great one-eyed chief falls, defeated by treachery. The moon used to stop to contemplate his feats, and there was not a man who didn't love him or fear him, but a traitor could do him in.

A year ago treachery also caught Lautaro by surprise.

"And you, what are you doing here?" asked the Spanish leader.

"I come to offer you Lautaro's head," said the traitor.

Lautaro did not enter Santiago as a conqueror at the head of his men. His head was brought in from Mount Chilipirco on the longest lance in the Spanish army.

Treachery is a weapon as devastating as typhus, smallpox, and hunger, all of which plague the Araucanians while the war destroys crops and plantings. Yet the farmers and hunters of these Chilean lands have other weapons. Now they know how to use horses, which previously struck terror into them: they attack on horseback, a whirlwind of mounted men, and protect themselves with rawhide armor. They know how to fire the arquebuses they take on the battlefield, and they tie swords to the tips of their lances. Behind moving tree branches, in the morning mist, they advance unseen. Then they feign retreat, so that the enemy horses will sink into swamps or break their legs in concealed traps. Smoke columns tell them which way the Spanish troops are heading: they bite them and disappear. They return suddenly and hurl themselves on the enemy when the sun burns brightest and the soldiers are frying in their armor plate. Horsemen are brought down with the slipknot lassos invented by Lautaro.

What is more, the Araucanians fly. Before going into battle they rub themselves with feathers of the swiftest birds.

(5 and 66)

Araucanian Song of the
Phantom Horseman

Who is this
riding on the wind,
like the tiger,
with his phantom body?
When the oaks see him,
when people see him,
they say in a whisper
one to the other:
"Look, brother, here comes
the ghost of Caupolicán."

(42)

1558: Michmaloyan
The Tzitzimes

They have caught and are punishing Juan Teton, Indian preacher of the village of Michmaloyan in the Valley of Mexico, and also those who listened and paid heed to him. Juan was going about announcing the last days of an era and the proximity of a year to end all years. At that point, he said, total darkness would fall, the verdure would dry up, and there would be hunger. All who failed to wash baptism out of their hair would turn into animals. *Tzitzimes,* terrifying black birds, would descend from the sky and eat everyone who had not washed off the mark of the priests.

The *tzitzimes* had also been announced by Martín Océlotl, who was captured and beaten, dispossessed and banished from Texcoco. He, too, said that there would be no flame at the festival of new fire and the world would end because of those who had forgotten the teachings of the fathers and grandfathers and no longer knew to whom they owed birth and growth. The *tzitzimes* will fall upon us through the darkness, he said, and devour women and men. According to Martín Océlotl, the missionary friars are *tzitzimes* in disguise, *enemies of all happiness, who don't know that we are born to die and that after death we will have neither pleasure nor joy.*

And the old lords who survive in Tlaxcala also have something to say about the priests: *Poor things,* they say. *Poor things. They must be sick or crazy. At noon, at midnight, and at the dawn hour, when everyone rejoices, they shout and cry. They must have something terribly wrong with them. They are men without any sense. They seek neither pleasure nor happiness, but sadness and loneliness.*

(109)

1558: Yuste

Who Am I? What Have I Been?

Breathing is a violent effort, and his head is on fire. His feet, swollen with gout, will no longer walk. Stretched out on the terrace, he who was monarch of half the world is in flight from his jesters and contemplates the dusk in this Estremaduran valley. The sun is departing beyond the purple mountains, and its last rays redden the shadows over the Jeronomite convent.

He has entered many a city as a conqueror. He has been acclaimed and hated. Many have given their lives for him; the lives of many more have been taken in his name. After forty years of traveling and fighting, the highest prisoner of his own empire wants to rest and be forgotten. Who am I, what have I been? In the mirror he has seen death entering. The deceiver or the deceived?

Between battles, by the light of campfires, he has signed more than four hundred loan agreements with German, Genoese, and Flemish bankers, and the galleons have never brought enough silver and gold from America. He who so loved music has heard more of the thundering of guns and horses than sacred lute melodies; and at the end of so much war his son, Philip, will inherit a bankrupt empire.

Through the fog, from the north, Charles had arrived in Spain when he was seventeen, followed by his entourage of Flemish merchants and German bankers, in an endless caravan of wagons and horses. At the time he could not even say good-morning in the language of Castile. But tomorrow he will choose it to say goodbye.

"Oh, Jesus!" will be his last words.

(41 and 116)

1559: Mexico City

The Mourners

The eagle of the Austrias opens his golden wings against the clear sky of the Mexican plateau. On a black cloth, surrounded by flags, glitters the crown. The catafalque renders homage to Charles V and also to death, *which has conquered so invincible a monarch*.

The crown, an exact replica of the one that adorned the emperor in Europe, has toured the streets of Mexico. On a damask cushion it was borne in procession. The multitude prayed and chanted behind it while the bells of all the churches rang out the death toll. The chief nobles paraded on horseback in mourning, black brocades, black velvet cloaks embroidered with gold and silver; and beneath a canopy, the archbishop, the bishops, and their spectacular miters broke through clouds of incense.

For several nights the tailors have not slept. The entire colony is dressed in mourning.

In the slums, the Aztecs are in mourning, too. They have been for months, nearly a year. The plague is exterminating them wholesale. A fever never known before the conquest draws blood from the nose and eyes and kills.

(28)

Advice of the Old Aztec Wise Men

Now that you see with your eyes,
take notice.
See how it is here: there is no joy,
there is no happiness.

Here on earth is the place of many tears,
the place where breath gives up
and where are known so well
depression and bitterness.

An obsidian wind blows and swoops
over us.
The earth is the place of painful joy,
of joy that pricks.

But even though it were thus,
though it were true that suffering is all,
even if things were thus on the earth,
must we always go with fear?
must we forever tremble?
must we live forever weeping?

So that we may not always go with groans,
so that sadness may not ever saturate us,
Our Father has given us
smiles, dreams, food,
our strength,
and finally
the act of love,
which sows people.

(110)

1560: Huexotzingo

The Reward

The native chiefs of Huexotzingo now bear the names of their new lords. They are called Felipe de Mendoza, Hernando de Meneses, Miguel de Alvarado, Diego de Chaves, or Mateo de la Corona. But they write in their own Náhuatl and in that language send a long letter to the king of Spain: *Unfortunates we, your poor vassals of Huexotzingo . . .*

They explain to Philip II that they cannot reach him in any other way, because they don't have the price of the journey, and they tell their story by letter. *How shall we speak? Who will speak for us? Unfortunates we.*

They never made war on the Spaniards. They walked twenty leagues to Hernán Cortés and embraced him, fed him, served him, and took charge of his sick soldiers. They gave him men and arms and timber to build the brigantines that assaulted Tenochtitlán.

After the Aztec capital fell, the Huexotzingans fought with Cortés in the conquest of Michoacán, Jalisco, Colhuacan, Pánuco, Oaxaca, Tehuantepec, and Guatemala. Many died. And afterward, *when they told us to break the stones and burn the carvings that we worshiped, we did it, and destroyed our temples . . . Whatever they ordered, we obeyed.*

Huexotzingo was an independent kingdom when the Spaniards came. They had never paid tribute to the Aztecs. *Our fathers, grandfathers, and ancestors did not know what tribute was and paid it to no one.*

Now, however, the Spaniards are demanding such high tribute in money and in corn that *we declare before Your Majesty that little time will pass before our city of Huexotzingo disappears and dies.*

(120)

1560: Michoacán

Vasco de Quiroga

Primitive Christianity, primitive communism: the bishop of Michoacán draws up ordinances for his evangelical communities. He was inspired in founding them by the *Utopia* of Thomas More, by the biblical prophets, and by the ancient traditions of America's Indians.

The communities created by Vasco de Quiroga, where no one is master of anyone or anything and neither hunger nor money is known, will not multiply throughout Mexico as he wished. The Council of the Indies will never take the foolish bishop's projects seriously nor even glance at the books that he obstinately recommends. But here utopia has returned to America, where it originated. Thomas More's chimera has been incarnated in the small communal world of Michoacán; and in times to come the Indians here will remember Vasco de Quiroga as their own—the dreamer who riveted his eyes on a hallucination to see beyond the time of infamy.

(227)

1561: Villa de los Bergantines

The First Independence of America

They crowned him yesterday. Curious monkeys trooped up among the trees. Fernando de Guzmán's mouth dripped guanábana juice, and there were suns in his eyes. One after the other, the soldiers knelt down before the throne of sticks and straw, kissed the hand of the elect, and swore fealty. Then they signed the declaration with a name or an X, all who were not women or servants or Indians or blacks. The scribe made it official, and independence was proclaimed.

The seekers of El Dorado, lost in midjungle, now have their own monarch. Nothing binds them to Spain except resentment. They have repudiated vassalage to the king across the sea: "I don't know him!" cried Lope de Aguirre yesterday, all bone and fury, raising his sword covered with mildew. "I don't know him or want to know him, nor to have him nor obey him!"

In the village's biggest hut the court is installed. By the light of candles, Prince Ferdinand eats endless cassava buns spread with honey. He is served by his pages, cup and ewer bearer, and valet; between buns he gives orders to his secretaries, dictates decrees to his scribes, and grants audiences and favors. The royal treasurer, chaplain, chief majordomo, and steward-taster wear tattered doublets and have swollen hands and split lips. The sergeant at arms is swarthy-skinned Lope de Aguirre, lame in one leg, one-eyed, almost a dwarf, who conspires by night and supervises the brigantine construction by day.

Ax- and hammerblows ring out. The Amazon currents have ground their ships to pieces, but ahead two new keels rise on the sand. The jungle offers good timber. They have made bellows out of horses' hides; nails, bolts, and hinges out of horseshoes.

Tortured by mosquitos and gnats, smothered by humid and fever-laden vapors, the men wait for the ships to grow. They eat grass and vulture meat, without salt. No dogs or horses are left, and the fishhooks bring up nothing but mud and decayed algae, but no one in the camp doubts that the hour of revenge has come. They left Peru months ago in search of the lake where according to legend there are solid gold idols as big as boys, and now they want to return to Peru on a war footing. They won't spend another day in pursuit of the promised land, because they realize that they already found it and are sick of cursing their bad luck. They will sail the Amazon, emerge into the ocean, occupy Margarita Island, invade Venezuela and Panama . . .

Those who sleep dream of the silver of Potosí. Aguirre, who never closes his remaining eye, sees it awake.

(123 and 164)

1561: Nueva Valencia del Rey

Aguirre

At center stage, ax in hand, appears Lope de Aguirre surrounded by dozens of mirrors. Outlined on the backdrop, the profile of King Philip II, black, enormous.

Lope de Aguirre (*to the audience*): On the road of our defeat, passing through death and misadventure, we took more than ten months to reach the mouth of the Amazon, which is a great, fearsome, and ill-starred river. Then we took possession of Margarita Island. There I cashed in twenty-five traitors on gallows or garrote. And then we made our way onto the mainland. King Philip's soldiers are trembling with fright! Soon we'll leave Venezuela . . . Soon we'll be entering the kingdom of Peru in triumph! (*He turns and confronts his own pitiful image in one of the mirrors.*) I crowned Fernando de Guzmán king on the Amazon River! (*Raises his ax and splits the mirror.*) I crowned him king and I killed him! Same with his captain of the guard and the lieutenant general and four captains! (*As he speaks he smashes all the mirrors one after the other.*) Same with his head steward and his chaplain! . . . And with a woman who was in on the plot against me, and that fellow born in Greece who thought himself such a big shot, and an admiral . . . and six more of their allies! . . . And I appointed new captains and a sergeant major! They wanted to kill me and I hanged them! (*Pulverizes the last of the mirrors.*) All of them! All of them! . . . (*He sits, almost suffocating, on the ground covered with glass. The ax held high in his fists, his eyes astray.*

Long silence.) As a lad I crossed the sea to Peru because I was worth more with a lance in my hand . . . A quarter of a century! . . . Mysteries, miseries . . . I dug out whole cemeteries to get silver and gold for others . . . I put up gallows in the middle of unborn cities . . . I hunted down crowds of people on my horse . . . Indians fleeing in terror through the flames . . . Gentlemen with fancy titles and borrowed silk clothes, sons of something or other, sons of nobody, agonizing in the jungle, frothing at the mouth, eating dirt, blood poisoned by arrows . . . Up in the mountains, warriors in steel armor pierced right through by blizzards more violent than any arquebus volley . . . A lot of them found graves in the bellies of vultures . . . A lot ended up as yellow as the gold they were hunting for . . . Yellow skin, yellow eyes . . . And the gold . . . (*Drops his ax. Painfully opens his hands, which are like claws. Shows his palms*.) Vanished . . . Gold turned into shadow or dew . . . (*Looks down incredulously. Long silence. Suddenly he rises. Back to the audience, raises his bony fist toward the huge outline of Philip II, projected with his pointed beard against the backdrop*.) Damn few of you kings go to hell, because there's damn few of you! (*Walks toward backdrop, dragging his lame leg*.) Ungrateful bastard! I lost my body defending you against the rebels in Peru! I gave you a leg and an eye and these hands that aren't much use to me! Now the rebel is me! Rebel till death for your ungratefulness! (*Faces audience, unsheathes his sword*.) Me, prince of the rebels! Lope de Aguirre the Pilgrim, Wrath of God, chief of the cripples! We don't need you, king of Spain! (*Colored lights go on at various points on the stage*.) We mustn't leave any minister of yours alive! (*Sword in hand, lunges at a beam of reddish light*.) Judges, governors, presidents, viceroys! War to the death against all court whores! (*The beam of light stays in place, indifferent to the sword cutting it*.) Usurpers! Thieves! (*The sword wounds the air*.) You have destroyed the Indies! (*Attacks beam of golden light*.) Lawyers, notaries, ink-shitters! How long must we endure your robberies in these lands won by us? (*Sword slashes beam of white light*.) Monks, bishops, archbishops! You won't even bury a poor Indian! For penitence you keep a dozen girls in the kitchen! Traffickers! Traffickers in sacraments! Swindlers! (*The sword's futile assaults on un-*

blinking beams of light, which multiply across the stage, con-
tinue. Aguirre begins to lose strength and looks ever more
alone and insignificant.)

(123 and 164)

1561: Nueva Valencia del Rey

From Lope de Aguirre's letter
to King Philip II

Over here we have got the measure of how cruel you are and how
you break your faith and word, so that in this country we give less
credit to your promises than to the books of Martin Luther, for
your viceroy the Marquis of Cañete hanged Martín de Robles, a
man outstandingly dedicated to your service, and the brave con-
quistador of Piru Tomás Vázquez, and poor Alonso Díaz, who
worked harder in the discovery of this land than Moses's scouts in
the desert . . .

Listen, listen, Spanish king, stop being cruel and ungrateful
to your vassals, because with your father and you comfortably
back in Spain away from all worries, your vassals have given you
at the cost of their blood and treasure all the many lands and
dominions that you have in these parts, and listen, king and sir,
you can't call yourself a just king and take any part of these lands
for which you ventured nothing without first rewarding those who
toiled and sweated . . .

Alas, what a terrible pity that the Imperial Caesar your father
should have conquered proud Germany with the forces of Spain,
spending so much money brought from these Indies discovered by
us, that our old age and exhaustion doesn't pain you enough for
you to relieve our hunger even for a day! . . .

(123)

1561: Barquisimeto

Order Restored

Abandoned by his men, who preferred the king's pardon or indulgences, Lope de Aguirre stabs to death his daughter Elvira, *to*

save her from becoming a mattress for blackguards, and confronts his executioners. He corrects their aim, not this way, not that way, lousy shot, and falls without commending himself to God.

When Philip reads the letter, seated on his throne a long way from here, Aguirre's head is fixed on a pike as a warning to all the pawns of European development.

(123 and 164)

1562: Maní

The Fire Blunders

Fray Diego de Landa throws into the flames, one after the other, the books of the Mayas.

The inquisitor curses Satan, and the fire crackles and devours. Around the incinerator, heretics howl with their heads down. Hung by the feet, flayed with whips, Indians are doused with boiling wax as the fire flares up and the books snap, as if complaining.

Tonight, eight centuries of Mayan literature turn to ashes. On these long sheets of bark paper, signs and images spoke: They told of work done and days spent, of the dreams and the wars of a people born before Christ. With hog-bristle brushes, the knowers of things had painted these illuminated, illuminating books so that the grandchildren's grandchildren should not be blind, should know how to see themselves and see the history of their folk, so they should know the movements of the stars, the frequency of eclipses and the prophecies of the gods and so they could call for rains and good corn harvests.

In the center, the inquisitor burns the books. Around the huge bonfire, he chastises the readers. Meanwhile, the authors, artist-priests dead years or centuries ago, drink chocolate in the fresh shade of the first tree of the world. They are at peace, because they died knowing that memory cannot be burned. Will not what they painted be sung and danced through the times of the times?

When its little paper houses are burned, memory finds refuge in mouths that sing the glories of men and of gods, *songs that stay on from people to people* and in bodies that dance to the sound of hollow trunks, tortoise shells, and reed flutes.

(205 and 219)

1563: Arauco Fortress

The History That Will Be

The noose tightens and strangles. In this frontier redoubt, twice burned down and rebuilt, water is almost exhausted. Soon they will have to drink their small urinations. So many arrows have fallen inside that the Spaniards use them as firewood for cooking.

The Araucanian chief approaches the foot of the rampart on horseback: "Captain! Do you hear me?"

Lorenzo Bernal leans his head over.

The native chief announces that they will surround the fort with straw and set fire to it. He says that they have not left anyone alive in Concepción.

"Nothing doing!" shouts Bernal.

"Surrender, Captain! You've no way out!"

"Not a chance! Never!"

The horse rears up on two legs.

"Then you'll die!"

"So we die," says Bernal, and yells: "But in the long run we'll win the war! There'll be more and more of us!"

The Indian replies with a chuckle.

"How? With what women?" he asks.

"If there are no Spanish ones, we'll have yours," says the captain slowly, savoring the words, and adds: *"And we'll make children on them who'll be your masters!"*

(130)

1564: Plymouth

Hawkins

The four ships, under command of Captain John Hawkins, await the morning tide. As soon as the water rises they will sail for Africa, to hunt people on the coasts of Guinea. From there they will head for the Antilles to trade slaves for sugar, hides, and pearls.

A couple of years ago, Hawkins made this voyage on his own. In a ship named *Jesus*, he sold three hundred slaves as contraband in Santo Domingo. Queen Elizabeth exploded with fury when she learned of it, but her anger vanished as soon as she saw the balance sheet of the voyage. In no time at all she made herself a business partner of the audacious Devonshire "seadog," and the Earls of Pembroke and Leicester and London's lord mayor bought first shares in the new enterprise.

As the sailors hoist the sails, Captain Hawkins harangues them from the bridge. The British navy will make his orders its own in centuries to come: *"Serve God every day!"* Hawkins orders at the top of his lungs. *"Love one another! Save your provisions! Watch out for fire! Keep good company!"*

(127, 187, and 198)

1564: Bogotá

Vicissitudes of Married Life

"Tell me, do I seem different?"

"Well, a bit."

"A bit what?"

"A bit fat, ma'am, if you'll excuse me."

"See if you can guess. Fat from eating or from laughing?"

"Fat from loving, I'd say, meaning no offense."

"No offense, woman, that's what I called you about . . ."

The lady is very worried. Her body has had little patience, unable to wait for the absent husband; and someone has told her that he's due back in Cartagena. When he sees her tummy, what won't he do, that dour man who cures headaches by cutting off heads?

"That's why I called you, Juana. Help me, you who can fly and can drink wine from an empty cup. Tell me. Is my husband coming in the Cartagena fleet?"

In a silver washbasin the black woman Juana García mixes waters, soils, bloods, weeds. She dips a little green book into the basin and lets it float. Then she buries her nose in it. "No," she says, "he's not coming. And if you want to see your husband, come and take a peek."

The lady bends over the basin. By the light of the candles she sees him. He is seated beside a pretty woman in a place of many silks, while someone cuts a dress of fancy cloth. "Oh, you faker! Tell me, Juana, what place is this?"

"The house of a tailor on the island of Santo Domingo."

In the dense water appears the image of the tailor cutting out a sleeve.

"Shall I stop it?" says the black woman.

"Yes, stop it!"

The hand emerges from the basin with a sleeve of fine cloth dripping between the fingers.

The lady trembles, but with fury.

"He deserves more fat bellies, the lousy pig!"

From a corner, a puppy snores with half-open eyes.

(194)

1565: Road to Lima

The Spy

On Don Antonio Solar's hacienda by the Lurín River, the melons have grown as big as suns. It is the first time that this fruit, brought from Spain, has been planted around here, and the foreman sends the master ten samples for his pleasure and pride. The size of these melons is comparable with that of the Cuzapa Valley radishes, of which they say five horses can be tied to their tops.

Two Indians take the foreman's offering to Lima in two sacks. He has given them a letter to deliver with the melons to Don Antonio Solar. "If you eat any of the melons," he warns them, "this letter will tell him about it."

When they are a couple of leagues from the city of the kings, the Indians sit down to rest in a ravine.

"How would this peculiar fruit taste?"

"Must be marvelous."

"How about trying it? One melon, just one."

"The letter will sing," one of the Indians recalls.

They look at the letter and hate it. They look around for a prison for it. They hide it behind a rock where it can't see anything, and devour a melon in quick bites, sweet juicy pulp, delicious beyond imagining. Then they eat another to even up the sacks. Then they pick up the letter, tuck it in their clothing, throw the sacks over their shoulders, and continue on their way.

(76)

1565: Yauyoa

That Stone Is Me

The king's official is awaiting the witch, skilled in deviltries, who has been summoned to come to explain herself. Face down at his feet lies the stone idol. The witch was caught communing secretly with the idol and will soon pay for her heresy. But before the punishment, the official wants to hear from her own lips her confession of talks with the Devil. While he waits for her to be brought, he amuses himself stomping on the idol and meditating on the fate of these Indians, whom God must be sorry to have made.

The soldiers throw down the witch and leave her trembling on the threshold.

Then the ugly old stone idol greets the ugly old witch in the Quechua language: *"Welcome, princess,"* says the hoarse voice from under the official's foot.

The official is flabbergasted and falls sprawling on the floor.

As she fans him with a hat, the old woman clutches the fainting man's coat and cries: "Don't punish me, sir, don't break it!"

The old woman wants to explain to him that divinities live in the stone and if it were not for the idol, she would not know her name, or who she is, or where she comes from and would be wandering the earth naked and lost.

(221)

Prayer of the Incas, Seeking God

Hear me,
from the sea up there where Thou livest,
from the sea down here where Thou art.
Creator of the world,
potter of man,
Lord of Lords,
to Thee,
with my eyes that despair to see Thee

or just for yearning to know Thee
if I see Thee,
know Thee,
ponder Thee,
understand Thee,
Thou wilt see me and know me.
The sun, the moon,
the day,
the night,
the summer,
the winter,
they don't walk idly,
but in good order,
to the appointed place
and to a good end.
Everywhere Thou carriest with Thee
Thy royal scepter.
Hear me,
listen to me.
Let me not tire out,
let me not die.

(105)

1565: Mexico City

Ceremony

The gilded tunic glints. Forty-five years after his death, Moctezuma heads the procession. The horsemen move at walking pace into the central square of Mexico City. Dancers step out to the thunder of drums and the lament of chirimía pipes. Many Indians, clad in white, hold up flowered branches; others, enormous clay cooking pots. The smoke of incense mingles with the aromas of spicy sauces.

Before Cortés's palace, Moctezuma dismounts.

The door opens. Among his pages, armed with tall, sharpened halberds, appears Cortés.

Moctezuma bows his head, crowned with feathers and gold and precious stones. Kneeling, he offers garlands of flowers. Cortés touches his shoulder. Moctezuma rises. With a slow gesture he tears off his mask and reveals the curly hair and high-pointed mustachio of Alonso de Avila.

Alonso de Avila, lord of gallows and knife, owner of Indians, lands, and mines, enters the palace of Martín Cortés, marquis of the Valley of Oaxaca. The son of a conquistador opens his house to the nephew of another conquistador.

Today the conspiracy against the king of Spain officially commences. In the life of the colony, all is not soirées and tournaments, card and hunting parties.

(28)

1566: Madrid

The Fanatic of Human Dignity

Fray Bartolomé de las Casas is going over the heads of the king and of the Council of the Indies. Will he be punished for his disobedience? At ninety-two, it matters little to him. He has been fighting for half a century. Are not his exploits the key to his tragedy? They have let him win many battles, but the outcome of the war was decided in advance. He has known it for a long time.

His fingers won't obey him anymore. He dictates the letter. Without anybody's permission, he addresses himself directly to the Holy See. He asks Pius V to order the wars against the Indians stopped and to halt the plunder that uses the cross as an excuse. As he dictates he becomes indignant, the blood rises to his head, and the hoarse and feeble voice that remains to him trembles.

Suddenly he falls to the floor.

(70 and 90)

1566: Madrid

Even if You Lose,
It's Still Worthwhile

The lips move, speak soundless words. "Forgivest Thou me, Lord?"

Fray Bartolomé pleads for mercy at the Last Judgment for having believed that black and Moorish slaves would alleviate the fate of the Indians.

He lies stretched out, damp forehead, pallid, and the lips do not stop moving. From far off, a slow thunderclap. Fray Bartolomé, the giver of birth, the doer, closes his eyes. Although always hard of hearing, he hears rain beating on the roof of the Atocha monastery. The rain moistens his face. He smiles.

One of the priests who accompanies him murmurs something about the strange light that has illumined his face. Through the rain, free of doubt and torment, Fray Bartolomé is traveling for the last time to the green worlds where he knew happiness.

"I thank Thee," say his lips in silence while he reads the prayers by the light of fireflies, splashed by the rain that strikes the palm-frond roof.

"I thank Thee," he says as he celebrates Mass in sheds without walls and baptizes naked children in rivers.

The priests cross themselves. The clock's last grains of sand have fallen. Someone turns over the hourglass so that time will not be interrupted.

(27, 70, and 90)

1568: Los Teques

Guaicaipuro

Never again will the river reflect his face, his panache of lofty plumes.

This time the gods did not listen to his wife, Urquía, who pleaded that neither bullets nor disease should touch him and that sleep, the brother of death, should never forget to return him to the world at the end of each night.

The invaders felled Guaicaipuro with bullets.

Since the Indians elected him chief, there was no truce in this valley nor in the Avila Mountains. In the newly born city of Caracas people crossed themselves when in a low voice they spoke his name.

Confronting death and its officials, the last of the free men has fallen shouting, *Kill me, kill me, free yourselves from fear*.

(158)

1568: Mexico City

The Sons of Cortés

Martín was the name of Hernán Cortés's oldest son, his blood son born of the Indian woman Malinche. His father died leaving him a meager annual pension.

Martín is also the name of Hernán Cortés's legitimate son, born of a Spanish woman, a count's daughter and niece of a duke. This Martín has inherited the coat of arms and the fortune: He is marquis of the Valley of Oaxaca, owner of thousands of Indians and leagues of this land that his father had humiliated and loved and chosen to lie in forever.

On a saddle of crimson velvet embroidered with gold, Martín the marquis used to wander the streets of Mexico. Behind him went his red-liveried guards armed with swords. Whoever crossed his path doffed his hat, paid homage, and joined his entourage. The other Martín, the bastard, was one of the retinue.

Martín the marquis wanted to break with Spain and proclaim himself king of Mexico. When the plot failed, he babbled regrets and named names. His life was spared.

Martín the bastard, who has served his brother in the conspiracy and everything else, is now writhing on the rack. At his side, the scribe records: *He was stripped and put in the cincha. On being admonished, he said he owed nothing.* The torturer gives a turn to the wheel. The cords break the flesh and stretch the bones.

The scribe records: *He is again admonished. Says he has no more to say than what he has said.*

Second turn of the wheel. Third, fourth, fifth.

(28)

1569: Havana

St. Simon Against the Ants

Ants harass the city and ruin the crops. They have devoured more than one heavy-sleeping Christian via the navel.

In extraordinary session, Havana's authorities resolve to ask the protection of a patron saint against the bibijaguas and other fierce ants.

Before the Reverend Alonso Álvarez, lots are drawn among the twelve apostles. The winner is St. Simon, whom they take as advocate *so that he may intercede with Our Lord God, that He may remove all ants from this community, the houses and haciendas of this town, and its environs*.

In return, the city will throw an annual party in honor of the blessed St. Simon, with sung vespers, Mass, compulsory-attendance procession, and bullfight.

(161)

1571: Mexico City
Thou Shalt Inform On Thy Neighbor

From the balconies hang coats of arms, gay carpets, velvets, banners. The armor of the knight of the Order of Santiago, who dips his standard before the viceroy, glitters. Pages raise their big axes around the immense cross nailed to the scaffold.

The inquisitor general is arriving from Madrid. Kettledrums and trumpets announce him. He comes on the back of a mule with jeweled trappings, amid countless lighted candles and black capes.

Under his supreme authority heretics will be tortured or burned. Centuries ago Pope Innocent IV ordered assassins of souls and robbers of the faith of Christ to be rewarded with torments; and much later Pope Paul III prohibited the torture to last more than an hour. Since then, inquisitors take a small break from their work every hour. The inquisitor general newly arrived in Mexico will see to it that green wood is never used in the executions, so that the city will not be choked with noxious smoke; and he will order them for clear days so that all may appreciate them. He will not bother with Indians, *since they are new in the faith, feeble folk, and of little substance*.

The inquisitor general takes his seat beside the viceroy. An artillery salvo greets him. The drums roll and the town crier proclaims the general edict of the faith. The edict orders everyone to inform on anyone they know or have seen or heard, not excepting wives, husbands, fathers, or anyone else, no matter how intimate.

All are obliged to denounce live or dead people who have said or believed *heretical, suspicious, erroneous, reckless, offensive, scandalous, or blasphemous words or opinions*.

(115 and 139)

1571: Madrid
Who Is Guilty, Criminal or Witness?

The face itself, or the mirror that reflects it? The king does not think twice about it. By decree he orders the confiscation of all the manuscripts left by Fray Bartolomé de Las Casas so that they may not fall into the hands of bad Spaniards and enemies of Spain. Especially worrying to Philip II is the possible publication or circulation in some manner of the extremely voluminous *History of the Indies*, which Las Casas could not finish and which survives, a prisoner under lock and key, in the San Gregorio monastery.

(70 and 90)

1572: Cuzco
Túpac Amaru I

He comes dragging his feet on the cobblestones. On the back of a dwarf donkey, a rope about his neck, Túpac Amaru approaches the scaffold. Ahead of him, the town crier proclaims him tyrant and traitor.

In the main square, the clamor swells up.

"Inca, why do they take you to cut off your head?"

The murmurings of the throng of natives become an uproar. *Let them have us all killed!* shriek the women.

High on the scaffold, Túpac Amaru raises a hand, rests it against his ear and calmly lets it fall back. Then the throng falls silent.

There is nothing but silence when the executioner's sword cleaves the neck of Huaina Cápac's grandson.

With Túpac Amaru, four centuries of the Inca dynasty and nearly forty years of resistance in the Wilcabamba Mountains come to an end. Now the storms of war, the harsh rhythm of the conches, will no longer fall on the valley of Cuzco.

(76)

The Vanquished Believe:

He will come back and move about the earth. The highest mountains know. Being the highest, they see the farthest.

He was the son of the sun and a simple woman.

He took the wind prisoner; and tied up the sun, his father, so that time might endure.

With harness and lash, he brought stones to the heights. With those stones he made temples and fortresses.

Wherever he went, the birds went. The birds greeted him and gladdened his steps. From much journeying his feet spilled blood. When the blood of his feet mixed with the soil, we learned to cultivate. We learned to speak when he told us: "Speak." He was stronger and younger than we.

We have not always had fear in our breasts. Not always bumped along, like the ups and downs of our roads. Our history is long. Our history was born on the day we were hauled from the mouth, the eyes, the armpits, and the vagina of the earth.

Inkarrí's brother Españarrí cut off Inkarrí's head. He has been. The head of Inkarrí turned into money. Gold and silver spurted from his shit-filled entrails.

The highest mountains know. Inkarrí's head is trying to grow toward his feet. The pieces of him will surely come together one day. On that day he will walk the earth followed by the birds.

(15 and 162)

1574: Mexico City

The First *Auto-da-Fé* in Mexico

Ever since the town criers spread the edict of the delations, denunciations have rained down against heretics and bigamists, witches and blasphemers.

The *auto-da-fé* is celebrated on the first Sunday in Lent. From sunrise until dusk the Holy Office of the Inquisition passes sentences on the scarecrows dragged from its cells and torture chambers. High on the sumptuous scaffold, surrounded by lancers and cheering crowds, work the hangmen. *No such multitude can be remembered at a public celebration or at any thing of very great solemnity ever offered on earth,* says the viceroy of New Spain, who attends the spectacle on a velvet throne with a cushion under his feet.

The punishments of *vela, soga, mordaza,* abjuration *de levi,* and one hundred and two hundred lashes are meted out to a silversmith, a cutler, a goldsmith, a scribe, and a cobbler *for having said that simple fornication is not mortal sin.* Various bigamists suffer similar inflictions, among them the Augustine friar Juan Sarmiento, who with his back one raw wound marches off to row in the galleys for five years.

The Negro Domingo, born in Mexico, and the mestizo Miguel Franco receive a hundred lashes each, the former *for having the custom of denying God,* the latter *because he made his wife confess to him.* A hundred, too, for the Sevillian apothecary Gaspar de los Reyes *for having said it was better to cohabit than to be married and that it was licit for the poor and afflicted to perjure themselves for money.*

To the galleys, *hard prison for the mischievous,* go various Lutherans and Jews, *who sucked their heresy in their mothers' milk,* a few Englishmen of the pirate John Hawkins's fleet, and a Frenchman *who called the pope and the king poltroons.*

An Englishman from the mines of Guanajuato and a French barber from Yucatán end their heretical days in the bonfire.

(139)

1576: Guanajuato

The Monks Say:

She came to Mexico twenty years ago. Two doves guided her to Guanajuato. She arrived without a scratch, although she crossed the sea and the desert, and those who carried her lost their way. The king sent her to us in gratitude for the wealth that never stops spurting from the bowels of these mountains.

For more than eight centuries she had lived in Spain. Hidden from the Moors, she survived in a cave in Granada. When Christians discovered and rescued her, they found no wound on her wooden body. She reached Guanajuato intact. She remains intact, performing miracles. Our Lady of Guanajuato consoles both poor and rich for their poverty; and she shields alike from the cold those who sleep outdoors and in a sheltered palace. In her infinite mercy she does not distinguish between servants and lords. No one invokes her and fails to receive divine favor.

By her grace many Indians of Guanajuato who go to her with repentance and faith are now being saved. She has stayed the sword of the Lord, who with just fury castigates the idolatries and sins of the Indians in Mexico. The afflicted who brought their supplications to her and paid due charity have not been touched by the pestilence.

In other areas, the Indian whom typhus does not kill dies of hunger or hardship. There are corpses in the fields and in the plazas, and there are houses filled with them in which all died and no one remained to tell of it. Throughout Mexico the pestilence is raising such a stink of putrefaction and smoke that we Spaniards have to go about holding our noses.

(79 and 131)

1576: Xochimilco
The Apostle Santiago *versus* the Plague

Here even nursing babies have paid tribute, in money and in corn. If the pestilence goes on, who will pay? Local hands have built the cathedral of Mexico. If the plague does not stop, who will sow these fields? Who will spin and weave in the workshops? Who will build cathedrals and pave streets?

The Franciscans discuss the situation in their monastery. Of the thirty thousand Indians in Xochimilco when the Spaniards came, four thousand are left, and that is an exaggeration. Many died fighting with Hernán Cortés, conquering men and lands for him, and more died working for him and for Pedro de Alvarado, and the epidemic is killing more.

Fray Jerónimo de Mendieta, the monastery guardian, comes up with the inspiration that saves the day.

They prepare to draw lots. An acolyte, blindfolded, stirs slips of paper in the silver dish. On each slip is written the name of a saint of proven prestige at the celestial court. The acolyte chooses one, and Father Mendieta unfolds it and reads: "It's the Apostle Santiago!"

From the balcony it is announced to the Indians of Xochimilco in their language. The apocalyptic monk speaks on his knees, raising his arms. "Santiago will defeat the pestilence!"

He promises him an altar.

(79 and 161)

1577: Xochimilco

St. Sebastian *versus* the Plague

During the tough years of the conquest, the clash of arms was heard from the tomb of Santiago on the eve of each battle; and the apostle fought with the invading hosts, lance in hand, on his white horse. Clearly the apostle Santiago has the habit of killing Indians but not of saving them. The plague, which barely scratches the Spaniards, continues massacring Indians in Xochimilco and other parts of Mexico.

From his cell as night falls, Father Mendieta hears shrieks and moans louder than the choruses of angels.

Someone has to intercede with the Lord, since the apostle Santiago is not interested, or Xochimilco will soon be Indianless. The Franciscans talk it over and decide to draw lots again. Fate picks the blessed Sebastian for saint-advocate.

They promise him an altar.

(79 and 161)

1579: Quito

Son of Atahualpa

Beto, Indian priest of the Archidona region, saw a vision of the Devil in the shape of a cow, who told him God was very annoyed with the Christians and was not going to defend them. Guami, Indian priest of Tambisa, spent five days in the other world. There he saw marvels and listened to God, and now he has the power of rain and the power of resurrection. Beto and Guami announce that Indians who don't join the rebellion will reap toads and snakes in eternally sterile fields.

The two prophets put themselves at the head of many lances. Southeast of Quito, the Quijo Indians rebel. They attack various towns and vainly await a rising in the mountains. The Inca's son, Francisco Atahualpa, captain of Spanish troops, imprisons the mountain plotters and staves off the insurrection. The Quijo Indians are left all alone.

After some battles comes defeat. The Spaniards oblige all Indians of the Quijo region and the surroundings of Quito to attend the execution of the prophets Beto and Guami. They parade them through the streets of Quito, torture them with hot pincers, hang them, quarter them, and exhibit the pieces. From the royal box, Captain Francisco Atahualpa watches the ceremony.

(156)

1580: Buenos Aires
The Founders

Nearly half a century ago, a Spanish captain sailed from Seville for these unrenowned shores. He sank the whole fortune he had made in the sack of Rome into the expedition. Here he founded a city, a fortress surrounded by huts, and upriver from here he went hunting for the silver mountain and the mysterious lake where the sun sleeps.

Ten years earlier, Sebastian Cabot had sought the treasure of King Solomon sailing up this Plate River—so innocent of its silvery name—which has only mud on one bank and sand on the other and leads to other rivers that lead to jungle.

Pedro de Mendoza's city didn't last long. While his soldiers, maddened by hunger, ate each other, the captain read Virgil and Erasmus and made pronouncements for immortality. In short order, the dream of another Peru having vanished, he wanted to go back to Spain. He didn't get there alive. Afterward came Alonso Cabrera, who set fire to Buenos Aires in the king's name. He could and did return to Spain. There he killed his wife and ended his days in a lunatic asylum.

Comes now Juan de Garay from Asunción. Santa María de los Buenos Aires is born again. With Garay come a bunch of Paraguayans, sons of conquistadors, who have received from their Guaraní mothers their first milk and the native language they speak.

The sword of Garay, stuck into this land, outlines the shadow of the cross. The founders' teeth chatter from cold and fear. The breeze plays rustling music in the treetops, and beyond, on the endless plains, Indians and phantoms silently spy on them.

(74, 97, and 99)

1580: London

Drake

"Three cheers for the gold of the galleons! Hurrah for the silver of Potosí!"

The Dragon is coming! cried the women, and church bells pealed out the alarm. In three years Francis Drake has circumnavigated the world. He has twice crossed the equator and sacked the Spanish Main, stripping ports and ships from Chile to Mexico.

Now he is returning with only one ship and a moribund crew of eighteen, but he brings treasure that multiplies by 120 the capital invested in the expedition. Queen Elizabeth, chief shareholder and author of the plan, converts the pirate into a knight. On the waters of the Thames the ceremony is performed. On the sword that dubs him is engraved this saying of the queen's: *Who strikes you strikes me, Drake*. On his knees, he offers Her Majesty an emerald brooch stolen in the Pacific.

Towering over the fog and soot, Elizabeth is at the summit of a nascent empire. She is the daughter of Henry VIII and Anne Boleyn, who for having produced a daughter lost her head in the Tower of London. The virgin queen devours her lovers, uses her fists on her maids of honor, and spits on her courtiers' clothes.

Francis Bacon will be the philosopher and chancellor of the new empire and William Shakespeare its poet. Francis Drake, captain of its ships. Scorner of storms, master of sails and winds, the pirate Drake moves at court as if climbing masts and rigging. Squat but hefty with fiery beard, he was born by the sea and has been brought up in the fear of God. The sea is his home; and he never launches an attack without a Bible pressing against the chest beneath his clothing.

(149, 187, and 198)

1582: Mexico City

What Color Is a Leper's Skin?

The lamp advances violating the darkness and pulls faces out of the murk, faces of specters, hands of specters, and nails them to the wall.

The official touches nothing, his gloved hands hidden beneath his cape, half closing his eyes as if fearing to infect them. He has come to check the implementation of the new order concerning San Lázaro Hospital. The viceroy has ordered that male patients should not mix. Whites and mestizos have to occupy one room, blacks and mulattoes another, Indians another. The females, however, are to be all together in one room whatever their color or condition.

(148)

1583: Copacabana

God's Aymara Mother

They cross Lake Titicaca in the cattail boat. She travels by his side, dressed for a fiesta. In the city of La Paz her tunic has been gilded. When they land, he puts his cloak over her to shield her from the rain; and with her in his arms, covered up, he enters the village of Copacabana. The rain stings the crowd that has come to receive them.

Francisco Tito Yupanqui enters the sanctuary with her and uncovers her. She is taken up to the altar. From on high, the Virgin of Copacabana embraces them all. She will protect against pestilence and sorrow and the bad weather of February.

The Indian sculptor has modeled her in Potosí. He has worked for nearly two years to give her appropriate beauty. Indians may only paint or carve images that imitate European models, and Francisco Tito Yupanqui did not want to violate the ban. He had intended to make a Virgin identical to Our Lady of Candelaria, but his hands have modeled this Andean body with big lungs hungry for air, large torso, and short legs, and this broad Indian face with fleshy lips and almond eyes that stare sadly at the bruised land.

(47 and 163)

1583: Santiago de Chile

He Was Free for a While

He raises himself on his hands and falls on his face. He tries to lean on an elbow and slips. He manages to bring up one knee and sinks into the mud.

Face down in the mud, beneath the rain, he weeps.

Hernando Maravilla had not wept under the two hundred lashes he received in the streets of Lima on the way to the harbor; and not a tear was seen on his face while he received another two hundred here in Santiago.

Now the rain lashes him, drawing off the dry blood and the mud.

"Wretch! That's how you bite the hand that feeds you!" said his owner, the long-widowed Doña Antonia Nabía, when they brought the fugitive slave back to her.

Hernando Maravilla had escaped because one day he saw a woman who was pretty as a picture and couldn't resist following her. They caught him in Lima, and the Inquisition questioned him. He was sentenced to four hundred lashes *for having said that marriages were made by the Devil and that the bishop was a nothing and that he shat on the bishop.*

He who was born in Africa, grandson of a medicine man, son of a hunter, twists himself around and weeps, his back raw, as the rain falls on Santiago de Chile.

(31 and 138)

1583: Tlatelolco

Sahagún

Lonelyme, lonelyme, sings the ringdove.

A woman offers flowers to a stone that has been smashed to pieces. "Lord," says the woman to the stone, "Lord, how you have suffered."

The old native wise men offer their testimony to Fray Bernardino de Sahagún: "Let us die," they plead, "since our gods have died."

Fray Bernardino de Ribiera, native of Sahagún: son of St. Francis, bare feet, patched cassock, seeker of the plenitude of Paradise, seeker of the memory of these vanquished peoples. For more than forty years Sahagún has been traveling through Mexico, the seigniory of Huexotzingo, Tula of the Toltecs, the Texcoco region, to rescue the images and words of times past. In the twelve books of the *General History of New Spain,* Sahagún and his young assistants have saved and assembled ancient voices, the fiestas of the Indians, their rites, their gods, their way of counting the passage of years and stars, their myths, their poems, their medicines, their tales of remote ages and of the recent European invasion . . . History sings in this first great work of American anthropology.

Six years ago King Philip II had those manuscripts and all the native codices copied and translated by Sahagún seized *so that no original or translation of them should remain.* Where have they ended up, those books suspected of perpetuating and publicizing idolatries? No one knows. The Council of the Indies has not replied to any of the despairing author-copier's pleas. What has the king done with these forty years of Sahagún's life and so many centuries of the life of Mexico? They say in Madrid that the pages have been used as spice wrappings.

Old Sahagún does not give up. At eighty he clutches to his breast a few papers saved from the disaster and dictates to his pupils in Tlatelolco the first lines of a new work, to be called *Divinatory Art.* Later he will go to work on a complete Mexican calendar. When he finishes the calendar, he will begin a Náhuatl-Spanish-Latin dictionary. And after the dictionary . . .

Outside, dogs howl, fearing rain.

(24 and 200)

1583: Ácoma

The Stony Kingdom of Cíbola

Captain Antonio de Espejo, who made a fast fortune on the frontier of Mexico, has responded to the siren call of the seven cities of gold. At the head of a few warrior horsemen he has undertaken the Odyssey to the north; and instead of the fabulous kingdom of Cíbola, he has found an immense desert, very occasionally peppered with villages in the shape of fortresses. No precious stones hang from the trees, because there are no trees except in the rare valleys; and there is no more glitter of gold than what the sun draws from the rocks when it beats down hard on them.

In those villages the Spaniards hoist their flag. The Indians still do not know that they will soon be obliged to change their names and raise temples to worship another god, although the Great Spirit of the Hopis told them some time ago that a new race would arrive, a race of fork-tongued men, bringing greed and boastfulness. The Hopis receive Captain Espejo with offerings of corn tortillas and turkeys and hides; and the Navajos of the high mountains welcome him bringing water and corn.

Beyond, a fortress of rock and mud soars into the purple sky. From the edge of the mesa, the village of the Ácomas dominates the valley, green with cornfields irrigated by canals and dams. The Ácomas, enemies of the Navajos, are famous for their ferocity. Not even Francisco Vázquez de Coronado, who came this way forty years ago, dared go near them.

The Ácomas dance in Captain Espejo's honor and lay at his feet colored cloths, turkeys, ears of corn, and deerskins.

A few years from now they will refuse to pay tribute. The assault will last three days and three nights. Survivors will have one foot chopped off with a single ax blow, and the chiefs will be thrown over the precipice.

(89)

Night Chant, a Navajo Poem

House made of dawn,
House made of evening light,
House made of dark cloud . . .
Dark cloud is at the house's door,
The trail out of it is dark cloud,
The zigzag lightning stands high upon it . . .
Happily may I walk,
Happily, with abundant showers, may I walk.
Happily, with abundant plants, may I walk.
Happily, on the trail of pollen, may I walk.
Happily may I walk.
May it be beautiful before me.

May it be beautiful behind me.
May it be beautiful below me.
May it be beautiful above me.
May it be beautiful all around me.
In beauty it is finished.

(42)

1586: Cauri

The Pestilence

Influenza does not shine like the steel sword, but no Indian can dodge it. Tetanus and typhus kill more people than a thousand greyhounds with fiery eyes and foaming jaws. The smallpox attacks in secret and the gun with a loud bang, amid clouds of sparks and sulfurous smoke, but smallpox annihilates more Indians than all the guns.

The winds of pestilence are devastating these regions. Anyone they strike, they blow down: they devour the body, eat the eyes, close the throat. All smells of decay.

Meanwhile, a mysterious voice ranges over Peru. It treads on the heels of the pestilence and penetrates the litanies of the dying, this voice that whispers, from one ear to another: "Whoever throws the crucifix out of his house will return from the dead."

(221)

1588: Quito

Grandson of Atahualpa

The golden columns, arabesques, and ornamentations sweat gold; the saints and adored virgins in their gilded robes, and the chorus of angels with little golden wings, pray gold: This is one of the houses that Quito offers to him who centuries ago was born in Bethlehem in manger straw and died naked.

The family of the Inca Atahualpa has an altar in this church of St. Francis, in the place of honor in the great transept beside the evangel. At the foot of the altar rest the dead. The son of Atahualpa, who was named Francisco like his father and his father's assassin, occupies the main tomb. God must have reserved glory for Captain Francisco Atahualpa if God listens, as they say, to the views of those in command with more attention than He pays to the screams of the commanded. The Inca's son knew how to suppress the native risings in the South. He brought as prisoners to Quito the rebel chiefs of Cañaribamba and Cuyes and was rewarded with the office of this city's director of public works.

Francisco's daughters and nieces have come to install the image of St. Catherine that a sculptor of Toledo, Juan Bautista Vázquez, has carved for a spot high on the Atahualpas' altar. Alonso, Francisco's son, sent the image from Spain; and the family is still unaware that Alonso died in Madrid while St. Catherine was crossing the ocean to this church.

Alonso Atahualpa, grandson of the Inca, died in prison. He could play the harp, the violin, and the clavichord. He wore only Spanish dress, cut by the best tailors, and for a long time had not paid the rent for his house. Gentlemen are not imprisoned for debt, but Alonso went to jail denounced by Madrid's most important tailors, jewelers, hatters, and glovemakers. Nor had he paid for the carving that his family now places, amid golden garlands, on the gilded altar.

(155 and 215)

1588: Havana

St. Martial *versus* the Ants

Rapacious ants continue to mortify people and undermine walls. They fell trees, devastate farmlands, and gobble fruit and corn and the flesh of the absentminded.

In view of patron St. Simon's inefficacy, the town council unanimously elects another protector.

The city promises to celebrate his day every year. St. Martial is the new shield of Havana against the assaults of bibijagua ants. St. Martial, who three centuries ago was bishop of Limoges, is known as a specialist and is said to have great influence with the Lord.

(161)

1589: Cuzco

He Says He Had the Sun

Rigid beneath the sheets, Mancio Serra de Leguízamo unburdens his conscience. Before a notary he dictates and swears: *"That we discovered these realms in such condition that there was not in all of them one thief, one vicious man, nor idler, nor was there an adulterous or bad woman . . ."*

Pizarro's old captain does not want to depart this world without saying for the first time: *"That the lands and mountains and mines and pastures and hunting grounds and woods and all manner of resources were governed or divided in such a way that everyone knew and had his property, without anyone else occupying or taking it . . ."*

Don Mancio is the last survivor of the army that conquered Peru. Over half a century ago he was one of those who invaded this sacred city of Cuzco, pillaged the treasures of its tombs and houses, and axed down the walls of the Temple of the Sun so clotted with gold that their resplendence made anyone who entered look like a corpse. He says he received the best part of the booty: the immense golden face of the sun, with its fiery rays and flames, which had dominated the city and blinded the people of Cuzco at the hour of dawn.

Don Mancio wagered the sun at cards and lost it in a night.

(118)

1592: Lima

An *Auto-da-Fé* in Lima

The wind carries off the ashes of three Lutheran Englishmen, captured on the island of Puná. One of them, Henry Oxley, was burned alive because he would not renounce his faith.

Smoke curls upward from the center of a circle of tall lances as the crowd grows delirious and the Tribunal of the Holy Office pronounces sentences of lashes and other pains and humiliations.

Several suffer punishment *for marrying twice or for simple fornication and other crimes of the sin of the flesh. For soliciting nuns* a Dominican friar, a Franciscan, an Augustinian, and a Jesuit are condemned. Juan de la Portilla, soldier, *for swearing by the ears of God*. Isabel de Angulo, soldier's wife, *because so that men would desire her she recited the words of the Consecration in a low voice*. Bartolomé de Lagares, sailor, *for affirming that, being a bachelor and paying for it, no sin was committed*. Lorenzo de la Peña, barber, *that because his wife's pew in church was taken, he said if that was the way of it, there was no God*.

The Sevillian Pedro Luis Enríquez goes off to ten years in prison *for having affirmed that by taking a rooster to a field where there was no sound of dogs, and cutting its head off at midnight, one would find a small stone like a hazelnut, rubbing one's lips with which would make the first pretty woman encountered die of love for the one doing this, and that killing a cat in January and inserting a bean into each of its joints and burying it, the beans growing from it, if bitten while looking at oneself in the mirror, would have the virtue of making one invisible; and because he said he was a tough fellow and a healer, in token of which he had a cross on his breast and another on the roof of his mouth, and claimed that in prison he saw splendors and smelled the sweetest of fragrances*.

(137)

1593: Guarapari

Anchieta

Ignacio de Loyola pointed to the horizon and ordered: "*Go, and set fire to the world!*"

José de Anchieta was the youngest of all the apostles who brought the message of Christ, the good news, to the jungles of Brazil. Forty years later, the Indians call him *Caraibebé*, man with wings, and they say that by making the sign of the cross Anchieta wards off storms and turns a fish into a ham and a dying man into an athlete. Choirs of angels descend from the sky to announce to him the arrival of galleons or the attacks of enemies, and God raises him from the earth when he kneels to say his prayers. His skinny body, burned by his hair shirt, sends off rays of light when he flagellates himself, sharing the torments of God's only son.

Brazil will be grateful to him for other miracles. From the hand of this tattered saint have come the first poems written in this land, the first Tupí-Guaraní grammar, and the first theatrical works, sacramental mystery plays in the indigenous language, which transmit the Gospel mixing native personages with Roman emperors and Christian saints. Anchieta has been Brazil's first schoolmaster and physician and the discoverer and chronicler of this land's animals and plants in a book that tells how the *guarás* change the color of their plumage, how the *peixe-boi* lays its eggs in the eastern rivers, and how the porcupine lives.

At sixty he continues founding cities and building churches and hospitals; on his bony shoulders he carries heavy beams along with the Indians. As if inspired by his clean and humble luminosity, the birds seek him out and people seek him out. He walks many leagues without complaining or letting them carry him in nets, through these regions where all has the color of heat and all is born and decays in an instant to be born again, fruit that becomes honey, water, death, seed of new fruits: the land boils, the sea boils with slow fire, and Anchieta writes on the sand, with a stick, his verses of praise to the Creator of everlasting life.

(10 and 38)

1596: London

Raleigh

Choreographer of tobacco, swaggering military artificer, Sir Walter Raleigh emits snakes of smoke from his nose and rings and spirals of it from his mouth as he says: "If they cut my head off, it will fall happily with my pipe between my teeth."

"You stink," comments his friend.

There is no one else in the tavern except a small black slave who waits patiently in the corner. Raleigh is telling how he discovered Earthly Paradise in Guyana the previous year, over there where El Dorado lies hidden. He licks his lips recalling the flavor of iguana eggs and closes his eyes describing the fruits and the leaves that never fall from the treetops.

"Listen, brother," he says. "This play of yours about the young lovers . . . Yes, that one, set in those forest glades, just marvelous. Set it in Verona and it smells of the cage. You got the wrong background, my dear man. That air over there . . ."

Raleigh's friend, a baldhead with mischievous eyes, knows that this Guyana is a swamp where the sky is always black with mosquitos, but he listens in silence and nods his head because he also knows that Raleigh isn't lying.

(198)

1597: Seville

A Scene in Jail

He was wounded and mutilated by Turks. He was attacked by pirates and scourged by Moors. He was excommunicated by the priests. He was in prison in Algiers and in Castro del Río. Now he is a prisoner in Seville. Seated on the floor beside the stone pallet, he dips his pen in the inkpot and wonders, eyes fixed on the candle flame, his good hand poised in the air.

Is it worthwhile to insist? King Philip's reply still hurts, when for the second time he asked for a job in America: *Seek what befits you over here*. If things have changed since then, they have changed for the worse. Before, he had at least the hope of a response. Since that time the black-clad king, detached from the world, is not talking to anyone except his own phantoms within the walls of the Escorial.

Miguel de Cervantes, alone in his cell, does not write to the king. He does not ask for any vacant office in the Indies. On a blank sheet he begins to relate the misadventures of a poet-errant, *one of those knights whose lance is on the rack, shield rusting, steed skin-and-bone, hound run away*.

Melancholy sounds ring through the prison. He does not hear them.

(46 and 195)

1598: Potosí

History of Floriana Rosales, Virtuous Woman of Potosí (Abbreviated Version of the Chronicle by Bartolomé Arzáns de Orsúa y Vela)

Because of her great beauty ever since the cradle, like a delicate pretty flower, and because her mother's name was Ana, they baptized her Floriana.

Schooled in virtue in the seclusion of the house, the dazzling young lady always avoided seeing and being seen, but this in itself set on fire the desires of suitors who surrounded her since she was twelve. Among them, those who most successfully pursued their suit were Don Julio Sánchez Farfán, mine owner, Captain Rodrigo de Albuquerque, and the governor of Tucumán, who passed this way en route to Lima and lingered in Potosí after spotting Floriana in church.

Out of pure spite, seeing himself rejected, the governor of Tucumán challenged Floriana's father to a duel, and they drew swords by a spring and cut each other about until some ladies, not without courage, interposed themselves.

Floriana burned with fury to see her father wounded and determined to avenge it with her own hand. She sent word to the governor that on the next night she would await him in a certain shop, where she wished to speak to him without witnesses.

The governor donned his best clothes—a department in which he was excessively vain, that abominable vice in men who have studied in the school of Heliogabalus, of whom Herodiano said that he despised Roman and Greek woolen clothing and wore gold and purple with precious stones in the Persian style, as Lampridio records. The governor arrived punctually, exquisitely arrayed, and at the designated hour Floriana appeared bringing amid the lovely flowers of her face the poisonous asp of her anger. Taking a broad and well-sharpened razor out of her sleeve, she rushed at him like a lioness to cut his face, hurling many an insult at him. The governor fended off the blade with his hand and produced a dagger.

Alert to the danger, Floriana threw over his face a bundle of cloth, behind which she was able to seize in both hands a stout stick which there and then sealed his fate. She gave the governor of Tucumán such a whack that he fell flat.

Heavyhearted and scared, Floriana's parents tried to hide her in their house, but it was not possible. The magistrate, the highest justice and police authority, came running and Floriana had no alternative to going up to her room and throwing herself out of the window into the street. God willed her skirt to catch on a projection from the window frame and she hung from it head downward.

A servant who knew Don Julio Sánchez Farfán and knew he loved her mistress told him to go to the alley behind the houses and see if Floriana was there, because she had just thrown herself from the window. But as Captain Rodrigo de Albuquerque saw Don Julio secretly talking to the servant, he followed him to the alley.

Don Julio arrived just when the afflicted Floriana, who had been suspended for some time, was pleading in mortal fear for help, saying that she was choking. Her knightly lover approached and, stretching out his arms, took her by the shoulders and gave her a hard pull, tumbling with her to the ground.

At that moment Captain Rodrigo turned up and with amorous words covered Floriana with his cape and raised her up. Seeing this, Don Julio, aflame with jealousy, got to his feet and taking out a dagger plunged it into the captain, calling him a scurvy traitor. With a mortal wound in his chest, the captain fell to the ground imploring for confession, hearing which Floriana cursed her fate and the ordeals of her honor and departed at full speed.

Floriana put on Indian clothing to escape from this town of Potosí, but when she was about to get on a mule somebody tipped off the magistrate, who came to the spot to put her in prison. When the magistrate saw Floriana, the blind child known as Cupid pierced his heart through with a terrible arrow. Panting, he took her by the hands and carried her off to the palace.

At ten o'clock that night, the hour when she had to go to the magistrate's bedroom, Floriana tied a rope to the balcony and let herself down into the hands of Don Julio, who awaited her below. The damsel told Don Julio that before moving a single step he must swear the security of her person and purity.

Seeing the danger they ran, for the flight had already been discovered, Don Julio took Floriana on his shoulders and ran, carrying her to the far-off Plaza del Gato. He flew over stones and mud, in a bath of sweat, and when he could finally sit down to rest and lowered Floriana from his back, he suddenly collapsed.

Thinking that he had just fainted, she put Don Julio's head in her lap. But noticing that he was dead, she sprang up with a start and fled to the barrios of San Lorenzo, in the month of March of that year 1598.

There she remained in concealment, resolved to maintain perpetual chastity and to continue till the end of her days being an obedient servant of the Lord.

(21)

Spanish Couplets to Be Sung and Danced

I have seen a man survive
with a hundred wounds from a lance
and later saw him die
from just a single glance.

Down in the sea a whale
sighed and sighed again
and his sighings told this tale:
"He who has love, has pain."

Today I want to sing
now that I have no sorrow,
in case the fates should bring
tears to my eyes tomorrow.

(196)

1598: Panama City

Times of Sleep and Fate

Simón de Torres, apothecary of Panama, would like to sleep but cannot take his eyes off the hole in the roof. Each time his lids close, his eyes open by themselves and fasten on the hole. Simón lights and puts out his pipe and lights it again, trying to discourage the mosquitos with the smoke and with his hand. He twists and turns, soaking and boiling in the bed that was left crooked by the shock it received the other day. The stars wink at him through the hole and he would like to stop thinking. So the hours pass until the rooster crows, either announcing the day or calling the hens.

A week ago a woman tumbled through the roof and fell on Simón.

"Who, who, who are you?" the apothecary stammered.

"We don't have much time," said she as she tore off her clothes.

In the morning she got up, shining, delicious, and dressed herself in no time flat.

"Where are you going?"

"To Nombre de Dios. I left the bread in the oven there."

"But that's twenty leagues away!" cried the apothecary.

"Only eighteen," she corrected him. And as she disappeared, she said: "Take care of yourself. Whoever enters me loses his memory."

(157)

1599: Quito

The Afro-Indians of Esmeraldas

They keep on the alert. They don't bat an eyelash. They are full of suspicion. That brush that robs them of their image, won't it rob them of their souls? The brush is magic like the mirror. Like the mirror, it takes possession of people.

From time to time, the horrible cold of Quito makes them sneeze, and the artist growls at them. Uncomfortable, half strangled by the ruffs, they resume the poses, rigid until the next sneeze. They have been in this city a few days and they still can't grasp why such powerful people have come to live in such a cold place, nor why the houses have doors, nor why the doors have locks, bolts, and padlocks.

Half a century ago a storm dashed a slave ship against the coastal reefs, near the mouth of the Esmeraldas River. The ship contained slaves from Guinea to be sold in Lima. The blacks took off and lost themselves in the woods. They founded villages and had children with native women, and those children multiplied, too. Of the three whose portrait Andrés Sánchez Gallque is now painting, two were born of that mixture of Africans and Ecuadorean women. The other, Francisco de Arobe, came from Guinea. He was ten at the time of the shipwreck.

They have been rigged out as distinguished gentlemen, tunics and cloaks, lace cuffs, hats, so as not to make a bad impression on the king when he receives, in Madrid, this portrait of his new subjects, *these barbarians who have been invincible up to now*. They also have lances in their hands, necklaces of teeth, and sea-shells over their Spanish dress; and on their faces are gold ornaments that pierce their ears, their nostrils, and their lips.

(176)

1599: Chagres River

The Wise Don't Talk

This is the shiniest road on earth. From sea to sea winds the long, silver trail. Countless strings of mules cross the jungle, weighed down by the metals of Potosí, en route to the galleons waiting in Portobello.

Little monkeys accompany the silver across Panama. Screaming without letup, they jeer at the muleteers and pelt them with guavas.

On the banks of the Chagres River, Fray Diego de Ocaña watches them admiringly. To cross the river, the monkeys form a chain from the crown of a tree, clutching each other by the tails: the chain swings and gathers speed until a strong shove hurls it to the highest branches on the other bank.

The Peruvian Indian carrying Ocaña's baggage comes up to

him and says: "Father, these are people. They don't talk so that the Spaniards won't notice it. If they see that they're people, they'll send them to work in the mines."

(157)

1599: La Imperial
Flaming Arrows

Rebellion breaks out on the Pacific coasts, and the repercussions shake the Andes cordillera.

Martín García Óñez de Loyola, nephew of St. Ignatius, came here from Peru with the fame of a tireless hunter and crack killer. There he captured Túpac Amaru, last of the Incas. Then they sent him as governor to Chile to tame the Araucanians. Here he killed Indians, stole sheep, and burned crops without leaving a grain. Now the Araucanians are parading his head on the point of a lance.

The Indians use Christians' bones as trumpets to sound the call to battle. War masks, armor of leather: The Araucanian cavalry devastates the South. Seven towns fall, one after the other, under a rain of fiery arrows. The hunted become the hunters. The Araucanians lay siege to La Imperial. To deny it water, they alter the course of the river.

Half of the realm of Chile, everything south of the Bío-Bío, becomes Araucanian again.

The Indians say, pointing at the lance: *This is my master. This won't be ordering me to dig gold, nor to bring herbs or firewood, nor to mind the cattle, nor to sow or reap. I want to stay with this master.*

(66 and 94)

1599: Santa Marta
They Make War to Make Love

Rebellion breaks out on the Caribbean coasts, and its repercussions shake the Sierra Nevada. The Indians are rising for the freedom to love.

At the fiesta of the full moon, the gods dance in the body of Chief Cuchacique and lend magic to his arms. From the villages

of Jeriboca and Bonda, the voices of war awaken the whole land
of the Tairona Indians and shake Masinga and Masinguilla, Zaca
and Mamazaca, Mendiguaca and Torama, Buritaca and Tairama,
Maroma, Taironaca, Guachaca, Chonea, Cinto and Nahuanje, Mamatoco, Ciénaga, Dursino and Gairaca, Origua and Durama, Di-
bocaca, Daona, Chengue and Masaca, Daodama, Sacasa, Cominca,
Guarinea, Mauracataca, Choquenca and Masanga.

Chief Cuchacique wears a jaguar skin. Arrows that whistle,
arrows that burn, arrows that poison: The Taironas burn chapels,
break crosses, and kill friars, fighting against the enemy god who
prohibits their customs.

Since time immemorial in these lands, anyone got a divorce
who wanted one, and siblings made love if they felt like it, and
women with men or men with men or women with women. Thus
it was in these lands until the men in black and the men in iron
came, they who throw to their dogs anyone loving as his ancestors
loved.

The Taironas celebrate their first victories. In their temples,
which the enemy calls houses of the Devil, they play the flute on
bones of the vanquished, drink corn wine, and dance to the lilt of
drums and shell trumpets. The warriors have closed all passes and
roads to Santa Marta and are preparing the final assault.

(189)

1600: Santa Marta
They Had a Country

The fire takes time to catch. How slowly it burns.

Grindings of metal, armored men in motion. The assault on
Santa Marta has failed and the governor has passed a sentence of
annihilation. Weapons and soldiers have arrived from Cartagena
in the nick of time and the Taironas, bled white by so many years
of tribute and slavery, scatter in defeat.

Extermination by fire. Burning villages and plantations, cornfields and cottonfields, cassava and potato crops, fruit orchards.
The irrigated plantings that delighted the eye and gave food, the
farmlands where the Taironas made love in full daylight, because
children made in the dark are born blind—everything burns.

How many worlds do these fires illuminate? The one that was and was seen, the one that was and was not seen . . .

Exiled at the end of seventy-five years of rebellions, the Taironas flee into the mountains, the most arid and remote places, where there is no fish and no corn. Far up there the invaders have expelled them, seizing their lands and uprooting their memory, so that in their remote isolation oblivion may descend upon the songs they sang when they lived together, a federation of free peoples, and were strong and wore robes of multicolored cotton and necklaces of gold and flashing stones: so that they should never again remember that their grandparents were jaguars.

Behind them they leave ruins and graves.

The wind whispers, souls in travail whisper, and fire dances in the distance.

(189)

Techniques of Hunting and Fishing

Deep in the Amazon jungle a fisherman of the Desana tribe sits on a high rock and contemplates the river. The waters slide down, carry fish, polish stones—waters gilded by the first light of day. The fisherman looks and looks, and feels that the old river turns into the flow of blood through his veins. The fisherman will not fish until he has won the hearts of the fishes' wives.

Nearby, in the village, the hunter gets ready. He has already vomited, and later bathed in the river, and is clean inside and out. Now he drinks infusions of plants that have the color of deer, so that their aromas may impregnate his body, and paints on his face the mask that the deer like best. After blowing tobacco smoke on his weapons, he walks softly to the spring where the deer drink. There he drops juice of the pineapple, which is the milk of the daughter of the sun.

The hunter has slept alone these last nights. He has not been with women nor dreamed of them, so that the animal he will hunt and pierce with lance or arrows should not be jealous.

(189)

1600: Potosí

The Eighth Wonder of the World

Caravans of llamas and mules carry to the port of Arica the silver that the Potosí mountain bleeds from each of its mouths. At the end of a long voyage the ingots arrive in Europe to finance war, peace, and progress there.

In exchange, from Seville or by contraband, Potosí receives the wines of Spain, the hats and silks of France, the lace, mirrors, and tapestry of Flanders, German swords, Genoese paper, Neapolitan stockings, Venetian glass, Cypriot wax, Ceylonese diamonds, East Indian marbles, the perfumes of Arabia, Malacca, and Goa, Persian carpets and Chinese porcelain, black slaves from Cape Verde and Angola, and dashing steeds from Chile.

Everything is very dear in this city, the dearest in the world. Only *chicha* corn liquor and coca leaves are cheap. The Indians, forcibly seized from the communities of all Peru, spend Sundays in the corrals dancing to their drums and drinking *chicha* till they roll on the ground. On Monday mornings they are herded into the mountain and, chewing coca and beaten with iron bars, they pursue the veins of silver, greenish-white serpents that appear and take flight through the entrails of this immense paunch, no light, no air. There the Indians toil all week, prisoners, breathing dust that kills the lungs, and chewing coca that deceives hunger and masks exhaustion, never knowing when night falls or day breaks, until Saturday ends and the bell rings for prayer and release. Then they move forward, holding lighted candles, to emerge on Sunday at dawn, so deep are the diggings and the infinite tunnels and galleries.

A priest newly come to Potosí sees them arriving in the city's suburbs, a long procession of squalid ghosts, their backs scarred by the lash, and remarks: "I don't want to see this portrait of hell."

"So shut your eyes," someone suggests.

"I can't," he says. "With my eyes shut I see more."

(21 and 157)

Prophecies

Last night they were married, before the fire as tradition demands, and heard the sacred words:

To her: *"When he ignites with the fire of love, do not be icy."*

And to him: *"When she ignites with the fire of love, do not be icy."*

By the glow of the fire they awaken, embrace, congratulate themselves with their eyes, and tell their dreams.

During sleep the soul travels outside the body and gets to know, in an eternity or the blink of an eye, what is going to happen. Beautiful dreams are to be shared; and to share them, couples awaken very early. Bad dreams, however, are to be thrown to the dogs.

Bad dreams, nightmares about abysses or vultures or monsters, may portend the worst. And the worst, here, is being forced to go to the Huancavélica mercury mines or to the far-off silver mountain of Potosí.

(150 and 151)

Ballad of Cuzco

A llama wished
to have golden hair,
brilliant as the sun,
strong as love
and soft as the mist
that the dawn dissolves,
to weave a braid
on which to mark,
knot by knot,
the moons that pass,
the flowers that die.

(202)

1600: Mexico City

Carriages

Carriages have returned to the broad streets of Mexico. More than twenty years ago the ascetic Philip II banned them. The decree said that use of a carriage turns men into idlers and accustoms them to a pampered and lazy life; and that this costs them muscle for the arts of war.

Now that Philip II is dead, carriages reign again in this city. Inside them, silks and mirrors; outside, gold and tortoise shell and coats of arms on the door. They exude an aroma of fine woods, roll smoothly as a gondola, rock like a cradle; behind the curtains the colonial nobility wave and smile. On his lofty perch, amid silken fringes and tassels, sits the disdainful coachman, almost like a king; and the horses are shod with silver.

Carriages are still banned for Indians, prostitutes, and those punished by the Inquisition.

(213)

1601: Valladolid

Quevedo

For twenty years Spain has reigned over Portugal and all its colonies, so that a Spaniard can walk the earth without treading on foreign soil. But Spain is the most expensive country in Europe: It produces ever fewer things and ever more coins. Of the thirty-five million escudos born six years ago, not even a shadow remains. The data recently published here by Don Martín González de Cellorigo in his *Treatise on Necessary Policy* are not encouraging: by virtue of chance and inheritance, every Spaniard who works maintains thirty more. For those with incomes, work is a sin. The gentry have the bedroom as a battlefield; and in Spain fewer trees grow than monks and beggars.

Galleys laden with the gold of America sail for Genoa. The metals arriving from Mexico and Peru do not even leave a smell in Spain. The feat of the conquest seems to have been achieved by German, Genoese, French, and Flemish merchants and bankers.

In Valladolid lives a crippled and myopic youth of pure blood, with a sharp sword and tongue. In the evenings, while his page removes his boots, he dreams up couplets. In the morning his snakes slither under the doors of the royal palace.

Head buried in his pillow, young Francisco de Quevedo y Villegas personifies in his head the force that turns a coward into a warrior and that softens up the most severe judge; and cursing this trade of poet, he rubs his eyes, draws up the lamp, and with one tug hauls from inside his head the verses that won't let him sleep. The verses tell of Don Doubloon, who

is honorably born in the Indies,
where the world accompanies him,
comes to die in Spain
and is buried in Genoa.

(64, 183, and 218)

1602: Recife

First Expedition Against Palmares

In the mills that press and squeeze sugarcane and men, each slave's work is measured as the weight of the cane and the pressure of the crusher and the heat of the oven are measured. The strength of a slave is exhausted in five years, but in only one year the owner will recover the price paid for him. When slaves cease to be useful hands and become useless mouths, they receive the gift of freedom.

In the mountains of northeastern Brazil hide the slaves who win freedom before sudden old age or early death topples them. The sanctuaries where the fugitives take refuge, in the groves of lofty palms in Alagoas, are called Palmares.

The governor general of Brazil sends out the first expedition against Palmares. It consists of a few poor whites and mestizos anxious to capture and sell blacks; a few Indians who have been promised combs, knives, and little mirrors; and many mulattoes.

Returning from the Itapicurú River, the commander of the expedition, Bartolomeu Bezerra, announces in Recife: *The core of the rebellion has been destroyed.* And they believe him.

(32 and 69)

The Four Parts of the World

An illustrated and enlarged edition of Cesare Ripa's *Iconology* is published in Rome. This dictionary of symbolic images shows the world as it looks from the north shore of the Mediterranean.

On top appears Europe, the queen, with her emblems of power. Horses and lances support her. With one hand she holds up the columns of the temple, with the other she holds a scepter. She has a crown on her head and other crowns lie at her feet, amid miters and books and paintbrushes, zithers, and harps. Next to the horn of plenty lie compass and ruler.

Beneath, to the right, Asia. She offers coffee, pepper, incense. Garlands of flowers and fruit adorn her. A kneeling camel awaits her.

At one side, Africa, a dusky Moorish woman topped by an elephant's head. On her breast, a necklace of coral. Around her the lion, the snake, the scorpion, and ears of grain.

Beneath everything America, *a woman with face fearsome to look upon.* She wears feathers over her naked olive skin. At her feet she has a newly severed human head and a lizard. She is armed with bow and arrows.

(125)

The Pack

Santiago's town council has purchased a new branding iron—of silver—to brand Indian slaves on the face. The governor, Alonso de Ribera, orders that a fifth part of the value of each Araucanian sold at the ports of Valdivia and Arica should go to the costs of war and maintenance of the soldiery.

One hunting expedition follows another. The soldiers cross the Bío-Bío and do their lashing out at night. They burn and butcher and return with men, women, and children roped around the neck. Once branded, they are sold to Peru.

The governor raises the spouted wine pitcher and toasts the

battles won. He toasts in the Flemish style, like Pedro de Valdivia. First, swig after swig to the gentlemen and ladies who come to his mind. When he finishes with people, he toasts saints and angels; and he never forgets to thank them for the pretext.

(94)

1605: Lima

The Night of the Last Judgment

Right after Christmas, nature's heavy artillery blew up the city of Arequipa. The cordillera exploded and the earth vomited the foundations of houses. People were left in fragments under the wreckage, crops burned under the cinders. The sea rose up, meanwhile, and smothered the port of Arica.

Yesterday, at dusk, a barefooted friar assembled a throng in Lima's plaza. He announced that this libertine city would collapse in the next few hours, and with it all its surroundings as far as the eye could see.

"No one will get away!" he howled. "Not the fastest horse nor the swiftest ship will be able to escape!"

At sunset, the streets are already filled with penitents scourging themselves by torchlight. Sinners proclaim their sins on the corners, and from the balconies rich folk throw silverware and party dresses down into the street. Hair-raising secrets are revealed out loud. Unfaithful wives tear up pavingstones and use them to beat their breasts. Thieves and seducers kneel before their victims, masters kiss the feet of their slaves, and beggars have not hands enough for so much charity. The Church receives more money than in all the Lents in its history. If not seeking a priest to confess to, people seek one to marry them. The churches are crammed with folk who want to nestle within their protection.

Then the dawn.

The sun shines on Lima as never before. Penitents look for ointments for their flayed backs, and masters pursue their slaves. Newlyweds inquire for their just-acquired husbands whom daylight has evaporated; people who repented of their sins wander the streets in search of new ones to commit. Sobs and curses are heard behind every door. There is no beggar who hasn't dropped from sight. The priests have also hidden themselves, to count the mountains of coins that God accepted last night. With the leftover cash, Lima's churches will buy in Spain the authentic feathers of the archangel Gabriel.

(157)

1607: Seville

The Strawberry

Captain Alonso González de Nájera, who has lived six years in Chile, remembers and relates.

He speaks of those who are born amid trumpets and drums, the noble host who wear coats of mail from the cradle and make a wall of their bodies against attacks by the Indians. He insists that rain pulls grains of gold out of the Chilean soil and that the Indians pay tribute with gold they take from the bellies of lizards.

.He also tells of a rare fruit, with the color and form of the heart, which explodes with sweet juices at the touch of the teeth. For vividness, flavor, and scent it could well compete with the most delectable fruits of Spain, *although over there in Chile they insult it by calling it a strawberry*.

(66)

1608: Puerto Príncipe

Silvestre de Balboa

In the mud and palm-frond house of Silvestre de Balboa, clerk of the Puerto Príncipe town council, the first epic poem in Cuba's history is born. The author dedicates his royal stanzas to Bishop Altamirano, who four years ago was kidnaped by the French pirate Gilbert Giron in the port of Manzanillo.

From the kingdom of Neptune rose seals and sea nymphs to the pirate's ship, sympathizing with the bishop, who would accept nothing in his defense. The people of Manzanillo managed to raise two hundred ducats, a thousand hides, and other provisions, and finally the Lutheran pirate freed his prisoner. To welcome the rescued bishop satyrs, fauns, and centaurs came down to the beach from the woods bringing guanábanas and other delicacies. From the meadows came nymphs loaded with mameys, prickly pears, pineapples, avocados, and tobacco, and petticoat-clad dryads descended from trees with arms full of wild pitahayas and fruit of the birijí and the tall jagua tree. The bishop also received guabinas, dajaos, and other river fish from naiads; and fountain and pond nymphs brought some tasty hicatee turtles from Masabo. When the pirates were ready to collect the ransom, a few lads, the flower of Manzanillo youth, fell on them and valiantly gave them what they deserved. It was a black slave named Salvador who pierced pirate Gilbert Giron's breast with his lance:

> Oh Creole Salvador, honorable slave!
> May your fame go soaring without end;
> for in praise of soldier so brave
> never should weary the tongue or the pen.

Filled with admiration and awe, Silvestre de Balboa invokes Troy and compares the Manzanillans with Achilles and Ulysses, after mixing them up with nymphs, fauns and centaurs. But amid all the portentous deities, the people of this village have been humbly immortalized—a black slave who behaved like a hero, and many of this island's fruits, herbs, and animals that the author calls and loves by their names.

(23)

1608: Seville
Mateo Alemán

Mateo Alemán boards the ship that is sailing for Mexico. To travel to the Indies he has bribed the king's secretary and demonstrated purity of blood.

Jewish on both father's and mother's sides, with one relative burned by the Inquisition, Mateo Alemán has invented for himself a super-Christian lineage and an imposing coat of arms and incidentally changed his mistress Francisca de Calderón into his eldest daughter.

The novelist knew how to learn the arts of his character Guzmán de Alfarache, *skilled in the business of flamboyant roguery,* who changes dress, name, and city to wipe away disgraces and escape from poverty. *I must dance to the same tune as all the others, as long as it may last,* explains Guzmán de Alfarache in the novel that all Spain is reading.

(6 and 147)

1608: Córdoba

The Inca Garcilaso

At sixty he leans over the table, wets the pen in the horn inkpot, and writes apologetically. He writes a meticulous and handsome prose. He praises the invader in the invader's tongue, which he has made his own. With one hand he salutes the conquest as the work of Divine Providence: the conquistadors, arms of God, have evangelized the New World, and tragedy has paid the price of salvation. With the other hand, he bids farewell to the kingdom of the Incas, *destroyed before it was known,* and invokes it with a nostalgia for paradise. One hand belongs to his father, a captain of Pizarro's. The other to his mother, Atahualpa's cousin, whom that captain humiliated and threw into the arms of a soldier.

Like America, the Inca Garcilaso de la Vega has been born of a rape. Like America, he lives torn to pieces.

Although he has been in Europe for half a century, he still listens, as if they were something recent, to the voices of his childhood in Cuzco, *things received in the mantillas and the milk:* in that devastated city he came into the world eight years after the Spaniards arrived, and in that city he drank from his mother's lips the stories that come down from that distant day when the sun dropped over Lake Titicaca the prince and princess born of his loves with the moon.

(76)

1609: Santiago de Chile

How to Behave at the Table

They told him of it this morning when they brought the steaming, aromatic chocolate. At one bound, the governor detached himself from the Holland sheets: The king of Spain has decided to legalize the enslavement of Indians captured in war.

The news took almost a year to cross the ocean and the cordillera. For some time now Araucanians have been sold in the presence of a public notary, and any who try to escape have their tendons cut; but the king's approval will shut the mouths of a few grumblers.

"*God bless this bread . . .*"

The governor offers a supper to the people-tamers of these unfriendly lands. The guests drink wine of the country from oxhorns and eat corn bread wrapped in corn leaves, the savory humita favored by the Indians. As indicated by Alfonso the Wise, they pick up with three fingers the strips of chili-peppered meat; and as Erasmus of Rotterdam recommended, they do not gnaw bones or throw fruit peelings under the table. After taking the hot quelén-quelén drink, they use a toothpick without either leaving it between the lips or parking it behind the ear.

(94 and 172)

1611: Yarutini

The Idol-Exterminator

They are smashing Cápac Huanca with pickaxes. The priest Francisco de Avila shouts to the Indians to get a move on. Many idols still remain to be discovered and broken to pieces in these lands of Peru, where he knows no one who refrains from the sin of idolatry. The divine anger never rests. Avila, scourge of sorcerers, never sits down.

But his slaves, who know, are hurt by each blow. This big rock is a man chosen and saved by the god Pariacaca. Cápac Huanca alone shared with him his corn *chicha* and his coca leaves when Pariacaca disguised himself in rags and came to Yarutini and begged for something to drink and chew. This big rock is a generous man. Pariacaca froze him and turned him into stone so that the punitory hurricane that blew everyone else away would not take him.

Avila has the pieces thrown down the cliff. In place of Cápac Huanca he puts up a cross. Afterward he asks the Indians for Cápac Huanca's history, and he writes it.

(14)

1612: San Pedro de Omapacha

The Beaten Beats

The symbol of authority, plaited rawhide tipped with cord, whistles through the air and bites. It tears off the skin in strips and splits the flesh.

Naked, bound to the punishment block, Cristóbal de León Mullohuamani, chief of the Omapacha community, endures the torment. His moans keep time with the whip.

From cell to stocks, from stocks to lash, the chief lives in agony. He dared to protest to the viceroy in Lima and has not delivered his quota of Indians. He was responsible for the lack of hands to bring wine from the plains to Cuzco and to spin and weave clothing as the magistrate ordered.

The executioner, a black slave, wields the lash with pleasure. This back is no better or worse than any other.

(179)

1613: London

Shakespeare

The Virginia Company is meeting great disappointment on the coast of North America, which lacks gold or silver; nonetheless, propaganda pamphlets circulate all over England claiming that the English are trading the Indians in Virginia *pearls of Heaven for pearls of earth*.

Not long ago, John Donne was exploring his mistress's body in a poem as one discovering America; and Virginia, the gold of Virginia, is the central theme of the celebrations of Princess Elizabeth's wedding. In honor of the king's daughter a masquerade by George Chapman is performed, which revolves around a great rock of gold, symbol of Virginia or of the illusions of its shareholders: gold, key to all powers, secret of life pursued by the alchemists, son of the sun as silver is daughter of the moon and copper is born of Venus. There is gold in the warm zones of the world, where the sun generously sows its rays.

In the wedding celebrations for the princess, a work by William Shakespeare is also staged, *The Tempest,* inspired by the wreck of a Virginia Company ship in the Bermudas. The great creator of souls and marvels locates his drama this time on an island in the Mediterranean that more resembles the Caribbean. There Duke Prospero meets Caliban, son of the witch Sycorax, worshiper of the god of the Patagonian Indians. Caliban is a *savage,* an Indian of the type Shakespeare has seen in some exhibition in London: *a thing of darkness,* more beast than man, who only learns to curse and has no capacity for judgment nor sense of responsibility. Only as a slave, or tied up like a monkey, could he find a place in human society; that is, European society, which he has absolutely no interest in joining.

(207)

1614: Lima

Minutes of the Lima Town Council: Theater Censorship Is Born

In this council it has been stated that, for lack of examination of the comedies presented in this city, there have been said many things injurious to parties and against the authorities and the honesty that is owing to this republic. In order that said improprieties may cease in the future, it behooves us to provide a remedy. And the question having been posed and discussed, it was agreed and so ordered that present and future authors of comedies be notified not to present or have presented in any form any comedy without its first being seen and examined and approved by the person duly named by this council, under pain of two hundred pesos . . .

(122)

1614: Lima

Indian Dances Banned in Peru

Wings of condor, head of parrot, skins of jaguar: the Peruvian Indians dance their ancestral Raymi on Corpus Christi day. In the Quechuan language they perform their invocations to the sun at the time of sowing, or pay the sun homage when there is a birth or at the harvest season.

To the end that with Our Lord's help occasions for falling into idolatry may be suppressed, and the devil may not continue exercising his deceits, the archibishop of Lima decides that *neither in the local dialect nor in the general tongue may dances, songs, or* taquies *be performed*. The archbishop announces terrible punishments and orders all native musical instruments to be burned, including the dulcet reed flute, the messenger of love:

By the shore you shall sleep,
At midnight I will come . . .

(21)

1615: Lima
Guamán Poma

At seventy, he leans over the table, wets the pen in the horn inkpot, and writes and draws defiantly. He is a man of hasty and broken prose. He curses the invader in the invader's tongue and makes it explode. The language of Castile keeps tripping over Quechua and Aymara words, but after all, Castile is Castile for the Indians, and *without the Indians Your Majesty isn't worth a thing*.

Today Guamán Poma de Ayala finishes his letter to the king of Spain. At the start it was addressed to Philip II, who died while Guamán was writing it. Now he wants it delivered into Philip III's own hand. The pilgrim has trekked from village to village, *the author walking over mountains with much snow*, eating if he could and always carrying on his back his growing manuscript of sketches and words. *The author has returned from the world . . . He went through the world weeping the whole way* and has finally reached Lima. From here he proposes to travel to Spain. How he will manage that, he doesn't know. What does it matter? No one knows Guamán, no one listens to him, and the monarch is very remote and very high up; but Guamán, pen in hand, treats him as an equal, addresses him familiarly, and explains to him what he should do.

Exiled from his province, naked, treated as a nothing, Guamán does not hesitate to proclaim himself inheritor of the royal dynasties of the Yarovilcas and Incas and calls himself king's counselor, first Indian chronicler, prince of the realm, and second-in-command. He has written this long letter out of pride: His lineage stems from the ancient lords of Huánuco, and he has incorporated in the name he gives himself the falcon and puma of his ancestors' coat of arms, they who ruled the lands of northern Peru before Incas and Spaniards.

To write this letter is to weep. Words, images, tears of rage. *The Indians are the natural owners of this realm and the Spaniards, natives of Spain, are strangers here in this realm.* The apostle Santiago, in military uniform, tramples on a fallen native. At banquets, the plates are heaped with miniature women. The muleteer carries a basket filled with the mestizo children of the priest. *Also it is God's punishment that many Indians die in mercury and silver mines. In all Peru, where there were a hundred not ten remain.* "Do you eat this gold?" asks the Inca, and the conquistador replies: "This gold we eat."

Today, Guamán finishes his letter. He has lived for it. It has taken him half a century to write and draw. It runs to nearly twelve hundred pages. Today, Guamán finishes his letter and dies.

Neither Philip III nor any other king will ever see it. For three centuries it will roam the earth, lost.

(124, 125, and 179)

1616: Madrid

Cervantes

"What news do you bring of our father?"

"He lies, sir, amid tears and prayers. All swelled up he is, and the color of ashes. He's already put his soul to rest with the notary and with the priest. The mourners are waiting."

"If only I had the balsam of Fierabrás . . . Two swallows of that and he'd get well right away!"

"And him going on seventy, and dying? With six teeth in his mouth and only one hand that works? With the scars from all them battles, and insults, and jailings? That balls stuff wouldn't do nothing for him, sir."

"I don't say two swallows. Two drops."

"It'd be too late."

"He's dead, you say?"

"Dying, sir."

"Take off your hat, Sancho. And you, Rocinante, lower your head. Ah, prince of arms! King of letters!"

"What'll we do without him, sir?"

"Nothing that doesn't do him homage."

"Where'll we be putting ourselves, so all alone?"

"We'll go where he wanted to go but couldn't."

"Where's that, sir?"

"To set right whatever is crooked on the shores of Cartagena, in the ravines of La Paz and the woods of Soconusco."

"Nice places to get your bones ground up."

"You must know, Sancho, my brother of so many roads and rides, that in the Indies glory awaits the knight-errant thirsting for justice and fame . . ."

"Well, it's been a while since we got beaten up . . ."

" . . . and their squires are rewarded with huge, never-explored kingdoms."

"Wouldn't there be some a bit closer?"

"And you, Rocinante, in the Indies horses are shod with silver and champ on gold bits. They're regarded as gods!"

"A thousand beatings ain't enough for him. He wants a thousand and one!"

"Shut up, Sancho."

"Didn't our father say that America is a refuge for scoundrels and a sanctuary for whores?"

"Shut up, I tell you!"

"Whoever embarks for the Indies, he said, leaves his conscience on the pier."

"So we'll go there to clean off the honor of him who fathered us as free men in prison!"

"Can't we just mourn him here?"

"Do you call such treachery homage? Ah, villain! We'll take to the road again. If he made us to sojourn in the world, we'll take him through the world. Reach me my helmet! Shield on arm, Sancho! My lance!"

(46)

1616: Potosí

Portraits of a Procession

Magic mountain of Potosí: On these high and hostile plains that offered only solitude and cold, the world's most populated city has been made to bloom.

Lofty silver crosses head the procession, which advances between two lines of banners and swords. On silver streets ring out the silver hooves of horses decked with velvets and pearl-studded bridles. For confirmation of those who rule and consolation of those who serve, silver passes in parade, gleaming, confident, strutting, sure that there is no space on earth or in heaven it cannot buy.

The city is dressed up for a fiesta; balconies display hangings and heraldries; from a sea of rustling silks, foam of lace, and cataracts of pearls, the ladies watch and admire the cavalcade that moves with a din of trumpets, shawms, and harsh drums. A few gentlemen have a black patch over an eye and lumps and wounds on their foreheads, which are signs not of war but of syphilis. Kisses and flirtations keep flying from balconies to street, from street to balconies.

Masked figures of Selfishness and Greed appear. Greed, from behind a mask of snakes, sings as his horse performs caprioles:

Root of all evils
They call me, and I never tire
Not to satisfy desire.

Selfishness, black breeches, black gold-embroidered doublet, black mask beneath black, many-plumed cap, answers:

If I have conquered love
And love conquers death, all agree
Nothing is stronger than me.

The bishop heads a long, slow army of priests and hooded penitents armed with tall candles and silver candelabra; then the heralds' trumpets impose themselves on the peal of church bells announcing the Virgin of Guadelupe, Light of the patient, Mirror of justice, Refuge of sinners, Consolation of the afflicted, green Palm, flowered Staff, luminous Rock. She appears on waves of gold and mother-of-pearl, in the arms of fifty Indians; stifled by so much jewelry, she observes with astonished eyes the turmoil of silver-winged cherubs and the spectacular display of her worshipers. On a white steed comes the Knight of the Burning Sword, followed by a battalion of pages and lackeys in white liveries. The knight hurls his hat into the distance and sings to the Virgin:

Brown as is my lady fair,
so much beauty she betrays
heaven and earth stand in a daze.

Lackeys and pages in purple livery run behind the Knight of Divine Love, who comes mounted at a trot, Roman-style horseman, purple silk coattails flying in the wind: he falls to his knees before the Virgin and lowers his laurel-crowned head, but when he puffs out his chest to sing his couplets, a volley of sulphur smoke erupts. The devils' float has invaded the street, and no one pays the smallest attention to the Knight of Divine Love.

Prince Tartar, worshiper of Mohammed, opens his bat wings, and Princess Proserpine, hair and trains of snakes, hurls from on high blasphemies that the retinue of devils applaud. Somewhere the name of Jesus Christ is pronounced, and the Inferno float blows up with a big bang. Prince Tartar and Princess Proserpine jump through the smoke and flames and fall as prisoners at the Mother of God's feet.

The street is covered with small angels, halos, and wings of sparkling silver, and violins and guitars, zithers and shawms sweeten the air. Musicians dressed as damsels celebrate the arrival of Mercy, Justice, Peace, and Truth, four elegant daughters of Potosí raised on litters of silver and velvet. The horses pulling their float have Indian heads and breasts.

Then comes the Serpent, coiling and weaving. On a thousand Indian legs the enormous reptile slithers along, now to the light of flaming torches, instilling fear and fire into the festivities and showing defiance and combat at the feet of the Virgin. When soldiers cut off his head with axes and swords, from the Serpent's entrails emerges the Inca with his pride smashed to pieces. Dragging his fantastic robes, the son of the Sun falls to his knees before the Divine Light. The Virgin sports a robe of gold, rubies, and pearls the size of chickpeas, and the gold cross on her imperial crown shines brighter than ever over her astonished eyes.

Then the multitude. Artisans of every trade, and rogues and beggars who could draw a tear from a glass eye: the mestizos, children of violence, neither slaves nor masters, go on foot. The law prohibits them from having horses or weapons, as it prohibits mulattos from using parasols, so that no one can conceal the stigma that stains the blood to the sixth generation. With the mestizos and mulattos come the quadroons and the half-black, half-Indian zambos and the rest of the mixtures produced by the hunter and his prey.

Bringing up the rear, a mass of Indians loaded with fruits and flowers and dishes of steaming food. They implore the Virgin for forgiveness and solace.

Beyond, some blacks sweep up the litter left by all the others.

(21 and 157)

1616: Santiago Papasquiaro

Is the Masters' God
the Slaves' God?

An old Indian prophet spoke of the free life. Clad in traditional raiment, he went through these deserts and mountains raising dust and singing, to the sad beat of a hollow tree trunk, about the ancestors' feats and the liberty lost. The old man preached war against those who had seized the Indians' lands and gods and made the Indians themselves burst their lungs in the Zacatecas' mines. Those who died in the necessary war would revive, he announced, and old people who died fighting would be reborn young and swift.

The Tepehuanes stole muskets and fashioned and hid bows and arrows, because they are bowmen as skilled as the Morning Star, the divine archer. They stole and killed horses to eat their agility, and mules to eat their strength.

The rebellion broke out in Santiago Papasquiaro, in the North of Durango. The Tepehuanes, the region's most Christian Indians, the first converts, trampled on the Host; and when Father Bernardo Cisneros pleaded for mercy, they answered *Dominus vobiscum.* To the south, in the Mezquital, they smashed the Virgin's face with machetes and swigged wine from the chalices. In the village of Zape, Indians clad in Jesuit surplices and bonnets chased fugitive Spaniards through the woods. In Santa Catarina, they used their clubs on Father Hernando del Tovar while saying to him: *Let's see if God saves you.* Father Juan del Valle ended up stretched on the ground naked, with his sign-of-the-cross hand up in the air, the other hand covering his never-used sex.

But the insurrection didn't last long. On the plains of Cacaria, colonial troops struck the Indians down. A red rain falls on the dead. The rain falls through air thick with powder and riddles the dead with bullets of red mud.

In Zacatecas the bells ring out, summoning to celebratory banquets. The owners of mines sigh with relief. There will be no shortage of hands for the diggings. Nothing will interrupt the prosperity of the realm. They will be able to continue urinating tranquilly into tooled silver chamberpots, and nobody will prevent their ladies from attending Mass accompanied by a hundred maids and twenty damsels.

(30)

1617: London

Whiffs of Virginia in the London Fog

Dramatis personae:

The King (James I of England, VI of Scotland). He has written: *Tobacco makes a kitchen of man's interior parts, dirtying them and infecting them with a sort of oily and greasy soot*. He has also written that anyone who smokes imitates *the barbarous and beastly manners of the wilde, godlesse, and slavish Indians* . . .

John Rolfe. English colonist in Virginia. One of the most distinguished members of that *peculiar people marked and chosen by the finger of God . . . for undoubtedly He is with us*—as Rolfe himself defines his countrymen. With seeds brought to Virginia from Trinidad, he has produced good mixtures of tobacco on his plantations. Three years ago he sent to London in the hold of the *Elizabeth* four casks full of leaves, which have launched the recent but already very fruitful tobacco trade with England. It can well be said that John Rolfe has put tobacco on the throne of Virginia, as a queen plant with absolute power. Last year he came to London with Governor Dale, seeking new colonists and new investments for the Virginia Company and promising fabulous profits for its shareholders; for tobacco will be to Virginia what silver is to Peru.

He also came to present to King James his wife, the Indian princess Pocahontas, baptized Rebecca.

Sir Thomas Dale.   Governor of Virginia until last year. Authorized the marriage of John Rolfe and Princess Pocahontas, first Anglo-Indian marriage in Virginia's history, on the understanding that it was an act of high political convenience that would contribute to the peaceful supply of grains and hands by the native population. However, in his request for permission, John Rolfe did not mention this aspect of the affair; nor did he make any mention of love, although he did take pains to deny emphatically any *unbridled desire* toward his handsome eighteen-year-old fiancée. Rolfe said he wished to wed this pagan *whose education hath been rude, her manners barbarous, her generation accursed, . . . for the good of this plantation, for the honour of our countrie, for the glory of God, for my own salvation, and for the converting to the true knowledge of God and Jesus Christ, an unbeleeving creature . . ."*

Pocahontas.   Also known as Matoaka when she lived with the Indians. Favorite daughter of the great chief Powhatan. After marrying Rolfe, renounced idolatry, changed her name to Rebecca, and covered her nudity with English clothes. Wearing crown hats and high lace collars at the neck, she came to London and was received at court. She spoke like an Englishwoman and thought like an Englishwoman; she devoutly shared her husband's Calvinist faith, and Virginia tobacco found in her the most able and exotic promoter it needed to plant itself in London. She died of an English disease. Sailing down the Thames en route to Virginia, while the ship awaited favorable winds, Pocahontas breathed her last in the arms of John Rolfe at Gravesend in March of this year 1617. She was not yet twenty-one.

Opechancanough.   Uncle of Pocahontas, elder brother of the great chief Powhatan. He gave the bride away in the Protestant church at Jamestown, a bare wooden church, three years ago. Spoke not a word before, during, or after the ceremony, but Pocahontas told Rolfe the story of her uncle. Opechancanough had once lived in Spain and in Mexico; he was then a Christian known as Luis de Velasco, but no sooner was he back in his country than he threw his crucifix, cape, and stole in the fire, cut the throats of the priests who accompanied him, and took back his name of Opechancanough, which in the Algonquin language means *he who has a clean soul*.

Some Globe Theatre actor has put this story together and now asks himself, confronting a mug of beer, what he will do with it. Write a love tragedy or a moral play about tobacco and its evil powers? Or perhaps a masquerade with the conquest of America as its theme? The play would have a sure success, because all London is talking about Princess Pocahontas and her fleeting visit here. That woman . . . a harem all by herself. All London dreams of her nude among the trees, with aromatic flowers in her hair. What avenging angel ran her through with his invisible sword? Did she expiate the sins of her pagan people, or was her death God's warning to her husband? Tobacco, illegitimate son of Proserpine and Bacchus . . . Does not Satan protect the mysterious pact between that weed and fire? Smoke that makes the virtuous giddy, isn't it the breath of Satan? And the hidden lechery of John Rolfe . . . And the past of Opechancanough, formerly known as Luis de Velasco, traitor or avenger . . . Opechancanough entering the church with the princess on his arm . . . Tall, erect, silent . . .

"No, no," concludes the indiscreet hunter of histories as he pays for his beers and walks out into the street, "This story is too good to write. As the gentle Silva, poet of the Indies, used to say: 'If I write it, what do I have left to tell my friends?' "

(36, 159, and 207)

1618: Lima

Small World

The owner of Fabiana Criolla has died. In his will he has lowered the price of her freedom from 200 to 150 pesos.

Fabiana has spent the night without sleeping, wondering how much her guaiacum-wood box full of powdered cinnamon would be worth. She does not know how to add, so she cannot calculate the freedoms she has bought with her work through the half century that she has been in the world, nor the price of the children who have been made on her and taken from her.

With the first light of dawn, the bird comes and taps its beak on the window. Every day the same bird announces that it is time to wake up and get going.

Fabiana yawns, sits up on the mat, and inspects her worn-down feet.

(31)

1618: Luanda

Embarcation

They have been caught in the hunters' nets and are marching to the coast, tied to each other at the neck, as drums of pain resound in the villages.

On the African coast, a slave is worth forty glass necklaces or a whistle with a chain or two pistols or a handful of bullets. Muskets and machetes, rum, Chinese silks, or Indian calicoes are paid for with human flesh.

A monk inspects the column of captives in the main square of the port of Luanda. Each slave receives a pinch of salt on the tongue, a splash of holy water on the head, and a Christian name. Interpreters translate the sermon: *Now you are children of God* . . . The priest instructs them not to think about the lands they are leaving and not to eat dog, rat, or horse meat. He reminds them of St. Paul's epistle to the Ephesians (*Slaves, serve your masters!*) and Noah's curse upon the children of Ham, who remained black through centuries of centuries.

They see the ocean for the first time, and the enormous, roaring beast terrifies them. They think the whites are taking them to some remote slaughterhouse to eat them and make oil and fat from them. Hippopotamus-hide whips drive them onto enormous canoes that cross the breakers. In the ships they face fore-and-aft guns with lighted fuses. The fetters and chains keep them from throwing themselves into the sea.

Many will die on the voyage. The survivors will be sold in the markets of America and again branded with hot irons.

They will never forget their gods. Oxalá, at once man and woman, will be disguised as St. Jeronimo and St. Barbara. Obatalá will be Jesus Christ; and Oshún, spirit of sensuality and fresh waters, will turn into the Virgins of Candelaria, the Conception, Charity, and Pleasures and will be St. Anne in Trinidad. Behind

St. George, St. Anthony, and St. Michael will lurk the lances of Ogum, god of war; and inside St. Lazarus, Babalú will sing. The thunders and fires of fearsome Shargó will transfigure St. John the Baptist and St. Barbara. In Cuba, Elegguá will continue having two faces, life and death, and in southern Brazil, Exú will have two heads, God and the Devil, to offer the faithful Solace and vengeance.

(68, 127, 129, and 160)

1618: Lima

Too Dark

The friends toss back their tattered capes and sweep the ground with their hats. Their respects duly paid, they exchange compliments: "That stump of yours, a bloody marvel!"

"Your chancre—what a masterpiece!"

Pursued by flies, they cross the empty lot.

They talk as they pee, backs to the wind.

"Long time no see."

"I been on the run like a fly. Suffering, suffering."

"Ay."

Lizard takes a crust from his pocket, breathes on it, polishes it, and invites Breadbeggar to be his guest. Seated on a rock, they contemplate the flowers on the thistles.

Breadbeggar takes a bite with his three teeth and reports: "Up at the courthouse, good handouts . . . Best damn place in Lima. But the porter threw me out. Kicked me out, he did."

"You don't mean Juan Ochoa?"

"Satan, more likely name for him. God knows I didn't do nothing to him."

"Juan Ochoa ain't there no more."

"That right?"

"They chucked him out like a dog. Now he ain't porter at the courthouse, nor nothing."

Breadbeggar, feeling avenged, smiles. He stretches his bare toes.

"Must've been because of his misdeeds."

"It wasn't that."

"Because he was too stupid, then?"

"No, no. Because he's the son of a mulatto and grandson of a nigger. Too bloody dark."

(31)

1620: Madrid

The Devil's Dances Come from America

Thanks to the corpse of St. Isidro, which slept beside him for the past few nights, King Philip III feels better. This noon he ate and drank without choking. His favorite dishes lit up his eyes, and he emptied the wineglass at a gulp.

Now he moistens his fingers in the bowl offered by a kneeling page. The pantryman reaches out the napkin to the majordomo of the week. The majordomo of the week passes it to the chief majordomo. The chief majordomo bows to the duke of Uceda. The duke takes the napkin. Bowing his head, he holds it out to the king. While the king dries his hands, the trencherman brushes crumbs from his clothes, and the priest offers God a prayer of thanks.

Philip yawns, loosens his high lace collar, asks what is the news.

The duke reports that the Hospital Board people have come to the palace. They complain that the public refuses to go to the theater since the king banned dances; and the hospitals live from the takings of the comedies. "Sir," the board people have told the duke, "since there have been no dances there have been no takings. The sick are dying. We have nothing to pay for bandages and doctors." Actors recite verses by Lope de Vega extolling the American Indian:

Taquitán mitanacuní,
Spaniard from here to there.
. . . In Spain there is no love
so it seems to me:
there selfishness is king
here love's the thing.

But what the public wants from America are the kind of salty songs and dances that set the most respectable folk on fire. No use for the actors to make the stones weep and the dead laugh, nor for proscenium arts to draw lightning out of cardboard clouds. "If the theaters stay empty," say the board people, groaning, "the hospitals will have to close."

"I told them," says the duke, "Your Highness would decide."

Philip scratches his chin, investigates his nails.

"If Your Majesty has not changed his mind . . . What is banned is banned and well banned."

The saraband and chaconne dances make sex shine in the dark. Father Mariana has denounced these dances, *inventions of negroes and American savages, infernal in words and in movements*. Even in processions their couplets eulogizing sin are heard; and when their lascivious tambourine and castanet rhythms burst forth, the very nuns in the convents can no longer control their feet and the Devil's ticklings galvanize their hips and bellies.

The king's eyes are following the flight of a big, lazy fly among the remains of the banquet. "You—what do you think?" the king asks the fly.

The duke thinks he is being addressed: "These clownish dances are music for a witches' sabbath, as Your Majesty has well said, and the place for witches is in the bonfires in the central plaza."

The goodies have disappeared from the table, but the smell sticks in the air.

Babbling, the king orders the fly: "You decide."

"Your Majesty's worst enemy couldn't accuse you of intolerance," insists the duke. "Your Majesty has been indulgent. In the time of the king your father, whom God keeps in glory . . ."

"Aren't you the one in command?" babbles Philip.

". . . anyone who dared to dance the saraband got a different reward. Two hundred lashes and a dose of the galleys!"

"You, I say," whispers the king and closes his eyes.

"You"—and a gob of foam, saliva that his mouth always produces to excess, appears on his lips.

The duke smells a protest and immediately shuts up and withdraws on tiptoe.

Drowsiness overtakes Philip, heavy eyelids, and he dreams of a plump, nude woman who devours playing cards.

(186)

1622: *Seville*

Rats

Father Antonio Vázquez de Espinosa, newly arrived from America, is the guest of honor.

While the servants serve slices of turkey with sauce, foamy waves break in the air; a high, white sea maddened by storm; and when the stuffed chickens come on, tropical rains explode over the table. Father Antonio relates that on the Caribbean coast it rains so hard that women become pregnant and their children are born waiting for it to stop; by the time it clears, they are already grown up.

The other guests, captives of the story and the banquet, eat and are silent; the priest has his mouth full of words and forgets the dishes. From the floor, seated on hassocks, children and women listen as if at Mass.

The crossing from the Honduran port of Trujillo to Sanlúcar de Barrameda has been quite a feat. The ships proceeded bump by bump, tormented by squalls; several ships were swallowed by the angry sea, and many sailors by sharks. But nothing was worse, and Father Antonio's voice lowers, nothing was worse than the rats.

In punishment for the many sins committed in America, and because no one bothers with confession and Communion as they should before going aboard, God filled the ships with rats. He put them in the storage holds among the victuals, and beneath the quarterdeck; in the stern saloon, in the cabins, and even on the pilot's seat; so many rats, and such big ones, that they aroused fear and admiration. Four quintals of bread the rats stole from the cabin where the priest slept, plus the biscuits that were under the hatchway. They wolfed the hams and the sides of bacon in the stern storechest. When thirsty passengers went looking for water, they found drowned rats floating in the containers. When hungry ones went to the hen coop, all they found were bones and feathers and perhaps one sprawling chicken with its feet gnawed off. Not even the parrots in their cages escaped. Sailors kept watch over the remaining water and food night and day, armed with clubs and knives, and the rats attacked them and bit their hands and ate each other.

Between olive and fruit courses, the rats have arrived. The desserts are intact. No one touches a drop of wine.

"Would you like to hear the new prayers I composed? Since old ones just didn't placate the wrath of the Lord . . ."

No one answers.

The men cough, raising napkins to mouths. The women who were on their feet giving orders to the servants have all disappeared. Those listening from the floor are cross-eyed and open-mouthed. The children see Father Antonio with long snout, enormous teeth, and mustachio and twist their necks looking for his tail under the table.

(201)

1624: Lima
People for Sale

"Walk!"
"Run!"
"Sing!"
"What blemishes does he have?"
"Open that mouth!"
"Is he drunk, or just cantankerous?"
"How much do you offer, sir?"
"And diseases?"
"He's worth twice that!"
"Run!"
"Better not cheat me, or I'll bring him back."
"Jump, you dog!"
"You don't get goods like that for nothing."
"Make him lift up his arms!"
"Make him sing good and loud!"
"This woman, with kids or without?"
"Let's see her teeth!"

They pull them by one ear. The buyer's name will be marked on the cheeks or forehead, and they will be work tools on the plantations, fisheries, and mines, or weapons of war on the battlefields. They will be midwives and wet nurses, giving life, and executioners and gravediggers taking it. They will be minstrels and bed-flesh.

The slave corral is right in the center of Lima, but the town council has just voted to move it. The blacks on offer will be lodged in a barracoon the other side of the Rímac River, beside the San Lázaro slaughterhouse. There they will be far enough from the city for the winds to carry off their rotten and contagious vapors.

(31 and 160)

1624: Lima

Black Flogs Black

Three African slaves have paraded the streets of Lima with bound hands and a rope around their necks. The executioners, also black, walked behind. At every few steps, a stroke of the lash, up to a total of a hundred; and when they fell down, extra lashes as a dividend.

The mayor gave the order. The slaves had brought playing cards into the cathedral cemetery, turning it into a gambling den, using gravestones as tables; and the mayor well knew that the lesson would not be lost on the blacks in general who have become so insolent and so numerous, and so addicted to making trouble.

Now the three lie in the patio of their master's house. Their backs are raw flesh. They howl as their wounds are washed with urine and rum.

Their master curses the mayor, shakes his fist, vows vengeance. One just doesn't play such games with other people's property.

(31)

1624: Lima

The Devil at Work

The moon shines bright as the church bells announce one o'clock. Don Juan de Mogroveso de la Cerda leaves the tavern and starts walking through the orange-blossom-scented Lima night.

At the Bargain Street intersection he hears strange voices or echoes; he stops and cups his ear.

A certain Asmodeo is saying that he has moved several times since his ship sailed from Seville. On arriving at Portobello he inhabited the bodies of various merchants *who call dirty tricks "deals" and robbery "business," and a picklock a measuring stick;* and in Panama he lived in a phony gentleman with a false name, *who knew by heart how to act like a duke, the routine of a marquis, and the litanies of a count . . .*

"Tell me, Asmodeo. Did this character observe the rules of modern gentry?"

"All of them, Amonio. He lied and never paid debts nor bothered himself with the Sixth Commandment; he always got up late, talked during Mass, and felt cold the whole time, which is said to be in the best of taste. Just think how hard it is to feel cold in Panama, which makes a good try at being our hell. In Panama the stones sweat and people say: 'Hurry up with the soup, it'll get hot.' "

The indiscreet Don Juan de Mogrovejo de la Cerda cannot see either Asmodeo or Amonio, who are talking at some distance, but he knows that such names do not occur in the *Lives of the Saints,* and the unmistakable smell of sulphur in the air is enough to get the drift of this eloquent conversation. Don Juan flattens his back against the tall cross at the Bargain Street intersection, whose shadow falls across the street to keep Amonio and Asmodeo at a distance; he crosses himself and invokes a whole squadron of saints to protect and save him. But pray he cannot, for he wants to listen. He is not going to lose a word of this.

Asmodeo says that he left the body of that gentleman to enter a renegade clergyman and then, en route to Peru, found a home in the entrails of a devout lady who specialized in selling girls.

"*So I got to Lima, and your advice about operating in its labyrinths would be most helpful. Tell me what goes on in these provincial wilds. . . . Are the fortunes here honestly won?*"

"*If they were, it would be less crowded in hell.*"

"*What's the best way of tempting the businessmen?*"

"*Just put them in business and leave them to it.*"

"*Do people here feel love or respect for their superiors?*"

"*Fear.*"

"*So what do they have to do to get ahead?*"

"*Not deserve to.*"

Don Juan invokes the Virgin of Atocha, searches for the rosary he has forgotten, and clutches the handle of his sword as the questioning and Amonio's quick answers proceed.

"About the ones who presume to be the best people, tell me, do they dress well?"

"They could, considering how busy they keep the tailors all year round."

"Do they grumble a lot?"

"In Lima it's always time for beefing."

"Now tell me, why do they call all the Franciscos Panchos, all the Luises Luchos, and all the Isabelas Chabelas?"

"First to avoid telling the truth, and second so as not to name saints."

An inopportune fit of coughing attacks Don Juan at that moment. He hears shouts of "Let's go! Let's be off!" and after a long silence he detaches himself from the protecting cross. Shaking at the knees, he moves on toward Merchant Street and the Provincia gates. Of the garrulous pair, not a puff of smoke remains.

(57)

1624: Seville

Last Chapter of the "Life of the Scoundrel"

The river reflects the man who interrogates it.

"So what do I do with my crook? Do I kill him off?"

From the stone wharf his ill-fitting boots go into a dance on the Guadalquivir. This guy has the habit of shaking his feet when he is thinking.

"I have to decide. I was the one who created him the son of a barber and a witch and nephew of a hangman. I crowned him prince of the underworld of lice, beggars, and gallows-fodder."

His spectacles shine in the greenish waters, fixed on the depths as he fires his questions: "What do I do? I taught him to steal chickens and implore alms for the sake of the wounds of Christ. From me he learned his trickery at dice and cards and fencing. With my arts he became a nuns' Don Juan and a notorious clown."

Francisco de Quevedo wrinkles his nose to keep his spectacles up. "It's my decision, and I must make it. There never was a novel in all literature that didn't have a last chapter."

He cranes his neck toward the galleons that lower their sails as they approach the docks.

"Nobody has suffered with him more than I have. Didn't I make his hunger my own when his belly groaned and not even explorers could find any eyes in his head? If Don Pablos has to die, I ought to kill him. Like me, he is a cinder left over from the flames."

From far off, a ragged lad stares at the gentleman who is scratching his head and leaning over the river. "Some old hag," the boy thinks. "Some crazy old hag trying to fish without a hook."

And Quevedo thinks: "Kill him? Doesn't everyone know it's bad luck to break mirrors? Kill him. Suppose I make the crime a just punishment for his evil life? A small dividend for the inquisitors and censors! Just thinking about their pleasure turns my stomach."

A flight of sea gulls explodes. A ship from America is weighing anchor. With a jump, Quevedo starts walking. The lad follows him, imitating his bowlegged gait.

The writer's face glows. He has found on the decks the appropriate fate for his character. He will send Don Pablos, the scoundrel, to the Indies. Where but in America could his days end? His novel has a dénouement, and Quevedo plunges abstractedly into this city of Seville, where men dream of voyages and women of homecomings.

(183)

1624: Mexico City

A River of Anger

The multitude, covering all of the central plaza and neighboring streets, hurls curses and rocks at the viceroy's palace. Paving stones and yells of *Traitor! Thief! Dog! Judas!* break against tightly closed shutters and portals. Insults to the viceroy mix with cheers for the archbishop, who has excommunicated him for speculating with the bread of this city. For some time the viceroy has been hoarding all the corn and wheat in his private granaries, and playing with prices at his whim. The crowd is steaming. *Hang him! Beat him up! Beat him to death!* Some demand the head of the officer who has profaned the Church by dragging out the archbishop; others want to lynch Mejía, who fronts for the viceroy's business deals; and everybody wants to fry the hoarding viceroy in oil.

Pikes, sticks, and halberds rise above heads; pistol and musket shots ring out. Invisible hands hoist the king's pennon on the roof of the palace, and trumpets wail for help; but no one comes to defend the cornered viceroy. The realm's top people have shut themselves in their palaces, and the judges and officials have slipped away through crannies. No soldier is obeying orders.

The walls of the prison on the corner do not resist the attack. The inmates join the furious tide. The palace portals fall, fire consumes the doors, and the mob invades the rooms, a hurricane that pulls draperies off the walls, breaks open chests, and devours whatever it meets.

The viceroy, disguised as a monk, has fled through a secret tunnel to the San Francisco monastery.

(72)

1625: Mexico City

How Do You Like Our City?

Father Thomas Gage, newly arrived, amuses himself on the Alameda promenade. With hungry eyes he watches the ladies float along beneath the tunnel of tall trees. None wears her fichu or mantilla below the waist, the better to show off swaying hips and a pretty walk; and behind each lady comes a retinue of flashy black and mulatto women, their breasts peeping from their décolletage. Fire and fun, they wear roses on their extra-high-heeled shoes, and amorous words are embroidered on the silk bands around their foreheads.

On an Indian's back the priest arrives at the palace.

The viceroy offers him pineapple preserve and hot chocolate and asks how he likes the city.

In the middle of Father Gage's eulogy of Mexico, its women, carriages, and avenues, the host interrupts: "Do you know that I saved my life by a hair? And a baldpate's hair at that . . ."

From the viceroy's mouth bursts a torrential account of last year's uprising.

After much smoke and blood and two helpings of chocolate drained sip by sip, Father Gage learns that the viceroy has spent a year in the San Francisco monastery and still cannot put his nose outside the palace without risking a hail of stones. However, the rebellious archbishop is suffering the punishment of exile in remote, miserable Zamora, a few priests have been sent to row in the galleys, and the hanging of three or four agitators sufficed to crush the insolence of the hoi polloi.

"If it were up to me, I'd hang the lot," says the viceroy. He rises from his chair, proclaims: "Yes, the lot! The whole of this damned city!" and sits down again. "These are lands always ready for rebellion," he breathes. "I have cleaned the bandits off the roads of Mexico!"

Confidentially, stretching his neck, he adds: "D'you know something? The children of Spaniards, the ones born here . . . Who was at the head of the mob? It was them! The Creoles! They think the country belongs to them, they want to rule . . ."

Father Gage stares with the eyes of a mystic at the heavy crystal candelabrum that threatens his head and says: "They give grave offense to God. A second Sodom . . . I saw it with my own eyes this evening. Worldly delights . . ."

The viceroy nods confirmation.

"For they shall soon be cut down like the grass." The priest passes sentence. "They shall wither as the green herb."

He takes the last sip of chocolate.

"Psalm Thirty-seven," he adds, gently resting the little cup on his plate.

(72)

1625: Samayac

Indian Dances Banned
in Guatemala

The monks proclaim that no memory or trace remains of the rites and ancient customs of the Verapaz region, but the town criers grow hoarse proclaiming the succession of edicts of prohibition.

Juan Maldonado, judge of the Royal Audiencia, now issues in the town of Samayac new ordinances *against dances injurious to the Indians' consciences and to the keeping of the Christian law they profess*, because such dances *bring to mind ancient sacrifices and rites and are an offense to Our Lord*. The Indians squander money on feathers, dresses, and masks and *lose much time in rehearsals and drinking bouts, which keep them from reporting*

*for work at the haciendas, paying their tribute, and maintaining
their households.*

Anyone dancing the *tun* will get a hundred lashes. In the *tun*,
the Indians have a *pact with demons*. The *tun*, or Rabinal Achí, is
a fertility dance dramatized with words and masks, and the *tun* is
also the hollow log whose beat is accompanied by long, resonant
trumpets as the drama of the son of the Quichés, prisoner of the
Rabinals, proceeds: The victors sing and dance in homage to the
greatness of the vanquished, who says a dignified farewell to his
land and mounts to the stake at which he will be sacrificed.

(3)

1626: Potosí

A Wrathful God

The lake stampedes, smashes the dike, and invades the city. Many
are ground to pieces by the flood. Mules drag bits of people out
of the mud. A mixture of Spaniards, Creoles, mestizos, and Indians
ends up in common graves. Potosí's houses look like broken corpses.

The fury of Lake Caricari does not abate until priests parade
the Christ of the True Cross through the streets. When they see
the procession approaching, the waters halt.

From the pulpits of all Peru the same sermons are heard in
these days: "Sinners! How long will you play games with the mercy
of the Lord? God has infinite patience. How long, sinners? Have
not the warnings and punishments been enough?"

In these broad and opulent realms, the bursting of Potosí's
lake is nothing new. Forty-five years ago a huge rock plunged
suddenly onto a community of Indian sorcerers in Achocalla, a few
leagues from the city of La Paz. The only survivor was the chief,
who was struck dumb and told the story by signs. Another immense
rock buried a community of heretical Indians shortly afterward in
Yanaoca, near Cuzco. In the following year, the earth opened and
swallowed men and houses in Arequipa; and as the city had not
learned the lesson, the earth showed its fangs a little later and left
nothing standing except the San Francisco monastery. In 1586, the
ocean overwhelmed the city of San Marcos de Arica and all its
harbors and beaches.

When the new century began, the Ubinas volcano blew up.

Its anger was such that the ashes crossed the cordillera by land and reached the coasts of Nicaragua by sea.

Two warning stars appeared in this sky in 1617. They would not go away. Finally they moved into the distance thanks to the sacrifices and promises of the faithful all over Peru, who prayed five novenas without a stop.

(142)

1628: Chiapas

Chocolate and the Bishop

He doesn't put in black pepper, as do those who suffer from chills on the liver. He doesn't add corn, because it bloats. He generously sprinkles cinnamon, which empties the bladder, improves the sight, and strengthens the heart; nor does he spare the hot, well-ground-up chilis. He adds orange-blossom water, white sugar, and achiote spice to give color, and never forgets the handful of anise, two of vanilla, and the powdered Alexandria rose.

Father Thomas Gage adores well-prepared foamy chocolate. If not dunked in chocolate, sweets and marzipans have no flavor. He needs a cup of chocolate at midmorning to keep going, another after dinner to get up from the table, and another to stretch out the night and keep drowsiness at bay.

Since he arrived in Chiapas, however, he hasn't touched it. His belly protests; but Father Thomas prefers living badly between dizziness and faintings if it avoids the fate that killed Bishop Bernardo de Salazar.

Until recently, the ladies of this city would go to Mass with a retinue of pages and maids who, in addition to carrying the velvet hassock, brought along a brazier, boiler, and cup to prepare chocolate. Having delicate stomachs, the ladies couldn't endure the ordeal of a prayer service without the hot elixir, still less a High Mass. So it was, until Bishop Bernardo de Salazar decided to ban the custom because of all the confusion and hubbub it caused it in the church.

The ladies took revenge. One morning the bishop turned up dead in his office. At his feet, broken in pieces, the cup of chocolate that someone had served him.

(72)

1628: Madrid

Blue Blood for Sale

Off the coast of Matanzas, in Cuba, the Spanish fleet has fallen into the hands of the pirate Piet Heyn. All the silver coming from Mexico and Peru will end up in Holland. In Amsterdam, Heyn gets promoted to grand admiral, and a national hero's welcome is prepared for him. From now on, Dutch children will sing:

> *Piet Heyn, Piet Heyn*
> *Short is your name*
> *but long is your fame.*

In Madrid, heads are clutched. Of the royal treasure, only a hole remains.

The king decides, among other emergency measures, to put new noble titles on the market. Nobility is granted *for distinguished deeds*. And what deed more distinguished than having the money to pay for it? For four thousand ducats, any plebeian can wake up a noble of ancient lineage; and he who last night was the son of a Jew or grandson of a Muslim can start the day with pure blood.

But secondhand titles can be had cheaper. Castile has plenty of nobles who would go around with their arses in the air if their capes didn't cover them, gentlemen of illusory grandeur who live brushing invisible crumbs from their jerkins and mustaches: they are offering to the highest bidder the right to use the *Don*, which is all they have left.

Those who have come down in the world have in common with those who ride in silver carriages only a sense of honor and nostalgia for glory, a horror of work—begging is less unworthy— and a disgust for bathing, which is a custom of Moors, foreign to the Catholic religion, and frowned on by the Inquisition.

(64 and 218)

Song About the Indies Hand,
Sung in Spain

To Ronda one goes for pears,
for apples to Argonales,
to the Indies for money
and to the Sierra for follies.

My husband went to the Indies
his poverty to end:
came back with a lot to tell me,
but precious little to spend.

My husband went to the Indies
and brought me back a dirk
with an inscription on it that tells you:
"If you want to eat, work."

The men go off to the Indies,
to the Indies for a golden lark.
Right here they have the Indies,
if they only wanted to work!

(19)

1629: Las Cangrejeras
Bascuñán

His head creaks and hurts. Stretched out in the mud amid the pile of dead, Francisco Núñez de Pineda y Bascuñán opens his eyes. The world is a mess of blood and mud, riddled with rain, which whirls and bounces and splashes and whirls.

Indians throw themselves on him. They tear off his armor and his iron helmet, dented by the blow that knocked him out, and jerkily strip him naked. Francisco manages to cross himself before they tie him to a tree.

The storm lashes his face. The world stops spinning. A voice from inside tells him through the yells of the Araucanians: "You are in a swamp in the Chillán region in your land of Chile. This rain is what dampened your powder. This wind is what blew out your fuses. You lost. Listen to the Indians who are arguing about your death."

Francisco mutters a last prayer.

Suddenly a gust of colored feathers bursts through the rain. The Araucanians make way for the white horse that charges up spurting fire from its nostrils and foam from its mouth. The rider, masked by a helmet, sharply reins in his horse. The horse rears up on two legs before Maulicán, winner of the battle. Everyone falls silent.

"It's the executioner," thinks Francisco. "Now it's all over."

The feathered horseman leans down and says something to Maulicán. Francisco hears only the voices of rain and wind. But when the horseman wheels around and disappears, Maulicán unties the prisoner, takes off his cape, and covers him with it.

Then the horses gallop southward.

(26)

1629: Banks of the Bío-Bío River

Putapichun

Soon they see a throng approaching from the far-off cordillera. Maulicán spurs his horse and advances to meet Chief Putapichun.

The group from the cordillera also has a prisoner, who stumbles along between the horses with a rope around his neck.

On a flat hillock, Putapichun sticks his three-pointed lance into the ground. He has the prisoner unbound and throws a branch at his feet.

"Name the three bravest captains of your army."

"I don't know," babbles the soldier.

"Name one," orders Putapichun.

"Don't remember."

"Name one."

He names Francisco's father.

"Another."

He names another. With each name he is told to break the branch. Francisco watches the scene with clenched teeth. The soldier names twelve captains. He has twelve sticks in his hand.

"Now dig a hole."

The prisoner throws the sticks into the hole, one by one, repeating the names.

"Throw dirt in. Cover them up."

Then Putapichun passes sentence. "Now the twelve brave captains are buried."

And the executioner brings down on the prisoner the club bristling with nails.

They tear out his heart. They invite Maulicán to take the first sip of blood. Tobacco smoke floats in the air as the heart passes from hand to hand.

Then Putapichun, swift in war and slow in word, says to Maulicán: "We came to buy the captain you have there. We know he is the son of Alvaro, the big chief who has caused our land to tremble."

He offers him one of his daughters, a hundred Castilian sheep, five llamas, three horses with tooled saddles, and several necklaces of precious stones. "All that would pay for ten Spaniards and leave something over."

Francisco swallows saliva. Maulicán stares at the ground. After a while he says:

"First I must take him for my father and the other chiefs of my Repocura region to see. I want to show them this trophy of my valor."

"We'll wait," Putapichun says calmly.

"My life is just one death after another," thinks Francisco. His ears hum.

(26)

1629: Banks of River Imperial

Maulicán

"You bathed in the river? Come up to the fire. You're shivering. Sit down and drink. Come, Captain, are you dumb? And you talking our language like one of us . . . Eat, drink. We have a long journey ahead. Don't you like our chicha? You don't like our unsalted meat? Our drums don't make your feet dance. You're in luck, Captain boy. You people burn the faces of captives with the iron that doesn't rub out. You're out of luck, Captain boy. Now your freedom is mine. I'm sorry for you. Drink, drink, tear that fear from your

heart. I'll hide you. I'll never sell you. Your fate is in the hands of
the Lord of the world and of man. He is just. So. Drink. More?
Before the sun arrives we'll be off to Repocura. I want to see my
father and celebrate. My father is very old. Soon his spirit will go
to eat black potatoes over beyond the snow peaks. Hear the footsteps of the night walking? Our bodies are clean and vigorous to
start the trip. The horses are waiting for us. My heart beats fast,
Captain boy. Hear the drums of my heart? Hear the music of my
happiness?"

(26)

1629: Repocura Region

To Say Good-Bye

Moon by moon, time has passed. Francisco has heard and learned
much in these months of captivity. He has learned, and someday
will write, the other side of this long Chile war, this *just war that
the Indians made against those who deceived and wronged them
and took them as slaves, and even worse.*

In the forest, kneeling before a cross of *arrayán* branches,
Francisco says prayers of gratitude. Tonight he will be hitting the
trail for Nacimiento fort. There he will be exchanged for three
captive Araucanian chiefs. He will make the journey protected by
a hundred lances.

Now he walks toward the settlement. Beneath a brush arbor
a circle of threadbare ponchos and muddy faces awaits him. The
strawberry or apple chicha passes from mouth to mouth.

The venerable Tereupillán receives the cinnamon-tree branch,
which is the word, and raising it, he makes a long speech of praise
for each of the chiefs present. Then he eulogizes Maulicán, the
brave warrior, who won such a valuable prisoner in battle and knew
how to take him alive.

"*It is not for generous hearts,*" says Tereupillán, "*to take life
in cold blood. When we took up arms against the Spanish tyrants
who held us under persecution and humiliation, only in battle I
felt no compassion for them. But afterward, when I saw them as
captives, it gave me great sadness and pain, and it hurt my soul
to perceive that truly we did not hate them as persons. Their greed,
yes. Their cruelties, their arrogance, yes.*"

Turning to Francisco, he says: *"And you, Captain, friend and comrade, who are going away and leaving us hurt, sad, and without consolation, do not forget us."*

Tereupillán drops the cinnamon branch in the center of the circle and the Araucanians shake the ground awake, stamping their feet.

(26)

1630: Motocintle

They Won't Betray Their Dead

For nearly two years Fray Francisco Bravo had been preaching in this village of Motocintle. One day he told the Indians he had been called back to Spain. He wanted to return to Guatemala, he said, and stay here forever with his beloved flock, but his superiors over there in Spain would not let him.

"Only gold could convince them," said Fray Francisco.

"Gold we don't have," said the Indians.

"Yes, you do," corrected the priest. "I know there's a seam of it hidden in Motocintle."

"That gold doesn't belong to us," they explained. "That gold belongs to our ancestors. We're just looking after it. If any were missing, what would we say to them when they return to the world?"

"I only know what my superiors in Spain will say. They'll say: 'If the Indians of that village where you want to stay love you so much, how come you're so poor?' "

The Indians got together to discuss the matter.

One Sunday after Mass, they blindfolded Fray Francisco and made him turn around until he was dizzy. Everybody went along behind him, from the oldest to children at the breast. When they reached the back of a cave, they took off the blindfold. The priest blinked, his eyes hurting from the glitter of gold, more gold than all the treasures of the Thousand and One Nights, and his trembling hands did not know where to start. He made a bag of his cassock and loaded up what he could. Afterward he swore by God and the holy gospels that he would never reveal the secret, and he received a mule and tortillas for his journey.

In the course of time the royal audiencia of Guatemala received a letter from Fray Francisco Bravo from the port of Veracruz. With great pain to his soul the priest was fulfilling his duty, *as an act of service to the king in an important and outstanding matter of business*. He described the possible location of the gold: "I think I went only a short distance from the village. There was a stream running to the left . . ." He enclosed some sample nuggets and promised to use the rest for devotions to a saint in Malaga.

Now mounted judge and soldiers descend upon Motocintle. Dressed in red tunic and with a white wand hanging from his breast, Judge Juan Maldonado exhorts the Indians to surrender the gold.

He promises and guarantees them good treatment.

He threatens them with severities and punishments.

He puts a few in prison.

Others he puts in the stocks and tortures.

Others he forces up the steps of the scaffold.

And nothing.

(71)

1630: Lima

María, Queen of the Boards

"Every day more problems and less husband!" says María del Castillo with a sigh. At her feet, the stagehand, the prompter, and the star actress offer consolation and breezes from their fans.

In the heavy dusk, the guards of the Inquisition took Juan from María's arms and threw him in jail because poisoned tongues said that he said, while listening to the Gospel: *"Hey! All there is is living and dying!"*

A few hours earlier, in the central plaza and along the four streets giving onto the merchants' corner, the Negro Lázaro had announced the viceroy's new orders concerning comedy playhouses.

The viceroy, Count Chinchón, orders that an adobe wall must separate women from men in the theater, under pain of imprisonment and fine for anyone invading the territory of the other sex. Also that comedies must ring down the curtain earlier, when the bells toll for prayers, and that men and women must leave by different doors so that the grave offenses being committed against God Our Father should not continue in the darkness of the alleyways. And as if that were not enough, the viceroy has decided that the price of tickets must come down.

"He'll never have me!" cries María. "No matter how much he lays siege to me, he'll never have me!"

María del Castillo, great chief of Lima's comedy stage, has kept intact the poise and beauty that made her famous, and after sixty long years she still laughs at the *covered ones* who wear their shawls over one eye; since both of hers are handsome, she looks, seduces, and frightens with open face. She was almost a child when she chose this magical profession, and she has been bewitching people from the Lima stage for half a century. Even if she wanted to, she explains, she could not now change theater for convent, for God would not want her for wife after three such thoroughly enjoyed marriages.

Although the inquisitors have left her husbandless and the government's decrees seek to scare the public, María swears she won't get into bed with the viceroy.

"Never, never!"

Against hell and high water, alone and by herself, she will continue presenting cape-and-sword works in her comedy playhouse behind the San Augustín monastery. Shortly she will be reviving *The Nun Lieutenant* by the well-known Spanish wit Juan Pérez de Montalbán and will produce two new and very salty plays so that everyone may dance and sing and thrill with emotion in this city where nothing ever happens, so boring that two aunts can die on you in the time it takes to yawn.

(122)

1631: Old Guatemala
A Musical Evening at the Concepción Convent

In the convent garden Juana sings and plays the lute. Green light, green trees, green breeze: The air was dead until she touched it with her words and music.

Juana is the daughter of Judge Maldonado, who apportions Indians in Guatemala among farms, mines, and workshops. The dowry for her marriage to Jesus was a thousand ducats, and six black slaves serve her in the convent. While Juana sings her own or others' words, the slaves, standing at a distance, listen and wait.

The bishop, seated before the nun, cannot keep his face under control. He looks at Juana's head bent over the neck of the lute, throat bare, mouth glowingly open, and orders himself to calm down. He is famous for never changing his expression when bestowing a kiss or a condolence, but now this immutable face wears a frown: His mouth twists and his eyelids flutter. His normally firm pulse seems foreign to this hand that tremblingly holds a wineglass.

The melodies, praises of God or profane plaints, rise into the foliage. Beyond stands the green-water volcano. The bishop would like to concentrate on the cornfields and wheatfields and springs that shine on its slope.

That volcano holds the water captive. Anyone approaching it hears seethings as in a stewpot. The last time it vomited, less than a century ago, it drowned the city that Pedro de Alvarado founded at its foot. Here the earth trembles every summer, promising furies; and the city lives on tenterhooks, between two volcanos that cut off its breath. One threatens flood, the other inferno.

Behind the bishop, facing the water volcano, is the fire volcano. By the flames coming from its mouth a letter can be read at midnight a league away. From time to time is heard a thunder as of many guns, and the volcano bombards the world with stones: It shoots out rocks so large that twenty mules could not move them, and it fills the sky with ash and the air with the stink of sulphur.

The girl's voice soars.

The bishop looks at the ground, wanting to count ants, but his eyes slip over to the feet of Juana, which her shoes hide and yet reveal, and his glance roves over that well-made body that palpitates beneath the white habit, while his memory suddenly awakes and takes him back to childhood. The bishop recalls those uncontrollable urges he used to feel to bite the Host in the middle of Mass, and his panic that it would bleed; then he takes off on a sea of unspoken words and unwritten letters and dreams never told.

After a while, silence has a sound. The bishop notices with a start that for some time Juana has not been singing and playing. The lute rests on her knees and she looks at the bishop, smiling broadly, with those eyes that not even she deserves. A green aura floats around her.

The bishop suffers an attack of coughing. The anise falls to the ground and he blisters his hands with applause.

"I'll make you a mother superior!" he cries, "I'll make you an abbess!"

(72)

Popular Couplets of the Bashful Lover

I want to say and I don't,
I'm speaking without any word.
I want to love and I don't
And I'm loving without being heard.

I've a pain from I don't know where,
That comes from I don't know what.
I'll be cured I don't know when
By someone whose name I forgot.

Each time you look at me
And I at you
With my eyes I say
What I don't say.
As I don't find you
I look, to remind you.

(196)

1633: Pinola

Gloria in Excelsis Deo

The chigger is smaller than a flea and fiercer than a tiger. It enters by the feet and knocks you out if you scratch. It does not attack Indians but has no mercy on foreigners.

Father Thomas Gage has been at war for two months, and as he celebrates his victory against the chigger he balances up his stay in Guatemala. If it were not for the chigger, he would have no complaint. The villages welcome him with trumpets beneath canopies of branches and flowers. He has the servants he wants, and a groom leads his horse by the bridle.

He collects his salary on the dot, in silver, wheat, corn, cacao, and chickens. The Masses he says here in Pinola and in Mixco are paid for separately, as well as baptisms, weddings, and burials, and the prayers he offers upon request against locusts, pests, or earthquakes. Counting in the offerings to the many saints in his charge and those at Christmas and Easter, Father Gage takes in more than two thousand escudos a year, free of dust and straw, in addition to wine and cassock free of cost.

The priest's salary comes from the tribute that the Indians pay to Don Juan de Guzmán, owner of these men and these lands. As only the married ones pay tribute and the Indians are quick to nose out and spread scandal, the officials force children of twelve and thirteen into matrimony, and the priest marries them while their bodies are still growing.

(72 and 135)

1634: Madrid

Who Was Hiding Under
Your Wife's Cradle?

The Supreme Council of the Holy Office of the Inquisition, watching over purity of blood, decides that in the future there will be an exhaustive investigation before its officials get married.

All who work for the Inquisition, porter and prosecutor, torturer and executioner, doctor and scullion, must state the two-century genealogy of the chosen woman *to obviate marriage with infected persons.*

Infected persons, that is: with liters or drops of Indian or black blood, or with great-great-grandfathers of the Jewish faith or Islamic culture or adherence to any heresy.

(115)

1636: Quito

The Third Half

For twenty long years he has been the big shot of the realm of Quito, president of the government and king of love, card table, and Mass. Everyone else walks or runs at the pace of his mount.

In Madrid, the Council of the Indies has found him guilty of fifty-six misdemeanors, but the bad news has not yet crossed the sea. He will have to pay a fine for the shop he has operated for twenty years in the royal audiencia, selling the silks and Chinese taffetas he has smuggled in, and for countless scandals involving married women, widows, and virgins; and also for the casino he installed in the embroidery room of his house beside the private chapel where he received communion every day. The turn of the cards has netted Don Antonio de Morga two hundred thousand pesos just in admissions collected, not counting the feats of his own deft, fleecing fingers. (For debts of ten pesos, Don Antonio has sentenced many Indians to spend the rest of their lives chained to looms in the mills.)

But the Council of the Indies' resolution has not yet reached Quito. That is not what worries Don Antonio.

He stands in his room naked before the tooled gold mirror and sees someone else. He looks for his bull's body and does not find it. Beneath the flaccid belly and between the skinny legs hangs mute the key that has known the combination to so many female locks.

He looks for his soul, but the mirror does not have it. Who has stolen the pious half of the man who preached sermons to friars and was more devout than the bishop? And the shine of his mystic's eyes? Only darkness and wrinkles above the white beard.

Don Antonio de Morga moves forward till he touches the mirror, and he asks for his third half. There must be a region where the dreams he once dreamed and has forgotten have taken refuge. There has to be: a place where the eyes, spent from so much looking, will have retained the colors of the world; and the ears, now almost deaf, its melodies. He searches for some taste that has not been broken, some smell that has not vanished, some warmth that the hand can yet feel.

He finds nothing that has been saved and was worth saving. The mirror gives back only an empty old man who will die tonight.

(176)

1637: Mouth of the River Sucre

Dieguillo

A few days ago Father Thomas Gage learned to escape from crocodiles. If you zigzag away from them, the crocodiles get confused. They can run only in a straight line.

On the other hand, no one has taught him how to escape from pirates. But does anyone really know how you flee from those stout Dutch ships in a slow, gunless frigate?

Fresh out of the Caribbean Sea, the frigate lowers its sails and surrenders. More deflated than the sails, the soul of Father Gage lies prone. Aboard with him is all the money he has collected in the twelve years he has spent in America warding off sacrilege and pulling the dead out of hell.

The skiffs come and go. The pirates take the bacon, the flour, the honey, the chickens, the fats, and the hides. Also nearly all of the fortune the priest was carrying in pearls and gold. Not all, because they have respected his bed, and he has sewn a good part of his belongings into the mattress.

The pirate captain, a hefty mulatto, receives him in his cabin. He does not offer his hand but a seat and a mug of spiced rum. A cold sweat breaks out on the priest's neck and runs down his back. He takes a quick drink. He has heard about this Captain Diego Guillo. He knows that he used to do his pirating under orders of the fearsome Pegleg, and is now on his own with a corsair's license from the Dutch. They say that Dieguillo kills so as not to lose his aim.

The priest implores, babbles that they have left him nothing but the cassock he has on. Refilling his mug, the pirate, deaf and without blinking an eye, tells of the mistreatment he suffered when he was a slave of the governor of Campeche.

"My mother is still a slave in Havana. You don't know my mother? Such a good heart, poor woman, that it puts you to shame."

"I am not a Spaniard," whines the priest. "I'm English." He

repeats it in vain. "My country is not an enemy of yours. Aren't England and Holland good friends?"

"Win today, lose tomorrow," says the pirate. He holds a swig of rum in his mouth, sends it slowly down his throat.

"Look," he orders, and tears off his jacket. He displays his back, the weals left by the lash.

Noises from the deck. The priest is thankful, for they muffle the wild beatings of his heart.

"I am English . . ."

A vein beats desperately in Father Gage's forehead. The saliva refuses to go down his throat.

"Take me to Holland. I beseech you, sir, take me to Holland. Please! A generous man cannot leave me this way, naked and without . . ."

With one jerk the pirate frees his arm from the thousand hands of the priest. He strikes the floor with a cane, and two men come in. "Take him out of here!"

He turns his back in farewell, looking at himself in the mirror. "If you hit Havana anytime," he says, "don't fail to look up my mother. Remember me to her. Tell her . . . Tell her I'm doing fine."

As he returns to his frigate, Father Gage feels cramps in his stomach. The waves are acting up, and the priest curses whoever it was who said, back there in Jerez de la Frontera, twelve years ago, that America was paved with gold and silver and you had to walk carefully not to trip over the diamonds.

(72)

1637: Massachusetts Bay

"God is an Englishman,"

said the pious John Aylmer, shepherd of souls, some years ago. And John Winthrop, founder of the Massachusetts Bay Colony, says that the English can take over the Indians' lands as legitimately as Abraham among the Sodomites: *That which is common to all is proper to none. This savage people ruleth over many lands without title or property.* Winthrop is the chief of the Puritans who arrived in the *Arbella* four years ago. He came with his seven sons. Reverend John Cotton said good-bye to the pilgrims on Southampton's docks, assuring them that God would fly overhead like an eagle leading them from old England, land of iniquities, to the promised land.

To build the new Jerusalem on a hilltop came the Puritans. Ten years before the *Arbella*, the *Mayflower* arrived at Plymouth, at a time when other Englishmen hungry for gold had already reached the Virginia coasts to the south. The Puritan families are fleeing from the king and his bishops. They leave behind them taxes and wars, hunger and diseases. They are also fleeing from threats of change in the old order. As Winthrop, Cambridge lawyer born into a noble cradle, says, *God Almightie in his most holy and wise providence hath soe disposed of the Condition of mankinde, as in all times some must be rich some poore, some highe and eminent in power and dignitie; others meane and in subjection*.

For the first time, the Indians saw a floating island. The mast was a tree, the sails white clouds. When the island stopped, the Indians put out in their canoes to pick strawberries. Instead of strawberries they found smallpox.

The smallpox devastated Indian communities and cleared the ground for God's messengers, God's chosen, people of Israel on the sands of Canaan. Those who had lived here for more than three thousand years died like flies. Smallpox, says Winthrop, was sent by God to oblige the English colonists to occupy lands depopulated by the disease.

(35, 153, and 204)

1637: Mystic Fort

From the Will of John Underhill, Puritan of Connecticut, Concerning a Massacre of Pequot Indians

They knew nothing of our coming. Drawing near to the fort, we yielded up ourselves to God and entreated His assistance in so weighty an enterprise . . .

We could not but admire at the providence of God in it, that

*soldiers so unexpert in the use of their arms, should give so complete
a volley, as though the finger of God had touched both match and
flint. Which volley being given at break of day, and themselves
fast asleep for the most part, bred in them such a terror, that they
brake forth into a most doleful cry; so as if God had not fitted the
hearts of men for the service, it would have bred in them a com-
miseration towards them. But every man being bereaved of pity,
fell upon the work without compassion, considering the blood they
had shed of our native countrymen, and how barbarously they had
dealt with them, and slain, first and last, about thirty persons . . .
Having our swords in our right hand, our carbines or muskets in
our left hand, we approached the fort . . .*

*Many were burnt in the fort . . . Others forced out . . . which
our soldiers received and entertained with the point of the sword.
Down fell men, women, and children; those that scaped us, fell
into the hands of the Indians that were in the rear of us. It is
reported by themselves, that there were about four hundred souls
in this fort, and not above five of them scaped out of our hands.
Great and doleful was the bloody sight to the view of young soldiers
that never had been in war, to see so many souls lie gasping on
the ground, so thick, in some places, that you could hardly pass
along. It may be demanded, Why should you be so furious (as some
have said)? Should not Christians have more mercy and compassion? But I would refer you to David's war. When a people is
grown to such a height of blood, and sin against God and man,
and all confederates in the action, there he hath no respect to
persons, but harrows them, and saws them, and puts them to the
sword, and the most terriblest death that may be. Sometimes the
Scr. ture declareth women and children must perish with their
parents. Sometimes the case alters; but we will not dispute it now.
We have sufficient light from the Word of God for our proceedings.*

(204)

1639: Lima

Martín de Porres

The bells of Santo Domingo church ring out the death toll. By the
candles' light, bathed in icy sweat, Martín de Porres has delivered
up his soul after much fighting against the Devil with the aid of

Most Holy Mary and of St. Catherine, virgin and martyr. He died in his bed, with a stone for pillow and a skull at his side, while the viceroy of Lima knelt and kissed his hand and implored his intercession for a small place for him up in Heaven.

Martín de Porres was the offspring of a black slave and her master, a gentleman of pure Spanish lineage, who did not impregnate her by way of using her as an object but rather to apply the Christian principle that in bed all are equal before God.

At fifteen, Martín was given to a monastery of Dominican friars. Here he performed his works and miracles. Being a mulatto, he was never ordained as a priest; but embracing the broom with love, he swept out each day the rooms, cloisters, infirmary, and church. Razor in hand, he shaved the monastery's two hundred priests; he nursed the sick and distributed clean clothes smelling of rosemary.

When he learned that the monastery was hard up for money, he went to see the prior: *"Ave María."*

"Gratia plena."

"Your Grace should sell this mulatto dog," he offered.

He put in his bed ulcerated beggars from the street, and prayed on his knees all night long. A supernatural light made him white as snow; white flames escaped from his face when he crossed the cloister at midnight, flying like a divine meteor, heading for the solitude of his cell. He walked through padlocked doors and sometimes prayed kneeling in the air, far off the ground; angels accompanied him to the choir holding lights in their hands. Without leaving Lima he consoled captives in Algiers and saved souls in the Philippines, China, and Japan; without budging from his cell he pealed the Angelus. He cured the dying with clothes dipped in black roosters' blood and powdered toad and with exorcisms learned from his mother. With the touch of a finger he stopped toothaches and turned open wounds into scars; he made brown sugar white and put out fires with a glance. The bishop had to forbid him to perform so many miracles without permission.

After matins he would strip and scourge his back with a whip of ox sinews tied in thick knots and cry as he drew blood: *"Vile mulatto dog! How long is your sinful life to last?"*

With imploring, tearful eyes always begging pardon, the first dark-skinned addition to the Catholic Church's lily-white sanctoral calendar has passed through the world.

(216)

1639: San Miguel de Tucumán

From a Denunciation of the Bishop of Tucumán,
Sent to the Inquisition Tribunal in Lima

With the sincerity and truth with which so sacred a tribunal should be addressed, I denounce the person of the Reverend Bishop of Tucumán, Don Fr. Melchor Maldonado de Saavedra, of whom I have heard things most gravely suspicious in our holy Catholic faith, which are of general currency through this whole bishopric. That in Salta, celebrating confirmations, a comely young girl came and he said to her: "Your Grace is better taken than confirmed"; and in Córdoba this last year of 1638 another came in the presence of many people and lifting his cassock he said: "Get out! I shouldn't be confirming you from below but from on top"; and with the first one he notoriously cohabited . . .

(140)

1639: Potosí

Testament of a Businessman

Through the curtains pokes the nose of the notary. The bedroom smells of wax and of death. By the light of the one candle the skull can be seen beneath the dying man's skin.

"What are you waiting for, you vulture?"

The businessman does not open his eyes but his voice sounds firm.

"My shadow and I have discussed and decided," he says. And sighs. And orders the notary: "You are not to add or subtract anything. Hear me? I'll pay you two hundred pesos in birds, so that with their feathers, and the ones you use to write, you can fly to hell. Are you listening? Ay! Each day I live is borrowed time. Every day it costs me more. Write, get going! Hurry up, man. I order that with a fourth part of the silver I leave, there should be built in the small square of the bridge a great latrine so that nobles and plebeians of Potosí may pay homage there every day to my memory. Another fourth part of my bullion and coins to be buried in the yard of this my house, and at the entrance to be kept four of the fiercest dogs, tied with chains and with plenty of food, to guard this interment.

His tongue does not tangle up and he continues, without taking a breath: "And with another fourth part of my wealth, that the most exquisite dishes be cooked and placed in my silver service and inserted in a deep ditch, with everything that remains in my larders, because I want the worms to gorge themselves sick as they will do with me. And I order . . ."

He wags his index finger, projecting a clublike shadow on the white wall: "And I order . . . that nobody whatever should attend my funeral, that my body be accompanied by all the asses that there are in Potosí, decked with the richest vestments and the best jewels, to be provided from the rest of my fortune."

(21)

The Indians Say:

The land has an owner? How's that? How is it to be sold? How is it to be bought? If it does not belong to us, well, what? We are of it. We are its children. So it is always, always. The land is alive. As it nurtures the worms, so it nurtures us. It has bones and blood. It has milk and gives us suck. It has hair, grass, straw, trees. It knows how to give birth to potatoes. It brings to birth houses. It brings to birth people. It looks after us and we look after it. It drinks chicha, accepts our invitation. We are its children. How is it to be sold? How bought?

(15 and 84)

1640: São Salvador de Bahia
Vieira

The mouth sparkles as it fires words lethal like gunfire. The most dangerous orator in Brazil is a Portuguese priest raised in Bahia, a Bahian to the soul.

The Dutch have invaded these lands, and the Jesuit Antonio Vieira asks the colonial gentry *if we are not just as dark-colored to the Dutch as the Indians are to us*.

From the pulpit the lord of the word rebukes the lords of the land and of the people: *"Does it make me a lord that I was born farther away from the sun, and others, slaves, that they were born closer? There can be no greater departure from understanding, no greater error of judgment among men!"*

In the little Ayuda church, oldest in Brazil, Antonio Vieira also accuses God, who is guilty of helping the Dutch invaders: *"Although we are the sinners, my God, today it is you who must repent!"*

(33, 171, and 226)

1641: Lima

Avila

He has interrogated thousands and thousands of Indians without finding one who is not a heretic. He has demolished idols and temples, has burned mummies; has shaved heads and skinned backs with the lash. At his passage, the wind of Christian faith has purified Peru.

The priest Francisco de Avila has reached seventy-five to find that his strength is failing him. He is half deaf and even his clothes hurt; and he decides not to leave the world without obtaining what he has wanted since he was a boy. So he applies to enter the Company of Jesus.

"No," says the rector of the Jesuits, Antonio Vázquez.

"No," because *although he claims to be a learned man and great linguist, Francisco de Avila cannot conceal his condition of mestizo.*

(14)

1641: Mbororé

The Missions

The *mamelukes* are coming from the region of San Pablo. Hunters of Indians, devourers of lands, they advance to the beat of a drum, raised flag and military order, thunder of war, wind of war, across

Paraguay. They carry long ropes with collars for the Indians they will catch and sell as slaves in the plantations of Brazil.

The *mamelukes* or *bandeirantes* have for years been devastating the missions of the Jesuits. Of the thirteen missions in the Guayrá, nothing is left but stones and charcoal. New evangelical communities have arisen from the exodus, downstream on the Paraná; but the attacks are incessant. In the missions the snake finds the birds all together and fattened up, thousands of Indians trained for work and innocence, without weapons, easy to pick off. Under the priests' tutorship the Guaranís share a regimented life, without private property or money or death penalty, without luxury or scarcity, and march to work singing to the music of flutes. Their sugarcane arrows are futile against the arquebuses of the *mamelukes,* who test the blades of their swords by splitting children in half and carry off shredded cassocks and caravans of slaves as trophies.

But this time, a surprise awaits the invaders. The king of Spain, scared by the fragility of these frontiers, has ordered firearms issued to the Guaranís. The *mamelukes* flee in disorder.

From the houses rise plumes of smoke and songs of praise to God. The smoke, which is not from arson but from chimneys, celebrates victory.

(143)

1641: Madrid
Eternity Against History

The count-duke of Olivares gnaws his fists and mutters curses. He commands much, after twenty years of doings and undoings at court, but God has a stronger tread.

The Board of Theologians has just turned down his project of channeling the Tagus and Manzanares rivers, which would be so welcomed by the plains of Castile. The rivers will remain as God made them, and the plans of engineers Carducci and Martelli will end up in the files.

In France, it is announced that the great Languedoc canal will soon be opened, to join the Mediterranean with the Garonne Valley. Meanwhile, in this Spain that has conquered America, the Board of Theologians decides that *he sins against Divine Providence*

who tries to improve what she, for inscrutable motives, has wished
to be imperfect. If God had desired that the rivers should be navigable, he would have made them navigable.

(128)

1644: Jamestown

Opechancanough

Before an English soldier shoots him in the back, Chief Opechancanough asks himself: "Where is the invisible guardian of my footsteps? Who has stolen my shadow?"

At the age of one hundred, he has been defeated. He had
come to the battlefield on a litter.

Over eighty years ago, Admiral Pedro Menéndez de Avilés
took him to Cádiz. He presented him at the court of Philip II: *Here
is a fine Indian prince of Florida.* They dressed him in breeches,
doublet, and ruff. In a Dominican monastery in Seville they taught
him the language and religion of Castile. Then in Mexico, the
viceroy gave him his name, and Opechancanough became Luis de
Velasco. Later he returned to the land of his fathers as interpreter
and guide to the Jesuits. His people thought he was returning from
the dead. He preached Christianity and then took off their clothes
and cut the Jesuits' throats and went back to his old name.

Since then he has killed many and seen much. He has seen
villages and fields devoured by flames and his brothers sold to the
highest bidder, in this region that the English baptized Virginia in
memory of a spiritually virginal queen. He has seen men swallowed
up by smallpox and lands devoured by enslaving tobacco. He has
seen seventeen of the twenty-eight communities that were here
wiped off the map and the others given a choice between diaspora
and war. Thirty thousand Indians welcomed the English navigators
who arrived at Chesapeake Bay one fresh morning in 1607. Three
thousand survive.

(36 and 207)

1645: Quito

Mariana de Jesús

Year of catastrophes for the city. A black bow hangs on every door. The invisible armies of measles and diphtheria have invaded and are destroying. Night has closed in right after dawn and the volcano Pichincha, king of snow, has exploded: a great vomit of lava and fire has fallen on the fields, and a hurricane of ash has swept the city.

"Sinners, sinners!"

Like the volcano, Father Alonso de Rojas hurls flame from his mouth. In the gleaming pulpit of the church of the Jesuits, a church of gold, Father Alonso beats his breast, which echoes as he weeps, cries, clamors: "Accept, O Lord, the sacrifice of the humblest of Your servants! Let my blood and my flesh expiate the sins of Quito!"

Then a young woman rises at the foot of the pulpit and says serenely: "I."

Before the people who overflow the church, Mariana announces that she is the chosen one. She will calm the wrath of God. She will take all the castigations that her city deserves.

Mariana has never played at being happy, nor dreamed that she was, nor ever slept for more than four hours. The only time a man ever brushed her hand, she was ill with a fever for a week after. As a child she decided to be the bride of God and gave Him her love, not in the convent but in the streets and fields: not embroidering or making sweets and jellies in the peace of the cloisters, but praying with her knees on thorns and stones and seeking bread for the poor, remedy for the sick, and light for those in the darkness of ignorance of divine law.

Sometimes Mariana feels called by the patter of rain or the crackle of fire, but always the thunder of God sounds louder: that God of anger with beard of serpents and eyes of lightning, who appears nude in her dreams to test her.

Mariana returns home, stretches out on her bed, and readies herself to die in place of all. She pays for God's forgiveness. She offers her body for Him to eat and her blood and her tears for Him to drink until he gets dizzy and forgets.

That way the plague will cease, the volcano will calm down, and the earth will stop trembling.

(176)

1645: Potosí

Story of Estefanía, Sinful Woman of Potosí (Abbreviation of Chronicle by Bartolomé Arzáns de Orsúa y Vela)

Estefanía was born in this imperial Town and grew up in beauty beyond the power of nature to enhance.

At fourteen, the lovely damsel left home, advised by other lost women; and her mother, seeing the abominable determination with which this daughter broke away, gave up the ghost within a few days.

This did not cause the daughter to mend her ways. Having already lost the priceless treasure of virginity, she dressed pro-fanely and became a public and scandalous sinner.

Seeing so much discredit and ill fame, her brother called her to his house and said: "Hurt you as it may, you must hear me. While you continue in mortal sin you are an enemy of God and a slave of the Devil, and furthermore you debase your nobility and dishonor all your lineage. Consider, sister, what you are doing, get out of that muck, fear God, and do penance." To which Estefanía replied: "What do you want of me, you bloody hypocrite?" And while the brother reproved her, she seized in a flash the dagger that hung on the wall and set on him with diabolical ferocity, saying: "This is the only answer your arguments deserve." She left him dead in a lake of blood and afterward disguised that misdeed by a pretense of sentiment, dressing herself in mourning and mak-ing much of her grief.

Also her aged father, sorrowing for the death of the good son and the scandal of the bad daughter, succeeded in confronting her with good arguments, to which the heartless girl listened against her will. Instead of mending her ways, she ended up loathing the venerable gentleman and at midnight she set fire to the roof of his house. The anguished old man sprang from his bed shouting at the top of his voice: "Fire, fire!" But the beams supporting the roof collapsed, and there and then the terrible element consumed him.

Seeing herself free, Estefanía gave herself with more wanton-ness to greater vices and sins.

In those days there came to Potosí a man of the realms of Spain, one of the most opulent merchants who came in those galleons to Peru, and the beauty and grace of that public sinner came to his attention. He solicited her, and when they were most enjoying their obscenities a former lover of the lady, armed with every weapon and with two thirsty pistols, turned up determined to avenge the affront.

The former lover found the woman alone, but she restrained his angry spirit with deceitful words, and when she had mitigated his fury she took a knife from her sleeve with great promptness and the wretch fell to the ground dead.

Estefanía mentioned the event to the rich merchant. After some months, being much tormented by jealousy, he threatened to bring her to justice for the homicide. In those days they went together to bathe in Tarapaya Lake. She threw off her rich clothing, revealing the snow of her body dotted with loveliest crimson, and threw herself naked into the water. The carefree merchant followed her, and when they were together in the middle of the lake, she pushed the luckless man's head into the water with all the strength of her arms.

Let it not be thought that her abominations stopped there. With one blow of a sword she ended the life of a gentleman of illustrious blood; and she killed two others with poison she inserted in a lunch. Her intrigues ended the days of others with swordthrusts in the breast, while Estefanía remained full of joy that blood should be shed on her account.

So it went up to the year 1645, when the sinful woman heard a sermon by Father Francisco Patiño, a servant of God whose admirable virtues Potosí was enjoying at the time, and God came to her aid with a ray of his divine grace. And so great was Estefanía's sorrow that she began to weep streams of tears, with great sighs and sobs that seemed to tear out her soul, and when the sermon ended she threw herself at the priest's feet pleading for confession.

The priest exhorted her to penitence and absolved her, it being well known with what felicity women surrender themselves into the serpent's hands, due to flaws inherited from her who tempted Adam. Estefanía rose from the confessor's feet like another Magdalene and when she was on her way home—oh, happy sinner!— she earned the appearance of Most Holy Mary, who said to her:

"Daughter, thou art forgiven. I have pleaded for you to my Son, because in your childhood you prayed with my rosary."

(21)

1647: Santiago de Chile
Chilean Indians' Game Banned

The captain general, Don Martín de Mujica, proclaims the prohibition of the game of chueca, which the Araucanians play according to their tradition, hitting a ball with curved sticks on a court surrounded by green boughs.

One hundred lashes for Indians who do not comply; and fines for others, because the infamous chueca has spread widely among the Creole soldiery.

The captain general's edict says that the ban is imposed *so that sins so contrary to the honor of God Our Father may be avoided* and because chasing the ball trains Indians for war: *The game gives rise to disturbances and thus afterward the arrow flies among them.* It is indecent, it says, that men and women foregather for the chueca almost naked, *clad in nothing but feathers and skins of animals on which they base their hopes of winning.* At the start of the game they invoke the gods to favor their prowess and speed their feet, and at the end, all in a big embrace, they drink oceans of chicha.

(173)

1648: Olinda
Prime Cannon Fodder

He was a boy when they took him from his African village, shipped him out from Luanda, and sold him in Recife. He was a man when he fled from the canefields and took refuge in one of the black bastions of Palmares.

As soon as the Dutch entered Brazil, the Portuguese promised freedom to slaves who would fight the invaders. The runaways of Palmares decided that the war was not theirs; it mattered little whether those who held the lash in canefields and sugarmills were Portuguese or Dutch. But he, Henrique Dias, went to volunteer.

Since then he commands a regiment of blacks who fight for the Portuguese Crown in northeastern Brazil. The Portuguese have ennobled him.

From Olinda, Captain Henrique Dias sends an intimidating letter to the Dutch army quartered in Recife. He says that his regiment, the Legion of the Henriques, consists of four nations: *Minas, Ardas, Angolans, and Creoles: These are so malevolent that they have and should have no fear; the Minas so wild that their reputation can subdue what they cannot reach with their arms; the Ardas so fiery that they want to cut everybody with a single blow; and the Angolans so tough that no work tires them. Consider, now, if men who have broken everything are not destined to break all Holland.*

(69 and 217)

1649: Ste. Marie des Hurons

The Language of Dreams

"Poor things," thinks Father Ragueneau, watching the Huron Indians surround with gifts and rituals a man who, last night, dreamed a mysterious dream. The community puts food in his mouth and dances for him; the young girls stroke him, rub him with ashes. Afterward, all seated in a circle, they set about interpreting the dream. They pursue the dream with flashed images or words and he keeps saying, "No, no" until someone says "river," and then among them all they succeed in capturing it: the river, a furious current, a woman alone in a canoe, she has lost the paddle, the river sweeps her away, the woman doesn't cry out, she smiles, looks happy. "Is it I?" asks one of the women. "Is it I?" asks another. The community invites the woman whose eyes penetrate the most obscure desires to interpret the symbols of the dream. While drinking herb tea, the clairvoyant invokes her guardian spirit and deciphers the message.

Like all the Iroquois peoples, the Hurons believe that dreams transfigure the most trivial things and convert them into symbols when touched by the fingers of desire. They believe that dreams are the language of unfulfilled desires and have a word, *ondinnonk*, for the secret desires of the soul that wakefulness does not recognize. Ondinnonks come forward in the journeys made by the soul while the body sleeps.

"Poor things," thinks Father Ragueneau.

For the Hurons, one who does not respect what dreams say commits a great crime. The dream gives orders. If the dreamer does not carry them out, the soul gets angry and makes the body sick or kills it. All the peoples of the Iroquois family know that sickness can come from war or accident, or from the witch who inserts bear teeth or bone splinters in the body, but also comes from the soul when it wants something that it is not given.

Father Ragueneau talks it over with other French Jesuits who preach in the area. He defends the Indians of Canada: *It's easy to call irreligion what is merely stupidity . . .*

Some priests see Satan's horns protruding from these superstitions and are scandalized because at the drop of a hat the Indians will dream against the Sixth Commandment and the next day plunge into therapeutic orgies. The Indians go about practically naked, looking at and touching each other in devilish liberty, and marry and unmarry whenever they want; and an order from a dream is all it takes to let loose the andacwandat fiesta, which is always the occasion for frenetic sinning. Father Ragueneau can't deny that the Devil can find fertile ground in this society without judges, or policemen, or jails, or property, where the women share command with the men and together they worship false gods, but he insists on the basic innocence of these primitive souls, still ignorant of God's law.

And when the other Jesuits tremble with panic because some Iroquois may dream one of these nights of killing a priest, Ragueneau recalls that that has already happened several times and that when it did, all that was necessary was to let the dreamer rip up a cassock while dancing his dream in an inoffensive pantomime.

"These are stupid customs," says Father Ragueneau, "but not criminal customs."

(153 and 222)

An Iroquois Story

It is snowing outside and in the center of the big house the old storyteller is talking, his face to the fire. Seated on animal skins, all listen as they sew clothing and repair weapons.

"The most splendid tree had grown in the sky," says the old man. "It had four big white roots, which extended in four directions. From this tree all things were born . . ."

The old man relates that one day wind completely uprooted the tree. Through the hole that opened in the sky fell the wife of the great chief, carrying a handful of seeds. A tortoise brought her soil on its shell so that she could plant the seeds, and thus sprouted the first plants that gave us food. Later that woman had a daughter, who grew and became the wife of the west wind. The east wind blew certain words in her ear . . .

The good storyteller tells his story and makes it happen. The west wind is now blowing on the big house; it comes down the chimney, and smoke veils all the faces.

Brother wolf, who taught the Iroquois to get together and listen, howls from the mountains. It is time to sleep.

One of these mornings, the old storyteller will not wake up. But someone of those who heard his stories will tell them to others. And later this someone will also die, and the stories will stay alive as long as there are big houses and people gathered around the fire.

(37)

Song About the Song of the Iroquois

When I sing
it can help her.
Yeah, it can, yeah!
It's so strong!

When I sing
it can raise her.
Yeah, it can, yeah!
It's so strong!

When I sing
her arms get straighter.
Yeah, it can, yeah!
It's so strong!

When I sing
her body gets straighter.
Yeah, it can, yeah!
It's so strong!

(197)

1650: Mexico City

The Conquerors and the Conquered

The family crest rears itself pompously in the ornamented iron over the gate, as if over an altar. The master of the house rolls up in a mahogany carriage, with his retinue of liveried attendants and horses. Within, someone stops playing the clavichord; rustlings of silks and tissues are heard, voices of marriageable daughters, steps on soft, yielding carpets. Then the tinkle of engraved silver spoons on porcelain.

This city of Mexico, city of palaces, is one of the largest in the world. Although it is very far from the sea, Spanish and Chinese ships bring their merchandise and silver shipments from the north end up here. The powerful Chamber of Commerce rivals that of Seville. From here merchandise flows to Peru, Manila, and the Far East.

The Indians, who built this city for the conquerors on the ruins of their Tenochtitlán, bring food in canoes. They may work here during the day, but at nightfall they are removed on pain of the lash to their slums outside the walls.

Some Indians wear stockings and shoes and speak Spanish in hope of being allowed to remain and thereby escape tribute and forced labor.

(148)

From the Náhuatl Song on the Transience of Life

We have but one turn at life.
In a day we go, in a night we descend
to the region of mystery.

We came here only to get to know each other.
We are here only in passing.
In peace and pleasure let us spend life.
Come and let's enjoy it!
Not those who live in anger:
broad is the earth.
How good to live forever,
never to have to die!

While we live, our spirit broken,
Here they harass us, here they spy on us.
But for all the misfortunes,
for all the wounds in the soul,
we must not live in vain!
How good to live forever,
never to have to die!

(77)

1654: Oaxaca

Medicine and Witchcraft

The Zapotec Indians, who before falling to earth were brightly
colored songbirds, told a few secrets to Gonzalo de Balsalobre.
After living among them for a time and after investigating the
mysteries of religion and medicine, Don Gonzalo is writing in
Oaxaca a detailed report that he will send to Mexico City. The
report denounces the Indians to the Holy Inquisition and asks for
punishment of the quackeries that monks and ordinary justice have
been unable to suppress. A while back, Alarcón left the university
to share for nine years the life of the Cohuixco Indian community.
He got to know the sacred herbs that cure the sick; and later he
denounced the Indians for devilish practices.

In the first period of the conquest, however, indigenous medicine aroused great curiosity in Europe, and marvels were attrib-
uted to America's plants. Fray Bernardino de Sahagún collected
and published the wisdom of eight Aztec doctors, and King Philip
II sent his personal physician, Francisco Hernández, to Mexico to
make a thorough study of native medicine.

For the Indians, herbs speak, have sex, and cure. It is little plants, aided by the human word, that pull sickness from the body, reveal mysteries, straighten out destinies, and provoke love or forgetfulness. These voices of earth sound like voices of hell to seventeenth-century Spain, busy with inquisitions and exorcisms, which relies for cures on the magic of prayer, conjurations, and talismans even more than on syrups, purges, and bleedings.

(4)

1655: San Miguel de Nepantla

Juana at Four

Juana goes about constantly chatting with her soul, which is her internal companion as she walks on the bank of the stream. She feels all the happier because she has the hiccups, and Juana grows when she has the hiccups. She stops and looks at her shadow, which grows with her, and measures it with a branch after each little jump of her tummy. The volcanos also grew with the hiccups when they were alive, before their own fire burned them up. Two of the volcanos àre still smoking, but they don't have the hiccups now. They don't grow anymore. Juana has the hiccups and grows. She gets bigger.

Crying, on the other hand, makes you smaller. For that reason old women and the mourners at funerals are the size of cockroaches. That isn't in her grandfather's books, which Juana reads, but she knows. These are things she knows from talking so much to her soul. Juana also talks to the clouds. To talk to the clouds you have to climb the hills or to the top branches of the trees.

"I am a cloud. We clouds have faces and hands. No feet."

(16 and 75)

1656: Santiago de la Vega

Gage

In a hammock stretched between two palms, the Anglican clergyman Thomas Gage dies in Jamaica.

Since the old days when he roamed the lands of America in a Catholic friar's cassock, preaching and spying and enjoying the chocolate and guava desserts, he dreamed of being the first English viceroy of Mexico. Back in London he switched sects and convinced Lord Cromwell that it was necessary and possible to fit out a good fleet to conquer the Spanish colonies.

Last year, Admiral William Penn's troops invaded the island of Jamaica. England seized from Spain the first bit of its American empire, and the inheritors of Columbus, marquises of Jamaica, lost the best of their revenues. Then the Reverend Thomas Gage delivered a patriotic Protestant sermon from the pulpit of the largest church in Santiago de la Vega, while the Spanish governor came in the arms of his slaves to surrender his sword.

(145)

1658: San Miguel de Nepantla
Juana at Seven

She sees her mother coming in the mirror and drops the sword, which falls with a bang like a gunshot, and Juana gives such a start that her whole face disappears beneath the broad-brimmed hat.

"I'm not playing," she says angrily as her mother laughs. She frees herself from the hat and shows her mustachios drawn with soot. Juana's feet move awkwardly in the enormous leather boots; she trips and falls and kicks in the air, humiliated, furious; her mother cannot stop laughing.

"I'm not playing," Juana protests, with tears in her eyes. "I'm a man! I'll go to the university, because I'm a man!"

The mother strokes her head. "My crazy daughter, my lovely Juana. I ought to whip you for these indecencies."

She sits beside her and says softly: "Better you were born stupid, my poor know-it-all daughter," and caresses her while Juana soaks her grandfather's huge cape with tears.

(16 and 75)

Juana Dreams

She wanders through the market of dreams. The market women have spread out dreams on big cloths on the ground.

Juana's grandfather arrives at the market, very sad because he has not dreamed for a long time. Juana takes him by the hand and

helps him select dreams, dreams of marzipan or of cotton, wings
to fly with in sleep, and they take off together so loaded down with
dreams that no night will be long enough for them.

(16 and 75)

1663: Old Guatemala
Enter the Printing Press

Bishop Payo Enríquez de Ribera is one of the most fervent advocates of forced labor for Indians. Without the allotments of Indians, the bishop reasons, who will cultivate the fields? And if
nobody cultivates the fields, who will cultivate souls?

When the bishop is preparing a document on the subject, he
receives from Puebla the first printing press to reach Guatemala.
The learned spiritual head of this diocese has had it brought with
cases of type, typography and all, so that his theological treatise
Explicatio Apologetica may be printed here.

The first book published in Guatemala is not written in Mayan
or in Castilian but in Latin.

(135)

1663: The Banks of the Paraíba River
Freedom

The hounds' baying and the slave-hunters' trumpeting have long
since faded away. The fugitive crosses a field of stubble, fierce
stubble higher than himself, and runs toward the river.

He throws himself on the grass, face down, arms open, legs
wide apart. He hears the accomplice voices of grasshoppers and
cicadas and little frogs. "I am not a thing. My history is not the
history of things." He kisses the earth, bites it. "I got my foot out
of the trap. I'm not a thing." He presses his naked body to the
dew-soaked ground and hears the sound of small plants coming
through the earth, eager to be born. He is mad with hunger, and
for the first time hunger gives him happiness. His body is covered
with cuts, and he does not feel it. He turns toward the sky as if
embracing it. The moon rises and strikes him, violent blows of

light, lashes of light from the full moon and the juicy stars, and he gets up and looks for his direction.

Now for the jungle. Now for the great screen of greenness.

"You heading for Palmares, too?" the fugitive asks an ant crawling up his hand. "Guide me."

(43)

Song of Palmares

Rest, black man.
The white doesn't come here.
If he comes,
the devil will take him.
Rest, black man.
The white doesn't come here.
If he comes, he'll leave
with a taste of our cudgels.

(69)

1663: Serra da Barriga

Palmares

On some nights when there is lightning, the incandescent crest of this mountain range can be seen from the Alagoas coast. In its foothills the Portuguese have exterminated the Caeté Indians, whom the pope had excommunicated in perpetuity for eating the first Brazilian bishop; and this is where fugitive black slaves have found refuge, for the last many years, in the hidden villages of Palmares.

Each community is a fortress. Beyond the high wooden palisades and the pointed-stake traps lie vast planted fields. The farmers work with their weapons within reach; and at night, when they return to the citadel, they count bodies in case anyone is missing.

Here they have two harvests of corn a year, and also beans, manioc, sugar, potatoes, tobacco, vegetables, and fruits; and they raise pigs and chickens. The blacks of Palmares eat much more and better than the people of the coast, where all-devouring sugar-cane, produced for Europe, usurps all of everyone's time and space.

As in Angola, the palm is king in these black communities: with its fiber they weave clothing, baskets, and fans; the fronds serve as roof and bed; from the fruit, the flesh is eaten, wine is made, and oil for lighting is extracted; from the husk, cooking fat and smoking pipes are made. As in Angola, the chiefs perform the noble office of blacksmith, and the forge occupies the place of honor in the plaza where the people have their assemblies.

But Angola is multiple; still more Africa as a whole. The Palmarians come from a thousand regions and a thousand languages. Their only common tongue is the one heard from the mouths of the masters, accompanying lash-delivered orders on slave ships and in canefields. Sprinkled with African and Guaraní words, the Portuguese language is now a bond of communication for those it formerly humiliated.

Folga nêgo.
Branco não vem cá

Since the Dutch were expelled from Pernambuco, the Portuguese have launched more than twenty military expeditions against this land of the free. An informant writes from Brazil to Lisbon: *Our army, which could tame the pride of Holland, has produced no result against those barbarians on its many and frequent incursions into Palmares . . .*

The Dutch had no better luck. Its expeditions, too, were without glory. Both Dutch and Portuguese have burned down empty villages and gotten lost in the thickets, turning this way and that like madmen in the violent rains. Both have made war against a shadow, a shadow that bites and runs; and each time they have claimed victory. Neither has succeeded in crushing Palmares nor in stopping the flight of slaves who leave King Sugar and his court without labor, although the Dutch crucified rebellious blacks and the Portuguese flog and mutilate to instill fear and set an example.

One of the Portuguese expeditions against Palmares has just returned, empty-handed, to Recife. It was headed by a black captain, Gonçalo Rebelo, who had two hundred black soldiers under his command. They cut the throats of the few prisoners they could take.

(69)

1665: Madrid
Charles II

The new monarch rocks and weeps. They hold him up from behind with braces tied to armpits and waist. At four, he does not know how to talk or walk, and they have to tear him from the nipples of his fourteen wet nurses to sit him on the throne of Spain.

He weeps because the crown, slipping down over his eyes, hurts him, and because he wants to go back to play with the elves and drink the warm milk of the fairies.

The weakling survives by a miracle, or thanks to the fact that they never bathed him even when he was born, although his head and neck are covered with purulent scabs. (Nobody bathes at the court, ever since Domingo Centurión died of a cold nine years ago.)

"Arrorró," babbles the king and cradles his foot against his ear.

(201)

1666: New Amsterdam
New York

With a few shots from their guns the English bring down the flag that waves over the fortress and seize the island of Manhattan from the Dutch, who had bought it from the Delaware Indians for sixty florins.

Recalling the arrival of the Dutch over half a century ago, the Delawares say: *The great man wanted only a little, little land, on which to raise greens for his soup, just as much as a bullock's hide would cover. Here we first might have observed their deceitful spirit.*

New Amsterdam, the most important slave market in North America, now becomes New York; and Wall Street is named after the wall built to stop blacks from escaping.

(136)

1666: London

The White Servants

Three ships full of white servants slip down the Thames toward the sea. When they open their hatches in the remote island of Barbados, the living will go to the sugar, cotton, and tobacco plantations and the dead to the bottom of the bay.

Spirits they call the traffickers in white servants, very skilled in the magic of evaporating people: They send to the Antilles whores and vagabonds kidnapped in the poor quarters of London, young Catholics hunted down in Ireland and Scotland, and prisoners awaiting the gallows in the Brixton jail for having killed a rabbit on private property. Stored under lock and key in the holds of the ships, the drunks captured on the docks wake up; with them on the voyage to the Americas are some lads lured by sweets, and many adventurers deceived by the promise of easy fortunes. Over there on the plantations of Barbados or Jamaica or Virginia, the juice will be squeezed from them until they have paid their price and the price of the passage.

The white servants dream of becoming owners of land and blacks. When they recover their freedom, after years of hard penitence and unpaid toil, the first thing they do is buy a Negro to fan them in the siesta hour.

There are forty thousand African slaves in Barbados. Births are registered in the plantation account books. At birth, a little Negro is worth half a pound sterling.

(11 and 224)

1666: Tortuga Island

The Pirates' Devotions

Jean David Nau, known as El Olonés, has just sacked Remedios and Maracaibo. His cutlass has made mincemeat of many Spaniards. Due to the weight of the stolen wealth, his frigates return at half speed.

El Olonés lands. Between his boots, his one friend and confidant, companion of his adventures and misadventures, wags his tail and barks. Behind comes a pack of men newly released from the spider web of the rigging, hungry for taverns and women and solid ground underfoot.

On these sands hot enough to boil turtles' eggs, the pirates stand in silence through a long Mass. Patched-up bodies, jackets stiff with filth, greasy prophets' beards, faces like knives notched by the years: If anyone dares to cough or laugh during the Mass, they fell him with a shot and cross themselves. Each pirate is an arsenal. At his waist, four knives and a bayonet in alligator-hide sheaths, and two naked pistols, boarding sword knocking against the knee, musket slung across his chest.

After Mass, the booty is divided. First, the mutilated. Whoever has lost his right arm gets six hundred pesos or six slaves. The left arm is worth five hundred pesos or five slaves, which is also the price of either of the legs. Anyone who left an eye or a finger on the coasts of Cuba or Venezuela has the right to a hundred pesos or one slave.

They stretch out the day's work with long drafts of spiced rum and end it with the turtle barbecue grand finale. Beneath the sand and covered with embers, the chopped turtle meat has been slowly baked in its shell with egg yolks and spices—the supreme party dish of these islands. The pirates light their pipes reclining on the sand, and abandon themselves to smoke and nostalgia.

When night falls, they cover with pearls the body of a mulatto woman and whisper horror stories and marvels to her, tales of hangings and boardings and treasure, and swear into her ear that they won't be sailing again soon. They drink and love without removing their boots: boots that tomorrow will polish the stones of the port, seeking a ship for another raid.

(61 and 65)

1667: Mexico City

Juana at Sixteen

In ships, the bell marks off the quarter hours of the watches. In mines and canefields, it summons Indian serfs and black slaves to work. In churches, it marks the hours and announces Masses, deaths, and fiestas.

But in the tower over the palace of the viceroy of Mexico there is a silent bell. It is said that inquisitors took it from the bell tower of an old Spanish village, removed the clapper, and expatriated it to the Indies no one knows how many years back. Ever since the maestro Rodrigo constructed it in 1530, this bell had always been clean and obedient. They say it had three hundred tones, according to the bell ringer's whim, and the whole village was proud of it. Until one night its long and violent pealing made everybody jump out of bed. The bell was sounding the alarm, unleashed by fear or joy or who knows what, and for the first time no one understood it. A crowd gathered in the atrium as the bell pealed madly on, and the mayor and the priest went up to the tower and, frozen with fear, confirmed that no one was there. No human hand moved it. The authorities took the case to the Inquisition. The Holy Office tribunal declared the pealing of the bell to be totally null and void, and it was silenced forever and exiled to Mexico.

Juana Inés de Asbaje walks out of the palace of her protector, the viceroy Mancera, and crosses the great plaza followed by two Indians who carry her trunks. Reaching the corner, she stops and looks back at the tower, as if called by the voiceless bell. She knows its history. She knows that it was punished for singing all on its own.

Juana heads for the Santa Teresa la Antigua convent. She will no longer be a lady of the court. In the serene light of the cloister and the solitude of a cell she will seek what she cannot find outside. She would have liked to study the mysteries of the world at the university, but women are born condemned to the embroidery frame and the husband chosen for them. Juana Inés de Asbaje will become a barefoot Carmelite and will call herself Sor Juana Inés de la Cruz.

(58 and 213)

1668: Tortuga Island

The Dogs

No Indians remain in this islet north of Haiti. But the dogs brought by the Spaniards to hunt them down and punish them stay on. The mastiffs, which have multiplied and go about in packs devouring wild boars, dispute the dominion of this land with French corsairs. Night after night their howls are heard from the thickets. Within their ramparts, the pirates tremble in their sleep.

Tortuga Island belongs to the enterprise created by French minister Colbert to run the slave traffic and piracy. The enterprise has named Bertrand d'Ogeron as governor, a gentleman of shining prestige among buccaneers and freebooters.

From France the governor brings a cargo of poison. It will be used to kill a few horses whose bodies will be spread about the island, bellies full of venom. This way he expects to put an end to the threat of the wild dogs.

(65)

1669: Town of Gibraltar

All the Wealth in the World

Henry Morgan's men keep scratching along the shores of Lake Maracaibo, seeking the buried treasure that El Olonés could not take with him. For all the time and effort invested, El Olonés did not have days long enough nor ships' holds big enough to load it.

After the usual cannonade, the landing. The pirates jump from their skiffs and enter the smoking village with drawn swords.

No one there, nothing there.

In the middle of the plaza, a tattered lad receives them, laughing. The enormous hat that covers his eyes has a broken brim hanging down over his shoulder.

"Secret! Secret!" he cries. He moves his arms like a windmill, beating off imaginary flies, and never stops laughing.

When a sword point scratches his throat, he whispers: "Don't sleep with your feet bare, or the bats will eat them."

Thick with smoke and powder, the air boils. Morgan seethes with heat and impatience. They tie up the lad. "Where did they hide the jewels?" They beat him. "Where's the gold?" They open the first gashes in his cheeks and his chest.

"I am Sebastián Sánchez!" he yells. "I am the brother of the governor of Maracaibo! Very important person!"

They cut off half an ear.

They drag him along. The lad leads the pirates to a cave, through a wood, and reveals his treasure. Hidden beneath boughs are two clay plates, the rusted point of an anchor, an empty shell, some colored feathers and stones, a key, and three small coins.

"I am Sebastián Sánchez!" the owner of the treasure keeps repeating as they kill him.

(65 and 117)

1669: Maracaibo

The Broken Padlock

At dawn Morgan discovers that Spanish ships have appeared out of the night and closed the entrance to the lake. He decides to attack. Ahead of his fleet he sends a sloop at full sail headlong against the Spanish flagship. The sloop has the war flag flying in defiance and contains all of the pitch, tar, and sulphur that Morgan has found in Maracaibo, and cases of gunpowder stashed in every corner. Its crew are a few wooden dolls dressed in shirts and hats. The Spanish admiral, Don Alonso del Campo y Espinoza, is blown into the air without discovering that his guns have fired into a powder keg.

Behind it charges the pirate fleet. Morgan's frigates break the Spanish padlock with cannon fire and gain the open sea. They sail off stuffed with gold and jewels and slaves.

In the shadow of the sails struts Henry Morgan, clothed from head to foot in the booty from Maracaibo. He has a gold telescope and yellow boots of Córdoba leather; his jacket buttons are emeralds mounted by Amsterdam jewelers. The wind lifts the lacy foam of his white silk shirt and carries from afar the voice of the woman who awaits Morgan in Jamaica, the flaming mulatto who warned him on the docks, when he said good-bye: "If you die, I'll kill you."

(65 and 117)

1670: Lima

"Mourn for us,"

the Indians of the Potosí mines had said to him wordlessly. And last year Count Lemos, viceroy of Peru, wrote to the king in Spain: *There is no people in the world so exhausted. I unburden my conscience to inform Your Majesty with due clarity: It is not silver that is brought to Spain, but the blood and sweat of Indians.*

The viceroy has seen the mountain that eats men. From the villages Indians are brought in strung together with iron collars, and the more the mountain swallows, the more its hunger grows. The villages are being emptied of men.

After this report to the king, Count Lemos bans week-long work periods in the asphyxiating tunnels. Beatings of drums, proclamations in the streets: In the future, the viceroy orders, Indians will work from sunrise to sunset, because *they are not slaves to spend the night in the mines*.

No one pays any attention.

And now, in his austere palace in Lima, he receives a reply from the Council of the Indies in Madrid. The council declines to suppress forced labor in the silver and mercury mines.

(121)

1670: San Juan Atitlán

An Intruder on the Altar

In midmorning, Father Marcos Ruiz lets the donkey carry him to the village of San Juan Atitlán. Who knows whether the gentle music of water and bells borne on the breeze comes from village or from dream? The friar yawns and does not hurry the pace, that soporific swing.

Much twisting and turning are required to get to San Juan Atitlán, a village deep in the asperities of the countryside; and it is well known that the Indians grow their crops in the most obscure corners of the mountains to pay homage, in those hideaways, to their pagan gods.

The first houses, and Fray Marcos begins to wake up. The village is deserted; no one comes out to greet him. He blinks strenuously on arriving at the church, overflowing with people, and his heart gives a violent jump when he manages to shoulder his way in, and he rubs his eyes to see what is happening: In the church, flower-bedecked and perfumed as never before, the Indians are worshiping the village idiot. Seated on the altar, covered from head to foot with the sacred vestments, dribbling and squinting, the idiot is receiving offerings of incense and fruit and hot food amid a torrent of hardly recognizable orations and hymns. No one hears the indignant cries of Fray Marcos, who retreats on the run in search of soldiers.

The spectacle infuriates the pious clergyman, but his surprise does not last long. After all, what can one expect from these idolaters, who ask pardon of a tree when they go to cut it down and do not dig a well without first making excuses to the ground? Don't they confuse God with some stone or other, the sound of a running stream, or a drizzle of rain? Don't they call carnal sin play?

(71)

1670: Masaya
"The Idiot"

For a moment, the sun breaks through clouds, then hides again, ashamed or scared by the brilliance of people here below, for the land is lit up with joy: dialogue dance, dance theater, saucy musical skits: on the verge of intelligibility, "the Idiot" directs the fiesta. The characters, wearing masks, speak a language of their own, neither Náhuatl nor Spanish, a mestizo language that has grown up in Nicaragua. It has been fed by the thousand idioms that the people have developed for talking defiantly and inventing as they talk, fiery chili from the imaginations of a people making fun of its masters.

An ancient Indian, a coarse fast talker, occupies the center of the stage. It is "the Idiot," otherwise known as Macho Mouse, mocker of prohibitions, who never says what he says or listens to what he hears, and so manages to avoid being crushed by the powerful: When the rogue cannot win the game, he draws; when he can't achieve a draw, he confuses.

(9)

1670: Cuzco
Old Moley

The walls of the cathedral, obese with gold, overwhelm this dark Virgin with the black hair streaming from under her straw hat and a baby llama in her arms. Her simple image is surrounded by a foamy sea of filigreed gold. Cuzco's cathedral would like to vomit out of its opulent belly this Indian Virgin, Virgin of despair, as not long ago its doormen rejected an old barefooted woman who tried to enter.

"Leave her alone!" cried the priest from the pulpit. "Let this Indian woman come in, she is my mother!"

The priest is Juan de Espinosa Medrano, known to all as Old Moley because God has covered his face with moles. When Old Moley preaches, crowds flock to the cathedral. The Peruvian church has no better orator. Furthermore, he teaches theology in the San Antonio seminary and writes plays. *Love Your Own Death*, his comedy in the Spanish language, the language of his father, resembles the pulpit from which he pronounces his sermons: pompous verses twisted into a thousand arabesques, ostentatious and extravagant like the colonial churches. At the same time, he has written in Quechua, his mother's language, a sacramental mystery play of simple structure and stripped phraseology, on the theme of the prodigal son. In this, the Devil is a Peruvian landlord, the wine is chicha, and the biblical calf is a fat pig.

(18)

1671: Panama City

On Punctuality in Appointments

More than two years have passed since Henry Morgan reached Panama in a canoe and at the head of a fistful of men stormed the ramparts of Portobello with a knife between his teeth. With a very small force and no culverins or cannon, he seized this impregnable bastion; and for not burning it down, he collected a mountain of gold and silver in ransom. The governor of Panama, defeated and disillusioned by this unheard-of feat, sent to ask Morgan for a pistol of the type he had used in the assault.

"Let him keep it for a year," said the pirate. "I'll be back to get it."

Now he enters the city of Panama, advancing among the flames, with the English flag streaming from one hand and a cutlass grasped in the other. Two thousand men and several cannons follow him. The fire turns night into day, another summer overtopping the eternal summer of these coasts; it devours houses and convents, churches and hospitals, and licks the lips of the buccaneer who yells: *"I'm here for money, not for prayers!"*

After much burning and killing, he moves off followed by an endless caravan of mules loaded with gold, silver, and precious stones.

Morgan sends his apologies to the governor for the delay.

(61 and 65)

1672: London

The White Man's Burden

The duke of York, brother of the king of England, founded the Company of Royal Adventurers nine years ago. English planters in the Antilles bought their slaves from Dutch slavers; but the Crown could not permit the purchase of such valuable articles from foreigners. The new enterprise, set up for trade with Africa, had prestigious shareholders: King Charles II, three dukes, eight earls, seven lords, a countess, and twenty-seven knights. In homage to the duke of York, the captains burned the letters DY with hot irons onto the breasts of the three thousand slaves they carried yearly to Barbados and Jamaica.

Now the enterprise is to be called the Royal Africa Company. The English king, who holds most of the stock, encourages slave-buying in his colonies, where slaves cost six times as much as in Africa.

Behind the ships, sharks make the trip to the islands, awaiting the bodies that go overboard. Many die because there is not enough water and the strongest drink what little there is, or because of dysentery or smallpox, and many die from melancholy: they refuse to eat, and there is no way to open their jaws.

They lie in rows, crushed against each other, their noses touching the deck above. Their wrists are handcuffed, and fetters wear their ankles raw. When portholes have to be closed in rough seas or rain, the small amount of air rises to fever heat, but with portholes open the hold stinks of hatred, fermented hatred, fouler than the foulest stench of slaughterhouse, and the floor is always slippery with blood, vomit, and shit.

The sailors, who sleep on deck, listen at night to the endless moans from below and at dawn to the yells of those who dreamed they were in their country.

(127, 160, and 224)

Mandingo People's Song of the Bird of Love

But let me, oh, Dyamberé!
You who wear the belt with the long fringes,
let me sing to the birds,
the birds that listen to the departing princess
and receive her last confidences.
And you, maidens, sing, sing
softly
"la, la"—the beautiful bird.
And you, Master-of-the-terrible-gun,
let me look at the bird of love,
the bird that my friend and I love.
Let me, master-of-the-splendid-tunic,
lord of raiment more brilliant
than the light of day.
Let me love the bird of love!

(134)

1674: Port Royal

Morgan

He was almost a child when they sold him, in Bristol, to a dealer. The captain who took him to the Antilles exchanged him for a few coins in Barbados.

In these islands he learned to break with one ax blow any branch that hit his face; and that there is no fortune that does not have crime for father and infamy for mother. He spent years robbing galleons and making widows. Fingers wearing gold rings, he simply chopped off. He became chief of the pirates. Correction, buccaneers. *Admiral of buccaneers.* From his toadlike neck always hangs his buccaneer's license, which legalizes his function and keeps him from the gallows.

Three years ago, after the sack of Panama, they took him to London as a prisoner. The king removed his chains, dubbed him knight of the court, and named him lieutenant governor of Jamaica.

The philosopher John Locke has drawn up the instructions for good government of this island, which is the headquarters of English buccaneers. Morgan will see to it that neither Bibles nor dogs to hunt fugitive slaves will ever be lacking and will hang his brother pirates every time his king decides to be on good terms with Spain.

Newly landed at Port Royal, Henry Morgan takes off his plumed hat, downs a shot of rum, and by way of a toast empties the bowl over his many-rolled wig. The buccaneers shout and sing, waving swords.

The horse that takes Morgan to the government palace is shod with gold.

(11 and 169)

1674: Potosí

Claudia the Witch

With her hand she moved clouds and brought on or held off storms. In the twinkling of an eye she brought people back from far-off lands and also from death. She enabled a magistrate of the Porco mines to see his native Madrid in a mirror; and she served at the table of Don Pedro de Ayamonte, who came from Utrera, cakes freshly baked in an Utrera oven. She caused gardens to bloom in deserts and turned the savviest lovers into virgins. She saved hunted people who sought refuge in her house by changing them into dogs or cats. For bad times, a bright face, she'd say, and hunger she'd beat off with a guitar: She played her guitar and shook her tambourine to revive the sick and the dead. If you were mute she could make you speak, if you talked too much she could stop you. She made open-air love with an extremely black devil right out in the countryside. After midnight, she flew.

She had been born in Tucumán, and this morning she died in Potosí. On her deathbed, she called a Jesuit priest and told him to take from a drawer certain lumps of wax and remove the pins that were stuck in them, so that five priests whom she had made sick could get well.

The priest offered her confession and divine mercy, but she laughed and died laughing.

(21)

1674: Yorktown

The Olympian Steeds

James Bullocke, a tailor of Yorktown, has challenged Matthew Slader to a horse race. The county court fines him for his presumptuousness and warns him that it is *contrary to Law for a Labourer to make a race being a Sport for Gentlemen.* Bullocke must pay two hundred pounds of tobacco in casks.

People on foot, gentry on horseback: the halo of aristocracy is the dust cloud that hooves raise along the road. Horses' hooves make and unmake fortunes. For races on Saturday afternoons, or for horsey talk in the evenings, the knights of tobacco emerge from the solitude of the plantation in silken clothes and curly wigs, and over mugs of cider or brandy discuss and make bets while dice roll on the table. They bet money or tobacco or black slaves, or white servants of the kind that pay their fare from England with years of work; but only on big nights of glory or ruin do they bet horses. A good horse is the measure of the worth of its owner, a tobaccocrat of Virginia who lives and commands on horseback and on horseback will die, flying like the wind to the heavenly gates.

In Virginia there is no time for anything else. Three years ago Governor William Berkeley could proudly remark: *I thank God, there are no free schools nor printing, and I hope we shall not have either for a hundred years; for learning has brought disobedience and heresy, and sects into the world, and printing has divulged them.*

(35)

1676: Valley of Connecticut

The Ax of Battle

With the first snows, the Wampanoag Indians rise. They are tired of seeing the New England frontier run south and west on speedy feet, and by the end of winter they have ravaged the Valley of Connecticut and are fighting less than twenty miles from Boston.

The horse drags its rider along the ground, his foot caught in a stirrup. An arrow has killed him. The victims of the plunder, swift warriors, strike and disappear; and so push the invaders toward the coast where they landed years ago.

(153 and 204)

1676: Plymouth

Metacom

Half of the Indian population has died in the war. Twelve English towns lie in ashes.

At the end of summer, the English bring to Plymouth the head of Metacom, the Wampanoag chief: Metacom, that is, Satan, who tried to seize from the Puritan colonists the lands that God had granted them.

The High Court of Plymouth discusses: *What do we do with Metacom's son? Hang him or sell him as a slave?* Taking into account Deuteronomy 24:16, the first Book of Kings 11:17, II Chronicles 25:4, and Psalms 137 to 139, the judges decide to sell Metacom's son, aged nine, in the Antillean slave markets.

As further proof of generosity, the victors offer the Indians a small piece of what used to be theirs: In the future the Indian communities of the region, whether or not they fought with Metacom, will be enclosed in four reserves in Massachusetts Bay.

(153 and 204)

1677: Old Road Town

Death Here, Rebirth There

The body, which knows little, doesn't know it, nor does the soul that breathes; but the soul that dreams, which knows the most, does: The black man who kills himself in America revives in Africa. Many slaves of this island of St. Kitts let themselves die by refusing food or eating only earth, ashes, and lime; and others tie a rope around the neck. In the woods, among the lianas that drape from the great weeping trees hang slaves who by killing themselves not only kill their memories of pain but also set forth in white canoes on the long voyage back to their ancestral homes.

A certain Bouriau, owner of plantations, strolls through the foliage, machete in hand, decapitating the hanged:

"Hang yourselves if you like!" he advises the live ones. "Over there in your countries you won't have a head! You won't be able to see or hear or talk or eat!"

Another planter, Major Crips, the harshest castigator of men, enters the wood with a cartful of sugar pans and sugarmill pieces. He seeks and finds his escaped slaves, who have gathered together and are tying knots and choosing branches, and says to them:

"Keep it up, keep it up. I'll hang myself with you. I'll accompany you. I've bought a big sugarmill in Africa, and there you'll work for me."

Major Crips selects a big tree, a huge ceiba, ties the rope around his neck, and threads the slipknot. The blacks watch him in a daze, but his face is just a shadow beneath the straw hat, a shadow that says: "Let's go, everybody! Quick! I need hands in Guinea!"

(101)

1677: Pôrto Calvo

The Captain Promises Lands, Slaves, and Honors

Early in the morning, the army moves off from Pôrto Calvo. The soldiers, volunteers, and draftees are marching against the free blacks of Palmares, who are going about the South of Pernambuco burning canefields.

Fernão Carrilho, senior captain of the Palmares war, addresses his troops after Mass: *"Great as is the host of our enemies, it is a host of slaves. Nature has created them more to obey than to resist. If we destroy them, we will have lands for our plantations, blacks for our service, and honor for our names. The blacks fight like fugitives. We will pursue them like lords!"*

(69)

1678: Recife

Ganga Zumba

Thanksgiving Mass in the mother church: the Governor of Pernambuco, Aires de Sousa de Castro, picks up the tails of his em-

broidered coat and kneels before the throne of the Most Holy.
Beside him, covered by an ample cape of red silk, kneels Ganga
Zumba, supreme chief of the Palmares federation.

Peal of bells, din of artillery and drums: The governor grants
to Ganga Zumba the title of sergeant at arms, and in proof of
friendship adopts two of his smallest children, who will take his
name. At the end of the peace talks held in Recife between delegates of the king of Portugal and representatives of Palmares, the
agreement is drawn up: The Palmares sanctuaries will be emptied.
All individuals born there are declared free, and those who have
the hot-iron brand will return to their owners.

"But I don't surrender," says Zumbí, Ganga Zumba's nephew.

Zumbí remains in Macacos, capital of Palmares, deaf to the
successive groups offering him pardon.

Of the thirty thousand Palmarinos, only five thousand accompany Ganga Zumba. For the others he is a traitor who deserves to
die and be forgotten.

"I don't believe in the word of my enemies," says Zumbí. "My
enemies don't believe it themselves."

(43 and 69)

Yoruba Spell Against the Enemy

When they try to catch a chameleon
under a mat,
the chameleon takes the color of the mat
and they can't tell which is which.
When they try to catch a crocodile
on the bottom of the river,
the crocodile takes the color of the water
and they can't distinguish him from the current.
When the Wizard tries to catch me
may I take on the agility of the wind
and escape with a puff!

(134)

1680: Santa Fe, New Mexico

Red Cross and White Cross

The knots in a rope of maguey announce the rebellion and indicate how many days to wait for it. The speediest messengers take it from village to village throughout New Mexico, until the Sunday of Wrath dawns.

The Indians of twenty-four communities rise. They are those that remain of the sixty-six that existed in these northern lands when the conquistadors arrived. The Spaniards succeed in suppressing the rebels in one or two villages.

"Surrender."

"I prefer death."

"You'll go to hell."

"I prefer hell."

But the avengers of pain advance destroying churches and forts, and after a few days are masters of the whole region. To wipe off the baptismal oils and get rid of the Christian names, the Indians plunge in the river and rub themselves with cleansing amole plants. Dressed up as monks, they drink to the recovery of their lands and their gods. They announce that they will never again work for others, that pumpkins will sprout all over the place, and that the world will be snowed under with cotton.

A noose is drawn around the city of Santa Fe, Spain's last redoubt in these remote regions. The chief of the Indians gallops up to the walls. He is armed with arquebus, dagger, and sword and wears a taffeta strip he found in a convent. He throws down at the foot of the wall two crosses, a white and a red one.

"The red cross is resistance. The white, surrender. Pick up whichever you choose!"

Then he turns his back on the besieged enemy and disappears in a puff of dust.

The Spaniards resist. But after a few days they raise the white cross. A while back they had come seeking the legendary golden cities of Cíbola. Now they begin the retreat southward.

(88)

1681: Mexico City

Juana at Thirty

After matins and lauds, she sets a top to spinning in the flour and studies the circles it draws. She investigates water and light, air and things. Why does an egg come together in boiling oil and separate in syrup? Forming triangles of pins, she seeks Solomon's ring. With one eye clamped to a telescope, she hunts stars.

They have threatened her with the Inquisition and forbidden her to open books, but Sor Juana Inés de la Cruz studies *the things that God created, which serve me as letters as this universal machine serves me as book.*

Between divine love and human love, between the fifteen mysteries of the rosary that hangs about her neck and the enigmas of the world, Sor Juana has set up a debate; and she passes many nights without sleep, praying, writing, when the endless war starts up again inside her between passion and reason. At the end of each battle, the first light of dawn enters her cell in the Jeronimite convent and helps Sor Juana remember what Lupercio Leonardo said, that one can both philosophize and cook supper. She creates poems on the table and puff pastry in the kitchen; letters and delicacies to give away, David's-harp music soothing to Saul as well as to David, joys of soul and mouth condemned by the advocates of pain.

"Only suffering will make you worthy of God," says the confessor, and orders her to burn what she writes, ignore what she knows, and not see what she looks at.

(49, 58, and 190)

1681: Mexico City

Sigüenza y Góngora

Since the end of last year, a comet has lit up the sky of Mexico. What evils does the angry prophet announce? What troubles will it bring? Will the sun like the great fist of God crash into the earth? Will the oceans dry up and no drop of water remain in the rivers?

"There is no reason why comets should be unlucky," says the wise man to the terrified people.

Carlos de Sigüenza y Góngora publishes his *Philosophical Manifesto Against the Stray Comets That the Empire Holds Over the Heads of the Timid*, a formidable indictment of superstition and fear. A polemic breaks out between astronomy and astrology, between human curiosity and divine revelation. The German Jesuit Eusebio Francisco Kino, who is visiting these regions, cites six biblical foundations for his affirmation that nearly all comets *are precursors of sinister, sad, and calamitous events*.

Kino disdainfully seeks to amend the theory of Sigüenza y Góngora, son of Copernicus, Galileo, and other heretics; and the learned Creole replies: *"Would you at least concede that there are also mathematicians outside of Germany, stuck though they may be among the reeds and bulrushes of a Mexican lake?"*

The Academy's leading cosmographer, Sigüenza y Góngora has intuited the law of gravity and believes that other stars must have, like the sun, planets flying around them. Calculating from eclipses and comets, he has fixed the dates of Mexico's indigenous history; and earth as well as sky being his business, he has also exactly fixed the longitude of this city (283° 23' west of Santa Cruz de Tenerife), drawn the first complete map of the region, and told it all in verse and prose works with the extravagant titles typical of his time.

(83)

1682: Accra

All Europe Is Selling Human Flesh

Not far from the English and Danish forts, a pistol shot away, rises the Prussian trading post. A new flag flies on these coasts, over the tree-trunk roofs of the slave depots and on the masts of ships that sail with full cargoes.

With their Africa Company the Germans have joined in the juiciest business of the period. The Portuguese hunt and sell blacks through their Company of Guinea. The Royal Africa Company operates for the English Crown. The French flag waves from ships of the Company of Senegal. Holland's Company of the West Indies is doing nicely. Denmark's enterprise specializing in the slave traffic is also called Company of the West Indies; and the Company of the South Sea lines the pockets of the Swedes.

Spain has no slave business. But a century ago, in Seville, the Chamber of Commerce sent the king a documented report explaining that slaves were the most lucrative of all merchandise going to America; and so they continue to be. For the right to sell slaves in the Spanish colonies, foreign concerns pay fortunes into the royal coffers. With these funds have been built, among other things, the Alcázars of Madrid and Toledo. The Negro Committee meets in the main hall of the Council of the Indies.

(127, 129, 160, and 224)

1682: Remedios

By Order of Satan

He trembles, twists, howls, dribbles. He makes the stones of the church vibrate. All around steams the red earth of Cuba.

"Satan, dog! Drunken dog! Talk or I'll piss on you!" threatens inquisitor José González de la Cruz, parish priest of Remedios, as he knocks down and kicks the black woman Leonarda before the main altar. Bartolomé del Castillo, notary public, waits without breathing. He clutches a thick bundle of papers in one hand, and with the other he waves a bird's quill in the air.

The Devil romps contentedly in the charming body of black Leonarda.

The inquisitor swings the slave around with a blow and she falls on her face, eats the dust, and bounces. She raises herself up, and turns, blazing and bleeding, handsome, on the checkerboard tiles.

"Satan! Lucifer! Nigger! Start talking, stinking shit!"

From Leonarda's mouth come flames and froth. Also noises that no one understands except Father José, who translates and dictates to the notary:

"She says she is Lucifer! She says there are eight hundred thousand devils in Remedios!"

More noises come from the black woman.

"What else? What else, dog?" demands the priest and lifts Leonarda by the hair.

"Talk, you shit!" He does not insult her mother because the Devil has none.

Before the slave faints, the priest shouts and the notary writes; "She says Remedios will collapse! She is confessing everything! I have him by the neck! She says the earth will swallow us up!"

And he howls: "A mouth of hell! She says Remedios is a mouth of hell!"

Everyone cries out. All the residents of Remedios jump about, screaming and shouting. More than one falls in a faint.

The priest, bathed in sweat, his skin transparent, and his lips trembling, loosens his grip on Leonarda's neck. The black woman collapses.

No one fans her.

(161)

1682: Remedios
But They Stay On

Eight hundred thousand devils. So there are more devils in the air of Remedios than mosquitos: 1,305 devils tormenting each inhabitant.

The devils are lame, ever since the Fall that all the world knows about. They have goats' beards and horns, bats' wings, rats' tails, and black skin. Circulating in Leonarda's body is more enjoyable to them because they are black.

Leonarda weeps and refuses to eat.

"If God wants to cleanse you," Father José tells her, "He will whiten your skin."

The plaintive song of cicadas and grasshoppers is that of souls in torment. Crabs are sinners condemned to walk crookedly. In the swamps and rivers live child-robbing goblins. When it rains, the scuffling of devils is heard from caves and crannies, furious because the flashes and sparks they have set off to burn down the skies are getting wet. And the harsh, nasal croak of frogs in the Boquerón fissure: is it foretelling rain, or is it cursing? Does the light that shines in the darkness come from the firefly? Those eyes, are they really the owl's? Against whom does the snake hiss?

The buzz of the blind nocturnal bat: if it brushes you with its wing, you will go straight to hell, which is down there beneath Remedios; there the flames burn but give no light, and eternal ice chatters the teeth of those who on earth sinned with randy heat.

"Stay back!"

At the smallest alarm, the priest makes one jump into the font of holy water.

"Satan, stay back!"

With holy water lettuces are washed. People yawn with their mouths shut.

"Jesus! Jesus!" the parishioners cross themselves.

There is no house unadorned by strings of garlic, no air that the smoke of sweet basil does not impregnate.

"They have feet but do not reach me, iron but do not wound me, nooses and do not bind me . . ."

But people stay on. No one leaves. No one abandons the town of Remedios.

(161)

1682: Remedios

By Order of God

The church bells, outlined against the sky, ring for service. All of Remedios turns out. The notary sits in his place to the right of the altar. The crowd presses in through the open doors.

There is a rumor that Father José is to hear testimony from God. It is hoped that Christ will unpin his right hand from the cross and swear to tell the truth, the whole truth, and nothing but the truth.

Father José advances to the main altar and opens the tabernacle. He raises the chalice and the host; and before the body and blood of the Lord, on his knees, formulates his request. The notary takes notes. God will show Remedios's inhabitants where they have to live.

If the Devil spoke through the mouth of Leonarda, Leonardo will be the vehicle for his invincible enemy.

With a bandage, the priest covers the eyes of Leonardo, a boy who does not reach to his waist, and Leonardo dips his hand in the silver pyx in which lie some bits of paper with names of places.

The boy picks one. The priest unfolds it and reads in a very loud voice: "Santa Maria de Guadalupe! Take note, notary!" And he adds triumphantly: "The Lord has had pity on us! He, in His infinite mercy, offers us protection! Up, people of Remedios! The time has come to go!"

And he goes.

He looks behind him. Few are following.

Father José takes everything along: chalice and host, lamp and silver candlesticks, images and wood carvings. But the barest handful of devout women and scared men accompany him to the promised land.

Slaves and horses drag their effects along. They take furniture and clothes, rice and beans, salt, oil, sugar, dried meat, tobacco, and also books from Paris, cottons from Rouen, and laces from Malines, all smuggled into Cuba.

The trek to Santa Maria de Guadalupe is long. Located there are the Hato del Cupey lands that belong to Father José. For years the priest has been seeking buyers for them.

(161)

1688: Havana

By Order of the King

All over Cuba it is the sole topic of conversation. Wherever people gather to gossip, bets are laid.

Will the people of Remedios obey?

Father José, abandoned by his faithful, remains alone and has to return to Remedios. But he continues his war, a stubborn holy war that has found echoes even in the royal palace. From Madrid, Charles II has ordered that the population of Remedios should move to the Hato del Cupey lands in Santa Maria de Guadalupe.

The government's captain general and the bishop of Havana announce that once and for all the king's will must be respected.

Patience is giving out.

The people of Remedios continue playing deaf.

(161)

1691: Remedios

Still They Don't Move

At dawn Captain Pérez de Morales arrives from Havana with forty well-armed men.

They stop at the church. One by one, the soldiers receive communion. Father José blesses their muskets and battle-axes.

They get the torches ready.

At noon, the town of Remedios is a big bonfire. From afar, on the road to his Hato del Cupey lands, Father José watches bluish smoke rise from the flaming rubble.

At nightfall, close to the ruins, the people emerge from hiding in the thickets.

Sitting in a circle, eyes fixed on the continuing clouds of smoke, they curse and remember. Many a time pirates have sacked this town. Some years back they carried off even the chalice of the Most Holy Sacrament, and a bishop was said to have died of disgust—a good thing, they said, that the scapulary hung on his breast at the time. But no pirate ever set fire to Remedios.

By the light of the moon, beneath a ceiba tree, the people hold a town council. They, who belong to this red-soiled clearing in the forest, resolve that Remedios shall be rebuilt.

The women clutch their young to their breasts and stare with the eyes of mother tigers ready to spring.

The air smells of burning but not of sulphur nor of Devil's dung.

The sounds rising among the trees are voices in discussion and a newly born babe wailing for some milk and a name.

(161)

1691: Mexico City
Juana at Forty

A stream of white light, limelight, sprays Sor Juana Inés de la Cruz, kneeling at center stage. Her back is turned, and she is looking upward. There bleeds an enormous Christ, arms open, on the lofty ramp lined with black velvet and bristling with crosses, swords, and flags. From the platform two prosecutors make their accusations.

Everything is black, and black the hoods that conceal the prosecutors' faces. However, one wears a nun's habit, and beneath the hood peep out the reddish rolls of a wig: it is the bishop of Puebla, Manuel Fernández de Santa Cruz, in the role of Sister Filotea. The other, Antonio Núñez de Miranda, Sister Juana's confessor, represents himself. His aquiline nose bulges from beneath the hood, moves as if it wanted to get free of its owner.

SISTER FILOTEA (*embroidering on a frame*): Mysterious is the Lord. Why, I ask myself, would He have put a man's head on the body of Sister Juana? So that she should concern herself with the wretched affairs of the earth? She does not deign to approach the Holy Scriptures.

THE CONFESSOR (*pointing at Sister Juana with a wooden cross*): Ingrate!

SISTER JUANA (*her eyes fixed on the Christ over the prosecutors' heads*): Indeed I repay badly the generosity of God. I only study to see whether studying will make me less ignorant, and I direct my footsteps toward the summits of Holy Theology; but I have studied many things and learned nothing, or almost nothing. The divine truths remain far from me, always far . . . I sometimes feel them to be so close yet know them to be so far away! Since I was a small child . . . at five or six I sought those keys in my grandfather's books, those keys . . . I read and read. They punished me and I read secretly, searching . . .

THE CONFESSOR (*to Sister Filotea*): She never accepted the will of God. Now she even writes like a man. I have seen the manuscripts of her poems!

SISTER JUANA: Searching . . . I knew quite early on that universities are not for women and that a woman who knows more than the Paternoster is deemed immodest. I had mute books for teachers and an inkpot for a schoolmate. When books were forbidden to me, as happened more than once in this convent, I studied the things of the world. Even cooking one can discover secrets of nature.

SISTER FILOTEA: The Royal and Pontifical University of the Pancake! The frying-pan campus!

SISTER JUANA: What can we women know except the philosophy of the kitchen? But if Aristotle had cooked, he would have written much more. That makes you laugh, does it? Well, laugh, if it pleases you. Men feel themselves to be very wise, just for being men. Christ, too, was crowned with thorns as King of Jests.

THE CONFESSOR (*erases his smile, hits the table with his fist*): Ever hear the like of that? The learned little nun! She can write little songs, so she compares herself with the Messiah!

SISTER JUANA: Christ also suffered from this unfairness. Is he one of *them*? So he must die! He is accused? So let him suffer!

THE CONFESSOR: There's humility for you!

SISTER FILOTEA: Really, my daughter, you scandalize God with your vociferous pride . . .

SISTER JUANA: My pride? (*Smiles sadly*) I used that up long ago.

THE CONFESSOR: The common people applaud her verses, so she thinks herself one of the elect. Verses that shame this house of God, exaltation of the flesh . . . (*coughs*) Evil arts of the male animal . . .

SISTER JUANA: My poor verses! Dust, shadow, nothing. Vain glory, all the applause . . . Did I ask for it? What divine revelation forbids women to write? By grace or curse, it was Heaven that made me a poet.

THE CONFESSOR (*looks at the ceiling and raises his hands in supplication*): She dirties the purity of the faith, and Heaven is to blame for it.

SISTER FILOTEA (*puts embroidery frame aside and clasps hands over stomach*): Sister Juana has much to sing to the human spirit, little to the divine.

SISTER JUANA: Don't the Gospels teach us that the celestial expresses itself in the terrestrial? A powerful force pushes my hand . . .

THE CONFESSOR (*waving the wooden cross, as if to strike Juana from afar*): Force of God, or force of the king of the proud?

SISTER JUANA: . . . and I'll continue writing, I'm afraid, as long as my body makes a shadow. I fled from myself when I took the habit, but I brought myself along, wretch that I am.

SISTER FILOTEA: She bathes in the nude. There are proofs.

SISTER JUANA: Oh, Lord, put out the light of my understanding! Leave only what suffices to keep Thy Law! Isn't the rest superfluous for a woman?

THE CONFESSOR (*screaming harshly like a crow*): Shame on you! Mortify your heart, ingrate!

SISTER JUANA: Put me out. Put me out, my God!

(*The play continues, with similar dialog, until 1693*).

(58 and 75)

1691: Placentia

Adario, Chief of the Huron Indians, Speaks to Baron de Lahontan, French Colonizer of Newfoundland

Nay, you are miserable enough already, and indeed I can't see how you can be more such. What sort of men must Europeans be? What species of creatures do they retain to? The Europeans, who must be forc'd to do good, and have no other prompter for the avoiding of Evil than the fear of punishment . . .

Who gave you all the countries that you now inhabit? By what right do you possess them? They always belonged to the Algonquins before. In earnest, my dear brother, I'm sorry for thee from the bottom of my soul. Take my advice, and turn Huron; for I see plainly a vast difference between thy condition and mine. I am master of myself and my condition. I am master of my own body, I have the absolute disposal of myself, I do what I please, I am the first and the last of my nation, I fear no man, and I depend only upon the Great Spirit. Whereas, thy body, as well as thy soul, are doomed to a dependence upon thy great Captain, thy Vice-Roy disposes of thee, thou hast not the liberty of doing what thou hast a mind to; thou art afraid of robbers, false witnesses, assassins, etc., and thou dependest upon an infinity of persons whose places have raised them above thee. Is it true or not?

(136)

1692: Salem Village

The Witches of Salem

"Christ knows how many devils there are here!" roars the Reverend Samuel Parris, pastor of the town of Salem, and speaks of Judas, the devil seated at the Lord's table, who sold himself for thirty coins, £3/15/0 in English pounds, the derisory price of a female slave.

In the war of the lambs against the dragons, cries the pastor, no neutrality is possible nor any sure refuge. The devils have planted themselves in his own house: a daughter and a niece of the Reverend Parris have been the first ones tormented by the army of devils that has taken this Puritan town by storm. The little girls fondled a crystal ball, wanting to know their fate, and saw death. Since that happened, many young girls of Salem feel hell in their bodies, the malignant fever burns them inside and they twist and turn, roll on the ground frothing at the mouth and screaming blasphemies and obscenities that the Devil puts on their lips.

The doctor, William Griggs, diagnoses evil spells. A dog is given a cake of rye flour mixed with the urine of the possessed girls, but the dog gobbles it up, wags his tail, and goes off to sleep in peace. The Devil prefers human habitations.

Between one convulsion and the next, the victims accuse.

Women, and poor ones, are the first sentenced to hang. Two whites, one black: Sarah Osborne, a bent old woman who years ago cried out to her Irish servant, who slept in the stable, and made her a place in her bed; Sarah Good, a disorderly beggar who smokes a pipe and grumbles when given alms; and Tituba, a black West Indian slave, mistress of a hairy devil with a long nose. The daughter of Sarah Good, a young witch aged four, is in Boston prison with fetters on her feet.

But the agonized screams of Salem's young girls do not cease, and charges and condemnations multiply. The witch-hunt spreads from suburban Salem Village to the center of Salem Town, from the town to the port, from the accursed to the powerful. Not even the governor's wife escapes the accusing finger. From the gallows hang prosperous farmers and businessmen, shipowners trading with London, privileged members of the Church who enjoy the right to Communion.

A sulphurous rain is reported over Salem Town, Massachusetts' second port, where the Devil, working harder than ever, goes about promising the Puritans cities of gold and French footwear.

(34)

1692: Guápulo

Nationalization of Colonial Art

In the sanctuary of Guápulo, a village overlooking Quito, Miguel de Santiago begins to show his canvases.

In homage to the local Virgin, who is a great miracle worker, Miguel de Santiago offers these mountains and plains, this cordillera and this sky, landscapes that would have little life if the people who move in them did not light them up: local people moving through local settings in procession or alone. The artist no longer copies works from Madrid or Rome about the life of St. Augustine. Now he paints the luminous city of Quito surrounded by volcanos, the towers of these churches, the Indians of Pujilí and Machángara Canyon, Bellavista Hill and the Valley of Guápulo; and the suns behind the mountains, the rising bonfire-smoke clouds, and the misty rivers that never stop singing all belong here.

Nor is it only Miguel de Santiago. The anonymous hands of indigenous or mestizo artisans sneak contraband llamas into their Christmas paintings instead of camels, and pineapples and palms and corncobs and avocados into church-façade greenery carvings; and even head-banded suns up close to the altars. On all sides there are pregnant Virgins, and Christs that grieve like men, like men of these parts, for the sadness of this world.

(215)

1693: Mexico City

Juana at Forty-Two

Lifelong tears, springing from time and pain, soak her face. She sees the world as profoundly and sadly clouded. Defeated, she bids it farewell.

For days she has been confessing the sins of her whole existence to the implacable Father Antonio Núñez de Miranda, and the rest is all penitence. With her own blood as ink she writes a letter to the Divine Tribunal, asking forgiveness.

Her *light sails and heavy keels* will no longer sail the seas of poetry. Sister Juana Inés de la Cruz abandons her human studies and renounces literature. She asks God for the gift of forgetfulness and chooses silence, or accepts it, and so America loses its best poet.

Her body will not survive long this suicide of the soul. *Let life be ashamed of lasting so long for me* . . .

(16, 49, and 58)

1693: Santa Fe, New Mexico

Thirteen Years of Independence

Thirteen years have passed since the bells of Santa Fe went mad celebrating the death of the God of the Christians and of Mary, his mother.

Thirteen years the Spaniards have taken to reconquer these wild lands of the North. While that truce of independence lasted, the Indians recovered their liberty and their names, their religion and their customs, but they also introduced into their communities the plow and the wheel and other instruments that the Spaniards brought.

For the colonial troops, the reconquest has not been easy. Each pueblo of New Mexico is a huge, tightly shut fortress, with board walls of stone and adobe several stories high. In the Rio Grande Valley live men not accustomed to obedience or servile labor.

(88)

Song of the New Mexican Indians to the Portrait That Escapes from the Sand

So I might cure myself,
the wizard painted,
in the desert, your portrait:
your eyes are of golden sand,
of red sand now your mouth,

of blue sand your hair
and my tears are of white sand.
All day he painted.
You grew like a goddess
on the immensity of the yellow canvas.
The wind of the night will scatter your shadow
and the colors of your shadow.
By ancient law nothing will remain for me.
Nothing, except the rest of my tears,
the silver sands.

(63)

1694: Macacos
The Last Expedition
Against Palmares

The great Indian-hunter, killer of Indians over many leagues, was born of an Indian mother. He speaks Guaraní, very little Portuguese. Domingos Jorge Velho is captain of the *mamelukes* of São Paulo, mestizos who have sown terror over half of Brazil in the name of their colonial lords and in ferocious exorcism of one half of their blood.

In the past six years, Captain Domingos has hired out his services to the Portuguese Crown against the Janduim Indians, rebelling in the hinterlands of Pernambuco and in Rio Grande do Norte. After a long campaign of carnage he arrives victorious at Recife, and there is contracted to demolish Palmares. They offer him fat booty in lands and blacks to sell in Rio de Janeiro and Buenos Aires and also promise him infinite amnesties, four religious orders' habits, and thirty military grades to distribute among his men.

With telescope slung over his naked chest, his greasy jacket open, Captain Domingos parades on horseback through the streets of Recife at the head of his mestizo officers and his rank-and-file Indian cutters of Indian throats. They ride amid clouds of dust and whiffs of gunpowder and rum, to applause and the fluttering of white handkerchiefs: this Messiah will save us from the rebellious blacks, the people believe or hope, convinced that the runaways are to blame for the lack of hands in the sugarmills as well as for the diseases and droughts that are devastating the Northeast, since God will not send health or rain while the Palmares scandal endures.

And the great crusade is organized. From all directions come volunteers, impelled by hunger, seeking sure rations. The prisons empty out, as even the jailbirds join the biggest army yet mobilized in Brazil.

The Indian scouts march ahead and the black porters bring up the rear. Nine thousand men cross the jungle, reach the mountains, and climb toward the summit, where the Macacos fortifications stand. This time they bring cannons.

The siege lasts several days. The cannons wreck the triple bulwark of wood and stone. They fight man to man on the edge of the abyss. There are so many dead that there is no place left to fall down, and the slaughter continues in the scrub. Many blacks try to flee, and slip down the precipice into the void; many choose the precipice and throw themselves off it.

Flames devour the capital of Palmares. From the distant city of Pôrto Calvo, the huge bonfire can be seen burning throughout the night. *Burn even the memory of it*. Hunting horns unceasingly proclaim the victory.

Chief Zumbí, wounded, has managed to escape. From the lofty peaks he reaches the jungle. He wanders through green tunnels, seeking his people in the thickets.

(38, 43, and 69)

Lament of the Azande People

The child is dead;
let us cover our faces
with white earth.
Four sons I have borne
in the hut of my husband.
Only the fourth lives.

I want to weep,
but in this village
sadness is forbidden.

(134)

1695: Serra Dois Irmãos

Zumbí

Jungle landscape, jungle of the soul. Zumbí smokes his pipe, his eyes locked on the high red rocks and caves open like wounds, and does not see that day is breaking with an enemy light, nor that the birds are flocking off in terrified flight.

He does not see the traitor approaching. He sees his comrade Antonio Soares and rises to embrace him. Antonio Soares buries a dagger several times in his back.

The soldiers fix the head on a lance point and take it to Recife, to putrefy in the plaza and teach the slaves that Zumbí was not immortal.

Palmares no longer breathes. This broad space of liberty opened up in colonial America has lasted for a century and resisted more than forty invasions. The wind has blown away the ashes of the black bastions of Macacos and Subupira, Dambrabanga and Obenga, Tabocas and Arotirene. For the conquerors, the Palmares century whittles down to the instant when the dagger polished off Zumbí. Night will fall and nothing will remain beneath the cold stars. Yet what does the wakeful know compared with what the dreamer knows?

The vanquished dream about Zumbí; and the dream knows that while one man remains owner of another man in these lands, his ghost will walk. He will walk with a limp, because Zumbí had been lamed by a bullet; he will walk up and down time and, limping, will fight in these jungles of palms and in all the lands of Brazil. The chiefs of all the unceasing black rebellions will be called Zumbí.

(69)

1695: São Salvador de Bahia

The Capital of Brazil

In this radiant city, there is a church for every day of the year,
and every day a saint's day. A glow of towers and bells and tall
palms, of bodies and of air sticky with *dendê* oil: today a saint is
celebrated, tomorrow a lover, in the Bahia of All Saints and of the
not-so-saintly. São Salvador de Bahia, seat of the viceroy and the
archbishop, is the most populated of all Portuguese cities after
Lisbon, and it envies Lisbon its monumental monasteries and golden
churches, its incendiary women and its fiestas and masquerades
and processions. Here strut mulatto prostitutes decked out like
queens, and slaves parade their masters on litters down leafy avenues amid palaces of delirious grandeur. Gregorio de Matos, born
in Bahia, thus portrays the noble gentry of the sugar plantations:

> In Brazil the gentlefolk
> are not all that gentle;
> their good manners, not all that good:
> So where do they belong?
> In a pile of money.

Black slaves are the brick and mortar of these castles. From
the cathedral pulpit Father Antonio Vieira insists on gratitude toward Angola, because without Angola there would be no Brazil,
and without Brazil there would be no Portugal, *so that it could be
very justly said that Brazil has its body in America and its soul in
Africa*: Angola, which sells Bantu slaves and elephants tusks; Angola, as the father's sermon proclaims, *with whose unhappy blood
and black but happy souls Brazil is nourished, animated, sustained,
served, and preserved.*

At almost ninety this Jesuit priest remains the worst enemy
of the Inquisition, advocate of enslaved Indians and Jews, and most
persistent accuser of the colonial lords, who believe that work is
for animals and spit on the hand that feeds them.

(33 and 226)

1696: Regla

Black Virgin, Black Goddess

To the docks of Regla, poor relation of Havana, comes the Virgin, and she comes to stay. The cedar carving has come from Madrid, wrapped in a sack, in the arms of her devotee Pedro Aranda. Today, September 8, is fiesta day in this little town of artisans and sailors, always redolent of shellfish and tar; the people eat meat and corn and beans and manioc, Cuban dishes, and African dishes, ecó, olelé, ecrú, quimbombó, fufú, while rivers of rum and earthquakes of drums welcome the black Virgin, *the little black one*, patron protector of Havana Bay.

The sea is littered with coconut husks and boughs of sweet basil, and a breeze of voices sings as night falls:

Opa ule, opa ule,
opa é, opa é,
opa opa, Yemayá.

The black Virgin of Regla is also the African Yemayá, silvered goddess of the seas, mother of the fish and mother and lover of Shangó, the womanizing and quarrel-picking warrior god.

(68 and 82)

1697: Cap Français

Ducasse

Gold escudos in hard cash, doubloons, double doubloons, big-shot gold and little-shot gold, gold jewelry and dishes, gold from chalices and crowns of virgins and saints: Filled with gold are the arriving galleons of Jean-Baptiste Ducasse, governor of Haiti and chief of the French freebooters in the Antilles. Ducasse has humbled Cartagena with his gun salvos; he has reduced to dust the cliff ramparts of the fortress, colossal lions of rock that rear up from the sea, and has left the church without a bell and the governor without rings.

To France goes the gold of the sacked Spanish colony. From

Versailles, Ducasse receives the title of admiral and a bushy wig of snow-white rolls worthy of the king.

Before becoming governor of Haiti and admiral of the royal fleet, Ducasse operated on his own, stealing blacks from Dutch slave ships and treasure from galleons of the Spanish fleet. Since 1691, he has been working for Louis XIV.

(11 and 61)

1699: Madrid
Bewitched

Although the herald has not blown his trumpet to announce it, the news flies through the streets of Madrid. The inquisitors have discovered who bewitched King Charles. The witch Isabel will be burned at the stake in the main plaza.

All Spain has been praying for Charles II. On waking, the monarch has been taking his posset of powdered snake, infallible for giving strength, but in vain: The penis has continued in a state of stupefaction, unable to make children, and from the royal mouth froth and foul breath have continued to emerge, and not one word worth hearing.

The curse did not come from a certain cup of chocolate with gallows bird's testicles, as some witches of Cangas had claimed; nor from the talisman that the king wore round his neck, as the exorcist Fray Mauro believed. Someone suggested that the king had been bewitched by his mother with tobacco from America or benzoin pills; and it was even rumored that the palace *maître d'hôtel*, the duke of Castellflorit, had served the royal table a ham larded with the fingernails of a Moorish or Jewish woman burned by the Inquisition.

The inquisitors have at last found the mess of pins, hairpins, cherrystones, and His Majesty's blond hairs that the witch Isabel had hidden near the royal bedroom.

The nose hangs down, the lip hangs down, the chin hangs down; but now that the king has been debewitched, his eyes seem to have lit up somewhat. A dwarf raises the candle to look at the portrait Carreño did of him years ago.

Meanwhile, outside the palace there is no bread or meat, fish or wine, as if Madrid were a besieged city.

(64 and 201)

1699: Macouba

A Practical Demonstration

To put some gusto into his slaves' work in this land of sluggishness and drowsiness, Father Jean-Baptiste Labat tells them he was black before coming to Martinique and that God whitened him as a reward for the fervor and submission with which he served his masters in France.

The black carpenter of the church is trying to make a difficult dovetailing of a beam and cannot get the angle right. Father Labat draws some lines with a ruler and compass, and he orders: "Cut it here."

The angle is right.

"Now I believe you," says the slave, looking him in the eyes. "No white man could do that."

(101)

1700: Ouro Prêto

All Brazil to the South

In the old days, the map showed Bahia close to the newly discovered mines of Potosí, and the governor general reported to Lisbon that *this land of Brazil and Peru are all one*. To turn the Paranapiacaba Mountains into the Andes cordillera, the Portuguese brought two hundred llamas to São Paulo and sat down to wait for the silver and gold to appear.

A century and a half later, the gold has turned up. The riverbeds and streams on the slopes of the Espinhaço Mountains are full of shiny stones. The São Paulo *mamelukes* found the gold when they were out hunting Cataguaz Indians.

The wind spread the news all through Brazil, and a multitude responded. To get gold in the Minas Gerais region, all you had to do was gather a handful of sand or pull up a tuft of grass and shake it.

With gold has come hunger. The price of a cat or a dog in the camps is 115 grams of gold, which is what a slave gets for two days' work.

(33 and 38)

1700: St. Thomas Island

The Man Who Makes Things Talk

Lugubrious bells and melancholy drums are sounding in this Danish island of the Antilles, a center for contraband and piracy. A slave walks up to the execution stake. Vanbel, the big boss, has condemned him because this black fellow turns on rain when he feels like it, kneeling before three oranges, and because he has a clay idol that answers all his questions and clears him of all doubts.

Smiling from ear to ear and with his eyes fixed on the stake surrounded by firewood, the condemned man approaches.

Vanbel intercepts him: "So you won't be chatting with your doll anymore, you black sorcerer!"

Without looking at him, the slave answers softly: "I can make that cane of yours talk."

"Stop!" Vanbel cries to the guards. "Unbind him!"

And before the waiting crowd he throws him his cane.

"Do it," he says.

The slave kneels. With his hands, he fans the cane stuck in the ground, makes a few turns around it, kneels again, and strokes it.

"I want to know," says the master, "whether the galleon that's due here has sailed yet. When it will arrive, who is aboard, what has happened . . ."

The slave takes a few steps backward.

"Come closer, sir," he suggests. "It will tell you."

His ear close to the cane, Vanbel hears that the ship sailed some time ago from Helsingør, in Denmark, but that on reaching the tropics a storm broke its small topsail and carried off the mizzensail. Vanbel's neck quivers like a frog's belly. The onlookers see him turn white.

"I don't hear anything," says Vanbel as the cane proceeds to tell him the names of the captain and the sailors.

"Nothing!" he screams.

The cane whispers to him: *The ship will arrive in three days.*

Its cargo will make you happy, and Vanbel explodes, tears off his wig, shouts: "Burn that Negro!"
He roars: "Burn him!"
He howls: "Burn that sorcerer!"

(101)

Bantu People's Song of the Fire

Fire that men watch in the night,
in the deep night.
Fire that blazest without burning, that shinest
without blazing.
Fire that fliest without a body.
Fire without heart, that knowest not
home nor hast a hut.
Transparent fire of palm leaves:
a man invokes thee without fear.
Fire of the sorcerers, thy father, where is he?
Thy mother, where is she?
Who has fed thee?
Thou art thy father, thou art thy mother,
Thou passest and leavest no trace.
Dry wood does not engender thee,
thou hast not cinders for daughters.
Thou diest and diest not.
The errant soul turns into thee, and no one
knows it.
Fire of the sorcerers, Spirit
of the waters below and the air above.
Fire that shinest, glowworm that lightest up
the swamp.
Bird without wings, thing without body, Spirit
of the Force of Fire.
Hear my voice:
a man invokes thee
without fear.

(134)

1700: Madrid

Penumbra of Autumn

He could never dress himself alone, or read fluently, or stand up by himself. At forty, a little old man without descendants, he lies dying surrounded by confessors, exorcists, courtiers, and ambassadors who dispute the throne.

The doctors, defeated, have removed the newly dead doves and the sheep's entrails from on top of him. Leeches no longer cover his body. They are not giving him rum to drink or the water of life brought from Malaga, because nothing is left but to wait for the convulsion that will tear him from the world. By the light of torches a bleeding Christ at the head of the bed presides over the final ceremony. The cardinal sprinkles holy water from the hyssop. The bedchamber smells of wax, of incense, of filth. The wind beats at the shutters of the palace, badly fastened with cord.

They will take him to the Escorial morgue, where the marble coffin with his name on it has awaited him for years. That was his favorite journey, but it is some time since he visited his own tomb or even stuck his nose outside. Madrid is full of potholes and garbage and armed vagabonds; and the soldiers, who keep alive on the thin soup of the monasteries, do not put themselves out to defend the king. The last times that he dared to go out, the Manzanares washerwomen and the street urchins ran after the carriage and hurled insults and stones at it.

Charles II, his bulging eyes red, trembles and raves. He is a small piece of yellow flesh that runs out beneath the sheets as the century also runs out, and so ends the dynasty that conquered America.

(201 and 211)

(End of the first volume of
Memory of Fire)

The Sources

1. Abbad y Lasierra, Augustín Iñigo. *Historia geográfica civil y natural de la isla de San Juan Bautista de Puerto Rico*. Río Piedras: Universidad, 1979.
2. Acosta Saignes, Miguel. *Vida de los esclavos negros en Venezuela*. Havana: Casa de las Américas, 1978.
3. Acuña, René, *Introducción al estudio del Rabinal Achí*. Mexico City: UNAM, 1975.
4. Aguirre Beltrán, Gonzalo. *Medicina y magia: El proceso de aculturación en la estructura colonial*. Mexico City: Instituto Nacional Indigenista, 1980.
5. Alegría, Fernando. *Lautaro, joven libertador de Arauco*. Santiago de Chile: Zig-Zag, 1978.
6. Alemán, Mateo. *Guzmán de Alfarache* (Benito Brancaforte, ed.). Madrid: Cátedra, 1979.
7. Alonso, Dámaso. *Cancionero y romancero español*. Estella: Salvat, 1970.
8. Alvarado, Pedro de. *Cartas de relación*, BAE, Vol. XXII. Madrid: M. Rivadeneyra, 1863.
9. Álvarez Lejarza, Emilio. *El Güegüence*, Managua, Distribuidora Cultural, 1977.
10. Amaral, Álvaro do. *O Padre José de Anchieta e a fundação de São Paulo*. São Paulo: Secretaría de Cultura, 1971.
11. Arciniegas, Germán. *Biografía del Caribe*. Buenos Aires: Sudamericana, 1951.
12. ———. *Amerigo y el Nuevo Mundo*. Mexico: Hermes, 1955.
13. ———. *El Caballero de El Dorado*. Madrid: Revista de Occidente, 1969.
14. Arguedas, José María. *Dioses y hombres de Huarochirí* (includes text by Pierre Duviols). Mexico: Siglo XXI, 1975.
15. ——— (with F. Izquierdo). *Mitos, leyendas y cuentos peruanos*. Lima: Casa de la Cultura, 1970.
16. Arias de la Canal, Fredo. *Intento de psicoanálisis de Juana Inés*. Mexico City: Frente de Afirmación Hispanista, 1972.
17. Armellada, Cesáreo de, and Carmela Bentivenga de Napolitano. *Literaturas indígenas venezolanas*. Caracas: Monte Ávila, 1975.
18. Arrom, José Juan. *El teatro hispanoamericano en la época colonial*. Havana: Anuario Bibliográfico Cubano, 1956.
19. ———. *Certidumbre de América*. Havana: Anuario Bibliográfico Cubano, 1959.
20. Arteche, José de. *Elcano*. Madrid: Espasa-Calpe, 1972.
21. Arzáns de Orsúa y Vela, Bartolomé. *Historia de la Villa Imperial*

de Potosí (Lewis Hanke and Gunnar Mendoza, eds.). Providence: Brown University Press, 1965.

22. Asturias, Miguel Ángel. *Leyendas de Guatemala*. Madrid: Salvat, 1970.

23. Balboa, Silvestre de. *Espejo de paciencia* (prologue by Cintio Vitier). Havana: Arte y Literatura, 1975.

24. Ballesteros Gaibrois, Manuel. *Vida y obra de fray Bernadino de Sahagún*. León: Inst. Sahagún, 1973.

25. Barrera Vázquez, Alfredo, and Silvia Rendón. *El Libro de los Libros de Chilam Balam*. Mexico: Fondo de Cultura Económica, 1978.

26. Bascuñán, Francisco Núñez de Pineda y. *Cautiverio feliz*. Santiago de Chile: Editorial Universitaria, 1973.

27. Bataillon, Marcel, and André Saint-Lu. *El Padre Las Casas y la defensa de los indios*. Barcelona: Ariel, 1976.

28. Benítez, Fernando. *Los primeros mexicanos: La vida criolla en el siglo XVI*. Mexico: Era, 1962.

29. ———. *La ruta de Hernán Cortés*. Mexico City: FCE, 1974.

30. ———. *Los indios de México*, Vol. V. Mexico City: Era, 1980.

31. Bowser, Frederick P. *El esclavo africano en el Perú colonial (1524–1650)*. Mexico City: Siglo XXI, 1977.

32. Boxer, C. R. *Race Relations in the Portuguese Colonial Empire (1415–1825)*. Oxford: Clarendon, 1963.

33. ———. *The Golden Age of Brazil (1695–1750)*. Berkeley: University of California, 1969.

34. Boyer, Paul, and Stephen Nissenbaum. *Salem Possessed: The Social Origins of Witchcraft*. Cambridge, Mass.: Harvard University, 1978.

35. Breen, T. H. *Puritans and Adventurers: Change and Persistence in Early America*. New York and Oxford: Oxford University, 1980.

36. Bridenbaugh, Carl. *Jamestown 1544–1699*. New York and Oxford: Oxford University, 1980.

37. Bruchac, Joseph. *Stone Giants and Flying Heads*. Trumansburg, N.Y.: Crossing, 1979.

38. Buarque de Holanda, Sergio. "A época colonial" in *História Geral da Civilização Brasileira (I)*. Rio de Janeiro and São Paulo: Difel, 1977.

39. Cabeza de Vaca, Álvar Núñez. *Naufragios y comentarios*. Madrid: Espasa-Calpe, 1971.

40. Cadogan, Leon. *La literatura de los guaraníes*. Mexico City: Joaquín Mortiz, 1965.

41. Carande, Ramón. *Carlos V y sus banqueros*. Barcelona: Crítica, 1977.

42. Cardenal, Ernesto. *Antología de poesía primitiva*. Madrid: Alianza, 1979.

43. Carneiro, Edison. *O quilombo dos Palmares*. Rio de Janeiro: Civilização Brasileira, 1966.

44. Carpentier, Alejo. *El arpa y la sombra*. Madrid: Siglo XXI, 1979.

45. Carvajal, Gaspar de. *Relación del nuevo descubrimiento del famoso río Grande de las Amazonas*. Mexico City: FCE, 1955.

46. Cervantes Saavedra, Miguel de. *El ingenioso hidalgo don Quijote de la Mancha*. Barcelona: Sopena, 1978.

47. Chacón Torres, Mario. *Arte virreinal en Potosí*. Seville: Escuela de Estudios Hispanoamericanos, 1973.

48. Chang-Rodríguez, Raquel. *Prosa hispanoamericana virreinal* (includes text by Mogrovejo de la Cerda). Barcelona: Hispam, 1978.

49. Chávez, Ezequiel A. *Ensayo de psicología de Sor Juana Inés de la Cruz*. Barcelona: Araluce, 1931.

50. Cieza de León, Pedro de. *La crónica del Perú*, BAE, Vol. XXVI. Madrid: M. Rivadeneyra, 1879.

51. Civrieux, Marc de. *Watunna: Mitología makiritare*. Caracas: Monte Ávila, 1970.

52. Colón, Cristóbal. *Diario del descubrimiento* (with notes by Manuel Alvar). Las Palmas: Cabildo de Gran Canaria, 1976.

53. ———. *Los cuatro viajes del Almirante y su testamento*. Madrid: Espasa-Calpe, 1977.

54. Cora, María Manuela de. *Kuai-Mare: Mitos aborígenes de Venezuela*. Caracas: Monte Ávila, 1972.

55. Corona Núñez, José. *Mitología tarasca*. Mexico: FCE, 1957.

56. Cortés, Hernán. *Cartas de relación*, BAE, Vol. XXII. Madrid: M. Rivadeneyra, 1863.

57. Cossío del Pomar, Felipe. *El mundo de los incas*. Mexico: FCE, 1975.

58. Cruz, Juana Inés de la. *Páginas escogidas* (Fina García Murruz, ed.). Havana: Casa de las Américas, 1978.

59. D'Ans, André Marcel. *La verdadera Biblia de los cashinahua*. Lima: Mosca Azul, 1975.

60. Davies, Nigel. *Los aztecas*. Barcelona: Destino, 1977.

61. Deschamps, Hubert. *Piratas y filibusteros*. Barcelona: Salvat, 1956.

62. Díaz del Castillo, Bernal. *Verdadera historia de los sucesos de la conquista de la Nueva España*, BAE, Vol. XXVI. Madrid: M. Rivadeneyra, 1879.

63. Di Nola, Alfonso M. *Canti erotici dei primitivi*. Rome: Lato Side, 1980.

64. Elliott, J. H. *La España imperial*. Barcelona: V. Vices, 1978.

65. Exquemelin, Alexandre O. *Piratas de América*. Barcelona: Barral, n.d.

66. Eyzaguirre, Jaime. *Historia de Chile*. Santiago: Zig-Zag, 1977.

67. ———. *Ventura de Pedro de Valdivia*. Madrid: Espasa-Calpe, 1967.
68. Franco, José Luciano. *La diáspora africana en el Nuevo Mundo*. Havana: Ciencias Sociales, 1975.
69. Freitas, Decio. *Palmares, la guerrilla negra*. Montevideo: Nuestra América, 1971.
70. Friede, Juan. *Bartolomé de las Casas: precursor del anticolonialismo*. Mexico: Siglo XXI, 1976.
71. Fuentes y Guzmán, Francisco Antonio de. *Obras históricas*. Madrid: BAE, 1969 and 1972.
72. Gage, Thomas. *Viajes en la Nueva España*, Havana: Casa de las Américas, 1980.
73. Gandía, Enrique de. *Indios y conquistadores en el Paraguay*. Buenos Aires: García Santos, 1932.
74. ———. *Historia de la conquista del río de la Plata y del Paraguay (1535–1556)*. Buenos Aires: García Santos, 1932.
75. Garcés, Jesús Juan. *Vida y poesía de Sor Juana Inés de la Cruz*. Madrid: Cultura Hispánica, 1953.
76. Garcilaso de la Vega, Inca. *Comentarios reales de los incas*. Madrid: BAE, 1960.
77. Garibay K., Ángel María (ed.). *Poesía indígena de la altiplanicie*. Mexico: UNAM, 1972.
78. Gerbi, Antonello. *La naturaleza de las Indias Nuevas*. Mexico City: FCE, 1978.
79. Gibson, Charles. *Los aztecas bajo el dominio español (1519–1810)*. Mexico City: Siglo XXI, 1977.
80. Godoy, Diego. *Relación a Hernán Cortés*, BAE, Vol. XXII. Madrid: M. Rivadeneyra, 1863.
81. Gómara, Francisco López de. *Primera y segunda parte de la Historia General de las Indias*, BAE, Vol. XXII. Madrid: M. Rivadeneyra, 1863.
82. Gómez Luaces, Eduardo. *Historia de Nuestra Señora de Regla* (booklet). Havana: Valcayo, 1945.
83. Gortari, Eli de. *La ciencia en la historia de México*. Mexico City: FCE, 1963.
84. Gow, Rosalind, and Bernabé Condori. *Kay Pacha*. Cuzco: Centro de Estudios Rurales Andinos, 1976.
85. Graham, R. B. Cunningham. *Pedro de Valdivia*. Buenos Aires: Inter-Americana, 1943.
86. Granada, Daniel. *Supersticiones del río de la Plata*. Buenos Aires: Guillermo Kraft, 1947.
87. Gridley, Marion E. *The Story of the Haida*. New York: Putnam's, 1972.
88. Hackett, Charles Wilson. "The Revolt of the Pueblo Indians of New

Mexico in 1680," *Quarterly of the Texas State Historical Association*, Vol. XV, No. 2, October 1911.

89. Hammond, George P., and Agapito Rey. *The Rediscovery of New Mexico (1580–1594)*. Albuquerque: University of New Mexico, 1966.

90. Hanke, Lewis. *Bartolomé de las Casas*. Buenos Aires: EUDEBA, 1968.

91. Harris, Olivia, and Kate Young (eds.). *Antropología y feminismo*. Barcelona: Anagrama, 1979.

92. Henestrosa, Andrés. *Los hombres que dispersó la danza*. Havana: Casa de las Américas, 1980.

93. Hernández Sánchez-Barba, M. *Historia de América*. Madrid: Alhambra, 1981.

94. Jara, Álvaro. *Guerra y sociedad en Chile*. Santiago de Chile: Editorial Universitaria, 1961.

95. ———. "Estructuras coloniales y subdesarrollo en Hispanoamérica," *Journal de la Société des Américanistes*, Vol. LXV. Paris, 1978.

96. Jerez, Francisco de. *Verdadera relación de la conquista del Perú y provincia del Cuzco*, BAE, Vol. XXVI. Madrid: M. Rivadeneyra, 1879.

97. Kirkpatrick, F. A. *Los conquistadores españoles*. Madrid: Espasa-Calpe, 1970.

98. Konetzke, Richard. *América Latina (II): La época colonial*. Madrid: Siglo XXI, 1978.

99. ———. *Descubridores y conquistadores de América*. Madrid: Gredos, 1968.

100. Krickeberg, Walter. *Mitos y leyendas de los aztecas, incas, mayas y muiscas*. Mexico City: FCE, 1971.

101. Labat, Jean-Baptiste. *Viajes a las islas de la América* (Francisco de Oraá, ed.). Havana: Casa de las Américas, 1979.

102. Las Casas, Bartolomé de. *Brevísima relación de la destrucción de las Indias*. Barcelona: Fontamara, 1979.

103. ———. *Historia de las Indias*. Mexico City: FCE, 1951.

104. ———. *Apologética historia de las Indias*. Mexico City: UNAM, 1967.

105. Lafone Quevedo, Samuel A. "El culto de Tonapa" in Valera Santillán and Santacruz Pachacuti, *Tres relaciones de antigüedades peruanas*. Asunción: Guarania, 1950.

106. Leal, Rine. *La selva oscura*. Havana: Arte y Literatura, 1975.

107. León-Portilla, Miguel. *El reverso de la Conquista. Relaciones aztecas, mayas e incas*. Mexico City: Joaquín Mortiz, 1964.

108. ———. *Los antiguos mexicanos*. Mexico City: FCE, 1977.

109. ———. *Culturas en peligro*. Mexico City: Alianza Editorial Mexicana, 1976.

110. ———. *La filosofía náhuatl*. Mexico City: UNAM, 1958.
111. Lévi-Strauss, Claude. *Lo crudo y lo cocido (Mitológicas, I)*. Mexico City: FCE, 1978.
112. ———. *De la miel a las cenizas (Mitológicas, II)*. Mexico City: FCE, 1978.
113. ———. *El origen de las maneras de mesa (Mitológicas, III)*. Mexico City: Siglo XXI, 1976.
114. ———. *El hombre desnudo (Mitológicas, IV)*. Mexico City: Siglo XXI, 1976.
115. Lewin, Boleslao. *La Inquisición en Hispanoamérica*. Buenos Aires: Proyección, 1962.
116. Lewis, D. B. Wyndham. *Carlos de Europa, emperador de Occidente*. Madrid: Espasa-Calpe, 1962.
117. Leydi, Roberto, Arrigo Polillo, and Tommaso Giglio. *Piratas, corsarios y filibusteros*. Barcelona: Maucci, 1961.
118. Lipschutz, Alejandro. *El problema racial en la conquista de América*. Mexico City: Siglo XXI, 1975.
119. ———. *Perfil de Indoamérica de nuestro tiempo*. Santiago de Chile: Andrés Bello, 1968.
120. Lockhart, James, and Enrique Orte. *Letters and People of the Spanish Indies: The Sixteenth Century*. Cambridge: Cambridge University Press, 1976.
121. Lohmann Villena, Guillermo. *El conde de Lemos, virrey del Perú*. Madrid: Escuela de Estudios Hispanoamericanos, 1946.
122. ———. *El arte dramático en Lima durante el Virreinato*. Madrid: Escuela de Estudios Hispanoamericanos, 1945.
123. López, Casto Fulgencio. *Lope de Aguirre, el Peregrino*. Barcelona: Plon, 1977.
124. López-Baralt, Mercedes. "Guamán Poma de Ayala y el arte de la memoria en una crónica ilustrada del siglo XVII," *Cuadernos Americanos*. Mexico City: May–June 1979.
125. ———. "La crónica de Indias como texto cultural: policulturalidad y articulación de códigos semióticos multiples en el arte de reinar de Guamán Poma de Ayala" (unpublished manuscript).
126. ———. *El mito taíno: Raíz y proyecciones en la Amazonia continental*. Río Piedras: Huracán, 1976.
127. Mannix, Daniel P., and M. Cowley. *Historia de la trata de negros*. Madrid: Alianza, 1970.
128. Marañón, Gregorio. *El conde-duque de Olivares (La pasión de mandar)*. Madrid: Espasa-Calpe, 1936.
129. Marchant, Alexander. *From Barter to Slavery*. Baltimore: Johns Hopkins, 1942.
130. Mariño de Lobera, Pedro. *Crónica del Reino de Chile*. Santiago de Chile: Editorial Universitaria, 1979.

131. Marmolejo, Lucio. *Efemérides guanajuatenses,* Vol. I. Guanajuato: Universidad, 1967.

132. Marriott, Alice, and Carol K. Rachlin. *American Indian Mythology.* New York: Apollo, 1968.

133. Martínez, José Luis. *El mundo antiguo, VI: América antigua.* Mexico City: Secretaría de Educación, 1976.

134. Martínez Fivee, Rogelio (ed.). *Poesía anónima africana.* Madrid: Miguel Castellote, n.d.

135. Martínez Peláez, Severo. *La patria del criollo.* San José, Costa Rica: EDUCA, 1973.

136. McLuhan, T. C. (ed.). *Touch the Earth (A Self-portrait of Indian Existence).* New York: Simon and Schuster, 1971.

137. Medina, José Toribio. *Historia del Tribunal de la Inquisición de Lima (1569–1820).* Santiago de Chile: Fondo Histórico y Bibliográfico J.T. Medina, 1956.

138. ———. *Historia del Tribunal del Santo Oficio de la Inquisición en Chile.* Santiago: Fondo J.T. Medina, 1952.

139. ———. *Historia del Tribunal del Santo Oficio de la Inquisición en México.* Santiago: Elzeviriana, 1905.

140. ———. *El Tribunal del Santo Oficio de la Inquisición en las provincias del Plata.* Santiago: Elzeviriana, 1900.

141. Méndez Pereira, Octavio. *Núñez de Balboa.* Madrid: Espasa-Calpe, 1975.

142. Mendoza, Diego de. *Chronica de la Provincia de S. Antonio de los Charcas. . . .* Madrid: n.p., 1664.

143. Montoya, Antonio Ruiz de. *Conquista espiritual hecha por los religiosos de la Compañía de Jesús en las provincias del Paraguay, Paraná, Uruguay y Tape.* Bilbao: El Mensajero, 1892.

144. Morales, Ernesto. *Leyendas guaraníes.* Buenos Aires: El Ateneo, 1929.

145. Morales Padrón, Francisco. *Jamaica española.* Seville: Escuela de Estudios Hispanoamericanos, 1952.

146. More, Thomas. *Utopía* (bilingual edition with introduction by Joaquim Mallafré Gabaldá). Barcelona: Bosch, 1977.

147. Mörner, Magnus. *Historia social latinoamericana (Nuevos enfoques).* Caracas: Universidad Católica Andrés Bello, 1979.

148. ———. *La Corona española y los foráneos en los pueblos de indios de América.* Stockholm. Instituto de Estudios Ibero-Americanos, 1970.

149. Mousnier, Roland. *Historia general de las civilizaciones.* Los siglos XVI y XVII. Barcelona: Destino, 1974.

150. Murra, John V. *La organización económica del Estado inca.* Mexico City: Siglo XXI, 1978.

151. ———. *Formaciones económicas y políticas del mundo andino.* Lima: Instituto de Estudios Peruanos, 1975.

152. Nabokov, Peter (ed.). *Native American Testimony*. New York: Harper and Row, 1978.

153. Nash, Gary B. *Red, White, and Black: The Peoples of Early America*. Englewood Cliffs, N.J.: Prentice-Hall, 1974.

154. Nebrija, Elio Antonio de. *Vocabulario español-latino* (facsimile ed.). Madrid: Real Academia Española, 1951.

155. Oberem, Udo. "Notas y documentos sobre miembros de la familia del Inca Atahualpa en el siglo XVI," *Estudios etno-históricos del Ecuador*, Casa de la Cultura Ecuatoriana, Núcleo del Guayas, 1976.

156. ———. *Los quijos*. Otavalo: Instituto Otavaleño de Antropología, 1980.

157. Ocaña, Diego de. *Un viaje fascinante por la América hispana del siglo XVI* (annotated by Fray Arturo Alvarez). Madrid: Studium, 1969.

158. Oliva de Coll, Josefina. *La resistencia indígena ante la conquista*. Mexico City: Siglo XXI, 1974.

159. Ortiz, Fernando. *Contrapunteo cubano del tabaco y el azúcar*. Havana: Consejo Nacional de Cultura, 1963.

160. ———. *Los negros esclavos*. Havana: Ciencias Sociales, 1975.

161. ———. *Historia de una pelea cubana contra los demonios*. Havana: Ciencias Sociales, 1975.

162. Ortiz Rescaniere, Alejandro. *De Adaneva a Inkarrí*. Lima: Retablo de Papel, 1973.

163. Otero, Gustavo Adolfo. *La vida social del coloniaje*. La Paz: La Paz, 1942.

164. Otero Silva, Miguel. *Lope de Aguirre, príncipe de la libertad*. Barcelona: Seix Barral, 1979.

165. Oviedo y Baños, José de. *Los Bélzares: El tirano Aguirre. Diego de Losada*. Caracas: Monte Avila, 1972.

166. Oviedo y Valdés, Gonzalo Fernández de. *Historia general y natural de las Indias*. Madrid: Real Academia de la Historia, 1851.

167. Palma, Ricardo. *Tradiciones peruanas* (1st and 2nd ed.). Buenos Aires: Espasa-Calpe, 1938 and 1940.

168. Pané, Ramón. *Relación acerca de las antigüedades de los indios* (José Juan Arrom, ed.). Mexico City: Siglo XXI, 1974.

169. Parry, J.H., and Philip Sherlock. *Historia de las Antillas*. Buenos Aires: Kapelusz, 1976.

170. Paz, Ramón. *Mitos, leyendas y cuentos guajiros*. Caracas: Instituto Agrario Nacional, 1972.

171. Peixoto, Afranio. *Breviario da Bahía*. Rio de Janeiro: Agir, 1945.

172. Pereira Salas, Eugenio. *Apuntes para la historia de la cocina chilena*. Santiago de Chile: Editorial Universitaria, 1977.

173. ———. *Juegos y alegrías coloniales en Chile*. Santiago: Zig-Zag, 1947.

174. Péret, Benjamin. *Anthologie des mythes, légendes et contes populaires d'Amérique*. Paris: Albin Michel, 1960.

175. Pérez Embid, Florentino. *Diego de Ordás, compañero de Cortés y explorador del Orinoco*. Seville: Escuela de Estudios Hispanoamericanos, 1950.

176. Phelan, John Leddy. *The Kingdom of Quito in the Seventeenth Century*. Madison: University of Wisconsin, 1967.

177. ———. *The Millennial Kingdom of the Franciscans in the New World*. Berkeley: University of California, 1970.

178. Plath, Oreste. *Geografía del mito y la leyenda chilenos*. Santiago de Chile: Nascimento, 1973.

179. Poma de Ayala, Felipe Guamán. *Nueva corónica y buen gobierno* (facsimile ed.). Paris: Institut d'Ethnologie, 1936.

180. Portigliotti, Giuseppe. *Los Borgia*. Madrid: J. Gil, 1936.

181. Portuondo, Fernando. *El segundo viaje del descubrimiento* (letters of Michele de Cúneo and Alvarez Chanca). Havana: Ciencias Sociales, 1977.

182. Prado, Juan José. *Leyendas y tradiciones guanajuatenses*. Guanajuato: Prado Hnos., 1953.

183. Quevedo, Francisco de. *Obras completas*. Madrid: Aguilar, 1974.

184. Quintana, Manuel J. *Los conquistadores*. Buenos Aires: Suma, 1945.

185. ———. *Vida de Francisco Pizarro*. Madrid: Espasa-Calpe, 1959.

186. Ramos Smith, Maya. *La danza en México durante la época colonial*. Havana: Casa de las Américas, 1979.

187. Real, Cristóbal. *El corsario Drake y el imperio español*. Madrid: Editora Nacional, n.d.

188. Recinos, Adrián (ed.). *Popol Vuh. Las antiguas historias del Quiché*. Mexico City: FCE, 1976.

189. Reichel-Dolmatoff, Gerardo and Alicia. *Estudios antropológicos*. Bogotá: Inst. Colombiano de Cultura, 1977.

190. Reyes, Alfonso. *Medallones*. Buenos Aires: Espasa-Calpe, 1952.

191. Rivet, Paul. *Etnographie ancienne de l'Équateur*. Paris: Gauthier-Villars, 1912.

192. Roa Bastos, Augusto (ed.). *Las culturas condenadas*. Mexico City: Siglo XXI, 1978.

193. Rodrigues, Nina. *Os africanos no Brasil*. São Paulo: Cía. Editora Nacional, 1977.

194. Rodríguez Fresle, Juan. *El carnero de Bogotá*, Bogotá: Ed. Colombia, 1926.

195. Rodríguez Marín, Francisco. *El Quijote: Don Quijote en América*. Madrid: Hernando, 1911.

196. ———. *Cantos populares españoles*. Seville: Alvarez, 1882–83.

197. Rothenberg, Jerome. *Shaking the Pumpkin: Traditional Poetry of the Indians of North America*. Garden City, N.Y.: Doubleday, 1972.

198. Rowse, A.L. *The England of Elizabeth*. London: Cardinal, 1973.
199. Rubio Mañé, J. Ignacio. *Introducción al estudio de los virreyes de Nueva España (1535–1746)*. Mexico City: UNAM, 1959.
200. Sahagún, Bernardino de. *Historia general de las cosas de la Nueva España* (annotated by Ángel Ma. Garibay K.). Mexico City: Porrúa, 1969.
201. Salas, Horacio. *La España barroca*, Madrid: Altalena, 1978.
202. Salazar Bondy, Sebastián (ed.). *Poesía quechua*. Montevideo; Arca, 1978.
203. Sapper, Karl. "El infierno de Masaya" in *Nicaragua en los cronistas de Indias* (anthology). Managua: Banco de América, 1975.
204. Segal, Charles M., and David C. Stineback. *Puritans, Indians and Manifest Destiny*. New York: Putnam's, 1977.
205. Sejourné, Laurette. *América Latina, I: Antiguas culturas precolombinas*. Madrid: Siglo XXI, 1978.
206. ———. *Pensamiento y religión en el México antiguo*. Mexico City: FCE, 1957.
207. Sheehan, Bernard. *Savagism and Civility*. Cambridge: Cambridge University, 1980.
208. Sodi, Demetrio. *La literatura de los mayas*. Mexico City: Mortiz, 1964.
209. Teitelboim, Volodia. *El amanecer del capitalismo y la conquista de América*. Havana: Casa de las Américas, 1979.
210. Tibón, Gutierre. *Historia del nombre y de la fundación de México*. Mexico City: FCE, 1975.
211. Tizón, Héctor. *La España borbónica*. Madrid: Altalena, 1978.
212. Toscano, Salvador. *Cuauhtémoc*. Mexico City: FCE, 1975.
213. Valle-Arizpe, Artemio de. *Historia de la ciudad de México según los relatos de sus cronistas*. Mexico City: Jus, 1977.
214. Vargas, José María. *Historia del Ecuador: Siglo XVI*. Quito: Universidad Católica, 1977.
215. ——— (ed.). *Arte colonial de Ecuador*. Quito: Salvat Ecuatoriana, 1977.
216. Velasco, Salvador. *San Martín de Porres*. Villava: Ope, 1962.
217. Vianna, Helio. *História do Brasil*. São Paulo: Melhoramentos, 1980.
218. Vicens Vives, J. (ed.). *Historia de España y América*. Barcelona: Vicens Vives, 1977.
219. Von Hagen, Víctor W. *El mundo de los mayas*. Mexico City: Diana, 1968.
220. ———. *Culturas preincaicas*. Madrid: Guadarrama, 1976.
221. Wachtel, Nathan. *Los vencidos: Los indios del Perú frente a la conquista española (1530–1570)*. Madrid: Alianza, 1976.
222. Wallace, Anthony F.C. "Dreams and the Wishes of the Soul: A Type

of Psychoanalytic Theory Among the Seventeenth-Century Iroquois," *The American Anthropologist*, Vol. 60, No. 2, 1958.

223. Watt, Montgomery. *Historia de la España islámica*. Madrid: Alianza, 1970.

224. Williams, Eric. *Capitalismo y esclavitud*. Buenos Aires: Siglo XX, 1973.

225. Wolf, Eric. *Pueblos y culturas de Mesoamérica*. Mexico City: Era, 1975.

226. Zavala, Silvio. *El mundo americano en la época colonial*. Mexico City: Porrúa, 1967.

227. ———. *Ideario de Vasco de Quiroga*. Mexico City: El Colegio de México, 1941.

Faces and Masks

Contents

Preface

This book

is the second volume of the trilogy *Memory of Fire*. It is not an anthology, but a work of literary creation. The author proposes to narrate the history of America, and above all the history of Latin America, reveal its multiple dimensions and penetrate its secrets. In the third volume this vast mosaic will reach to our own times. *Faces and Masks* embraces the eighteenth and nineteenth centuries.

At the head of each text is indicated the year and place of occurrence of the episode. The numbers in parentheses below show the principal works consulted by the author in his search for information and points of reference. Documentary sources are listed at the end of the book.

Literal transcriptions are italicized.

Acknowledgments

In addition to the friends mentioned in *Genesis*, who continued collaborating through this second volume, many others have facilitated the author's access to the necessary bibliography. Among them, Mariano Baptista Gumucio, Olga Behar, Claudia Canales, Hugo Chumbita, Galeno de Freitas, Horacio de Marsilio, Bud Flakoll, Piruncha and Jorge Galeano, Javier Lentini, Alejandro Losada, Paco Moncloa, Lucho Nieto, Rigoberto Paredes, Rius, Lincoln Silva, Cintio Vitier, and René Zavaleta Mercado.

This time the following nobly undertook to read the first draft: Jorge Enrique Adoum, Mario Benedetti, Edgardo Carvalho, Antonio Doñate, Juan Gelman, María Elena Martínez, Ramírez Contreras, Lina Rodríguez, Miguel Rojas-Mix, Nicole Rouan, Pilar Royo, César Salsamendi, José María Valverde, and Federico Vogelius. They suggested several changes and caught foolish and silly mistakes.

Once again Helena Villagra accompanied the work step by step, sharing tailwinds and setbacks, to the last line with mysterious patience.

This book

is dedicated to Tomás Borge, to Nicaragua.

I don't know who I am,
nor just where I was bedded.
Don't know where I'm from
nor where the hell I'm headed.

I'm a piece of fallen tree,
where it fell I do not know.
Where can my roots be?
On what sort of tree did I grow?
                    (Popular verses
                     of Boyacá, Colombia)

Promise of America

The blue tiger will smash the world.

Another land, without evil, without death, will be born from the destruction of this one. This land wants it. It asks to die, asks to be born, this old and offended land. It is weary and blind from so much weeping behind closed eyelids. On the point of death it strides the days, garbage heap of time, and at night it inspires pity from the stars. Soon the First Father will hear the world's supplications, land wanting to be another, and then the blue tiger who sleeps beneath his hammock will jump.

Awaiting that moment, the Guaraní Indians journey through the condemned land.

"Anything to tell us, hummingbird?"

They dance without letup, ever lighter and airier, intoning the sacred chants that celebrate the coming birth of the other land.

"Shine your rays, shine your rays, hummingbird!"

From the sea coasts to the center of America, they have sought paradise. They have skirted jungles and mountains and rivers in pursuit of the new land, the one that will be founded without old age or sickness or anything to interrupt the endless fiesta of living. The chants announce that corn will grow on its own and arrows shoot into the thickets all by themselves; and neither punishment nor pardon will be necessary, because there won't be prohibition or blame.

(72 and 232)*

1701: Salinas Valley
The Skin of God

The Chirigua Indians of the Guaraní people sailed down the Pilcomayo River years or centuries ago, and reached the frontier of the empire of the Incas. Here they remained, beneath the first of these Andean heights, awaiting the land without evil and without death.

The Chiriguans discover paper, the written word, the printed word, when after a long journey the Franciscan monks of Chuquisaca appear carrying sacred books in their saddlebags.

As they didn't know paper or that they needed it, the Indians

* These numbers refer to the documentary sources consulted by the author as listed on pages 261–76.

had no word for it. Today they give it the name *skin of God*, because paper is for sending messages to friends far away.

(233 and 252)

1701: São Salvador de Bahia
Voice of America

Father Antonio Vieira died at the turn of the century, but not so his voice, which continues to shelter the defenseless. The words of this missionary to the poor and persecuted still echo with the same lively ring throughout the lands of Brazil.

One night Father Vieira spoke about the ancient prophets. They were not wrong, he said, in reading destinies in the entrails of the animals they sacrificed. In the entrails, he said. In the entrails, not the heads, because a prophet who can love is better than one who can reason.

(351)

1701: Paris
Temptation of America

In his study in Paris, a learned geographer scratches his head. Guillaume Deslile draws exact maps of the earth and the heavens. Should he include El Dorado on the map of America? Should he paint in the mysterious lake, as has become the custom, somewhere in the upper Orinoco? Deslile asks himself whether the golden waters, described by Walter Raleigh as the size of the Caspian Sea, really exist. And those princes who plunge in and swim by the light of torches, undulating golden fish: are they or were they ever flesh and bone?

The lake, sometimes named El Dorado, sometimes Parima, figures on all maps drawn up to now. But what Deslile has heard and read makes him doubt. Seeking El Dorado, many soldiers of fortune have penetrated the remote new world, over there where the four winds meet and all colors and pains mingle, and have found nothing. Spaniards, Portuguese, Englishmen, Frenchmen, and Germans have spanned abysses that the American gods dug with nails and teeth; have violated forests warmed by tobacco smoke puffed by the gods; have navigated rivers born of giant trees the gods tore out by the roots; have tortured and killed Indians the gods created out of saliva, breath, or dream. But that fugitive gold has vanished and always vanishes into the air, the lake disappearing before anyone can reach it. El Dorado seems to be the name of a grave without coffin or shroud.

In the two centuries that have passed since the world grew and became round, pursuers of hallucinations have continued heading for the lands of America from every wharf. Protected by a god of navigation and conquest, squeezed into their ships, they cross the immense ocean. Along with shepherds and farmhands whom Europe has not killed by war, plague, or hunger, go captains and merchants and rogues and mystics and adventurers. All seek the miracle. Beyond the ocean, magical ocean that cleanses blood and transfigures destinies, the great promise of all the ages lies open. There, beggars will be avenged. There, nobodies will turn into marquises, scoundrels into saints, gibbet-fodder into founders, and vendors of love will become dowried débutantes.

(326)

Sentinel of America

Long, long ago in the Andean cordillera, the Indians lived in perpetual night. The condor, oldest of all flying creatures, was the one who brought them the sun. He dropped it, a little ball of gold, among the mountains. The Indians picked it up and, blowing as hard as they could, blew it up toward the sky where it remains suspended forever. With the golden rays the sun sweated, the Indians modeled the animals and plants that inhabit the earth.

One night the moon rose, ringed by three halos, to shine upon the peaks: the halo of blood announced war; the halo of flame, fire; and the black halo was the halo of disaster. Then the Indians fled into the cold, high wilderness and, carrying the sacred gold, plunged into the depths of lakes and into volcanos.

The condor, bringer of the sun to the Andeans, is the caretaker of that treasure. With great gliding wings he soars over the snowy peaks and the waters and the smoking craters. The gold warns him when greed approaches. The gold cries out, and whistles, and shouts. The condor swoops down. His beak picks out the eyes of the thieves, and his claws tear their flesh.

Only the sun can see the back of the condor, his bald head, his wrinkled neck. Only the sun knows his loneliness. Seen from the earth, the condor is invulnerable.

(246)

1701: Ouro Prêto

Conjuring Tricks

The silver mountain of Potosí is not an illusion, nor do the deep tunnels of Mexico contain only delirium and darkness; nor do the rivers of central Brazil sleep on beds of fool's gold.

The gold of Brazil is apportioned by lottery or by fists, by luck or by death. Those who don't lose their lives make immense fortunes, one-fifth of which is owed to the Portuguese king. Yet, when all's said and done, that royal fifth is but a fable. Heaps and heaps of gold escape as contraband, and even as many guards as the region's dense forests have trees could not stanch its flow.

The friars of the Brazilian mines devote more time to trafficking in gold than to saving souls. Hollow wooden saints serve as containers. For the monk Roberto way off by the coast, forging dies is as simple as telling his rosary, and so illicit gold bars come to sport the royal seal. Roberto, a Benedictine monk of the Sorocaba monastery, has also manufactured an all-powerful key that vanquishes any lock.

(11)

1703: Lisbon

Gold, Passenger in Transit

A few years ago a governor-general of Brazil made some prophesies that were as accurate as they were useless. From Bahia, João de Lencastre warned the king of Portugal that hordes of adventurers would turn the mining region into a sanctuary for criminals and vagabonds; and even graver, with gold the same might happen to Portugal as to Spain, which as soon as it receives its silver from America kisses it a tearful goodbye. Brazilian gold might enter by the Bay of Lisbon and, without ever stopping on Portuguese soil, continue its voyage up the River Tagus en route to England, France, Holland, Germany . . .

As if to echo the governor's voice, the Treaty of Methuen is signed. Portugal will pay with Brazilian gold for English cloth. With gold from Brazil, another country's colony, England will give its industrial development a tremendous push forward.

(11, 48, and 226)

1709: *The Juan Fernández Islands*

Robinson Crusoe

The lookout reports distant gunfire. To investigate it, the freebooters of the Duke change course and head for the coast of Chile.

The ship approaches the Juan Fernández Islands. From a string of bonfires, a canoe, a splash of foam comes toward it. Onto the deck climbs a tangle of hair and filth, trembling with fever, emitting noises from its mouth.

Days later, Captain Rogers has the story. The shipwrecked man is one Alexander Selkirk, a Scottish colleague well versed in sails, winds, and plunder. He arrived off the Valparaíso coast with the expedition of the pirate William Dampier. Thanks to Bible, knife, and gun, Selkirk has survived more than four years on one of those uninhabited islands. He has learned the art of fishing with goats' intestines, cooked with salt crystallized on the rocks, and lighted his world with seal oil. He built a hut on high ground and beside it a corral for goats. He marked the passage of time on a tree trunk. A storm brought him the remains of some wreck and also an almost-drowned Indian. He called the Indian Friday because that was the day of his arrival. From him he learned the secrets of the plants. When the big ship came, Friday chose to stay. Selkirk swore to him that he would return, and Friday believed him.

Within ten years, Daniel Defoe will publish in London his novel about the adventures of a shipwrecked sailor. Selkirk will be Robinson Crusoe, native of York. The expedition of the British pirate Dampier, who had ravaged the coasts of Peru and Chile, will become a respectable commercial enterprise. The desert island without a history will jump from the Pacific Ocean to the mouth of the Orinoco, and the shipwrecked sailor will live there twenty-eight years. Robinson will save the life of a savage cannibal. "Master" will be the first word he teaches him in English.

Selkirk marked with a knife-point the ears of each goat he caught. Robinson will undertake the subdivision of the island, his kingdom, into lots for sale; he will put a price on every object he gets from the wrecked ship, keep accounts of all he produces on the island and a balance of every situation, the "debit" of bad fortune and the "credit" of good. Robinson will endure, like Selkirk, the tough tests of solitude, fear, and madness; but at the hour of rescue Alexander Selkirk is a shivering wretch who cannot talk and is scared of everything. Robinson Crusoe, on the other hand, invincible tamer of nature, will return to England with his faithful Friday, totting up accounts and planning adventures.

(92, 149, and 259)

1711: Paramaribo
The Silent Women

The Dutch cut the Achilles tendon of a slave escaping for the first time, and one who makes a second try gets the right leg amputated; yet there is no way to stop the spreading plague of freedom in Surinam.

Captain Molinay sails downriver to Paramaribo. His expedition is returning with two heads. He had to behead the captured women, one named Flora, the other Sery, because after the torture they were in no condition to walk through the jungle. Their eyes are still fixed heavenward. They never opened their mouths in spite of the lashes, the fire, and the red-hot pincers, stubbornly mute as if they had not spoken a word since that remote day when they were fattened up and smeared with oil, and stars or half-moons were engraved on their shaven heads to fit them for sale in the Paramaribo market. Always mute, this Flora and Sery, as the soldiers kept asking where the fugitive slaves hid out: they stared upwards without blinking, following clouds stout as mountains that drifted high in the sky.

(173)

They Carry Life in Their Hair

For all the blacks that get crucified or hung from iron hooks stuck through their ribs, escapes from Surinam's four hundred coastal plantations never stop. Deep in the jungle a black lion adorns the yellow flag of the runaways. For lack of bullets, their guns fire little stones or bone buttons; but the impenetrable thickets are their best ally against the Dutch colonists.

Before escaping, the female slaves steal grains of rice, corn, and wheat, seeds of bean and squash. Their enormous hairdos serve as granaries. When they reach the refuges in the jungle, the women shake their heads and thus fertilize the free land.

(173)

The Maroon

The crocodile, disguised as a log, basks in the sun. The snail revolves its eyes on the point of little horns. The male bird courts the female with circus acrobatics. The male spider climbs up the female's perilous web—bedsheet and shroud—where he will embrace and be devoured. A band of monkeys leaps to seize wild fruits in the branches. The monkeys' screams daze the thickets, drowning out the litanies of cicadas, the questionings of birds. But strange footsteps sound on the carpet of leaves and the jungle falls quickly silent. Paralyzed, it draws into itself and waits. When the first gunshot rings out, the whole jungle stampedes in flight.

The shot announces a hunt for runaway slaves: *cimarrones*, in the Antillean phrase meaning "arrow that seeks freedom." Used by Spaniards for the bull that takes off for the woods, it passes into other languages as *chimarrão, maroon, marron* to designate the slave who in every part of America seeks the protection of forests and swamps and deep canyons; who, far from the master, builds a free domain and defends it by marking false trails and setting deadly traps.

The maroon is the gangrene of colonial society.

(264)

1711: Murrí

They Are Never Alone

There are Indian maroons too. To shut them in under the control of friars and captains, prisons are built. The newly born village of Murrí, in the region of the Chocó, is one.

Some time back, huge canoes with white wings arrived here, seeking the rivers of gold that flow down from the cordillera; and since then, Indians have been fleeing. Countless spirits accompany them as they journey through forests and across rivers.

The witch doctor knows the words that call the spirits. To cure the sick he blows his conch shell toward the foliage where the peccary, the bird of paradise, and the singing fish live. To make the well sick, he puts into one of their lungs the butterfly of death. The witch doctor knows that there is no land, water, or air empty of spirits in the Chocó region.

(121)

1711: Saint Basil's Refuge

The Black King, the White Saint and His Sainted Wife

More than a century ago, the Negro Domingo Bioho fled from the galleys in Cartagena of the Indies and became warrior-king of the swamplands. Hosts of dogs and musketeers went hunting for him, and Domingo was hanged several times. On various days of great public enthusiasm Domingo was dragged through the streets of Cartagena tied to the tail of a mule, and several times had his penis chopped off and nailed to a long pike. His captors were rewarded with successive grants of land and repeatedly given the title of marquis; but within the maroon palisades of the Dique Canal or of the lower Cauca, Domingo Bioho reigns and laughs with his unmistakable painted face.

The free blacks live on constant alert, trained from birth to fight, protected by ravines and precipices and deep ditches lined with poisonous thorns. The most important of the refuges in the region, which has existed and resisted for a century, is going to be named after a saint, Saint Basil, whose effigy is soon expected to arrive on the Magdalena River. Saint Basil will be the first white man authorized to enter here. He will arrive with mitre and staff of office and will bring with him a little wooden church well stocked with miracles. He will not be scandalized by the nudity, or ever talk in a master's voice. The maroons will provide him with a house and wife. They will get him a saintly female, Catalina, so that in the other world God will not wed him to an ass and so that they may enjoy this world together while they are in it.

(108 and 120)

The Maríapalito

There is much animal life in the region where Domingo Bioho reigns forever and a day within his palisades. Most feared are the tiger, the boa constrictor, and the snake that wraps himself around the vines and glides down into the huts. Most fascinating are the mayupa fish that shits through his head, and the maríapalito.

Like the spider, the female maríapalito eats her lovers. When the male embraces her from behind, she turns her chinless face to

him, measures him, with her big, protuberant eyes, fastens her teeth
in him and lunches off him with absolute calm, until nothing remains.

The maríapalito is extremely devout. She always keeps her arms
folded in prayer and prays as she eats.

(108)

1712: Santa Marta
From Piracy to Contraband

From the green foothills of the Sierra Nevada, which wets its feet in
the sea, rises a belltower surrounded by houses of wood and straw.
In them live the thirty white families of the port of Santa Marta. All
around, in huts of reed and mud, sheltered by palm leaves, live the
Indians, blacks, and mixtures whom no one has bothered to count.

Pirates have always been the nightmare of these coasts. Fifteen
years ago the bishop of Santa Marta had to take apart the organ of
the church to improvise ammunition. A week ago English ships penetrated the cannon fire of forts guarding the bay and calmly met the
dawn on the beach.

Everybody fled into the hills.

The pirates waited. They didn't steal so much as a handkerchief
or burn a single house.

Mistrustful, the inhabitants approached one by one; and Santa
Marta has now become a pleasant market. The pirates, armed to the
teeth, have come to buy and sell. They bargain, but are scrupulous
in paying.

Far away over there, British workshops are growing and need
markets. Many pirates are becoming contrabandists although not one
of them knows what the devil "capital accumulation" means.

(36)

1714: Ouro Prêto
The Mine Doctor

This doctor does not believe in drugs, nor in the costly little powders
from Portugal. He mistrusts bleedings and purges and has small use
for the patriarch Galen and his tablets of laws. Luis Gomes Ferreira
advises his patients to take a daily bath, which in Europe would be
a clear sign of heresy or insanity, and prescribes herbs and roots of

the region. Dr. Ferreira has saved many lives, thanks to the common sense and ancient experience of the Indians, and to the aid of the "white handmaiden," sugarcane brandy that revives the dying.

There is little he can do, however, about the miners' custom of disemboweling each other with bullet or knife. Here, every fortune is fleeting, and shrewdness is worth more than courage. In the implacable war of conquest against this black clay in which suns lie concealed, no science has any role to play. Captain Tomás de Souza, treasurer to the king, went looking for gold and found lead. The doctor could do nothing for him but make the sign of the cross. Everyone believed the captain had a ton of gold stashed away, but the creditors found only a few slaves to divide up.

Rarely does the doctor attend a black patient. In the Brazilian mines slaves are used and scrapped. In vain Ferreira recommends more careful treatment, telling the bosses they sin against God and their own interests. In the places where they pan for gold, and in the galleries below ground, no black lasts ten years, but a handful of gold buys a new child, who is worth the same as a handful of salt or a whole hog.

(48)

1714: Vila Nova do Príncipe

Jacinta

She hallows the ground she walks on. Jacinta de Siquiera, African woman of Brazil, is the founder of this town of Príncipe and of the gold mines in the Quatro Vintens ravines. Black woman, verdant woman, Jacinta opens and closes like a carnivorous plant swallowing men and birthing children of all colors, in this world still without a map. Jacinta advances, slashing open the jungle, at the head of the scoundrels who come on muleback, barefoot, armed with old rifles, and who, when they enter the mines, leave their consciences hanging from a branch or buried in a swamp: Jacinta, born in Angola, slave in Bahia, mother of the gold of Minas Gerais.

(89)

1716: Potosí

Holguín

The viceroy of Lima, Don Rubico Morcillo de Auñón, enters Potosí beneath a hundred and twenty triumphal arches of tooled silver, through a tunnel of canvases depicting Icarus and Eros, Mercury, Endymion, the Colossus of Rhodes, and Aeneas fleeing from Troy.

Potosí, poor Potosí, is not what it once was. Its population down by half, the city receives the viceroy on a street of wood, not of silver. But as in the days of wonder and glory, trumpets and drums resound: pages in gallant liveries light up with wax torches the parade of captains on horseback, governors and judges, magistrates, ambassadors . . . With nightfall comes the radiant masquerade: the city offers the dust-covered visitor the homage of the twelve heroes of Spain, the twelve peers of France, and the twelve Sibyls. In garish costumes the valiant Cid and Emperor Charles salute him, plus as many nymphs and Arab princes and Ethiopian kings as ever existed in the world or in dreams.

Melchor Pérez Holguín depicts this day of prodigies. One by one, he paints the thousand personages, and Potosí, and the world's most generous mountain, in earth and blood and smoke hues lustered with silver, and paints his own image at the foot of the vast canvas: Holguín, eagle-nosed mestizo in his fifties, long black hair streaming from beneath his slouch hat, palette raised in one hand. He also paints two old characters leaning on canes, and writes the words coming from their mouths:

"So many marvels all at once, who ever did see?"

"Never saw nothing this grand in a hundred and some years."

Perhaps Holguín doesn't know that the marvel is the thing he is creating, believing he is just copying; nor does he know that his work will remain alive when the pomp of Potosí has been blotted from the face of the earth and no one can remember any viceroy.

(16 and 215)

1716: Cuzco

The Image Makers

Holguín's mentor, Diego Quispe Tito, died shortly after his eyes died. In the initial fog of blindness he managed to paint his own likeness en route to Paradise, with the imperial tassel of the Incas on his forehead. Quispe was the most talented of the Indian artists of Cuzco. In his works, parrots soar among the angels and alight on a Saint Sebastian riddled with arrows. American faces, birds, and fruits appear smuggled into landscapes of Europe or of Heaven.

While the Spaniards burn flutes and ponchos in the Plaza Mayor, the image makers of Cuzco find a way to paint bowls of avocados, rocoto chilis, chirimoyas, strawberries, and quinces on the table of the Last Supper, and to paint the Infant Jesus emerging from the belly of the Virgin and the Virgin sleeping on a bed of gold, in the embrace of Saint Joseph.

The people raise crosses of corn, or adorn them with garlands of potatoes; and at the foot of the altars there are offerings of squashes and watermelons.

(138 and 300)

Mary, Mother Earth

In churches hereabouts it is common to see the Virgin crowned with feathers or protected by parasols, like an Inca princess, and God the Father in the shape of a sun amid monkeys holding up columns and moldings adorned with tropical fruits, fish, and birds.

An unsigned canvas shows the Virgin Mary in the silver mountain of Potosí, between the sun and the moon. On one side is the pope of Rome, on the other the king of Spain. Mary, however, is not on the mountain but *inside* it; she *is* the mountain, a mountain with woman's face and outstretched hands. Mary-mountain, Mary-stone, fertilized by God as the sun fertilizes the land.

(137)

Pachamama

In the Andean highlands, the Virgin is *mama* and the land and time are also *mama*.

Earth, mother earth—the Pachamama—gets angry if someone drinks without inviting her. When she is extremely thirsty, she breaks the vessel and spills out its contents.

To her is offered the placenta of the newly born, which is buried among flowers so that the child may live; and so that love may live, lovers bury their knotted hair.

The goddess earth takes into her arms the weary and the broken who once emerged from her, opens to give them refuge at the journey's end. From beneath the earth, the dead make her flower.

(247)

Mermaids

In the main portico of the cathedral of Puno, Simón de Asto will carve two mermaids in stone.

Although mermaids symbolize sin, the artist will not sculpt monsters. He will create two handsome Indian girls, gay charango-players who will love without a shadow of guilt. These Andean mermaids, Quesintuu and Umantuu, in ancient times rose from the waters of Lake Titicaca to make love with the god Tunupa, the Aymara god of fire and lightning, who in passing left a wake of volcanos.

(137)

1717: Quebec
The Man Who Didn't Believe in Winter

The way Rabelais told it and Voltaire repeats it, the cold of Canada is so cold that words freeze as they emerge from the mouth and are suspended in midair. At the end of April, the first sun cleaves the ice on the rivers and spring breaks through amid crackings of resurrection. Then, only then, words spoken in the winter are heard.

The French colonists fear winter more than the Indians, and envy the animals that sleep through it. Neither the bear nor the marmot knows the ills of cold: they leave the world for a few months while winter splits trees with a sound like gunshots and turns humans into statues of congealed blood and marbleized flesh.

The Portuguese Pedro da Silva spends the winter carrying mail in a dog sled over the ice of the Saint Lawrence River. In summer he travels by canoe, and sometimes, due to the winds, takes a whole month coming and going between Quebec and Montreal. Pedro carries decrees from the governor, reports by monks and officials, offers by fur traders, promises from friends, secrets of lovers.

Canada's first postman has worked for a quarter of a century without asking winter's permission. Now he has died.

(96)

1717: Dupas Island
The Founders

The map of Canada fills a whole wall. Between the east coast and the great lakes, a few cities, a few forts. Beyond, an immense space of mystery. On another wall, beneath the crossed barrels of muskets, hang the scalps of enemy Indians, darkened by tobacco smoke.

Seated on a rocking chair, Pierre de La Vérendrye bites his pipe. La Vérendrye doesn't hear the bawlings of his newly born son as he squints at the map and lets himself go down the torrential rivers that no European has yet navigated.

He has returned alive from the battlefields of France, where they had given him up for dead from a shot in the breast and various saber wounds. In Canada he has plenty to eat, thanks to the wheat in his fields and his wounded lieutenant's pension; but he is bored to delirium.

His wounded legs will travel farther than his wildest daydreams. La Vérendrye's explorations will make this map look foolish. Heading west in search of the ocean that leads to the China coasts, he will reach places to the north where the musket barrel explodes from the cold when fired, and farther south than the unknown Missouri River. This child who is crying beside him in his wooden cradle will be the discoverer of the invincible wall of the Rocky Mountains.

Missionaries and fur traders will follow in his footsteps. So it has ever been. So it was with Cartier, Champlain, and La Salle.

Europe pays good prices for the skins of beavers, otters, martens, deer, foxes, and bears. In exchange for the skins, the Indians get weapons to kill each other, or die in the wars between Englishmen and Frenchmen who dispute their lands. The Indians also get firewater, which turns the toughest warrior into skin and bone, and diseases more devastating than the worst snowstorms.

(176 and 330)

Portrait of the Indians

Among the Indians of Canada there are no paunches nor any hunchbacks, say the French friars and explorers. If there is one who is lame, or blind, or one-eyed, it is from a war wound.

They do not know about property or envy, says Pouchot, and call money *the Frenchmen's snake*.

They think it ridiculous to obey a fellow man, says Lafitau. They elect chiefs who have no privilege whatsoever; and if one gets bossy, they depose him. Women give opinions and decisions on par with men. Councils of elders and public assemblies have the final word; but no human word has precedence over the voice of dreams.

They obey dreams as Christians do the divine mandate, says Brébeuf. They obey them every day, because the soul speaks through dreams every night; and when winter comes to an end and the ice of the world is broken, they throw a big party dedicated to dreams. Then the Indians dress up in costumes and every kind of madness is permitted.

They eat when they are hungry, says Cartier. Appetite is the only clock they know.

They are libertines, Le Jeune observes. Both women and men can break their marriage vows when they like. Virginity means nothing to them. Champlain has found women who have been married twenty times.

According to Le Jeune, they do not like working, but they delight in inventing lies. They know nothing of art, unless it be the art of scalping enemies. They are vengeful: for vengeance they eat lice and worms and every bug that enjoys human flesh. They are incapable, Biard shows, of understanding any abstract idea.

According to Brébeuf, the Indians cannot grasp the idea of hell. They have never heard of eternal punishment. When Christians threaten them with hell, the savages ask: *And will my friends be there in hell?*

(97)

Songs of the Chippewa Indians in the Great Lakes Region

Sometimes
I go about pitying myself
while I am carried by the wind
across the sky.

• • •

The bush
is sitting under a tree
and singing.

(38 and 340)

1718: São Jose del Rei

The Pillory

The horde of adventurers level forests, open mountains, divert rivers; and as long as fire evokes a sparkle in the rusty stones, the pursuers of gold eat toads and roots, and found cities under the double sign of hunger and punishment.

Erection of the pillory marks the birth of each city in the Brazilian gold region. The pillory is the center of everything, and around it will be the houses, and on the hilltops, churches: the pillory, with a crown on top and two iron rings to bind the hands of slaves deserving the lash.

Raising his sword before it, the count of Assumar is giving official birth to the town of São Jose del Rei. The journey from Rio de Janeiro has taken him four months and on the way he has had to eat monkey meat and roast ants.

This land makes the count of Assumar, governor of Minas Gerais, panicky and sick. He considers the spirit of revolt second nature for these intractable and rootless people. Here the stars induce disorder, he says; the water exhales uprisings and the earth gives off tumultuous vapors; the clouds are insolent, the winds rebellious, the gold outrageous.

The count has every runaway slave beheaded and organizes militias to put down black subversion. The *raceless ones*, neither white nor black, wretched offspring of master and slave, or mixtures of a thousand bloods, are the hunters of fugitive slaves. Born to live outside the law, all they are good for is dying as killers. They, the mulattos and mestizos, are abundant. Here, with no white women, there is no way of complying with the will of the king, who has ordered from Lisbon the avoidance of *defective and impure offspring*.

(122 and 209)

1719: Potosí

The Plague

Three years ago heaven sent a warning, *horrendous fire, presaging calamity*. The comet—maverick sun, crazy sun—pointed its accusing tail at the mountain of Potosí.

At the beginning of this year a child with two heads was born in the San Pedro barrio and the priest wondered whether to do one or two baptisms.

Despite comet and monster, Potosí persists in its French styles, clothing, and customs *reproved by God, shameful to sex, offensive to nature and a scandal to civic and political decency.* The city celebrates the Shrovetide carnival as usual, binge and uproar *very contrary to honesty*; and when six lovely damsels proceed to dance in the nude, the plague strikes.

Potosí suffers a thousand ills and deaths. God is merciless with the Indians, who shed rivers of blood to pay for the city's sins. According to Don Matías Ciriaco y Selda, *scientific and highly qualified physician*, to avenge himself God has used the evil influence of Saturn to turn the blood into urine and bile.

(16)

1721: Zacatecas
To Eat God

Bells ring out summoning all to the celebration. The mining center of Zacatecas has signed a peace pact with the Huichol Indians.

Long ago having fallen back into the Nayarit mountains, the Huichols have defended their independence for two centuries, invulnerable to constant assault. Now they are submitting to the Spanish crown. The pact guarantees that they will not be forced to serve in the mines.

On pilgrimages to their sacred lands, the Huichols have had no alternative but to pass through the region of mines, which is always hungry for hands. Grandfather Fire protects them from scorpion and snake, but can do little against the Indian-hunters.

The long trek to the Viricota plateau through an endless stony wilderness is a journey to their place of origin along the road of the gods. In Viricota the Huichols relive the ancestral deer hunt; they return to the eternal moment when the Lord of the Deer raised his horns to the newly risen sun, when he sacrificed himself so that human life would be possible, when he fertilized the corn with his own blood.

The deer, god of gods, inhabits a cactus, the peyote, which is extremely hard to find. The small and ugly peyote conceals itself among the rocks. When the Huichols discover it, they shoot arrows at it; and when they trap it, it weeps. Then they bleed it and skin it and cut the flesh into strips. Around the campfire, the Huichols eat the sacred cactus and then the trance sets in. At the edge of madness, in the ecstasy where all is forever and all is never, they are gods— while the communion lasts.

(31)

If You Inadvertently Lose Your Soul

That Huichol Indian woman about to give birth, what is she doing? She is remembering. She remembers intensely the night of love from which comes the child about to be born. She thinks about it with all the strength of that memory, that happiness, her body opening, joyful with that joy she had, sending forth a good Huichol who will be worthy of the joy that made him.

A good Huichol takes care of his soul, shining life force, but everyone knows that soul is smaller than an ant, softer than a whisper, a little nothing, a puff of wind. In any careless moment it can be lost.

A young lad trips and rolls down the mountainside. The soul, tied to him by no more than a silken spider's thread, detaches as he falls. The young Huichol, dizzy, sickening, calls haltingly to the guardian of the sacred songs, the wizard-priest.

That old Indian scratching at the mountainside, what is he looking for? He retraces the sick lad's trail. He climbs, silently, among the sharp rocks, searching the foliage leaf by leaf, looking under little stones. *Where did life fall? Where does it lie in fright?* He walks slowly, listening alertly because lost souls weep or sometimes whistle like the breeze.

When he finds the missing soul, the wizard-priest lifts it with the tip of a feather, wraps it in a tiny ball of cotton, and carries it in a little hollow reed back to its owner, who will not die.

(124)

1726: Montevideo Bay
Montevideo

East of the bend in the Uruguay River, the rolling prairie nurtures more cows than clover. The *bandeirantes* of Brazil, swallowers of frontiers, covet this enormous mine of meat and hides; and now the Portuguese flag flutters on the River Plata coast, over the Colonia del

Sacramento fortress. To stop their onslaught, the king of Spain orders a town built on Montevideo Bay.

Under the protection of cannon and cross, the new city emerges. It blooms on a point of earth and rock beaten by the wind and threatened by Indians. From Buenos Aires come the first settlers, fifteen young people, nineteen children, and a few slaves who do not figure on the list—black hands for the ax, the hoe, and the gallows, breasts to give milk, a voice to cry wares.

The founders, almost all illiterate, get knightly privileges from the king. They try out the right to call themselves "Don" over rounds of maté, gin, and cigars:

"Your health, Don."

"Here's to yours."

The general store smells of maté and tobacco. It is the first house to have a wooden door and adobe walls among the cowhide huts scattered in the shadow of the fort. The store offers drinks, talk, and guitars, and also sells buttons and frying pans, biscuits and what-have-you.

Out of the general store, the cafe will be born. Montevideo will be the city of cafes. No corner will be a corner without a cafe as an accessory for secrets and noise, a little temple where all loneliness can take refuge, all encounters be celebrated, with cigarette smoke serving as incense.

(278 and 315)

1733: Ouro Prêto

Fiestas

Arches of flowers span the streets of Ouro Prêto, and in their shade the Holy Sacrament parades between walls of silks and damasks. The Four Winds and the Seven Planets come and go on horses sheathed with jewels, and on lofty thrones gleam the Moon and the Nymphs and the Morning Star, with their corteges of angels. After a week of fireworks and continuous celebration, the procession chants thanksgivings to Gold, hallelujahs to the Diamond, and devotions to God.

Diamonds are a novelty in the region. Until recently they were used to keep score in card games. When it was discovered what these little crystals were, the king of Portugal presented the first ones to

God and the pope and then bought from the Vatican the very costly title of Most Faithful King.

The streets of Ouro Prêto rise and fall steeply like knife blades, its people divided between summits and abysses. The fiestas of those at the top are displays of obligatory celebration, but the fiestas of those at the bottom provoke suspicion and punishment. Dark skins conceal threats of witchcraft and dangers of rebellion. The songs and music of the poor are a sin. The mulatta who likes to laugh risks prison or banishment, and on a Sunday of merriment a black slave can lose his head.

(209)

1736: Saint John's, Antigua
Flare-ups

They sealed their oath drinking from the same earthenware bowl a mixture of rum, grave dirt, and rooster's blood, and an earthquake of drums exploded. They had the powder ready to blow up the governor and all the chief gentry of the British island of Antigua. So the prosecutor told it. So the judges believed.

Six black slaves die of hunger, lashed to the stake, and another five are broken to pieces. Seventy-seven are burned alive. Two others save themselves by telling lies that condemn their fathers to the fire.

The conspirators are charcoal or putrid meat, but they wander along the beach at dawn. While the low tide bares marvels in the sand, fishermen cross paths with the dead, who are seeking water and food to continue their journey to the beyond.

(78)

1738: Trelawny Town
Cudjoe

Plants and people stream with sweat in the hairy mountains of western Jamaica. Even the sun hides itself when the long wail of the horn announces that the enemy chief has arrived at the pass.

This time Colonel Guthrie does not come to fight. The English slavers offer peace to the maroons. They promise to respect the freedom they have won in long years of war and recognize their ownership of the lands they live on. In exchange, the maroons turn themselves into gendarmes of their imprisoned brothers: from now on, they will help punish slave rebellions on the sugar plantations and will return fugitives who come here seeking refuge.

Chief Cudjoe goes out to meet Colonel Guthrie. Cudjoe wears a brimless hat and a jacket that once was blue and had sleeves. The red dust of Jamaica imparts one color to skin and clothing, but not even a button is missing on the colonel's vest and the whiteness of his rolled wig can still be discerned. Cudjoe falls to the ground and kisses his boots.

(78, 86 and 264)

1739: New Nanny Town
Nanny

After dealing with Cudjoe, chief of the Leeward maroons, Colonel Guthrie marches east, but some unknown hand slips a deadly poison into his rum, and he falls like lead from his horse.

Some months later, at the foot of a very high mountain, Captain Adair secures peace in the east. Sporting a ceremonial sword and a silvery hat, Quao, chief of the Windward maroons, accepts his conditions. But on these eastern cliffs Nanny has more power than Quao. The scattered Windward bands obey her, as do the squadrons of mosquitos. Nanny, a large woman of fiery clay, mistress of the gods, wears nothing but a necklace of English soldiers' teeth.

No one sees her, everyone sees her. They say she is dead, but she hurls herself naked, a black bombshell, into the center of the battle. She squats with her back to the enemy, and her magnificent ass catches the bullets. Sometimes she sends them back with interest and sometimes she turns them into balls of cotton.

(78 and 264)

Pilgrimage in Jamaica

They come from holes in the trees, holes in the ground, chinks between rocks.

Rains and rivers do not hold them back. They cross marshes, ravines, forests. Neither fog nor the fierce sun sidetracks them. Slowly, implacably, they descend from the mountains. They march in profile, on a straight course, without deviations. Their shells gleam in the sun. Battalions of warrior males head the pilgrimage. At any sign of danger they raise their weapons, their claws. Many die or lose an arm opening the way. The soil of Jamaica creaks, covered by this immense army of crabs.

The journey to the sea is long. After two or three months they arrive exhausted—those that arrive. Then the females come forward and let themselves be covered by the waves, and the sea pulls out their eggs.

Of the millions that began the journey to the sea, few return. But the sea incubates, beneath the sand, a new crab people. And before long this new people sets out for the mountains whence came their mothers; and there is no one to stop them.

The crabs have no heads. They arrived late at the distribution of heads that was made by the god king in his cotton and copper palace back in Africa. Crabs have no heads, but they dream and know.

(86)

1742: Juan Fernández Islands

Anson

The Chileans believe that the waves of this ocean are horses with foaming mouths that witches ride with reins of gulfweed. The waves hurl their assault upon the boulders which do not believe in witches, and the rocky castles submit to the beating with remote disdain. High above, dignified as a king, a billy goat with venerable beard contemplates the spray. Few goats remain on the Juan Fernández Islands. Years ago the Spaniards brought from Chile a pack of dogs to seize this easy food, thus denying it to the pirates.

Commander Anson's men vainly hunt the shadows of horns among rocks and precipices, and think they recognize the mark of Alexander Selkirk on the ears of a goat they catch. The English flag flies intact from the ships' masts. Lord George Anson's fleet will return to London devastated by hunger and scurvy, but the booty will be so splendid that forty ox-carts will not suffice to haul it from the port. In the name of perfecting Cartography, Geography, Astronomy, Geometry and the Art of Navigation, scientist Anson has hunted down various Spanish ships with his guns and set fire to several towns, taking everything, down to wigs and embroidered underwear.

In these years the British Empire is coming to birth in the translation from piracy to contraband; but Anson is a pirate of the old school.

(10)

1753: Sierra Leone River
Let Us Praise the Lord

The revelation of God came in the flashes of lightning. Captain John Newton was converted to Christianity on a night of blasphemy and drunkenness when a sudden storm was on the point of sending his ship to the bottom of the ocean.

Since then he is one of the Lord's elect. Every evening he preaches a sermon. He says grace before each meal and starts every day singing psalms which the crew hoarsely repeat in chorus. In Liverpool, at the end of each voyage, he pays for a special ceremony of thanksgiving to the All-Highest.

While awaiting a cargo at the mouth of the Sierra Leone River, Captain Newton puts fears and mosquitos to flight and beseeches God to protect the ship *African* and all her crew, and to ensure that the merchandise he is about to load reaches Jamaica intact.

Captain Newton and his numerous colleagues are engaged in a triangular trade between England, Africa, and the Antilles. At Liverpool they load cloth, rum, rifles, and knives which they exchange for men, women, and children on the African coast. The ships steer a course for the Caribbean islands, and there exchange the slaves for sugar, molasses, cotton, and tobacco which they take to Liverpool to start the cycle again.

In his leisure hours the captain contributes to the sacred liturgy by composing hymns. On this night, shut up in his cabin, he begins to write a new one as he waits for the slave caravan, delayed because a few slaves tried to kill themselves by eating clay on the way. He already has the title. The hymn will be called "How Sweet the Sound of Jesus' Name." The first verses are done, and the captain hums possible melodies beneath the accomplice lamp that swings from the upper deck.

(193)

1758: Cap Français

Macandal

Before a large assembly of runaway slaves, François Macandal pulls a yellow handkerchief out of a glass of water.

"First it was the Indians."

Then a white handkerchief.

"Now, whites are the masters."

He shakes a black handkerchief before the maroons' eyes. The hour of those who came from Africa has arrived, he announces. He shakes the handkerchief with his only hand, because he has left the other between the iron teeth of the sugar mill.

On the plains of northern Haiti, one-handed Macandal is the master of fire and poison. At his order cane fields burn; and by his spells the lords of sugar collapse in the middle of supper, drooling spit and blood.

He knows how to turn himself into an iguana, an ant, or a fly, equipped with gills, antennae, or wings; but they catch him anyway, and condemn him; and now they are burning him alive. Through the flames the multitude see his body twist and shake. All of a sudden, a shriek splits the ground, a fierce cry of pain and exultation, and Macandal breaks free of the stake and of death: howling, flaming, he pierces the smoke and is lost in the air.

For the slaves, it is no cause for wonder. They knew he would remain in Haiti, the color of all shadows, the prowler of the night.

(63 and 115)

1761: Cisteil

Canek

The Maya Indians proclaim the independence of Yucatán and announce the forthcoming independence of America.

"Spanish power has brought us nothing but troubles. Nothing but troubles."

Jacinto Uc, who makes trumpets sound by caressing the leaves of trees, crowns himself king. Canek, *black snake*, is his chosen name. The king of Yucatán ties around his neck the mantle of Our Lady of the Conception and harangues the other Indians. They have rolled grains of corn on the ground and sung the war chant. The prophets, the men with warm breasts enlightened by the gods, have said that he who diēs fighting will reawaken. Canek says he is not king for love of power, that power craves more and more power, and that when the jug is full the water spills out. He says he is king against the power of the powerful, and announces the end of serfdom and whipping posts and of Indians lining up to kiss the master's hand.

"They won't be able to tie us up: they'll run out of rope."

In Cisteil and other villages the echoes multiply, words become screams; and monks and captains roll in blood.

(67 and 144)

1761: Merida
Fragments

After much killing, they have taken him prisoner. Saint Joseph has been the patron saint of this colonial victory. They accuse Canek of scourging Christ and of stuffing Christ's mouth with grass. He is convicted. He is to be broken alive with iron bars in the main square of Merida.

Canek enters the square on muleback, his face almost hidden by an enormous paper crown. On the crown his infamy is spelled out: *Risen against God and against the King.*

They chop him up bit by bit, without permitting him the relief of death, worse than an animal's fate in a slaughterhouse; then they throw the fragments of him into the bonfire. A prolonged ovation punctuates the ceremony. Beneath the ovation, it is whispered that the serfs will put ground glass in the masters' bread.

(67 and 144)

1761: Cisteil
Sacred Corn

The executioners throw Canek's ashes into the air, so that he won't revive on the day of the Last Judgement. Eight of his chiefs die by garroting and two hundred Indians have an ear cut off. Hurting what is most sacred, soldiers burn the rebel communities' seedcorn plantings.

The corn is alive. It suffers if it is burned; its dignity is hurt if it is trodden on. Perhaps the corn dreams about the Indians, as the

Indians dream about the corn. It organizes space and time and history for the people made of corn flesh.

When Canek was born, they cut his navel cord over a corncob. In the name of the newly born, grains of corn stained with his blood were planted. From this cornfield he fed, and drank clear water containing the light of an evening star, and so grew up.

(1, 67, 144, and 228)

1763: Buraco de Tatú
The Subversives Set a Bad Example

The guides, who can see as well on a moonless night as by day, elude the traps. Thanks to them, the soldiers are able to cross the labyrinth of treacherous sharpened stakes, and swoop down at dawn on the free blacks' village.

Smoke of gunpowder, smoke of flames: the air is thick and sour down by the beach at Itapoã. By midday nothing remains of the Buraco de Tatú, the fugitive slaves' refuge which for twenty years has been such an offense to the nearby city of São Salvador de Bahia.

The viceroy has sworn to cleanse Brazil of runaway slaves, but they sprout up on all sides. In vain Captain Bartolomeu Bueno lops off four thousand pairs of ears in Minas Gerais.

Rifle butts force into line those who did not fall in defense of the Buraco de Tatú. All are branded on the chest with the letter *F* for fugitive, and returned to their owners. Captain Joaquim da Costa Cardoso, who is short of cash, is selling children at bargain prices.

(264 and 284)

Communion

History, the pink-veiled lady offering her lips to those who win, will have much to hide. She will feign absent-mindedness or sicken with fake amnesia; she will lie that the black slaves of Brazil were meek and resigned, even happy.

But plantation owners oblige the cook to sample each dish before their eyes. Among the delights of the table lurk poisons that promise long agonies. Slaves kill; and they also kill themselves or flee, which are their ways of robbing the master of his chief wealth. Or they rise

up, believing and dancing and singing, which is their way of redemption and resurrection.

The smell of cut sugarcane inebriates the plantation air, and fires
burn in the earth and in human breasts: the fire tempers the whips,
drums rumble. The drums invoke the ancient gods, who fly to this
land of exile in response to the voices of their lost children, enter
them, make love to them, and, pulling music and howls from their
mouths, give them back their broken life intact.

In Nigeria or Dahomey, the drums ask fecundity for the women
and the fields. Not here. Here the women bear slaves and the fields
crush them. The drums do not ask for fecundity, but vengeance; and
Ogum, the god of iron, sharpens daggers instead of plows.

(27)

Bahia Portrait

Those in command in Bahia say that *the black man does not go to
Heaven, pray as he might, because he has rough hair that pricks Our
Lord.* They say he does not sleep: he snores. That he does not eat:
he swallows. That he does not talk: he mumbles. That he does not
die: he comes to an end. They say that God made the white man and
painted the mulatto. The black man, the Devil shat.

Any black fiesta is suspect of homage to Satan, that atrocious
black with tail, claws, and trident, but those in command know that
if the slaves amuse themselves from time to time, they do more work,
live more years and have more children. Just as the *capoeira*—ritual
and mortal hand-to-hand combat—purports to be a colorful game,
the *candomblé* pretends to be nothing but dance and noise. Furthermore, Virgins or saints to lend a disguise are never lacking. No
one stops Ogum from turning into Saint George, the blond cavalier,
and the mischievous black gods even conceal themselves in the wounds
of Christ.

In the slaves' Holy Week, it is a black that administers justice
to the traitor, blowing up the white Judas, a puppet painted with
lime; and when the slaves parade the Virgin in procession, the black
Saint Benedict is at the center of all homage. The Church does not
recognize this saint. According to the slaves, Saint Benedict was a
slave like themselves, a cook in a monastery, and angels would stir
the pot while he said his prayers.

Anthony is the saint preferred by the masters. Saint Anthony sports military stripes, draws a salary, and specializes in policing blacks. When a slave escapes, the master throws the saint into the corner with the trash. Saint Anthony remains in penitence, face down, until the dogs catch the runaway.

(27 and 65)

Your Other Head, Your Other Memory

From the sundial of the San Francisco monastery, a lugubrious inscription reminds passersby how time flies: *Every hour that passes wounds thee and the last will kill thee*.

The words are written in Latin. The black slaves of Bahia do not know Latin or how to read. From Africa they brought happy and scrappy gods: the blacks are with them, to them they go. Whoever dies, enters. The drums beat so that the deceased will not get lost and will arrive safely in Oxalá. There, in the house of the creator of creators, awaits his other head, the immortal head. We all have two heads and two memories. A head of clay, which will turn to dust; and another, forever invulnerable to the gnawings of time and of passion. One memory that death kills, a compass that expires with the journey; and another memory, the collective memory, which will live as long as the human adventure in the world lives.

When the air of the universe first stirred and breathed, and the god of gods was born, there was no separation between earth and heaven. Now they seem to be divorced; but heaven and earth join again each time someone dies, each time someone is born, and each time someone receives the gods in a throbbing body.

(361)

1763: Rio de Janeiro
Here

A quarter of a century ago, Luis da Cunha proposed to the king of Portugal that he move with all his court from Lisbon to Rio de Janeiro, and that in this city he proclaim himself Emperor of the West. The capital of the empire should be here, at the center of abundance, because Portugal could not live without the riches of Brazil but Brazil, Luis da Cunha warned, could easily live without Portugal.

For the time being the throne remains in Lisbon, but the center of the colony is displaced from north to south. Bahia, the sugar port, yields to Rio de Janeiro, port of gold and diamonds. Brazil is growing southward and westward, beating against Spanish frontiers.

The new capital occupies the most beautiful spot in the world. Here the mountains look like pairs of lovers, the air has aromas that make you laugh, and a warm breeze excites the birds. Things and people are made of music, and the sea so sparkles before your eyes that it would be a pleasure to drown yourself.

(48)

1763: Tijuco
The World Inside a Diamond

Among lofty red rocks which look like dragons undulates the red earth hurt by man's hand. The region of diamonds exhales a fiery dust that reddens the walls of the city of Tijuco. A stream flows at its side and in the distance are mountains the color of the sea or of ashes. From the bed of the river come diamonds which will cross the mountains, and sail from Rio de Janeiro to Lisbon and from Lisbon to London, where they are cut, their price multiplying several times over, later to lend brilliance to the whole world.

Many diamonds escape as contraband. Although the corpus delicti may be the size of a flea's eye, clandestine miners who have been caught lie without graves, meat for crows; and the slave suspected of swallowing what he shouldn't gets a violent purge of hot chili.

Every diamond belongs to the king of Portugal and to João Fernandes de Oliveira, who reigns here by right of the king's contract. Beside him is Chica da Silva, also known as Chica Who Commands. A mulatta, she wears European clothes barred to the dark-skinned, and shows off by going to Mass on a litter followed by a cortege of black women decked out like princesses. In the church, she occupies the place of honor. There is no noble hereabouts who does not bend his spine before her hand covered with gold rings, and none who misses her gatherings at the mansion in the mountains. There, Chica da Silva throws banquets and theater parties—performances of *The Charms of Medea* or some other fashionable play—and afterwards takes her guests for a sail on the lake that Oliveira had dug for her because she wanted ocean and there was no ocean. They mount a gilded stairway to the dock and cruise in a grand vessel crewed by ten sailors.

Chica da Silva wears a wig of white rolls. The rolls cover her forehead and hide the mark left by the branding iron when she was a slave.

(307)

1763: Havana
Progress

A year ago the English arrived at Cojímar beach with guns blazing.

While Havana signed the surrender, after a long siege, the slave ships waited outside the port. When they anchored in the bay, buyers grabbed up their merchandise. Merchants customarily follow warriors. A single slave trafficker, John Kennion, sold seventeen hundred slaves during the British occupation. He and his colleagues doubled the work force on the plantations, which were so antiquated that they still grew all kinds of food and had only one machine, the mill that crushes sugarcane, turning at the pace of circling oxen.

British dominion over Cuba hardly lasts ten months, but the Spaniards scarcely recognize the colony they get back. The English have given it such a shaking that Cuba awakens from its long agrarian siesta. In times to come this island will turn into an immense sugar factory, grinding up slaves and ravaging everything else. Tobacco farms, cornfields, and vegetable patches will be razed. Forests will be devastated and streams dried up. Each black slave will be squeezed out in seven years.

(222)

The Slaves Believe:

The gods move blood and sap. In every blade of Cuban grass breathes a god, and that's why the forest is alive. Temple of African gods, home of African ancestors, the forest is sacred and keeps secrets. If anyone fails to greet it, its anger rises and it denies health and fortune. One must offer it a gift to receive the leaves that heal wounds and ward off misfortune. One must greet it with ritual words—or whatever words come out. Everyone talks with the gods as he feels or is able.

No god is all good or all bad. The same one may save or kill. The breeze refreshes and the hurricane destroys, but both are air.

(56)

The Ceiba Tree

"Good evening, mother Ceiba. Bless you."

The imposing ceiba is a tree of mystery. The ancestors and the gods favor it. The flood respected it. It is secure from lightning and hurricanes.

One may not turn one's back on it or walk in its shade without permission. Anyone striking an ax to its sacred trunk feels the ax-blow on his own body. They say that at times it consents to die by fire, fire being its favorite son.

It opens when you ask it for shelter, and to defend the fugitive it covers itself with thorns.

(56)

The Royal Palm

In this haughty palm lives Shangó, the black god who calls himself Saint Barbara when he disguises himself as a Christian woman. The leaves of its crest are his arms. From on high he fires his heavenly artillery. Shangó eats fire, wears lightning, talks thunder, and shakes the earth with his rays. He turns enemies into ash.

Warrior and satyr, Shangó never tires of joking and loving. The gods hate him; the goddesses are crazy about him. He took his brother Ogum's woman Oyá, who is said to be the Virgin of Candelaria and fights at Shangó's side with two swords. In the rivers he makes love to Oshún, and together they eat delicacies of sugar and cinnamon.

(28 and 56)

1766: The Fields of Areco
The Wild Horses

In Buenos Aires, the twenty Indian children from the Jesuits' San Javier mission choir have sung in the cathedral and in several full churches; and the public has shown its gratitude for these voices from heaven. The Guaraní orchestra of violins and one-stringed *trompas marinas* has also worked miracles.

The musicians set out on their return journey, led by Fray Hermann Paucke. Two weeks' traveling separates them from their homes on the coast. On the way, Paucke collects and sketches all he sees: plants, birds, customs.

In the fields of Areco, Paucke and his Guaraní musicians witness the sacrifice of maverick horses. Peons bring these wild horses to the corrals mixed in with domesticated ones, and there they halter them and take them out one by one into open country. Then they turn them over and with a single slash, open their bellies. The mavericks still gallop, treading on their entrails, until they roll on the grass; and the next day dawns on bones whitened by dogs.

The wild horses wander through the pampa in troops that are more like shoals, flying fish slithering between air and grass, and spread their contagion of freedom among the domesticated horses.

(55)

1767: Misiones

The Story of Seven Villages

The king of Spain had made his father-in-law, the king of Portugal, a present of seven villages. He offered them empty, but they were inhabited. Those villages were seven missions founded by Jesuit fathers, for Guaraní Indians, east of the upper Uruguay River. Like many other missions of the Guaraní region, they had served as bulwarks for the constantly assaulted frontier.

The Guaranís declined to get out. Change their pasturelands, like a flock of sheep, because the man said so? The Jesuits had taught them to make clocks, plows, bells, clarinets, and books printed in their Guaraní language; but they had also taught them to make guns to defend themselves against the slave hunters.

Portuguese and Spanish soldiers chase the Indians off and the Indians slip back by night. Again they are chased off and again they return, but this time transformed into thunderous winds, a storm of lightning that sets fortresses afire.

Everyone knows the monks are on their side. *The will of the king is the will of God*, say the superiors of the Order of Loyola, *an impenetrable will that puts us to the test: When Abraham obeyed the divine voice, and raised the sword against the neck of his own son Isaac, God sent an angel to stay the blow at the critical moment*. But the Jesuit priests refuse to immolate the Indians. To no avail the archbishop of Buenos Aires threatens to excommunicate both Indians and priests. In vain the Church hierarchy orders the burning of the

gunpowder and destruction of the guns and lances with which the missions have a thousand times stopped Portuguese attacks against the Spanish frontier.

Long is the war of the seven villages against the two crowns. In the battle of Caybaté hill, fifteen hundred Indians fall. The seven missions are razed, but the king of Portugal cannot enjoy the king of Spain's gift.

The kings never forgive the offense. Three years after the battle of Caybaté, the king of Portugal expels the Jesuits from all his dominions. And now the king of Spain follows suit.

(76 and 189)

1767: Misiones
The Expulsion of the Jesuits

The instructions arrive from Madrid in envelopes sealed with wax. Viceroys and governors execute them immediately throughout America. They seize the Jesuit fathers at night by surprise and immediately ship them to far-off Italy. More than two thousand priests go into exile.

The king of Spain punishes the sons of Loyola, who have become such sons of America, for repeated disobedience and the suspected planning of an independent Indian kingdom.

No one weeps for them as do the Guaranis. The Jesuits' many missions in the Guaraní region announced the promised land without evil and without death; and the Indians called the priests *karaí*, a name reserved for their prophets. From the wreckage of the San Luis Gonzaga mission, the Indians send a letter to the governor of Buenos Aires. *We are not slaves*, they say. *We don't like your custom of every man for himself instead of helping one another*.

Soon all is broken up. Common property and the communal system of production and life disappear. The best missionary estancias are sold to the highest bidder. Churches, factories, schools fall apart. Undergrowth invades pastures and wheat fields. Pages are torn from books to make cartridges for gunpowder. The Indians flee into the forest or stay to become vagabonds, whores, and drunks. To be born Indian is once again an insult or a crime.

(189)

1767: Misiones

They Won't Let Their Tongues Be Torn Out

In the print shops of the Paraguay missions some of the best books of colonial America have been published, religious books in the Guaraní language, with typefaces and engravings carved in wood by Indians.

Guaraní was the spoken and written language of the missions. After the expulsion of the Jesuits, Castilian is imposed as the obligatory and only language.

No one resigns himself to becoming dumb and without memory. No one pays any attention.

(117)

1769: London

The First Novel Written in America

Ten years ago the bells of London wore themselves out celebrating the victories of the British Empire. The city of Quebec had fallen after intense bombardment, and France had lost her dominions in Canada. The young general James Wolfe, who commanded the English army, had announced that he would crush *the Canadian plague*, but died before seeing it happen. According to the gossip, Wolfe would measure himself when he awoke and find himself a bit taller each day, until a bullet interrupted his growth.

Now Frances Brooke publishes a novel in London, *The History of Emily Montague*, which depicts Wolfe's officers conquering hearts in the land conquered by their guns. The author, a plump and pleasant Englishwoman, lives and writes in Canada. In the form of two hundred and twenty-eight letters, she relates her impressions and experiences in the new British colony and weaves in some romances between uniformed English gallants and the breathless young ladies of Quebec high society. Their well-educated passions lead to matrimony, via the fashion house, the ballroom, and picnics on the islands. The magnificent waterfalls and noble lakes provide a fitting backdrop.

(50, 52, and 176)

Indians and Dreams in
the Novel of Frances Brooke

The Indians retain most of their ancient superstitions. I should particularize their belief in dreams, of which folly even repeated disappointments cannot cure them . . . As I happened to smile at the recital a savage was making of a prophetic dream, from which he assured us of the death of an English officer whom I knew to be alive, "You Europeans," said he, "are the most unreasonable people in the world; you laugh at our belief in dreams, and yet expect us to believe things a thousand times more incredible."

(50)

1769: Lima

Viceroy Amat

At the hour when families kneel to say the rosary, the holy, holy, holy, the novena, and prayers for the dead, the trot of the viceroy's carriage heading for the theater is heard. A murmur of scandal echoes through half-open Venetian blinds. Prayers stop short. Gossip breaks forth. The brusque viceroy of Lima, a rascal, rogue, and knave, has lost his head to a small-time comedienne.

Night after night, Don Manuel de Amat y Junyent attends any zarzuela, farce, mystery or comedy in which Micaela Villegas waggles her hips and stomps her heels on the stage. He doesn't care about the plot. When Micaela, that exquisite pure cinnamon, that cinnamon in flower starts singing her cajoleries, the old viceroy's wig flies off. He applauds madly and punches holes in the floor with his cane. She answers him rolling her eyes, smiling beneath the indispensable beauty spot, and offering her breasts in sequined curtsies.

The viceroy has been a man of the barracks, not of parties and balls. A scowling bachelor with five big scars won in the North African wars, he came to Lima to clean horse- and cattle-thieves off the roads and throw out idlers and loafers. Under this leaden sky, more roof than sky, he wanted to kill himself, but conquered the temptation by hanging people.

Eight years after his arrival the viceroy has learned to steal, to eat rocote chilis and spicy guinea pig, and to study décolletages with an opera glass. The ship that brought him from Valparaíso had a naked woman as figurehead on its prow.

(26 and 245)

1769: Lima

La Perricholi

Like all women of Lima, Micaela Villegas displays her bosom but hides her feet, protects them with tiny shoes of white satin. Like the others, she enjoys wearing rubies and sapphires even on her belly, be they only paste, as hers were.

Daughter of a poor provincial mestizo, Micaela made the rounds of this city's shops for the pure pleasure of seeing or feeling Lyons silks and Flanders woollens, and bit her lips when she discovered a gold and diamond necklace around the neck of a highborn lady's kitten.

Micaela got into the theater and was transformed into queen, nymph, fashion plate, or goddess as long as the performance lasted. Now she is First Courtesan all day and all night, too. A cloud of black slaves surrounds her, her jewelry is above suspicion and counts kiss her hand.

The ladies of Lima avenge themselves by calling her Perricholi. The viceroy himself had so baptized her, trying to say *perra chola* (mestizo bitch) with his toothless mouth. They say he put this curse on her, as a sort of exorcism, while carrying her up the steps to his lofty bed, because she stirred in him dangerous panics and burnings and wet and dry sensations that took him back trembling to his early years.

(95, 245, and 304)

The Snack Clock

With the milkwoman at seven o'clock begins the bustle of Lima. Behind her, in an odor of sanctity, comes the vendor of herb teas.

At eight the curds-seller passes.

At nine, a voice offers cinnamon candies.

At ten, tamales seek mouths to delight.

Eleven is the hour of melons and coconut candies and toasted corn.

At noon, bananas and passion fruit, pineapples, milky *chirimoyas* of green velvet, and avocados promising soft pulp promenade through the streets.

At one, come the cakes of hot honey.

At two, a hawker offers *picarones*, buns that invite choking; and behind her come the corn sugarcakes steeped in cinnamon that no tongue can forget.

At three, appears the vendor of *anticuchos*, roasted broken hearts, followed by the peddlers of honey and sugar.

At four, the chili-vendor sells spice and fire.

Cebiche, raw fish steeped in lime, marks five o'clock.

At six, nuts.

At seven, *mazamorra* pastries baked to a T on open tile roofs.

At eight, ice creams of many flavors and colors, fresh gusts of wind, push the doors of night wide open.

(93 and 245)

1771: Madrid
Royal Summit

Big crates arrive at the palace from the incandescent deserts of Peru. The Spanish monarch reads the report of the official who sends them: this is the complete tomb of a Mochica chief, much older than the Incas; the descendants of the Mochicas and of the Chimús now live in dire penury and there are ever fewer of them; their valleys are in the hands of a *few greedy Spaniards*.

The cases are opened. A seventeen hundred-year-old king appears at the feet of Charles III. He has teeth, nails and hair still intact, and flesh of parchment stuck to his bones, and his majestic raiment gleams with gold and feathers. His scepter, a god of corn garlanded with plants, accompanies the remote visitor; and the vases that were buried with him have also made the journey to Madrid.

The king of Spain, dumbfounded, contemplates the ceramics that surround his defunct colleague. The king of the Mochicas lies amid pleasures. The ceramics represent pairs of lovers embracing and entering each other in a thousand ways, ignorant of original sin, enjoying themselves without knowing that for this act of disobedience we have been condemned to live on the earth.

(355)

1771: Paris

The Age of Enlightenment

In Europe the venerable walls of cathedrals and palaces are cracking. The bourgeoisie is on the offensive, armed with steam engines and volumes of the *Encyclopedia* and other unstoppable battering rams of the industrial revolution.

Budding from Paris are defiant ideas which, flying over the heads of *hoi polloi*, set their seal on the century. A time of the *fury to learn* and the *fever of intelligence*, the Age of Enlightenment raises up human reason, the reason of the minority who think, against the dogmas of the Church and the privileges of the nobility. Condemnations, persecution, and exile only stimulate the learned sons of the English philosophers and of prolific Descartes, *he who started by doubting everything*.

No subject is out of bounds for the philosophers of the Enlightenment, from the law of gravity to ecclesiastical celibacy. The institution of slavery merits their constant attack. Slavery contradicts nature, says Denis Diderot, director of the *Encyclopedia, Reasoned Dictionary of the Sciences, Arts, and Professions*: a man cannot be the property of his master for the same reason that a child cannot be his father's property, nor a woman her husband's, nor a servant his employer's, nor a subject his king's, and anyone thinking the opposite is confusing persons with things. Helvetius has said that *no barrel of sugar reached Europe that is not stained with blood*; and Candide, Voltaire's character, meets in Surinam a slave missing a hand devoured by a sugar mill, and a leg cut off for trying to escape:

"At this price you eat sugar in Europe."

If we admit that blacks are human beings, we admit how little Christian we are, says Montesquieu. All religion that hallows slavery deserves to be prohibited, says the Abbé Raynal. For Jean-Jacques Rousseau, slavery makes him ashamed to be a man.

(95 and 98)

1771: Paris

The Physiocrats

More than a crime, slavery is an economic error, say the physiocrats. In the last issue of the *Citizen's Ephemerides* Pierre Dupont de Nemours explains that slavery perpetuates archaic methods of agriculture and slows the development of France's colonies in the Antilles and on the mainland of America. Despite continuous replacement of the spent labor force, slavery means waste and a depreciation of invested capital. Dupont de Nemours proposes that calculations should take into account losses incurred by the early death of slaves, fires set by runaways and the cost of the constant war against them, the appallingly bad preparation of harvests, and tools ruined by ignorance or ill will. Ill will and laziness, he says, are weapons that the slave uses to recover a part of his personality stolen by the master; and his ineptitude results from the absolute lack of incentive to develop his intelligence. It is slavery, not nature, that makes the slave.

Only a free labor force proves efficiently productive, according to the economist-philosophers of the Physiocrat school. They believe that property is sacred, but only in freedom can it fully achieve the production of value.

(98)

1771: Paris

The Minister of Colonies Explains Why Mulattos Should Not Be Freed from Their Congenital "State of Humiliation"

His Majesty has considered that such a favor would tend to destroy the differences that nature has placed between whites and blacks, and that political prejudice has been careful to maintain as a distance which people of color and their descendants will never be able to bridge; finally, that it is in the interest of good order not to weaken the state of humiliation congenital to the species, in whatever degree it may perpetuate itself; a prejudice all the more useful for being in the very heart of the slaves and contributing in a major way to the due peace of the colonies . . .

(139)

1772: Cap Français

France's Richest Colony

The monks have denied last rites to the diva of the Cape Comedy, Mademoiselle Morange, whose irreparable loss to Haiti is mourned in six theaters and more than six bedrooms. No dead artiste deserves to be prayed for, the theater being an infamous occupation eternally condemned; but one of the actors, bell in hand and crucifix on breast, in black cassock and shining tonsure, marches singing psalms in Latin at the head of the dead virtuosa's cortege.

Before it reaches the cemetery, the police are already chasing off the baritone and his accomplices, who vanish in a split second. But the people protect and hide them. Who does not feel sympathy for these show folk who fan the insufferable languors of Haiti with breezes of cultural madness?

On the stages of this colony, France's richest, plays just opened in Paris are applauded, and the theaters are like Paris's—or, at least, would like to be. Here, though, the public is seated according to color of skin: in the center, ivory; on the right, copper; and on the left, ebony, a few free blacks.

The affluent sail into the theaters in a flutter of fans, the heat releasing floods beneath their powdered wigs. Each white woman resembles a jewelry store: gold, pearls, and diamonds make a dazzling frame for damp breasts leaping out of silk, demanding obedience and desire.

Haiti's most powerful colonists live on guard against the sun and the cuckold's horns. They do not leave home until after dusk, when the heat is less punishing, and only then dare to show themselves in litters or carriages drawn by many horses. The ladies are notorious for indulging in much love and much widowhood.

(115 and 136)

1772: Léogane
Zabeth

Ever since she learned to walk she was in flight. They tied a heavy chain to her ankles, and chained, she grew up; but a thousand times she jumped over the fence and a thousand times the dogs caught her in the mountains of Haiti.

They stamped the fleur-de-lis on her cheek with a hot iron. They put an iron collar and iron shackles on her and shut her up in the sugar mill, where she stuck her fingers into the grinder and later bit off the bandages. So that she might die of iron they tied her up again, and now she expires, chanting curses.

Zabeth, this woman of iron, belongs to Madame Galbaud du Fort, who lives in Nantes.

(90)

1773: San Mateo Huitzilopochco

The Strength of Things

The church of this village is a sorry wreck. The priest, newly arrived from Spain, decides that God cannot go on living in such a miserable and broken-down house, and sets to work. To raise solid walls, he orders the Indians to bring stones from some nearby ruins from the times of idolatry.

No threat or punishment can make them obey. The Indians refuse to move those stones that still lie where the grandfathers of their grandfathers worshiped the gods. Those stones promise nothing, but they prevent forgetting.

(132 and 322)

1774: San Andrés Itzapan

Dominus Vobiscum

The Indians are forced to spit every time they mention one of their gods. They are forced to dance new dances, the Dance of the Conquest and the Dance of Moors and Christians, which celebrate the invasion of America and the humiliation of the infidels.

They are forced to cover up their bodies, because the struggle against idolatry is also a struggle against nudity, a dangerous nudity that, according to the archbishop of Guatemala, produces in anyone seeing it *much lesion in the brain*.

They are forced to repeat from memory the Praise Be to God, the Hail Mary, and the Our Father.

Have Guatemala's Indians become Christians?

The doctrinal friar of San Andrés Itzapan is not very sure. He says he has explained the mystery of the Holy Trinity by folding a cloth and showing it to the Indians: *Look, a single cloth folded into three. In the same way God is one in three*. And he says this convinced the Indians that God is made of cloth.

The Indians parade the Virgin on feathered platforms. Calling her Grandmother of the Light, they ask her each night that tomorrow may bring the sun; but they venerate more devoutly the serpent that she grinds underfoot. They offer incense to the serpent, the old god who gives a good corn crop and good deer hunting and helps them to kill enemies. More than Saint George they worship the dragon, covering it with flowers; and the flowers at the feet of the horseman

Santiago pay homage to the horse, not to the apostle. They recognize themselves in Jesus, who was condemned without proof, as they are; but they adore the cross not as a symbol of his immolation, but because the cross has the shape of the fruitful meeting of rain and soil.

(322)

1775: *Guatemala City*
Sacraments

The Indians only perform Easter rites if they coincide with days of rain, harvesting, or planting. The archbishop of Guatemala, Pedro Cortés Larraz, issues a new decree warning that forgetfulness may imperil salvation of the soul.

Nor do the Indians come to Mass. They do not respond to announcements or to the bell. They have to be sought out on horseback in villages and fields and dragged in by force. Absence is punished with eight lashes, but the Mass offends the Mayan gods and that has more power than fear of the thong. Fifty times a year, the Mass interrupts work in the fields, the daily ceremony of communion with the earth. For the Indians, accompanying step by step the corn's cycle of death and resurrection is a way of praying; and the earth, that immense temple, is their day-to-day testimony to the miracle of life being reborn. For them all earth is a church, all woods a sanctuary.

To escape the punishment of the pillory in the plaza, some Indians come to the confessional, where they learn to sin, and kneel before the altar, where they eat the god of corn by way of communion. But they only bring their children to the baptismal font after having offered them, deep in the forest, to the old gods. Before them they celebrate the joys of resurrection. All that is born, is born again.

(322)

1775: *Huehuetenango*
Trees that Know, Bleed, Talk

The monk enters Huehuetenango through mists of incense. He thinks the infidels are paying homage in this way to the true God. But the mothers cover their new babies with cloths, so that the priest may not make them sick by looking at them. The clouds of incense are not for gratitude or welcome, but for exorcism. The copal resin burns and the smoke drifts up in supplication to the ancient Maya gods to halt the plagues that the Christians have brought.

The copal, which bleeds incense, is a sacred tree. Sacred are the ceiba, which by night becomes a woman, and the cedar, and all the trees that know how to listen to human woes.

(322)

1775: Gado-Saby
Bonny

A hail of bullets opens the way for the eight hundred soldiers from Holland. The maroon village of Gado-Saby crackles and falls. Behind a curtain of smoke and fire, the traces of blood disappear at the edge of the forest.

Swiss colonel Fourgeaud, veteran of the European wars, decides to camp among the ruins. At dusk mysterious voices sound from the brush, and a whistling of shots obliges the soldiers to throw themselves on the ground.

The troop spends the night surrounded by shots, insults, and chants of defiance and victory. The maroons, invisible, burst out laughing when Colonel Fourgeaud, from the ground, promises freedom and food in return for surrender.

"Hungry dog!" cry a thousand voices from the foliage. *"Scarecrow!"*

The voices call the Dutch soldiers *white slaves*, and announce that chief Bonny will very soon be master of this whole land of Surinam.

When dawn breaks the siege, Colonel Fourgeaud discovers that his men have been wounded not by bullets but by little stones and buttons and coins. He also discovers that the maroons have spent the night carting into the forest sacks of rice, cassava, and yams, while the volleys of projectiles and words kept the Dutchmen immobilized.

Bonny has been responsible for the maneuver. Bonny, leader of the maroons, does not have the branding iron's mark on his body. His mother, a slave, fled from the master's bed and gave him free birth in the forest.

(264)

1776: Cape Coast Castle

Alchemists of the African Slave Trade

Captain Pegleg Clarke has spent a long time bargaining on the coast of Africa. The ship stinks. The captain orders his sailors to bring the already purchased slaves up on deck and give them a bath; but hardly have their chains been removed when the blacks jump into the sea and swim toward their land. The current devours them.

The loss of the merchandise hurts the honor of Captain Clarke, old-time shepherd of these flocks, and damages the prestige of the Rhode Island slave traders. North American shipyards take pride in building the most secure ships for the Guinea traffic. Their floating prisons are so effectively constructed that only one slave rebellion occurs in four and a half years, an average four times smaller than the French, and half as much as England's specialized enterprises can boast.

The thirteen colonies that will soon be the United States of America have much to thank their slave traders for. Rum, good medicine for the soul and for the body, is turned into slaves on the African coast. Then those blacks become molasses in the Antillean islands of Jamaica and Barbados. From there, the molasses heads north and becomes rum in the distilleries of Massachusetts, and then the rum crosses the ocean again to Africa. Each voyage is rounded off with sales of tobacco, lumber, ironware, flour, and salted meat, and with purchases of spices in the islands. The blacks left over go to the plantations of South Carolina, Georgia, and Virginia.

Thus the slave trade produces profits for seamen, merchants, moneylenders, and owners of shipyards, distilleries, sawmills, meat salting plants, flour mills, plantations, and insurance companies.

(77 and 193)

1776: Pennsylvania

Paine

Its title is *Common Sense*. The pamphlet was published early this year and has circulated through the North American colonies like water or bread. The author, Tom Paine, an Englishman who came to these lands a couple of years ago, pleads for declaring independence without further ado: *A government of our own is our natural right. Why do we hesitate?*

There is something exceedingly ridiculous, says Paine, *in the composition of a monarchy*. In the best of cases, Paine considers government a necessary evil; in the worst, an intolerable evil. And monarchy is the worst of cases. One honest man, he says, *is of more worth than all the crowned ruffians that ever lived*, and he calls George III *the Royal Brute of Great Britain*.

Throughout the world, he says, liberty is fiercely hunted down. In Europe it is regarded as a foreigner; Asia and Africa long since expelled it; and the English have warned it to get out. Paine exhorts American colonists to turn this soil into a refuge for free men: *O! receive the fugitive, and prepare in time an asylum for mankind.*

(243)

1776: Philadelphia
The United States

England has never paid too much attention to her thirteen colonies on North America's Atlantic coast. They have no gold, silver, or sugar. They were never indispensable to her; she never prevented them from growing. They have walked alone, so it has been since that remote time when the Pilgrims first trod the stony lands they called New England—and the soil was so hard that they had to plant seeds with bullets, or so it was said. Now well developed, the thirteen English colonies have to run away.

The thirteen colonies are hungry for the West. Many pioneers dream of taking off over the mountains, with rifle, ax, and a handful of corn as baggage; but the British crown has drawn the frontier on the crests of the Appalachians and reserved the lands beyond for Indians. The thirteen colonies are hungry for a world. Already their ships ride all the oceans; but the British crown forces them to buy what it wants them to buy and sell where it says they should sell.

With one jerk they break the ties. The thirteen colonies refuse to continue paying obedience and money to the king of such a remote island. They hoist their own flag, decide to call themselves the United States of America, reject tea, and proclaim that rum, a national product, is the patriotic drink.

All men are created equal, says the Declaration of Independence. The slaves, half a million black slaves, don't even hear about it.

(130 and 224)

1776: Monticello

Jefferson

The writer of the Declaration of Independence, the United States' birth certificate, is a man of a thousand talents and concerns.

Tireless reader of thermometers, barometers, and books, Thomas Jefferson seeks and finds, pursuing the revelations of nature and wanting to embrace all dimensions of human thought. He is assembling a fabulous library and a universe of stones, fossils, and plants; and he knows all that can be known about neoplatonic philosophy, Latin grammar, the structure of the Greek language, and the organization of society throughout history. He knows everything about his land of Virginia, every son and grandfather of every family, every blade of grass; and he is up-to-date on all the technical novelties in the world. He enjoys trying out steam engines, new types of plows, and original methods of producing butter and cheese. He imagined his mansion of Monticello and designed and built it faultlessly.

The Puritans counted the population by "souls." Jefferson counts it by "individuals of the human species." Within the species, blacks are almost equal. Black have fair memories and no imagination, and their poor intelligence could never understand Euclid. Aristocrat of Virginia, Jefferson preaches democracy, a democracy of proprietors, and freedom of thought and religion; but he defends the hierarchies of sex and color. His educational plans do not include women, or Indians, or blacks. Jefferson condemns slavery and is, and will continue to be, a slave owner. Mulattas attract him more than white women, but loss of racial purity panics him and he thinks the mixture of bloods is the worst of the temptations besetting the white colonist.

(41 and 161)

1777: Paris

Franklin

The most famous of North Americans arrives in France on a desperate mission. Benjamin Franklin comes to ask help against the English colonial troops, who have occupied Philadelphia and other patriot redoubts. Using all the weight of his personal prestige, the ambassador proposes to kindle fires of glory and revenge in French breasts.

There is no king or commoner on earth who hasn't heard of

Franklin, since he sent up a kite and and discovered that heavenly fires and thunders express not the wrath of God but electricity in the atmosphere. His scientific discoveries emanate from daily life. The most complicated resides in the most commonplace: dawn and its never-repeated patterns, oil that is thrown on water and calms its waves, the fly drowned in wine that revives in the sun. Observing that sweat keeps the body fresh on days of stifling heat, Franklin conceives a system for producing cold by evaporation. He also invents and produces stoves and watches and a musical instrument, the glass harmonica, which inspires Mozart; and since the constant changing of spectacles for reading or distant vision bores him, he cuts lenses and fits them in a single frame and thus gives birth to bifocals.

But Franklin makes himself most popular when he notices that electricity seeks out sharp points, and defeats lightning by placing a pointed iron rod on top of a tower. Franklin being the spokeman for the American rebels, the king of England has decreed that British lightning rods should have rounded tips.

(79)

If He Had Been Born a Woman

Of Benjamin Franklin's sixteen brothers and sisters, Jane is the one most resembling him in talent and strength of will.

But at the age when Benjamin leaves home to make his own way, Jane marries a poor saddler, who accepts her without dowry, and ten months later bears her first child. From then on, for a quarter of a century, Jane has a child every two years. Some of them die, and each death opens a wound in her breast. Those that live demand food, shelter, instruction, and consolation. Jane spends whole nights cradling those that cry, washes mountains of clothing, bathes stacks of children, rushes from market to kitchen, washes piles of dishes, teaches ABC's and chores, toils elbow to elbow with her husband in his workshop, and attends to the guests whose rent helps to fill the stewpot. Jane is a devoted wife and exemplary widow; and when the children are grown up, she takes charge of her own ailing parents and of her unmarried daughters and her orphaned grandchildren.

Jane never knows the pleasure of letting herself float in a lake, drifting over the surface hitched to the string of a kite, as Benjamin enjoys doing despite his years. Jane never has time to think, nor allows herself to doubt. Benjamin continues to be a fervent lover, but Jane doesn't know that sex can produce anything except children.

Benjamin, founder of a nation of inventors, is a great man of all the ages. Jane is a woman of her age, like almost all women of all the ages, who has done her duty on this earth and expiated her share of blame in the Biblical curse. She has done all she could to keep from going mad and sought, in vain, a little silence.

Her case will awaken no interest in historians.

(313)

1778: Philadelphia
Washington

The first among the soldiers is also the most prestigious among the farmers, the swiftest among the horsemen, the best marksman among the hunters. He gives no one his hand, nor lets anyone look him in the eye. No one calls him George. From his mouth come no eulogies, nor any complaints either; and he always sets an example of composure and bravery, no matter his sufferings from ulcers, toothaches, and fevers.

With the help of men and weapons from France, George Washington's army seizes the city of Philadelphia from British hands. The war for the independence of the United States, blackcoats against redcoats, becomes long and painful.

(224 and 305)

1780: Bologna
Clavijero Defends the Accursed Lands

One of the Jesuits expelled from America, Francisco Javier Clavijero, writes in Italy his *Ancient History of Mexico*. In four volumes the priest tells *the life of a people of heroes*, marking the dawn of national and historical consciousness in native-born people who are beginning to call New Spain "Mexico" and already speak the word "fatherland" with pride. The work assumes the defense of America, so much under attack in these years from Paris, Berlin, or Edinburgh: *If America had no wheat, neither did Europe have corn . . . If America had no pomegranates or lemons, now she has them; but Europe never had, has not, and cannot have chirimoyas, avocados, bananas, chicoza-potes . . .*

With innocence and passion Clavijero attacks the Encyclopedists who describe the New World as an emporium of abominations. Count Buffon says that in America the skies are miserly and the rains rot the soil; that the lions are bald, small and cowardly and the tapir is a vest-pocket elephant; that over there horses, pigs, and dogs become dwarfs and that the Indians, cold as serpents, have no soul, nor fire for females. Voltaire, too, speaks of hairless lions and men, and Baron Montesquieu explains that warm countries produce despicable peoples. Abbé Guillaume Raynal is offended because in America mountain ranges extend from north to south instead of from east to west as they should, and his Prussian colleague Corneille de Pauw portrays the American Indian as a flabby, degenerate beast. According to de Pauw, the climate over there leaves animals sickly and without tails; the women are so ugly that they are confused with men; and the sugar has no taste, the coffee no aroma.

(73 and 134)

1780: Sangarara

America Burns from Mountains to Sea

Two centuries have passed since the executioner's blade cleaved the neck of Túpac Amaru, last of the Incas, in the Plaza Mayor of Cuzco. The myth born of his death is now fulfilled. The prophecy is coming to pass: the head rejoins the body and a reborn Túpac Amaru attacks.

José Gabriel Condorcanqui, Túpac Amaru II, enters the village of Sangarara to the music of giant seashells, *to cut off the bad government of so many thieving drones who rob the very honey from our combs.* Behind his white horse, a desperate army assembles. They fight with slingshots, sticks, and knives, these naked soldiers. They are mostly Indians who *spill out their lives in bloody vomit* in the depths of Potosí or burn themselves out in workshops and haciendas.

Thunder of drums, clouds of banners, fifty thousand men crowning the sierra: Túpac Amaru, liberator of Indians and blacks, scourge of *those who have put us in such a lamentable state of dying*, advances and destroys. Messengers at the gallop rouse whole communities to rebellion from the valley of Cuzco to the coasts of Arica and the frontiers of Tucumán, *because those who fall in this war are sure of resurrection later.*

Many mestizos join the rebellion. Also some Creoles, of European blood but American birth.

(183 and 344)

1780: Tungasuca
Túpac Amaru II

Antonio Oblitas, slave of the magistrate Arriaga, hoisted a strong rope, hangman's rope, mule's rope, in the plaza of this town of Tungasuca, and for a whole week the wind rocked the body of Arriaga, boss of Indians, owner of blacks, owner of Antonio.

This hand that paints is the hand that hanged. Antonio Oblitas is painting the portrait of the man who ordered the freedom of all the slaves in Peru. For lack of easel, the board rests against some sacks of corn. Creating color over the rough wood, come and go the brushes of Antonio, hangman of his master, nevermore a slave. Túpac Amaru poses on a horse, out in the open. He is not wearing his usual black velvet jacket or his three-cornered hat. The inheritor of the Incas wears the royal insignias of the son of the sun: like his forebears, on his head the feather headdress and triple crown and hanging tassel; on his breast the golden sun; and in one fist the scepter of authority bristling with barbs. Around the motionless horseman appear scenes of the recent victory against colonial troops. From Antonio's hand spring little soldiers and puffs of smoke, Indians at war, flames devouring the church of Sangarara and prisoners escaping from the jail.

The painting is born between two battles, during the armed truce. Túpac and his horse have been posing for some time. They are so stony that Antonio wonders if they are breathing. Bright colors spread across the board, very slowly. The painter immerses himself in this long moment of truce. Thus the artist and his model escape from time; stave off, while the work lasts, defeat and death.

(137, 183, and 344)

1780: Pomacanchi
The Workshop Is an Enormous Ship

that sails over American lands, a galley that never stops advancing, propelled night and day by Indians who row toward a port they will never reach. Toward the coast that retreats, the Indians row and row; and the whip wakes them up when sleep overcomes them.

Men and women, children and old people spin, weave, and elaborate cotton and wool in the workshops. The laws promise hours and wages, but the Indians, thrown into these great slave quarters or prisons, only leave them when their burial hour arrives.

South of Cuzco, Túpac Amaru goes about freeing Indians tied to the looms. The winds of the great rebellion deprive viceroys of sleep in Lima, Buenos Aires, and Bogotá.

(170 and 320)

A Colonial Poem: If the Indians Triumph . . .

. . . they will make us toil
the way they toil now
and to the extent we despoil now
they will despoil us back.
All of us can expect to lack
house, hacienda, or splendors,
nobody will win honors
and all will nobodies be:
we will belong to Indians free
and they'll ride herd upon us.

(183)

1781: Bogotá
The Commoners

The archbishop of Bogotá trembles with rage and the leather of his chair groans. His hands, sweetmeat hands, ornamented with rubies and emeralds, clutch his purple robe. The Most Illustrious Don Antonio Caballero y Góngora curses with his mouth full, although he is not eating, for his tongue is as fat as the rest of him.

Outrageous news has come from the town of Socorro. The commoners, people without rank, have risen against the new taxes, and have appointed rich Creoles as captains. Both rich and poor are hit by the taxes, which punish everything from tallow candles to honey, sparing not even the wind: the tax on transient merchants is called the *wind sales tax*.

In Socorro, city of rocks, the rebellion that the viceroy in Bogotá saw coming has come. It happened one market day, right in the plaza.

A plebeian woman, Manuela Beltrán, pulled the decree from the doors of City Hall, tore it to pieces and stamped on it; soon after, the people hurled themselves upon the stores and burned down the jail. Now thousands of commoners, armed with sticks and hoes, are heading for Bogotá beating drums.

Spanish arms collapse in the first battle. The archbishop, who commands more authority than the viceroy, decides to go out and meet the insurrectionists. To deceive them with promises he will march at the head of the court commission. His mule stares at him in panic.

(13 and 185)

1781: Támara
The Plainsmen

Yelling Túpac Amaru's name, fifteen hundred Indians come galloping from the plains east of the Andes. They seek to gain the cordillera, to join the tide of commoners marching on Bogotá. The governor of the plains flees and saves his neck.

These rebels are Indians of the savannas of rivers that flow into the Orinoco. On the beaches of the Orinoco, where turtles deposit their eggs, they once held their markets. There they gathered, since the remotest of remote times, with the Indians of Guyana and Amazonia, exchanging salt, gold, clay pots, baskets, nets, dried fish, turtle oil, arrow poison, and red dye to protect the naked body from mosquitos. Snail conches were the currency, until Europeans arrived eager for slaves and offered axes, scissors, mirrors, and brandy in exchange for men. Then the Indians began to enslave one another, and to sell their brothers, and every hunter was also hunted; and many died of measles or smallpox.

(121 and 185)

1781: Zipaquirá
Galán

In the village of Zipaquirá the peace treaty is signed. The archbishop dictates it, swears to it by the evangels and consecrates it with a high Mass.

The agreement justifies the rebels. Soon this piece of paper will be cinders, and the rich Creole captains well know it; but they too need to dispel as soon as possible the stunning storm, the *supreme disorder of the plebeians*, which grow constantly, darkening the skies of Bogotá and threatening wealthy Americans as much as the Spanish crown.

One of the rebel captains refuses to enter the trap. José Antonio Galán, who had his baptism of fire in the mulatto battalion of Cartagena, carries on the struggle. He marches from town to town, from one hacienda to another, freeing slaves, abolishing tribute and dividing up lands. *Union of the Oppressed Against the Oppressors*, proclaims his banner. Friends and enemies call him *the Túpac Amaru of Here and Now*.

(13 and 185)

Popular Ballad of the Commoners

*Let the drumbeats stop
and you, lend an ear
for this is the true ballad
and voice of the commoner:
The goat is pulled toward the hills
and hills toward the sky;
the sky toward God knows where
and right now neither do I.
The rich pull at the poor.
The Indian, worth only a little,
gets pulled by both poor and rich
till he splits right down the middle . . .*

(13)

1781: Cuzco
The Center of the Earth, the House of the Gods

Cuzco, the sacred city, wants to be itself again. The black stones of ancient times, tightly pressed together in loving embrace, victors over the furies of the earth and of man, want to shake themselves loose of the churches and palaces which crush them.

Micaela Bastidas stares down at Cuzco and bites her lips. Túpac

Amaru's wife is looking at the center of the earth, the spot chosen by the gods, from the crest of a hill. Right there, the color of clay and smoke so close that one could touch it, waits the capital of the Incas.

A thousand times Micaela has insisted in vain. The new Inca will not attack. Túpac Amaru, son of the sun, refuses to kill Indians. Túpac Amaru, incarnation of the founder of all life, living promise of resurrection, cannot kill Indians. And it is Indians, under the command of chief Pumacahua, who defend this Spanish bastion.

A thousand times Micaela has insisted, and a thousand times insists, and Túpac is silent. She knows now that there will be a tragedy in the Plaza of Tears, and knows that no matter what, she'll go on to the end.

(183 and 344)

1781: Cuzco
Dust and Sorrow Are the Roads of Peru

Riddled with bullets, some seated and others prone, they still defended themselves and infuriated us by hurling many stones . . . Slopes of the sierras, a litter of corpses: among the dead and the spears and the broken banners, the victors pick up here and there a carbine.

Túpac Amaru does not enter the sacred city as a conqueror, heading his tumultuous troops. He enters Cuzco on the back of a mule, loaded with chains which drag over the pavestones. Between two files of soldiers, he goes to the prison. The church bells ring out in a frenzy.

Túpac Amaru had escaped by swimming across the River Combapata and was taken by surprise in an ambush in the town of Langui— sold out by one of his captains, Francisco Santa Cruz, who was also his compadre.

The traitor does not look for a rope to hang himself. He collects two thousand pesos and a title of nobility.

(183 and 344)

1781: Cuzco
Sacramental Ceremony
in the Torture Chamber

Bound to the rack, Túpac Amaru lies naked and bloody. The torture chamber of Cuzco's prison is gloomy and low-ceilinged. A shaft of light falls on the rebel chief, violent bruising light. José Antonio de Areche wears a rolled wig and military dress uniform. Areche, representative of the king of Spain, commanding general of the army, and supreme judge, is seated beside the crank. When he moves it, another turn of the rope convulses the arms and legs of Túpac Amaru and stifled groans are heard.

ARECHE: Ah king of kings, little king sold for a contemptible price! Don José I, agent in the pay of the British crown! Money married to the ambition for power . . . Who should be surprised by the wedding? It's normal enough . . . British arms, British money. Why don't you deny it, eh? Poor devil. (*He rises and strokes Túpac Amaru's head.*) The Lutheran heretics have thrown dust in your eyes and a dark veil over your brain. Poor devil. José Gabriel Túpac Amaru, absolute and natural lord of these dominions . . . Don José I, monarch of the New World! (*Unrolls a parchment and reads out loud.*) "Don José I, by the grace of God, Inca, King of Peru, Santa Fe, Quito, Chile, Buenos Aires and continents of the southern seas, duke of the Superlative, Lord of the Caesars and Amazons, with dominion in the great Paitití, Commissioner of divine mercy . . ." (*Turns suddenly toward Túpac Amaru.*) Deny it! We found this proclamation in your pockets . . . You promised freedom . . . The heretics have taught you the evil arts of contraband. Wrapped in the flag of freedom, you brought the cruelest of tyrannies. (*Walks around the figure bound to the rack.*) "They treat us like dogs," you said. "They skin us alive," you said. But did you by any chance even pay tribute, you and your fellows? You enjoyed the privilege of using arms and going on horseback. You were always treated as a Christian of pure-blooded lineage! We gave you the life of a white man and you preached race hatred. We, your hated Spaniards, have taught you to speak. And what did you say? "Revolution!" We taught you to write, and what did you write? "War!" (*Sits. Turns his back on Túpac Amaru and crosses his legs*.) You have laid Peru waste. Crimes, arson, robberies, sacrileges . . . You and your terrorist henchmen have brought hell to these provinces. So the Spaniards leave the Indians licking the dirt, do they? I have already ordered forcible sales stopped and workshops opened and fair wages paid. I have suppressed tithes and tariffs . . . Why did you continue the war, if good treatment has been reestablished? How many thousands of deaths have you caused, you sham emperor? How much pain have you inflicted on the invaded lands? (*Rises and leans toward Túpac Amaru, who does not open his eyes*.) So the labor draft is a crime and of every hundred Indians who go to the mines, twenty return? I have ordered an end to compulsory work. And anyway, wasn't the detestable labor draft invented by your forebears? The Incas . . . No one has treated the Indians worse. You blaspheme the European blood that runs in your veins, José Gabriel Condorcanqui Noguera . . . (*Pauses and speaks while encircling the body of the victim*.) Your sentence is ready. I conceived it, wrote it, signed it. (*His hand cuts the air over Túpac's mouth*.) They will haul you to the scaffold and the executioner will cut out your tongue. They will tie you to four horses by the hands and feet. You will be quartered. (*Passes his hand over the bare torso*.) They will throw your trunk on the bonfire on Mount Picchú and the ashes in the air. (*Touches the face*.) Your head will hang from a gallows for three days in the town of Tinta and afterwards will be nailed to a pole at the gate of the town, with a crown of eleven iron spikes, for your eleven titles of emperor. (*Strokes Túpac's arms*.) We will send one arm to Tungasuca and the other will be exhibited in the capital of Carabaya. (*And his legs*.) One leg to the town of Livitaca and the other to Santa Rosa de Lampa. The houses you have lived in will be obliterated. We will throw salt on your lands. Infamy will fall upon your descendants through all the centuries. (*Lights a candle and holds it over Túpac Amaru's face*.) You still have time. Tell me: who carries on the rebellion you started? Who are your accomplices? (*Wheedling*.) You have time. I offer you the gallows. You have time to avoid so much humiliation and suffering. Give me names. Tell me. (*Lowers his ear*.) You are your own hangman, Indian butcher! (*Again sweetens his tone*.) We'll cut out the tongue of your son Hipólito. We'll cut out the tongue of Micaela, your woman, and garrote her . . . All right, don't repent, but save her. Her. Save your wife from an infamous death. (*Moves nearer. Waits*.) God knows the crimes you must carry with you. (*Violently twists the torture crank, and a ghastly cry is heard.*) Silence won't get you anything before the tribunal of the All-Highest, arrogant Indian! (*Pityingly.*) Oh, it saddens me that a soul chooses to go like that to eternal condemnation . . . (*With fury.*) For the last time! Who are your accomplices?

TÚPAC AMARU: (*Raising his head with a tremendous effort, opens his eyes and finally speaks.*) Here there are no accomplices but you and me. You as oppressor, I as liberator, both of us deserve death.

(183 and 344)

1781: Cuzco
Areche's Order Against Inca Dress and to Make Indians Speak Spanish

Indians are forbidden to wear the dress of the gentry, and especially of the nobility, which serves only to remind them of what the ancient Incas wore, bringing back memories that merely cause them to feel more and more hatred for the ruling nation; apart from looking ridiculous and hardly in keeping with the purity of our religion, since it features in various places the sun which was their first deity; this order extends to all provinces of this Southern America, totally abolishing such clothing . . . and at the same time all paintings or portraits of the Incas . . .

And to the end that these Indians should rid themselves of the hatred they have conceived against Spaniards, that they should dress in clothing prescribed by law, and that they should adopt our Spanish customs and speak the Castilian language, schools shall be more vigorously encouraged than heretofore, with the most stern and just punishment for those who do not use them, after a due period of time for their enlightenment . . .

(345)

1781: Cuzco
Micaela

In this war, which has made the earth groan with birth pains, Micaela Bastidas has had neither rest nor comfort. This woman with the neck of a bird has traveled constantly from region to region *making more people*, and sending to the front new fighters, and a few rifles, and the telescope someone asked for, and coca leaves and ripe ears of corn. Horses galloped incessantly back and forth across the mountains with her orders, safe-conducts, reports, and letters. She sent many messages to Túpac Amaru urging him to hurl his troops upon Cuzco once and for all, before the Spaniards could fortify their defenses and dishearten and disperse the rebels. *Chepe*, she wrote, *Chepe, my dearest one: Enough warnings I've given you* . . .

Pulled by a horse's tail, Micaela enters the main plaza of Cuzco, which the Indians call the Plaza of Tears, inside a leather bag, the kind in which maté is brought from Paraguay. Horses are also dragging to the gallows Túpac Amaru and Hipólito, their son. Another son, Fernando, looks on.

(159 and 183)

1781: Cuzco
Sacred Rain

The boy wants to turn his head, but the soldiers force him to look. Fernando sees how the executioner tears out the tongue of his brother Hipólito and pushes him down the steps from the scaffold. The executioner hangs two of Fernando's uncles, and then the slave Antonio Oblitas, who had painted Túpac Amaru's portrait, and afterward he cuts him to bits with an ax; and Fernando sees. With chains on his hands and irons on his feet, between two soldiers who force him to look, Fernando sees the executioner apply the garrote to Tomasa Condemaita, the woman chief of Acos, whose women's battalion has dealt the Spanish army tremendous blows. Then Micaela Bastidas mounts the scaffold and Fernando sees less. His eyes cloud over as the executioner reaches for Micaela's tongue, and a curtain of tears covers the boy's eyes when they sit his mother down to finish off the torture: the iron collar does not quite strangle her fine neck and it is necessary to *fasten nooses around her neck and pull from different directions, finishing her off with kicks in the belly and breasts*.

Fernando, born of Micaela nine years ago, now sees nothing and hears nothing. He doesn't see that they are bringing in his father, Túpac Amaru, and lashing him to the cinches of four horses by the hands and feet, his face turned skyward. The horsemen dig in their spurs heading for the four points of the compass, but Túpac Amaru doesn't split. *They have him up in the air, looking like a spider*; spurs tear at the bellies of the horses, which rear up on their hind legs to muster all their forces, but Túpac Amaru doesn't split.

It is the season of long dryness in the Valley of Cuzco. Precisely at noon, as the horses struggle and Túpac Amaru doesn't split, a violent downpour bursts from the sky: drops fall heavy as clubs, as if God or the Sun or someone had decided that it was the moment for the kind of rain that leaves the world blind.

(183 and 344)

The Indians Believe:

Jesus has clothed himself in white to come to Cuzco. A child shepherd sees him, plays with him, follows him. Jesus is a child too, and runs between earth and air: he crosses the river without getting wet, and slips very softly through the sacred valley of the Incas, careful not to scrape these recently wounded lands. From the slopes of the peak Ausangate, whose icy breath radiates the energy of life, he walks toward Mount Coylloriti. At the foot of this mountain, shelter of ancient divinities, Jesus lets fall his white tunic. He climbs up the rock and stops. Then he enters the rock.

Jesus has wanted to give himself to the conquered, and for them he turns into stone, like the ancient gods of this region, stone that says and will say: *I am God, I am you, I am those who fell*.

Forever the Indians of the Valley of Cuzco will go up in procession to greet him. They will purify themselves in the waters of the torrent, and with torches in their hands will dance for him, dance to give him joy: so sad is Jesus, so broken, there inside.

(301)

The Indians Dance to the Glory of Paradise

Far from Cuzco, Jesus' sadness has also stricken the Tepehua Indians. Ever since the new god arrived in Mexico, the Tepehuas had been going to church with a musical band, offering him dances, costume games, tasty tamales, and good drink; but nothing gave him happiness. Jesus continued to grieve, his beard pressed against his breast, and so it went until the Tepehuas invented the Dance of the Old Ones.

It is danced by two men in masks. One is the Old Lady, the other the Old Man. The two Old Ones come from the sea with offerings of shrimp and traverse the town of San Pedro leaning on feathered canes, their bodies twisted by age. Before altars improvised in the streets, they stop and dance while the cantor sings and a musician beats a turtle shell. The naughty Old Lady waggles her hips and offers herself, and pretends to run away; the Old Man follows her and catches her from behind, embraces her and hoists her shoulder high. She kicks her legs in the air, dying of laughter, and pretends to defend herself with blows from her cane, happily clutching the body of the Old Man, who keeps grabbing at her, staggering and laughing as everyone applauds.

When Jesus saw the Old Ones making love, he raised his head and laughed for the first time. He laughs now every time the Tepehuas perform this impious dance for him.

In remote times, the Tepehuas, who have rescued Jesus from his sadness, were born from balls of cotton, there on the slopes of the Sierra of Veracruz. Instead of "it's dawning," they say, "God is here."

(359)

1781: Chincheros
Pumacahua

In the center gleams the Virgin of Montserrat. Mateo García Pumacahua is on his knees giving thanks. His wife and a group of relatives and captains appear in procession behind him. Pumacahua wears Spanish dress, vest and coat, shoes with buckles. Beyond him, the battle is fought, little soldiers and guns that look like toys: Pumacahua the puma beats the dragon Túpac Amaru. *Veni, vidi, vici* is written above.

After several months a nameless artist has finished his work. Over the door of the church of the town of Chincheros appear the images that will perpetuate the glory and the faith of chief Pumacahua in the war against Túpac Amaru.

Pumacahua, also a descendant of the Incas, has received a medal from the king of Spain and a plenary indulgence from the bishop of Cuzco.

(137 and 183)

1781: La Paz
Túpac Catari

He spoke only Aymara, the language of his people. He proclaimed himself viceroy of these lands that are not yet called Bolivia, and named his wife vicereine. He set up his court on the heights dominating the city of La Paz, hidden in a hollow, and laid siege to it.

He walked with a limp and an extraordinary brilliance lit up his eyes, deeply sunk in his young and already furrowed face. He dressed in black velvet, gave orders with a cane and fought with a spear. He beheaded priests suspected of celebrating denunciatory Masses and cut off the arms of spies and traitors.

Julián Apaza had been a sacristan and a baker before becoming Túpac Catari. Together with his wife, Bartolina Sisa, he organized an army of forty thousand Indians which kept in check troops sent by the viceroy from Buenos Aires.

Despite the defeats and massacres he suffered there was no way to catch him. Traveling at night he eluded every attempt at encirclement, until the Spaniards offered the governorship of Achacachi, on the banks of Lake Titicaca, to his best friend Tomás Inca Lipe, known as *the good*.

(183)

1782: La Paz
Rebel Women

Spanish cities of the New World, born as offerings to God and the king, have an enormous heart of beaten earth. In each city's main plaza are the gallows and the seat of government, the cathedral and the jail, the courthouse and the market. People stroll around the gallows and the fountain, to and fro in the main plaza, fortified plaza, garrison plaza, pass cavalier and beggar, silver-spurred horseman and barefoot slave, devout ladies taking their souls to Mass, and Indians delivering chicha in potbellied clay jugs.

Today there is a show in the main plaza of La Paz. Two women, leaders of the native rebellion, will be sacrificed. Bartolina Sisa, wife of Túpac Catari, emerges from the jail with rope around neck, tied to the tail of a horse. Gregoria Apaza, sister of Túpac Catari, is brought out on a donkey. Each of them carries a cross of sticks, like a scepter, in the right hand, and has a crown of thorns fastened on her head. Before them, prisoners sweep the ground clear with branches. Bartolina and Gregoria make several turns around the plaza, suffering in silence the stones and laughter of those who mock them as Indian queens, until the hour of the gallows strikes. Their heads and hands, the sentence reads, will be paraded through the towns of the region.

The sun, the old sun, also attends the ceremony.

(183 and 288)

1782: *Guaduas*

With Glassy Eyes,

from a wooden cage, the head of José Antonio Galán gazes at the town of Charalá. In Charalá, where he was born, they are exhibiting his right foot. A hand of his is nailed up in the plaza of Socorro.

The cream of colonial society has repented of the sin of insolence, these rich Creoles who prefer to keep paying tribute and obedience to the Spanish monarch, thus avoiding the *contagious plague* that Galán, like Túpac Amaru, like Túpac Catari, incarnated and spread in their days of fury. Galán, chief captain of the commoners' insurrection, has been betrayed and hunted down by those who were his comrades. In a hut he fell, after a long pursuit, together with his last twelve men.

Don Antonio Caballero y Góngora, the pompous archbishop, sharpened the sword that beheaded Galán. While throwing on the fire the treaty of peace, so promising, so deceiving, the Most Illustrious One added infamies against *the spiteful plebeian*. Galán has been quartered not merely as a rebel, but also as *a man of most obscure birth and lover of his own daughter*.

Now the archbishop has two thrones. Besides the apostolic one, he has acquired the viceregal throne of Bogotá.

(13 and 185)

1782: Sicuani
This Accursed Name

Diego Cristóbal, first cousin of Túpac Amaru and continuer of his war in Peru, has signed a peace treaty. The colonial authorities have promised pardon and a general amnesty.

Stretched out on the ground, Diego Cristóbal swears fidelity to the king. Multitudes of Indians come down from the mountains and surrender their arms. The marshal stages a banquet of merry toasts and the bishop a Mass of thanksgiving. From Lima, the viceroy orders all houses to be illuminated for three nights.

Within a year and a half, in Cuzco, in the Plaza of Happiness, the executioner will tear to pieces the flesh of this cousin of Túpac Amaru, with red-hot pincers, before hanging him from the gallows. His mother will also be hanged and quartered. The judge, Francisco Díaz de Medina, had passed sentence to the effect that *it is not fitting either for the King or for the State that any seed or race of this or any Túpac Amaru should remain, considering the great clamor and impression that this accursed name has aroused in the natives*.

(183)

1783: Panama City
For Love of Death

Ever since dawn the ground has been steaming, pleading for a drink, and the living seek shade and fan themselves. If the heat shrivels the living, what will it not do to the dead, who have no one to fan them?

The important dead lie in the churches. So much does custom require in the dry tableland of Castile, and so it has to be also in this fiery furnace of Panama. The faithful stand on memorial stones, or kneel on them, and from below death whispers to them: *Soon I'll come for you*. More than the panic of dying or the memory of irreparable loss though, it is the stink of putrefaction that brings tears to the eyes.

Sebastián López Ruiz, sage researcher into nature, writes a report showing that, here, this custom from over there is the enemy of hygiene and fatal for public health, and that it would be healthier to bury the gentry of Panama in some distant cemetery. The reply, when it comes, says in effect that the dead are well placed in the churches; and that what has been and is, will continue to be.

(323)

1783: Madrid

The Human Hand Vindicated

To the four winds trumpets proclaim that the king of Spain has decided to redeem the human hand. From here on, the gentleman who does manual work will not lose his noble condition. The king says that industriousness dishonors neither him who performs it, nor his family, and that no artisanship is unworthy of Spaniards.

Charles III wants to bring his reign up to date. His minister Campomanes dreams of promoting industry, popular education, and agrarian reform. From its great imperial feat in America, Spain gets the honors and other European monarchies get the benefits. How long will the silver of the colonies go on paying for merchandise that Spain does not produce? What is the point of the Spanish monopoly if the products leaving the port of Cadiz are English, French, Dutch, or German?

Knightly gentlemen, who in Spain are as abundant as monks, have hands that serve either to die for Spain or to kill her. Even if they are penniless, they don't lower themselves to produce anything except glory. A long time ago those hands forgot how to work, as a hen's wings have forgotten how to fly.

(175)

1785: Mexico City

Lawyer Villarroel Against the Pulque Saloon

Every pulque saloon is an office where adulteries, concubinages, rapes, pickpocketings, robberies, homicides, brawls, knifings, and other crimes are hatched . . . They are theaters in which men and women are transformed into the most abominable furies from hell, their mouths spewing the most refined obscenities, the vilest words, and most dissolute, infamous, offensive, and provocative things that the greatest of libertines could hardly utter if they were not perturbed by the fumes of the most fetid and disgusting of drinks . . . These are the effects of the negligence, the omissions and the tolerance of judges, who are not horrified at the sight of men and women lying in the streets as if they were dogs, exposed to being run over by a coachman as drunk as themselves, as often happens, dispatching them to eternity in such an unhappy situation as the one in which they find themselves.

(352)

The Pulque Saloon

When the viceroy expelled pulque from Mexico City, the outcast found shelter in the suburbs.

Liquor of the green plants . . . In taverns on the outskirts, the barman never stops coming and going between the big vats and the eager mugs, *you stun me, you kill me, you make me walk on all fours*, while a newborn child cries disconsolately in one corner and an old man sleeps off the effects in another.

Horses, donkeys, and fighting cocks, tethered to iron rings, grow old waiting outside. Inside, the bright-colored vats bear defiant names: "Don't stretch me out," "The stuff for the strong," "The brave one" . . . Inside, law does not exist, nor the time of day. Dice roll on the earth floor and flowery gambling cards are flung down on a barrel-top. Some fool sings to the sound of a merry harp, others pair off to kick up dust in a dance, a monk chats with a soldier and the soldier promises to get tough with a muleteer, *I am plenty tough, I'm too tough*, and the potbellied barman chimes in: *What about another?*

(153 and 266)

Pulque

Perhaps pulque brings their old gods back to the Indians. They offer it to them, sprinkling it on the ground or in the fire or raising a mug to the stars. Perhaps the gods are always thirsty for the pulque they sucked from the four hundred teats of mother Mayahuel.

Perhaps, too, the Indians drink to fortify themselves and to get even; certainly they drink to forget and to be forgotten.

According to the bishops, pulque is to blame for laziness and poverty and brings idolatry and rebellion. *Barbarous vice of a barbarous people*, says one of the king's officers. Under the effect of the maguey's heavy wine, he says, *the child denies the father and the vassal his lord*.

(153 and 331)

The Maguey

Armed with green swords, the maguey stands up to drought and hail, the icy nights and furious suns of the deserts of Mexico.

Pulque comes from the maguey, *the tree that gives suck*, and from the maguey come forage for animals, beams and tiles for roofing, fencing posts and fuel for fires. Its fleshy leaves provide rope, pouches, matting, soap, and paper, the paper of the ancient codices; and its thorns make good pins and needles.

The maguey only flowers when it is going to die. It opens and flowers as if saying farewell. A lofty stalk, perhaps a mast, perhaps a penis, shoots from the heart of the maguey toward the clouds in a burst of yellow flowers. Then the great stalk falls and with it falls the maguey, torn out by the root.

It is unusual to find a flowering maguey in the arid Mezquital valley. Hardly has it begun to shoot up when the Indian castrates it and turns the wound downward, and thus the maguey yields up its pulque, which quenches thirst, feeds, and consoles.

(32 and 153)

The Mug

The Mexican potter has a long history. Three thousand years before Hernán Cortés, his hands were converting clay into receptacles or human figures which fire hardened against time. Much later on, the Aztecs explained that a good potter *gives being to clay and makes things live*.

This ancient tradition still flourishes in a daily multiplication of bottles, jars, pots, and, above all, drinking mugs: the ivorylike mugs of Tonalá, the tough mugs of Metepec, the bulging shiny ones of Oaxaca, the humble little ones of Chilililco; the reddish mugs of Toluca, dripping black tears . . . The mug of cooked clay presides over fiestas and kitchens and accompanies prisoner and beggar. It receives the pulque, scorned by the crystal glass, and it is the gift of lovers:

When I die, old lady, take my clay if you can
And fashion a mug with this refrain:
If you thirst for me, drink;
And if it stops at the brink,
That will be kisses from your old man.

(18, 153, and 294)

1785: Mexico City

Fiction in the Colonial Era

The viceroy of Mexico, Matías de Gálvez, signs a new edict in favor of Indian workers. The Indians are to receive fair wages, good food, and medical attention; and they will have two rest hours at noon, and be able to change employers whenever they like.

(146)

1785: Guanajuato

The Wind Blows Where It Wants

An abyss of light opens in the clear air and between the black walls of the sierra shines the desert. In the desert, a glitter of domes and towers, rise Mexico's mining towns. Guanajuato, as densely populated as the viceroy's capital, is the most distinguished. Its owners go to Mass in sedan chairs followed by swarms of beggars through a labyrinth of lanes and alleys, Kiss Lane, Slide Lane, Four Winds Lane; and between the cobblestones polished by the feet of time grow grasses and phantoms.

In Guanajuato church bells organize life; and chance governs it. Some mysterious slippery-fingered joker deals the cards. They say that here one treads on gold and silver wherever one goes, but everything depends on the veins that snake underground and offer and deny themselves at their whim. Yesterday, a fortunate gentleman celebrated his stroke of luck, and toasted everybody in the best wine, and paid for flute and guitar serenades, and bought fine Cambray lace and velvet trousers and silk lamé jackets and camisoles from Holland; and today the thread of silver that made him knight for a day disappears without trace.

The life of the Indians, on the other hand, does not hang on chance. Breathing mercury in the alloy factories leaves them forever

with the shakes and toothless, and their chests burst from breathing
murderous dust and pestilent vapors in the mines. Sometimes exploding dust blows them to bits, and sometimes they slip into the
void when they go down carrying stones or when they come up
carrying on their backs the foremen who call Indians their "little
horses."

(6, 261, and 349)

1785: Guanajuato
Silver Portrait

Using the language of fluttering fans, ladies chat in the leafy gardens.
Somebody pees against the wall of a church and on one side of the
plaza two beggars, sitting in the sun, pick at each other's lice. Beneath
a stone archway a distinguished doctor in a huge cloak talks of the
Rights of Man, and a monk moves down the lane muttering eternal
condemnations against the drunks, whores, and rowdies who cross
in front of him. Not far from the city, *collectors* hunt Indians with
lassos.

Guanajuato has long since dethroned Potosí. The world queen
of silver is hungry for labor. The workers, *free wage earners*, don't
see a coin in all their lives, but are prisoners of debt. Their children
will inherit the debts and also the fear of pain and prison and hunger,
and of the old gods and the new.

(261 and 349)

1785: Lisbon
The Colonial Function

The Portuguese crown orders Brazil's textile workshops closed down;
in the future they must only produce rustic clothing for slaves. In the
name of the queen, Minister Melo e Castro issues the orders. The
minister observes that *in most of the captaincies of Brazil have been
set up, and are spreading ever more wildly, various factories and
manufactories of cloth of differing qualities, including even gold and
silver braid*. These, he says, are *pernicious transgressions*. If they
continue, *the result will be that all the utilities and wealth of these
most important colonies will end up as the patrimony of their inhabitants*. Brazil being such a fertile land, so abundant in fruits, *said*

inhabitants will become totally independent of their dominant me-tropolis: consequently it is indispensably necessary to abolish said factories and manufactories.

(205)

1785: Versailles
The Potato Becomes a Great Lady

Two and a half centuries ago the Spanish conquistadors brought her from Peru. Since she came so highly recommended by the Indians, Europe destined her for hogs, jailbirds, and the dying. The potato has been jeered and castigated whenever she has tried to escape from pigsties, prisons, and hospitals. In several places she was banned; and in Besançon she was accused of causing leprosy.

Antoine Parmentier got to know the potato in jail. Parmentier was in a Prussian prison and they didn't provide anything else to eat. At first he thought her stupid, but later he came to love her and discovered her charm and savoriness.

Free again in Paris, Parmentier organizes a banquet. D'Alem-bert, Lavoisier, American ambassador Benjamin Franklin, and other celebrities attend. Parmentier offers them an all-potato menu: potato bread, potato soup, potato puree, salads of potatoes enlivened with dressings to taste, fried potatoes, potato buns and pastries. For dessert, potato tart. To drink, potato brandy. Parmentier makes a speech in her defense. He extolls her nutritive virtues, proclaims her necessary for the palate and for the blood, and says the potato could conquer hunger in Europe, being invulnerable to hailstorms and easily cultivated. The guests, abrim with potatoes, applaud him with emotion and conviction.

Then Parmentier convinces the king. Louis XVI orders potatoes planted in the Sablons estates near Paris, and has them surrounded by a permanent guard of soldiers. Thus, he excites curiosity and desire for the forbidden fruit.

The definitive consecration takes place at Versailles. Queen Marie Antoinette, decked out like a garden with potato flowers, bestows the royal kiss on the cheek of Antoine Parmentier. King Louis, who has still not lost his head, embraces Parmentier. All the nobility of France attends the apotheosis of the potato, in this kingdom where the art of good cuisine is the only religion without atheists.

(156 and 250)

The Potato Was Born of
Love and Punishment,
As They Tell It in the Andes

The Inca, they say, condemned two lovers who violated the sacred laws. Let them be buried alive and together, he decided.

She had been a virgin consecrated to the Sun god. She had fled from the temple to give herself to a peasant serf.

Alive and together, the Inca decided. They were buried in a deep pit, tied together, face up; and not a complaint was heard as the dirt covered them.

Night fell and the stars moved in unaccustomed courses. Shortly afterward, gold disappeared from the riverbeds, and the fields of the kingdom became sterile, nothing but dust and stones. Only the soil that covered the lovers was immune to the drought.

The high priests counseled the Inca to disinter the lovers, burn them and scatter their ashes to the wind. So let it be, decided the Inca.

But they could not find them. They dug wide and deep and found nothing but a root. That root multiplied and from then on the potato was the staff of the Andean people.

(248)

1790: Paris
Humboldt

At age twenty, Alexander von Humboldt discovers the ocean and revolution.

At Dunkirk the ocean struck him dumb, and in Calais the moon blossoming from the waves drew a shout of wonder. Astonishment at the sea, revelation of the revolution: in Paris, a year after July Fourteenth, Humboldt lets himself go in the sweet whirlwind of streets in fiesta, merges into the people who dance and sing to their newborn liberty.

He has lived in search of answers and found questions. Without let-up he has inquired of books, of the heavens, and of the earth, pursuing the enigmas of the soul and the mysteries of the cosmos and the secrets of beetles and stones, always in love with the world and with men and women who fill him with dizziness and panic. *Alexander will never be happy*, says his brother Wilhelm, his mother's favorite child.

At twenty, fever of living, fever of going places, Humboldt swears eternal fealty to the banners of the French revolution and swears he will cross the ocean, like Balboa and Robinson Crusoe, to the lands where it is always noon.

(30 and 46)

1790: Petit Goâve
The Missing Magic

The heft of the purse can at times achieve more than the color of the skin. In Haiti, poor mulattos are blacks, and free blacks who have accumulated enough cash are mulattos. Rich mulattos pay immense fortunes to become white, although few obtain the magic document that permits the offspring of master and slave to become a doctor, to style himself Monsieur, to wear a sword, or to touch a white woman without losing an arm.

From a gallows hangs the mulatto who claimed the rights of a citizen, recently proclaimed in Paris, and high on a pike through the town of Petit Goâve rides the head of another mulatto who wanted to be a deputy.

(115)

1791: Bois Caiman
The Conspirators of Haiti

The old slave woman, intimate of the gods, buries her machete in the throat of a black wild boar. The earth of Haiti drinks the blood. Under the protection of the gods of war and of fire, two hundred blacks sing and dance the oath of freedom. In the prohibited voodoo ceremony aglow with lightning bolts, two hundred slaves decide to turn this land of punishment into a fatherland.

Haiti is based on the Creole language. Like the drum, Creole is the common speech of those torn out of Africa into various Antillean islands. It blossomed inside the plantations, when the condemned needed to recognize one another and resist. It came from African languages, with African melody, and fed on the sayings of Normans and Bretons. It picked up words from Caribbean Indians and from

English pirates and also from the Spanish colonists of eastern Haiti. Thanks to Creole, when Haitians talk they feel that they touch each other.

Creole gathers words and voodoo gathers gods. Those gods are not masters but lovers, very fond of dancing, who convert each body they penetrate into music and light, pure light of undulating and sacred movement.

(115 and 265)

Haitian Love Song

I burn like firewood.
My legs shake like sugarcanes.
No dish tempts my mouth.
The strongest drink becomes water.
When I think of you,
my eyes brim up
and my reason falls vanquished
by my pain.
Isn't it very true, my beauty,
that soon you will be back?
Oh, come back to me, my ever faithful!
Believing is less sweet than feeling!
Don't delay too much.
It hurts a lot.
Come and free from his cage
the hungry bird.

(265)

1792: Rio de Janeiro
The Conspirators of Brazil

Barely half a century ago the mines of Brazil were expected to last as long as the world, but the gold and the diamonds steadily grow less, and the tributes that must be paid to the queen of Portugal and her court of parasites weigh ever more heavily.

Since that time, many voracious bureaucrats have been sent in from Portugal, and not a single mining technician. From there they have stopped the cotton looms producing anything but clothing for slaves, and from there they have banned both the exploitation of iron, which lies at arm's reach, and the production of gunpowder.

To break with Europe, *which sucks us like a sponge*, a handful of gentlemen entered a conspiracy. Three years ago, owners of mines and haciendas, monks, poets, doctors, veteran smugglers, organized a rising which aimed to convert this colony into an independent republic, in which blacks and native-born mulattos would be free and everyone would wear Brazilian clothes.

Before the first musket shot rang out, informers went to work. The governor jailed the Ouro Prêto conspirators. Under torture, they confessed; and they accused each other in enthusiastic detail. Basílio de Britto Malheiro pleaded innocent explaining that anyone fated to be born in Brazil copies the bad habits of blacks, mulattos, Indians, and other ridiculous folk. Cláudio Manuel da Costa, most illustrious of the prisoners, hanged himself in his cell, or was hanged, for not confessing, or for confessing too much.

There was one who remained silent. Lieutenant Joaquim Jose da Silva Xavier, known as *Sacamuelas*, the tooth-puller, only opened his mouth to say:

"I am the only one responsible."

(205 and 209)

1792: Rio de Janeiro
Tooth-Puller

They look like cadavers in the candlelight. Bound by enormous chains to the bars of the windows, the accused have been listening to the judge for eighteen hours, without missing a word.

The judge took six months to formulate the sentence. Far into the night, they find out: six are condemned. These six will be hanged, beheaded, and quartered.

Then the judge falls silent while the men who wanted independence for Brazil exchange reproaches and apologies, insults and tears, stifled cries of repentance or protest.

Early in the morning comes the queen's pardon. Five of the guilty six will not die but be exiled. But one, the only one who betrayed nobody and was betrayed by all, will walk to the gallows at dawn. For him the drums will beat and the mournful voice of the town crier will resound through the streets announcing the sacrifice.

Tooth-puller is far from white. He entered the army as a lieutenant and lieutenant he always remained, pulling teeth to round out his pay. He wanted Brazilians to be Brazilians. The birds that disappear behind the mountains as the sun rises know it well.

(205)

1794: Paris

"The remedy for man is man,"

say the black sages, and the gods always knew it. The slaves of Haiti are no longer slaves.

For five years the French revolution turned a deaf ear. Marat and Robespierre protested in vain. Slavery continued in the colonies. Despite the Declaration of the Rights of Man, the men who were the property of other men on the far plantations of the Antilles were born neither free nor equal. After all, the sale of blacks from Guinea was the chief business of the revolutionary merchants of Nantes, Bordeaux, and Marseilles; and French refineries lived on Antillean sugar.

Harassed by the black insurrection headed by Toussaint L'Ouverture, the Paris government finally decrees the liquidation of slavery.

(71)

1794: Mountains of Haiti

Toussaint

He came on the scene two years ago. In Paris they call him the *Black Spartacus*.

Toussaint L'Ouverture has the body of a tadpole and lips that occupy almost all of his face. He was a coachman on a plantation. An old black man taught him to read and write, to cure sick horses, and to talk to men; but he learned on his own how to look not only with his eyes, and he knows how to see flight in every bird that sleeps.

(71)

1795: Santo Domingo

The Island Burned

Scared by the freeing of the slaves in Haiti, the king of Spain cedes the territory of Santo Domingo to France. A stroke of the pen wipes out the frontier that cut the island in half, dividing the poorest of

Spanish colonies from the richest of French colonies. Don Manuel Godoy, the leading light at court, says in Madrid that the rebellion in Haiti has turned the whole island into an *accursed land for whites*.

This had been Spain's first colony in America. Here the empire had had its first tribunal, its first cathedral, its first university; from here the conquering hosts had sailed for Cuba and Puerto Rico. Such a birth presaged a glorious destiny, but two centuries ago Governor Antonio de Osorio turned this colony into smoke.

Day and night Osorio labored at roasting the sinful land, going from palm to palm burning houses and fortresses and boats, mills and pigsties and corrals and fields, spraying it all with salt. With his own hands, he strangled those who resisted. In the crackle of flames sounded the trumpets of the Last Judgement. After a year and a half of continuous burning, the arsonist stood up on the island he had destroyed and received from the king of Spain two thousand ducats for his work of redemption by fire.

Governor Osorio, verteran of the Flanders wars, had purified this ground. He had begun by burning the northern cities, because it was on that coast that the English and Dutch pirates landed bringing Bibles *of the sect of Luther* and spreading the heretical custom of eating meat on Good Friday. He had started in the north; and then he just couldn't stop.

(216)

1795: Quito

Espejo

He passed through history cutting and creating.

He wrote the sharpest words against the colonial regime and its methods of education, *an education for slaves*, and he disemboweled the pompous style of the Quito rhetoricians. He nailed up his diatribes on the doors of churches and at busy street corners, so that they would multiply from mouth to mouth, because *writing anonymously might very well remove the disguise from the false wise men and cause them to appear clothed in their true and natural ignorance*.

He wanted an America governed by those born there. He urged that the cry of independence should ring out simultaneously in all the viceroyalities and tribunals, and that the colonies should unite, to become fatherlands under democratic, republican governments.

He was the son of an Indian. At birth he received the name of Chusig, which means barn owl. To become a physician he decided to call himself Francisco Javier Eugenio de Santa Cruz y Espejo, a name suggesting ancient lineage; and only thus could he practice and spread his discoveries against smallpox and other pestilences.

He founded, edited, and wrote from cover to cover *First Fruits of Culture*, Quito's first journal. He was director of the public library. They never paid him his salary.

Charged with crimes against the king and against God, Espejo was shut up in a filthy cell. There he died, from confinement, and with his last breath asked forgiveness of his creditors.

The city of Quito does not list in its register of principal citizens the death of this precursor of Hispanic American independence, who was the most brilliant of its sons.

(17 and 249)

Espejo Mocks the Oratory of These Times

I bid farewell to the volatile breezes of inspiration; I lose the pulsing oscillations of life, when I hear these fulgurous incomprehensibilities of rhetorical concepts. What delicious satisfaction to hear the melodious swans of oratory, trilling with gutteral sonority, chirping dirges in their sweet syllables! What savory intervals of glorious contentmeni the soul perceives in the harmonious echoes of their oracular descriptions!

(17)

1795: Montego Bay
Instruments of War

The prestige of Cuban dogs is well merited. With them the French have hunted down many fugitive blacks in the mountains of Haiti, and a few Cuban dogs were enough to defeat the Miskito Indians, who had wiped out three Spanish regiments on the coasts of Nicaragua.

The English landowners of Jamaica send Colonel William Dawes Quarrell to Cuba to get dogs. The Assembly says the security of the island and the lives of the inhabitants demand it. Dogs are instruments of war. Don't the Asians use elephants in their battles? The most civilized and polished nations of Europe, so reason the English planters, pursue enemy infantry on horses. Why not use dogs then to track down the hideouts of runaway slaves, since blacks are more savage than dogs anyway?

Colonel Quarrell gets what he wants in Cuba, thanks to the good offices of Doña María Ignacia de Contreras y Justíz, marchioness of San Felipe and Santiago, countess of Castile, and owner and mistress of the Bejucal. Men and dogs embark in the schooner *Mercury*.

Mists of dusk in Montego Bay. The beasts arrive in Jamaica. In a flash the streets empty out, doors are shut tight. Forty Cuban rangers fall into line to the light of torches. Each leads three enormous dogs, tied to his belt by straining chains.

(86 and 240)

1795: Havana

Did the Gallilean Rebel Imagine He Would Be a Slave Overseer?

On Cuba's sugar plantations, the slaves do not suffer from neglect. The master redeems them by labor and shortens their stay in this vale of tears; and the monks save them from hell. The Church receives five percent of sugar production for teaching the slaves that God made them slaves, that the body is enslaved but the soul is free, that the pure soul is like white sugar, cleansed of brown taint in purgatory, and that Jesus Christ is the great overseer who watches, awards merits, punishes, and recompenses.

At times Jesus Christ is not only the overseer, but the master in person. The count of Casa Bayona washes the feet of twelve blacks, on Holy Thursday night, sits them down at his table and shares his supper with them. The slaves express their gratitude by setting fire to his sugar mill, and twelve heads end up on a row of lances beside the cane fields.

(222)

1796: Ouro Prêto

El Aleijadinho

El Aleijadinho, *the Little Cripple*, creator of abundances, sculpts with his stump. This sculptor of the loftiest beauties in Brazil's mining region is repugnantly ugly. One of the slaves he bought tried to kill himself to escape from serving such a horrendous master. His sickness, leprosy or syphilis or some mysterious curse, is devouring him bite by bite. For each bit of flesh that it tears from him, he gives the world new marvels of wood or stone.

In Congonhas do Campo they are awaiting him. Can he make it? Will he have the strength left to carve the twelve prophets and raise them against the sky of bluest blue? Will those who prophesied the love and anger of God dance their tormented dance of wounded animals?

No one believes he has life enough left for so much. Slaves carry him through the streets of Ouro Prêto, always hidden beneath his hood, and tie the chisel to what remains of his hand. Only they see the ravages of his face and body. Only they draw close to this monstrosity. Antonio Francisco Lisboa, El Aleijadinho, is falling to pieces; and no urchin dreams of hitting him with a spitball.

(29 and 118)

1796: Mariana

Ataíde

Manuel da Costa Ataíde puts gold and colors on the figures that El Aleijadinho carves in wood. And he is a painter famous in his own right. In churches, Ataíde creates heavens of this earth. Using the pigments of flowers and plants, he paints the Virgin with the face of María do Carmo, a woman born here, brown madonna from whom spring the sun and the stars; and he paints little angel musicians and singers with very fleshy eyelids and lips, nappy hair and startled or mischievous eyes. The mulatto angels are his children and the Virgin his children's mother.

In the San Francisco church in Mariana, African features mark the patron saint of Assisi who turned wolves into lambs. Next to him live white saints with real hair and the faces of madwomen.

(123)

1796: São Salvador de Bahia

Night and Snow

The mulatta lover offers a sexual spree, the white wife social prestige. To achieve a white wife, the mulatto has to whiten himself. If he has plenty of money, he buys some document that erases the stigma of the slave grandmother and permits him to wear sword and hat, leather buskins and silk parasol. He also has a portrait painted which his grandchildren can display without a blush in the living room. Artists have arrived in Brazil who know how to give a European appearance to any tropical model. Oval gold frames surround the head of the patriarch, a man with pink skin and straight hair and a grave and watchful expression.

(65 and 119)

1796: Caracas
White Skin For Sale

The Spanish crown no longer considers Indian lineage vile; black blood, on the other hand, *darkens births* for many generations. Rich mulattos can buy certificates of whiteness for five hundred silver coins.

To remove the stain that greatly afflicts him, the king pronounces Diego Mejías Bejarano, mulatto of Caracas, to be *white so that his sad and inferior condition should not be an impediment to his use, treatment, alternatives and mode of dress vis-à-vis other subjects*.

In Caracas, only whites can attend Mass in the cathedral or kneel on carpets in any church. The master race are known as *Mantuans* because the mantilla is the privilege of white ladies. No mulatto may be a priest or a doctor.

Mejías Bejarano has paid up the five hundred coins, but the local authorities decline to obey. An uncle of Simón Bolívar and the other *Mantuans* of the town council declare that the royal warrant *is frightening for the inhabitants and creoles of America*. The town council asks the king: *How is it possible for the white inhabitants and natives of this province to admit at their side a mulatto descended from their own slaves, or from the slaves of their fathers?*

(174 and 225)

1796: San Mateo
Simón Rodríguez

A mouse's ears, bourbon nose, mouth like a mailbox. A red tassel straggles from the cap that covers his premature baldness. The spectacles, wedged above the eyebrows, rarely help the blue, avid, darting eyes. Simón Carreño, Rodríguez by chosen name, wanders about preaching strange doctrines.

This reader of Rousseau claims that schools should be opened to the people, to those of mixed blood; that girls and boys should share the same classrooms, and that it would be more useful for the country to raise masons, blacksmiths, and carpenters than gentlemen and monks.

Simón the teacher and Simón the pupil. Simón Rodríguez is twenty-five years old and Simón Bolívar, the richest orphan in Venezuela, inheritor of mansions and plantations, owner of a thousand black slaves, is thirteen.

Far from Caracas, the teacher initiates the boy into the secrets of the universe and speaks to him of liberty, equality, fraternity; he reveals to him the hard life of the slaves who work for him, and tells him that the forget-me-not is also called *myosotis palustris*. He shows him how the foal is born of the belly of the mare, and cacao and coffee complete their cycles. Bolívar becomes a swimmer, a hiker, and a horseman; he learns to sow, to build a chair, and to name the stars in the sky of Aragua. Master and pupil cross Venezuela, camping wherever they may be, and together get to know the land that made them. By the light of a lantern they read and discuss *Robinson Crusoe* and Plutarch's *Lives*.

(64, 116, and 298)

1797: La Guaira

The Compass and the Square

The flight of his teacher interrupts Bolívar's education. Simón Rodríguez, suspected of plotting against the king, changes his name to Simón Robinson. From the port of La Guaira he sails to Jamaica and exile.

The plotters wanted an independent and republican America, without native tribute or black slavery, free from king and pope, where people of all races would be brothers and sisters in reason and in Jesus Christ.

Creole Masons, of the lodge founded by Francisco de Miranda in London, headed up the movement. Also accused are three Spanish Masons, exiled in Caracas. Frenchmen, schooled in revolutions and guillotines, are said to be in the conspiracy as well. Raids bring to light more banned books than dangerous weapons.

In the main plaza of Caracas, "Spain" is drawn and quartered: José María de España, chief of the plot.

(191 and 298)

1799: London

Miranda

It is thirty years since Francisco de Miranda left Venezuela. In Spain he was a victorious warrior. He became a Mason in Cadiz and left on a tour of Europe seeking arms and money for the independence of America. On a magic carpet he has journeyed from court to court, with no baggage but a flute, the false title of count, and many letters of introduction. He has dined with kings and he has slept with queens. In France, the revolution made him a general. The people of Paris acclaimed him as a hero, but Robespierre condemned him as a traitor; and to save his head, Miranda crossed the Channel to London with a false passport, a wig, and sunglasses.

The head of the English government, William Pitt, receives him in his office. He sends for General Abercromby, and the three talk while crawling on hands and knees over huge maps spread on the floor.

MIRANDA (*in English*): It should be clear that all this is to be done for the independence and freedom of those provinces, without which . . . (*gazing at the ceiling, he switched to Spanish*) . . . it would be an infamy.

ABERCROMBY (*nodding his head*): Independence and freedom.

MIRANDA: I need four thousand men and six warships. (*Points a finger at the map.*) We should start by attacking Caracas and . . .

PITT: Don't be offended, but I'll speak frankly to you. I prefer the oppressive government of Spain to the abominable system of France.

MIRANDA (*shuts his eyes and whispers in Spanish*): The enemy of my enemy is my friend. The enemy of my enemy is my friend. The enemy . . .

PITT: I wouldn't want to push the Americans into the calamities of such a revolution.

MIRANDA: I understand and share your concern, Your Excellency. Precisely for that I ask for the alliance, so that together we may fight against the monstrous principles of French liberty. (*Returns to the map.*) Caracas will fall without any difficulty . . .

ABERCROMBY: And if the colored people take up arms? And if they get control, as in Haiti?

MIRANDA: In my country the flag of liberty is in the hands of illustrious citizens of such civilized customs as Plato would have wanted for his republic. (*Slides his hand to the province of Santa Fe. The three fasten their eyes on the port of Cartagena.*)

ABERCROMBY: It looks difficult.

MIRANDA: It looks invulnerable. But I know a spot where the defense is extremely weak. On the right flank of the rampart . . .

(150 and 191)

Miranda Dreams of Catherine of Russia

Sometimes, very late at night, Miranda returns to Saint Petersburg and conjures up Catherine the Great in her intimate Winter Palace chambers. The endless train of the empress's gown, which thousands of pages hold up in the air, is a tunnel of embroidered silk through which Miranda rushes until he sinks into a sea of lace. Seeking the body that burns and waits, Miranda loosens golden fasteners and ropes of pearls and makes his way among rustling materials. Beyond the ample puffed skirt he is scratched by the wires of the crinoline, but manages to penetrate this armor and arrives at the first petticoat, tearing it off with one pull. Beneath it he finds another, and another and another, many petticoats of pearly smoothness, onion skins which his fingers peel with less and less spirit, and when with a great effort he breaks through the last petticoat the corset appears, invulnerable bastion defended by an army of belts and hooks and little laces and buttons, while the august lady, flesh that never tires, groans and beseeches.

1799: Cumaná

Two Wise Men on a Mule

The New World is too big for the eyes of the two Europeans who have just landed at Cumaná. The port sparkles on the river, set aflame by the sun, houses of white timber or bamboo beside the stone fort, and beyond, green sea, green land, the glowing bay. All truly new, never used, never seen: the plumage of the flamingos, the beaks of the pelicans, the sixty-foot coconut trees and the immense velvety flowers, tree trunks padded with lianas and foliage, the eternal siesta of the crocodiles, the skyblue, yellow, red crabs . . . There are Indians sleeping nude on the warm sand, and mulattas dressed in embroidered muslin, their bare feet caressing the places they tread. Here there is no tree that does not offer forbidden fruit from the center of the lost garden.

Alexander von Humboldt and Aimé Bonpland rent a house facing the main plaza, with a good flat on which to stand the telescope. Looking upward from this roof they see an eclipse of the sun and a shower of meteors, the angry sky spitting fire through a whole night, and looking down they see how the buyers of slaves open the mouths of blacks newly arrived at the Cumaná market. In this house they experience the first earthquake of their lives; and from it they go out to explore the region. They classify ferns and rare birds and look for Francisco Loyano, who suckled his son for five months and had tits and pure, sweet milk as long as his woman was sick.

Later Humboldt and Bonpland set out for the southern highlands. They carry their instruments: sextant, compass, thermometer, hygrometer, magnetometer. They also bring paper for drying flowers, bistouries for bird, fish, and crab autopsies; and ink and pen to sketch all the wonders. They go on muleback, weighed down with equipment, the German with the black top hat and blue eyes and the Frenchman with the insatiable magnifying glass.

Perplexed, the forests and mountains of America open up to these two lunatics.

(30 and 46)

1799: Montevideo
Father of the Poor

Francisco Antonio Maciel has founded the first meat-salting plant on this bank of the River Plata. His, too, is the soap and tallow candle factory. The lamplighter who patrols Montevideo's streets at nightfall, torch in hand and ladder on shoulder, lights Maciel's candles.

When not touring his fields, Maciel is at the salting plant checking the strips of jerky he will sell to Cuba or Brazil, or at the docks inspecting the hides he exports. He often accompanies his brigantines, which bear the names of saints, beyond the bay. Montevideans call him *Father of the Poor*, because he always has time, though it seems a miracle, to succor the sick left in the hands of God. Anywhere and at any hour the pious Maciel will stretch out a plate asking alms for the charity hospital he founded. Nor does he forget to visit blacks who spend Eastertide in the barracks at the mouth of the Miguelete River. He personally fixes the minimum price of each slave that his ships bring from Rio de Janeiro or Havana. Those with a complete set of teeth go for two hundred pesos; those who know the arts of masonry and carpentry, for four hundred.

Maciel is the most important of the Montevidean businessmen specializing in the exchange of cow meat for people meat.

(195 and 251)

1799: Guanajuato
Life, Passion, and Business of the Ruling Class

All through the century that is dying, the owners of the Guanajuato and Zacatecas mines have been buying titles of high nobility. Ten mine owners have become counts and six marquises. While they planted family trees and tried on wigs, a new labor code was transforming their workers into debt-slaves. During the eighteenth century Guanajuato has multiplied eightfold its production of silver and gold.

Meanwhile, the magic wand of money has also touched seven Mexico City merchants, farm laborers from the mountains of northern Spain, and made them marquises and counts.

Some mine owners and merchants, anxious for aristocratic prestige, buy lands as well as titles. Throughout Mexico, innumerable haciendas advance, devouring the traditional lands of Indian communities.

Others prefer to go in for usury. The moneylender José Antonio del Mazo, for example, risks little and wins much. *Friend Mazo*, writes Francisco Alonso Terán, *is one of those who do the most business in Guanajuato. If God gives him long life, he will contain the whole city in his belly*.

(49 and 223)

1799: Royal City of Chiapas
The Tamemes

Don Augustín de las Quentas Zayas, governor of Chiapas, plans a new road from the River Tulijá to Comitán, on the way to Guatemala. Twelve hundred Tamemes will transport the necessary materials.

The Tamemes, two-legged mules, are Indians capable of carrying up to a hundred and seventy-five pounds. With ropes around their foreheads, they tote enormous bundles on their backs—even people seated in chairs—and thus cross high mountains and skirt precipices with one foot in life and the other out.

(146 and 321)

1799: Madrid
Fernando Túpac Amaru

On the street, someone plucks lamentations from a guitar. Inside, Fernando Túpac Amaru shakes with fever and dies dreaming that he is drooling snow.

The son of Peru's great chieftain does not reach his thirtieth year. Poor as a rat, he ends in Madrid his brief life of exile and prison.

Twenty years ago, violent rain swept the main plaza of Cuzco, and since then it has not stopped raining in the world.

The doctor says Fernando has died of melancholy.

(344)

1800: Apure River
To the Orinoco

America flames and spins, burned and dizzied by its suns. Giant trees embrace over the rivers and in their shade glows the canoe of the sages.

The canoe progresses pursued by birds and by hungry hordes of gnats and mosquitos. Slapping continuously, Humboldt and Bonpland defend themselves against the onslaughts of the lancers, which penetrate clothing and skin and reach to the bone, while the German studies the anatomy of the manatee, the fat fish with hands, or the electricity of the eel or the teeth of the piraña, and the Frenchman collects and classifies plants or measures a crocodile or calculates its age. Together they draw maps, register the temperature of the water and the pressure of the air, analyze the mica in the sand and the conches of snails and the passage of Orion's belt across the sky. They want America to tell them all it knows and here not a leaf or pebble is dumb.

They camp in a small cove, unloading the troublesome instruments. They light a fire to ward off mosquitos, and to cook. Suddenly, the dog barks as if to warn of an approaching jaguar, and runs to hide beneath Bonpland's legs. The toucan that Humboldt carries on his shoulder picks nervously at his straw hat. The undergrowth creaks and from among the trees appears a naked man, copper skin, Indian face, African hair:

"Welcome to my lands, gentlemen."

And he bows to them: "Don Ignacio, at your service."

Don Ignacio makes a face at the improvised fire. The sages are roasting a capybara rat. "That's Indian food," he says disdainfully, and invites them to sup in his house in splendid venison freshly hunted with an arrow.

Don Ignacio's house consists of three nets slung between trees not far from the river. There he presents them to his wife, Doña Isabela, and his daughter, Doña Manuela, not as naked as he is. He offers the travelers cigars. While the venison is browning, he riddles them with questions. Don Ignacio is hungry to know the news of the court of Madrid and the latest on those endless wars that are so wounding Europe.

(338)

1800: Esmeralda del Orinoco
Master of Poison

They sail on down river.

At the foot of a rocky mountain, at the remote Christian mission of Esmeralda, they meet the master of poison. His laboratory is the cleanest and neatest hut in the village. The old Indian, surrounded by smoking cauldrons and clay jugs, pours a yellowish juice into banana leaf cones and palm leaf funnels: the horrifying curare falls drop by drop, and bubbles. The arrow anointed with this curare will enter and kill better than the fang of a snake.

"Better than anything," says the old man, as he chews some liana and tree bark into a paste. "Better than anything you people make."

And Humboldt thinks: *He has the same pedantic tone and the same starchy manner as our pharmacists.*

"You people have invented black powder," the old man continues, as very slowly, with meticulous hand, he pours water onto the paste.

"I know it," he says after a pause, "that powder isn't worth a

damn. It's noisy. It's unreliable. Powder can't kill silently and it kills
even when you miss your aim."

He revives the fire under the kettles and pots. From within the
smoke he asks, "Know how to make soap?"

"He knows," says Bonpland.

The old man looks at Humboldt with respect. "After curare," he
says, "soap is the big thing."

(338)

Curare

Guam, the child-god of the Tukan Indians, managed to reach the
kingdom of poison. There he caught the daughter of Curare and made
love to her. She had spiders, scorpions, and snakes hidden between
her legs. Each time he entered that body, Guam died; and on reviving
he saw colors that were not of this world.

She took him to her father's house. Old Curare, who ate people,
licked himself. But Guam turned himself into a flea, and in that form
entered the old man's mouth, slithered down to his liver and took a
bite. Curare covered his mouth, nose, ears, eyes, his navel, asshole
and his penis, so that the flea would have no way to escape; but Guam
tickled him inside and got out with the sneeze.

He flew back to his country, and in his bird's beak carried a little
piece of Curare's liver.

So the Tukan Indians got poison, as the men of much time, the
guardians of memory, tell it.

(164)

1800: Uruana
Forever Earth

Opposite the island of Uruana, Humboldt meets the Indians who eat
earth.

Every year the Orinoco rises, *the Father of rivers*, flooding its
banks for two or three months. While the flood lasts, the Otomacos
eat soft clay, slightly hardened by fire, and on that they live. It is
pure earth, Humboldt confirms, not mixed with corn flour or turtle
oil or crocodile fat.

So these *wandering Indians* travel through life toward death, clay wandering toward clay, erect clay eating the earth that will eat them.

(338)

1801: Lake Guatavita

The Goddess at the Bottom of the Waters

On the maps of America, El Dorado still occupies a good part of Guyana. The lake of gold takes flight when its hunters approach, and curses and kills them; but on the maps it is a tranquil blot of blue joined to the upper Orinoco.

Humboldt and Bonpland decipher the mystery of the elusive lake. In the glittering mica on a mountain which the Indians call Golden Mountain, they discover part of the hallucination; and another in a little lake which in the rainy season invades the vast plain neighboring the source waters of the Orinoco and then, when the rains cease, disappears.

In Guyana lies the phantom lake, that most tempting of America's deliriums. Far away, on the plateau of Bogotá, is the true El Dorado. After covering many leagues by canoe and mule, Humboldt and Bonpland discover it in the sacred Lake Guatavita. This mirror of waters faithfully reflects even the tiniest leaf in the woods surrounding it: at its bottom lie the treasures of the Muisca Indians.

To this sanctuary came princes, their naked bodies gleaming with gold dust, and at the center of the lake dropped their goldsmiths' finest works, then plunged in themselves. If they came up without a single speck of gold on the skin, the goddess Furatena had accepted their offerings. In those times the goddess Furatena, snake goddess, governed the world from the depths.

(326 and 338)

1801: Bogotá

Mutis

The old monk talks as he peels oranges and an unending shower of gold spirals down into a pan between his feet.

To see him, to listen to him, Humboldt and Bonpland have detoured from their southward route and have gone upriver for forty days. José Celestino Mutis, patriarch of America's botanists, is put to sleep by speeches but enjoys intimate chats as much as anyone.

The three men, sages ever astonished by the beauty and mystery of the universe, exchange plants, ideas, doubts, discoveries. Mutis is excited by talk of Lake Guatavita, the salt mines of Zipaquirá, and the Tequendama waterfall. He praises the map of the Magdalena River which Humboldt has just drawn, and discreetly suggests some changes with the sureness of one who has traveled much and knows much, and knows very deep inside himself that something of him will remain in the world.

And he shows everything and tells everything. While he eats and offers oranges, Mutis speaks of the letters that Linnaeus wrote him, and of how much those letters taught him, and of the problems he had with the Inquisition. And he recalls and shares his discoveries about the curative powers of quinine bark, and the influence of the moon on the barometer, and the cycles of flowers, which sleep as we do and stretch and wake up little by little, unfurling their petals.

(148)

1802: The Caribbean Sea
Napoleon Restores Slavery

Squadrons of wild ducks escort the French army. The fish take flight. Through a turquoise sea, bristling with coral, the ships head for the blue mountains of Haiti. Soon the land of victorious slaves will appear on the horizon. General Leclerc stands tall at the head of the fleet. Like a ship's figurehead, his shadow is first to part the waves. Astern, other islands disappear, castles of rock, splendors of deepest green, sentinels of the new world found three centuries ago by people who were not looking for it.

"*Which has been the most prosperous regime for the colonies?*"
"*The previous one.*"

"*Well, then, put it back,*" Napoleon decided.

No man, born red, black, or white can be his neighbor's property, Toussaint L'Ouverture had said. Now the French fleet returns slavery to the Caribbean. More than fifty ships, more than twenty thousand soldiers, come from France to bring back the past with guns.

In the cabin of the flagship, a female slave fans Pauline Bonaparte and another gently scratches her head.

(71)

1802: Pointe-à-Pitre

They Were Indignant

On the island of Guadeloupe, as in all French colonies, free blacks become slaves again. Black citizens reappear in their owners' inventories and wills as saleable goods; once more they form part of the tool inventories of plantations, the equipment of ships, and the arsenal of the army. The colonial government summons whites who have left the island and guarantees them the return of their property. Blacks unclaimed by their owners are sold off for the public treasury.

The hunt becomes a butchery. The authorities of Guadeloupe pay forty-four francs for each rebel head. The hanged rot in perpetuity on top of Constantine Hill. In Pointe-à-Pitre's Place Victoria, the bonfire of blacks never goes out and the flames rise higher than the houses.

Three whites protest. For their dignity, for their indignation, they are condemned. Millet de La Girardière, a several-times-decorated French army officer, is sentenced to death in an iron cage, exposed to the public, sitting naked on a spiny leaf. The other two, Barse and Barbet, will have their bones broken before being burned alive.

(180)

1802: Chimborazo Volcano

On the Roofs of the World

They climb over clouds, amid abysses of snow, clinging to the rough body of Chimborazo, tearing their hands against the naked rock.

They have left the mules half-way up. Humboldt carries on his shoulder a bag full of stones that speak of the origin of the Andean cordillera, born of an unusual vomiting from the earth's incandescent belly. At seventeen thousand feet Bonpland has caught a butterfly, and higher up an incredible fly, and they have continued climbing, despite the bitter cold and vertigo and slippings and the blood that spurts from their eyes and gums and parted lips. Mist envelops them as they climb blindly up the volcano, until a shaft of light breaks through and strips bare the summit, that high white tower, before the astounded travelers. Is it real, could it be? Never has any man climbed so close to the sky, and it is said that on the roofs of the world appear horses flying to the clouds and colored stars at noon. Is it a hallucination, this cathedral of snow rearing up between north and south skies? Are not their bruised eyes deceiving them?

Humboldt feels an abundance of light more intense than any delirium: we are made of light, Humboldt feels, of light ourselves, and of light the earth and time, and he feels a tremendous urge to tell it right away to brother Goethe, over there at his home in Weimar.

(338)

1803: Fort Dauphin
The Island Burned Again

Toussaint L'Ouverture, chief of the free blacks, died a prisoner in a castle in France. When the jailer opened the padlock at dawn and slid back the bolt, he found Toussaint frozen in his chair.

But life in Haiti moved on, and without Toussaint the black army has beaten Napoleon Bonaparte. Twenty thousand French soldiers have been slaughtered or died of fevers. Vomiting black blood, dead blood, General Leclerc has collapsed. The land he sought to enslave proves his shroud.

Haiti has lost half its population. Shots are still heard, and hammers nailing down coffins, and funeral drums, in the vast ash-heap carpeted with corpses that the vultures spurn. This island, burned two centuries ago by an exterminating angel, has been newly eaten by the fire of men at war.

Over the smoking earth those who were slaves proclaim independence. France will not forgive the humiliation.

On the coast, palms, bent over against the wind, form ranks of spears.

(71)

1804: Mexico City
Spain's Richest Colony

Theology professors still earn five times more than their colleagues in surgery or astronomy, but Humboldt finds in Mexico City an astonishing nursery of young scientists. This is the heritage of some Jesuit priests, friends of experimental physics, the new chemistry, and certain theories of Descartes, who despite the Inquisition taught and contaminated here; and it is also the work of the viceroy Revillagigedo, a man open to the winds of time, defier of dogmas, who a few years ago governed these lands with anguished concern about the lack of machines and laboratories and modern books to read.

Humboldt discovers and praises the School of Mining and its learned professors, while Mexico produces more silver than all the rest of the world, a river of silver flowing to Europe through the port of Veracruz. At the same time, Humboldt warns that cultivated land is little and badly worked, and that the colonial monopoly of commerce and the poverty of the people block the development of manufacturing. *Mexico is the land of inequality*, he notes. *The monstrous inequality of rights and fortunes* hits one in the face. Counts and marquesses paint newly purchased coats-of-arms on their carriages, and the people live in a misery that is the enemy of all industry. The Indians suffer atrocious penury. As in all of America, here too, *more or less white skin decides what class a man occupies in society*.

(163 and 217)

1804: Madrid

The Attorney General of the Council of the Indies advises against overdoing the sale of whiteness certificates,

to the end that persons of color should not seek to generalize these favors believing that these make them equal to whites with no difference but the accident of color, and believing themselves able to obtain all destinies and employments and to form links with any legitimate and mixture-free family . . . consequences which it is fitting to avoid in a monarchy, where the classification of classes contributes to better order, security, and good government . . .

Colored or brown persons stemming from infected mixtures constitute a very inferior species which, due to its vitiated nature, its arrogance, and inclination for freedom, has been and is little attached to our government and nation . . .

(174)

1804: Catamarca

Ambrosio's Sin

Bound to a post in the main plaza of Catamarca, Ambrosio Millicay receives twenty-five strokes of the lash.

The mulatto Ambrosio, who belongs to the commander Nieva y Castillo, was denounced to the authorities for having committed the crime of learning to read and write. They flayed his back with lashes *as a lesson to those pen-pushing Indians and mulattos who wish to ape Spaniards*.

Prone on the paving stones, Ambrosio groans and raves and dreams of vengeance. *"Pardon me,"* he pleads in his dream, and, plunges in the knife.

(272)

1804: Paris

Napoleon

The solemn chords of the organ invoke the sixty kings who have ruled France, and perhaps too the angels, while the pope offers the crown to Napoleon Bonaparte.

Napoleon wreathes his own brow with the laurel of the Caesars. Then he descends, slowly, majestic in ermine and purple, and places on Josephine the diadem that consecrates her as the first empress in France's history. In a gold and crystal coach they have reached the throne of this nation, the small foreigner, great warrior, sprouted from the harsh mountains of Corsica, and his wife Josephine, born in Martinique, an Antillean whose embrace they say will burn you to a crisp. Napoleon, the artillery lieutenant who hated Frenchmen, becomes Napoleon I.

The founder of the dynasty that is inaugurated today has rehearsed this coronation ceremony a thousand times. Each personage in the retinue, each actor, has dressed as he prescribed, has placed himself where he wanted, has moved the way he ordered.

"Oh, José! If our father could see us . . . "

The voracious relatives, princes and princesses of France's new nobility, have done their duty. True, the mother, Laeticia, has refused to come, and is in the palace murmuring grudges, but Napoleon will order David, the official artist, to give Laeticia a prominent place in the painting which will tell posterity of these ceremonials.

The guests overflow the cathedral of Notre Dame. Among them, a young Venezuelan cranes his neck to miss no detail. At twenty, a hallucinated Simón Bolívar attends the birth of the Napoleonic monarchy: *I am no more than a diamond on the handle of Bonaparte's sword* . . .

During these days, in a gilded salon in Paris, Bolívar has met Alexander von Humboldt. The adventurer-sage, newly arrived from America, has said to him, *"I think your country is ripe for independence, but I don't see the man who can* . . .*"*

(20 and 116)

1804: Seville

Fray Servando

For wanting the independence of Mexico, and for believing that the pagan god Quetzalcoatl was the apostle Saint Thomas in person, Fray Servando has been sentenced to exile in Spain.

From prison to prison, from escape to escape, the Mexican heretic has been a guest of the most varied Spanish dungeons. But this artist of the file, the tunnel, and the high jump has managed to travel far on the old continent.

Globetrotter, globe breaker: a bird with agile wings and beak of steel, Fray Servando defends himself against Europe's fascination by cursing all he sees. *I am a Mexican*, he repeats at every step, and thinks Frenchwomen have faces like snub-nosed, big-mouthed frogs; that in France men are like women and women like children; that the Italian language is made for lying; and that Italy is the homeland of the superlative and the bogus, although it has one worthwhile city, Florence, because it is something like a Mexican city. Against Spain, the impertinent friar recites a whole rosary of insults: he says the Spaniards imitate the French like monkeys; that the Court is a brothel and the Escorial no more than a pile of stones; that the Basques drive nails with their foreheads, and the Aragonese likewise, except with the point upward; that the Catalans don't move a step without a lantern and won't admit any relative to their homes who doesn't bring food; and that the Madrileños are dwarfed stringers of rosaries and inheritors of prisons, condemned to a climate of eight months' winter and four months' hell.

Now, in the Seville jail, Fray Servando is pulling lice from his
chest by the fistful while an army of bedbugs makes waves in his
blanket and the fleas mock his slaps and the rats his lunges with a
stick. They all want to lunch off Fray Servando and he pleads for a
truce. He needs a moment of peace to round out the details of his
next escape, which he already has nearly complete.

(318 and 346)

1806: Island of Trinidad

Adventures, Misadventures

After many years of futile waiting, Francisco de Miranda leaves London. The English have paid him a fairly good salary, given him a few
promises and some benevolent smiles, but not a bullet for his liberating expedition. Miranda escapes from the chessboard of British
diplomacy and tries his luck in the United States.

In New York he gets a ship. Two hundred volunteers accompany
him. He lands on the Venezuelan coasts of the Gulf of Coro, after
thirty-six years of exile. He has promised his recruits a glorious welcome, flowers and music, honors and treasure, but he meets silence.
No one responds to the proclamations that announce freedom. Miranda occupies a couple of towns, covers them with flags and words,
and quits Venezuela before the five thousand soldiers from Caracas
can wipe him out.

On the island of Trinidad he receives outrageous news. The
English have seized the port of Buenos Aires and plan the conquest
of Montevideo, Valparaíso, and Veracruz. From London, the War
Minister has given clear instructions: *The novelty will consist, simply
and solely, of substituting the dominion of His Britannic Majesty for
the dominion of the Spanish king.*

Miranda will return to London, to his house in Grafton Street,
and loudly voice his protest. There they raise his annual pension from
three hundred to seven hundred pounds sterling.

(150)

1808: Rio de Janeiro
Judas-Burning Is Banned

By will of the Portuguese prince, recently arrived in Brazil, the traditional burning of Judases during the Holy Week is to be banned in the colony. To avenge Christ and avenge themselves the people would throw on the fire, one night in the year, the marshal and the archbishop, the rich merchant, the big landlord and the chief of police; the naked ones have enjoyed seeing how the rag dolls, sumptuously adorned and filled with firecrackers, twist in pain and explode amid the flames.

From now on, those in power will not suffer even in Holy Week. The royal family, who have just come from Lisbon, demand silence and respect. An English ship has rescued the Portuguese prince with all his court and jewelry, and brought them to these remote lands.

This efficacious maneuver removes the Portuguese dynasty from the dangerous onslaught of Napoleon Bonaparte, who has invaded Spain and Portugal, and it affords England a useful center of operations in America. The English have taken a tremendous beating on the River Plata. Expelled from Buenos Aires and Montevideo, they now launch their next penetration through Rio de Janeiro, through the most helplessly unconditional of their allies.

(65 and 171)

1809: Chuquisaca
The Cry

of "America" explodes in Chuquisaca. While Spain seethes, up in arms against the French invaders, America rebels. The Creoles repudiate the throne that Joseph Bonaparte, brother of Napoleon, occupies in Madrid.

Chuquisaca is first. The rebellion of America's Salamanca announces that Spain will lose her dominion over the Indies.

Chuquisaca, formerly La Plata and Charcas, and the Sucre to be, lies at the foot of two mountains in love. From its patios and gardens rises the aroma of citrus blossoms, and through its streets pass more knightly gentlemen than commoners. Nothing is so abundant here as cloaks and clerical tonsures. Very Chuquisacan are doctors, stiff as their gilt-handled canes, and friars who go about sprinkling houses with hyssop.

Here, the world seemed immutable and secure. Astoundingly, the shrill cry of liberty has come from this mouth accustomed to falsetto Latin. La Paz and Quito and Buenos Aires will immediately echo it. To the north, in Mexico . . .

(5)

1810: Atotonilco
The Virgin of Guadalupe
Versus the Virgin of Remedios

Making its way through curtains of dust, the multitude crosses the town of Atotonilco.

"Long live America and death to the bad government!"

Father Miguel Hidalgo hauls from the church the image of the Virgin of Guadalupe and ties it to a spear. The raised standard glows over the crowd.

"Long live Our Lady of Guadalupe! Death to the Spanish dogs!"

Fervor of revolution, passion of religion. The bells have rung out from the church of Dolores, the priest Hidalgo calls for struggle, and the Mexican Virgin of Guadalupe declares war on the Spanish Virgin of Remedios. Indian Virgin defies white Virgin; the one who chose a poor Indian on the hill of Tepeyac marches against the one who saved Hernán Cortés in the flight from Tenochtitlán. Our Lady of Remedios will dress up as a general; and by order of the viceroy the firing squad will riddle with bullets the standard of the Virgin of Guadalupe.

Mother, queen, and goddess of the Mexicans, the Virgin of Guadalupe was called Tonantzin by the Aztecs before the archangel Gabriel painted her image in the Tepeyac sanctuary. Year after year the people stream to Tepeyac in procession, *Ave Virgin and Pregnant, Ave Damsel with Child*, go on their knees up to the rock where she appeared, to the crack from which roses bloomed, *Ave Possessed of God, Ave Most Beloved of God*, drink water from its springs, *Ave that Maketh God a Nest*, and beseech love and miracles, protection, counsel, *Ave Maria, Ave Ave.*

Now the Virgin of Guadalupe advances, killing for the independence of Mexico.

(178)

1810: Guanajuato
El Pípila

Hidalgo's troops storm out of the mountain scrub, and fall upon Guanajuato with volleys of stones. The mining town joins the insurgent avalanche.

Despite the havoc wrought by the king's fusillades, the multitude flood the streets, a surge that sweeps the soldiers aside and beats up against that bastion of Spanish power, the Corn Exchange. There, beneath the vaulted ceilings of its thirty halls, lie eight thousand bushels of corn and an incalculable fortune in silver, gold bars, and jewels. The lords of the colony, scared out of their wits, have locked themselves in with all of their treasure.

In vain, the dandies beg for mercy. Throat-cuttings, looting, a vast drunken spree follows, and the Indians strip the dead to see if they have tails.

El Pípila, a miner, is the hero of the day. They say he hoisted an enormous stone slab onto his back, scuttled like a turtle through the rain of bullets, and with a lighted torch and plenty of pitch set fire to the Corn Exchange door. They say that El Pípila's name is Juan José Martínez and they say he has other names too, all the names of the Indians who are or have ever been in the mines of Guanajuato.

(197)

1810: Guadalajara
Hidalgo

Everybody knew, in the town of Dolores, that the priest Hidalgo had the bad habit of reading as he walked through the streets, the great wings of his hat between the sun and the pages, and that it was a sheer miracle that neither horses nor the Inquisition ever hit him, because more dangerous than reading was what he read. At a slow pace the priest moved through the cloud of dust in the streets of Dolores, always with some French book covering his face, one of those books that talk of the social contract and the rights of man and the freedoms of citizens; and if he didn't greet people it was because of his thirst for erudition, not rudeness.

The priest Hidalgo rebelled along with the twenty Indians who made bowls and pots with him, and at the end of a week there were fifty thousand of them. Then the Inquisition went to work on him.

The Holy Office of Mexico has pronounced him *a heretic, apostate of religion, denier of the virginity of Mary, materialist, libertine, advocate of fornication, seditious, schismatic, and sectarian of French liberty.*

The Virgin of Guadalupe invades Guadalajara at the head of an insurgent army. Miguel Hidalgo has the portrait of King Ferdinand removed from the walls and replies to the Inquisition with a decree abolishing slavery, confiscating the goods of Europeans, ending the tributes paid by Indians, and recovering farmlands from those who have usurped them.

(127, 203, and 321)

1810: Pie de la Cuesta
Morelos

He is a country priest, like Hidalgo. Like Hidalgo, he was born in the Tarascan country, in the mountains of Michoacán where Bishop Vasco de Quiroga had created, two and a half centuries earlier, his communist utopia—lands of redemption later laid waste by plagues and by the forced labor of thousands of Indians dragged to the mines of Guanajuato.

"With violence I go to the hot lands of the south."

José María Morelos, shepherd and muleteer, parish priest of Carácuaro, joins the revolution. He takes the road with twenty-five spearmen and a few shotguns. Behind the white silk kerchief that binds his head, the troop keeps growing.

In search of Atoyac Indians hidden in the palm groves, Morelos crosses the little town of Pie de la Cuesta.

"Who goes there?"

"Holy God," say the Indians.

Morelos talks to them. From now on, to the cry of *"Who goes there?"* people will answer, *"America."*

(332 and 348)

1811: Buenos Aires
Moreno

Great fortunes in a few hands, thought Mariano Moreno, are stagnant waters that do not bathe the earth. *So as not to escape from tyrants without destroying tyranny*, parasitical capital amassed in colonial business would have to be expropriated. Why seek in Europe, at the price of extortionate interest, money that is more than abundant at home? From abroad should be brought machines and seeds, instead of Stoddard pianos and Chinese vases. The State, thought Moreno, should become a great entrepreneur of a newly independent nation. The revolution, he thought, should be terrible and astute, implacable with enemies and vigilant towards onlookers.

Fleetingly he held power, or thought he did.

"Thanks be to God," breathed the merchants of Buenos Aires. Mariano Moreno, *the demon of hell*, has died on the high seas. His friends French and Beruti go into exile. Castelli is sentenced to prison.

Cornelio Saavedra orders copies of Rousseau's *Social Contract*, which Moreno had published and circulated, rounded up; and he warns that no Robespierre has any place on the River Plata.

(2 and 267)

1811: Buenos Aires
Castelli

There were two of them: a pen and a voice. A Robespierre who wrote, Mariano Moreno, and another who spoke. *They are all perverse*, said a Spanish commandant, *but Castelli and Moreno are very perverse indeed.* Juan José Castelli, the great orator, is in jail in Buenos Aires.

Usurped by conservatives, the revolution sacrifices the revolutionaries. The charges pile up: Castelli is a womanizer, a drunk, a cardsharp, and a profaner of churches. The prisoner, agitator of Indians, seeker of justice for the poor, spokesman for the American cause, cannot defend himself. Cancer has attacked his mouth. His tongue has to be amputated.

The revolution falls dumb in Buenos Aires.

(84)

1811: Bogotá
Nariño

We have changed masters, writes Antonio Nariño in Colombia.

La Bagatela, the newspaper founded, directed, and edited by him from cover to cover, deprives puppets of heads and big shots of pedestals. Nariño proclaims that the patriotic uprising of the Colombians is turning into a masked ball and demands that independence be declared once and for all. He also demands, voice crying in the desert, that the right of the poor to vote be recognized and that the will of the naked plebeian is worth as much as that of the gentleman sheathed in velvet.

We have changed masters, he writes. Some months ago the people invaded the main square of Bogotá, the men took the viceroy prisoner and the women threw the vicereine into the whores' prison. The ghost of José Antonio Galán, the commoners' captain, charged at the head of the infuriated multitude. Then the doctors and bishops and merchants and masters of lands and slaves were badly scared. Swearing to avoid at any price *the errors of the libertines of France*, they helped the viceregal couple to escape secretly.

We have changed masters. Colombia is governed by gentlemen in very starched shirts and cassocks with many buttons. *Even in Heaven there are hierarchies*, preaches the Canon of the Cathedral, *and not even the fingers of the hand are equal*. The ladies cross themselves, lowering a thicket of curls, flowers, and ribbons beneath the black mantilla. The Junta of Notables issues its first decrees. Among other patriotic measures, it resolves to despoil the despoiled Indians of all that remains to them. Under the pretext of freeing them from tribute, the Junta seizes the Indians' communal lands to force them to serve in the big haciendas which feature a pillory in the middle of the patio.

(185 and 235)

The World Upside Down,
Verses for Guitar Accompanied by Singer

When you paint the world upside down
You see it in all its error:
The dog flees the fox in terror,
Thief chases judge in his gown.
The feet look down on the head,
The mouth drags along in the mire,
Water is put out by fire,
Letters are taught by the blind,
The carter is pulling the wagon,
The oxen are riding behind.

On the banks of a man sits a river,
Sharpening his horse in the shade
And watering his blunted blade.

(179)

1811: Chilapa

Potbelly

In Mexico, military order is vanquishing popular tumult. Hidalgo has been executed in Chihuahua. It is said that he renounced his ideas, after four months of chains and torture. Independence now has only the forces that follow Morelos to rely on.

Ignacio López Rayón sends Morelos an urgent message of warning: *I have it from good sources that the viceroy has paid an assassin to kill you. I cannot tell you any more about this man, except that he is very potbellied . . .*

At dawn, in a burst of hooves, the messenger reaches the camp at Chilapa.

At noon, the assassin comes to offer his services to the national cause. Arms crossed, Morelos gets a broadside of patriotic speeches. Without saying a word he sits the assassin down on his right and invites him to share his dinner. He watches the assassin eating, as the man stares at his plate.

In the evening they sup together. The assassin eats and talks and chokes. Morelos, courteous statue, seeks out his eyes.

"I have a bad presentiment," he says suddenly and waits for the eyes to tense, the chair to creak, and then offers relief: "My rheumatism again. Rain."

His somber expression cuts short a laugh.

He lights a cigar. Studies the smoke.

The assassin dares not get up. He stammers thanks. Morelos faces him closely. "I shall be curious," he says.

He notices the assassin giving a start and counts the beads of sweat on his forehead. He draws out the question: "Are you sleepy?"

And without a pause: "Would you do me the honor of sleeping beside me?"

They stretch out, separated by a candle fluttering in its death agonies, yet undecided whether to die or not. Morelos turns his back. He breathes deeply, perhaps snores. Before dawn he hears a horse's hooves fading into the distance.

At midmorning, he asks his assistant for paper and pen.

A letter to Ignacio López Rayón: *Thanks for the tip. In this camp there is no one more potbellied than I.*

(348)

1811: East Bank Ranges
"Nobody is more than anybody,"

say the mounted cowboys. The land cannot have an owner, because the air doesn't have one. They know no better roof than the stars, nor any glory that compares with the freedom to wander aimlessly on friend horse across the prairie that rolls like the sea.

Having herds to drive in the open country is to have almost everything. The gauchos eat only meat, because the verdure is grass and grass is for cows. The roast is topped off with tobacco and rum, and with guitars that sing of events and miracles.

The gauchos, *loose men* whom the estates use and discard, join forces with José Artigas. The ranges east of the Uruguay River take fire.

(227 and 278)

1811: Banks of the Uruguay River
Exodus

Buenos Aires makes a deal with the viceroy and withdraws the troops that were besieging Montevideo. José Artigas refuses to observe the armistice, which restores his land to the Spaniards, and vows to carry on the war *even if it be with teeth, with nails.*

The leader emigrates northward to organize an army of independence. A dispersed people unites and is born in his tracks, a roving host that joins wild cowboys with peons and laborers, patriots of the estancias. To the north march women who heal wounds or take up a spear and monks who all along the march baptize newborn soldiers. The formerly well-sheltered opt for the rigors of outdoor life, those who lived quietly choose danger. Marching northward are masters of letters and the knife, loquacious doctors and worried bandits in debt for some death. Tooth-pullers and miracle workers, deserters from ships and forts, fugitive slaves. All are marching. Indians burn their huts and join up, bringing along only arrows and bolas.

Northward goes the long caravan of carts, horses, people on foot. As they go, the land that will be called Uruguay is stripped of those who want a fatherland. The land itself goes with its children, goes in them, and nothing is left behind. Not even an ash, not even silence.

(277)

1812: Cochabamba
Women

From Cochabamba, many men have fled. Not one woman. On the hillside, a great clamor. Cochabamba's plebeian women, at bay, fight from the center of a circle of fire.

Surrounded by five thousand Spaniards, they resist with battered tin guns and a few arquebuses; and they fight to the last yell, whose echoes will resound throughout the long war for independence. Whenever his army weakens, General Manuel Belgrano will shout those words which never fail to restore courage and spark anger. The general will ask his vacillating soldiers: *Are the women of Cochabamba present?*

(5)

1812: Caracas
Bolívar

An earthquake demolishes Caracas, La Guaira, San Felipe, Barquisimeto, and Mérida. They are the Venezuelan cities which have proclaimed independence. In Caracas, center of the Creole insurrection, ten thousand lie dead beneath the ruins. Nothing is heard but supplications and curses as people seek bodies among the stones.

Can God be Spanish? The earthquake has swallowed the gallows erected by the patriots and has not left standing one of the churches which had sung the Te Deum in honor of the nascent republic. In the ruined Mercedes church the column bearing Spain's imperial coat of arms still stands. Coro, Maracaibo, Valencia and Angostura, cities loyal to the king, have not suffered a scratch.

In Caracas, the air burns. From the ruins rises a dense dust which the eye cannot penetrate. A monk harangues the people, proclaiming that God will no longer tolerate such effrontery.

"*Vengeance!*"

The multitude presses around him in what was the San Jacinto convent. Perched on the ruins of the altar, the monk demands punishment for those who brought on God's wrath.

"*Vengeance!*" roars the scourge of Christ, and his accusing finger points at a patriot officer who, his arms crossed, contemplates the scene. The crowd turns against the officer—short, bony, in a brilliant uniform—and advances to crush him.

Simón Bolívar neither implores nor retreats: he attacks. Sword in hand he plunges through the frenzy, mounts the altar and with one blow topples the apocalyptic monk.

The people, silent, disperse.

(116)

1813: Chilpancingo
Independence Is Revolution or a Lie

In three military campaigns Morelos has won a good part of Mexico. The Congress of the future republic, a wandering Congress, travels behind its leader. The deputies sleep on the ground and eat soldiers' rations.

By the light of a thick tallow candle Morelos draws up the essentials of the national Constitution. He proposes a free, independent, and Catholic America; substitutes an income tax for Indian tributes and increases the wages of the poor; confiscates the goods of the enemy; establishes freedom of commerce, but with tariff barriers; suppresses slavery and torture and liquidates the caste system, which bases social differences on the color of skin, *so that only vice and virtue distinguish one American from another*.

The rich Creoles go from shock to shock as Morelos's troops march along expropriating fortunes and dividing up haciendas. A war against Spain or a rising of the serfs? This is not the sort of independence they were hoping for. They will make another.

(348)

1814: San Mateo
Boves

In Venezuela the word *independence* still does not mean much more than *freedom of commerce* for rich Creoles.

Blacks and browns look to the chief of the Spaniards, a Hercules with red beard and green eyes, as their leader. Slaves run away to find José Tomás Rodríguez Boves, *Papa* Boves. Ten thousand prairie horsemen set fire to plantations and cut masters' throats in the name of God and the king. Boves's flag, a skull on black ground, promises pillage and revenge, war to the death against the cacao oligarchy who want independence from Spain. On the plains of San Mateo, Boves rides his horses into the mansion of the Bolívar family and carves his name with a knife on the door of the main vestibule.

The spear does not repent; the bullet does not repent. Before killing with lead, Boves shoots salvos of gunpowder, for the pleasure of seeing the expressions on his victims' faces. Among his bravest soldiers he divides up the young ladies of the best families. He enjoys bullfighting elegant patriots, after sticking banderillas in their necks. He cuts heads off as if it were a joke.

Before long now, a spear will pierce him. He will be buried with bound feet.

(160)

1815: San Cristóbal Ecatepec
The Lake Comes for Him

On the thorny ridge of Tezmalaca the Spaniards catch José María Morelos. After so many mistakes and defeats, they hunt him down in the brambles, his clothing in shreds, without weapons or spurs.

They chain him. They insult him. Lieutenant-Colonel Eugenio Villasana asks, "What would you do if you were the winner, and I the defeated?"

"*Give you two hours to confess,*" says the priest Morelos, "*and shoot you.*"

They take him to the secret cells of the Inquisition.

They humiliate him on his knees. They shoot him in the back.

The viceroy says that the rebel died repentant. The Mexican people say that the lake heard the firing squad's blast and overflowed to carry off the body.

(178 and 332)

1815: Paris

Navigators of Seas and Libraries

Julien Mellet, writer and traveler, relates his adventures in South America to the European public. Among other things he describes *a very lively and lascivious dance* much done in Quillota, in Chile, and which was brought *by the blacks from Guinea*. Pretending to look the other way, Mellet copies a description of a dance of Montevideo's blacks, as published by the traveler Anthony Helms eight years previously in London. Helms had stolen his text line by line from the book that Dom Pernetty published in Paris in 1770. Pernetty, for his part, had portrayed at first hand the dance of the Montevideo slaves with words astonishingly similar to those that Father Jean Baptiste Labat had devoted to the blacks of Haiti, in a book published half a century earlier in The Hague.

From the Caribbean to the Chilean city of Quillota, passing through Montevideo, and from The Hague to Paris, passing through London, those passages of Father Labat's have traveled much further than their author. Without passport or disguise.

(19)

1815: Mérida, Yucatán

Ferdinand VII

The starched gentlemen of Yucatán cross the Plaza de Armas in Mérida, whitened by dust and sun, and enter the cathedral in very solemn procession. From the shade of its portico, the Indian tamale and necklace vendors don't understand why the bells ring so merrily, or know whose is that crowned head that the gentlemen carry on a banner.

The colonial aristocracy is celebrating the news from Madrid. It has been belatedly learned that the French were driven out and Ferdinand VII reigns in Spain. Messengers report that the cry being heard around the monarch is *"Long live chains!"* As court jesters tinkle their little bells, King Ferdinand orders the guerrillas who brought him to the throne jailed or shot, revives the Inquisition, and restores the privileges of the clergy and nobility.

(339)

1815: Curuzú-Cuatiá

The Hides Cycle on the River Plata

On the tip of a spear, the sharp-edged half-moon reaches for the fleeing animal's legs. Just one slash: the horseman strikes with sure aim, and the calf limps and gasps and falls. The horseman dismounts. He cuts the throat and begins to skin.

He does not always kill that way. Easier to drive the maverick cattle with yells into the corrals and knife them there, thousands and thousands of wild cattle or horses stampeded to their death; easier yet to surprise the animals in the hills by night, while they sleep.

The gaucho pulls off the hide and stakes it out in the sun. Of the remainder, what the mouth doesn't want is left for the crows.

The Robertson brothers, John and William, Scottish merchants, go around these lands with sacks that look like sausages, stuffed with gold coins. From an estancia in Curuzú-Cuatiá they send ten thousand hides to the town of Goya, in sixty carts.

The enormous wooden wheels creak as they turn, and goads urge the oxen on. The carts cut through the countryside. They climb hills, cross swamps and swollen rivers. At nightfall the encircled carts form a hearth. While the gauchos smoke and drink maté, the air thickens with the aroma of meat browning on the embers. After the roast, yarns are exchanged and guitars heard.

From the town of Goya, the hides will travel on to the port of Buenos Aires and cross the ocean to the tanneries of Liverpool. The price will have multiplied many times when the hides return to the River Plata, converted into boots, shoes, and whips of British manufacture.

(283)

1815: Buenos Aires

The Bluebloods Seek a King in Europe

The goose-quill pen writes: *José Artigas, traitor to his country*.

In vain they have offered him gold and glory. Shopkeepers expert in yard-measures and precise balances, the patricians of Buenos Aires calculate the price of Artigas dead or alive. They are ready to pay six thousand duros for the head of the leader of the rebel camps.

To exorcise these lands of the gaucho devil, Carlos de Alvear offers them to the English: *These provinces*, Alvear writes to Lord Castlereagh, *want to belong to Great Britain without any conditions*. And he implores Lord Strangford: *The British Nation cannot abandon to their fate the inhabitants of the River Plata in the very act of throwing themselves into its generous arms* . . .

Manuel de Sarratea journeys to London in search of a monarch to crown in Buenos Aires. The interior, republican and federal, threatens the privileges of the port, and panic prevails over any oath of allegiance. In Madrid, Manuel Belgrano and Bernardino Rivadavia, who had been ardent republicans, offer the throne to the Infante Francisco de Paula, brother of Ferdinand VII. The port city's emissaries promise hereditary power embracing all the River Plata region, Chile, and even Peru. The new independent kingdom would have a blue and white flag; freedom and property would be sacred and the court would be formed by distinguished Creoles promoted into dukes, counts, and marquesses.

Nobody accepts.

(2 and 278)

1815: Purification Camp
Artigas

Here, where the river gets mad and boils up in eddies and whirlpools, on a purple tableland surrounded by hollows and canyons, General Artigas governs. These thousand hearths of poor Creoles, these huts of mud and straw and leather windows, are the capital of the confederation of peoples of the River Plata interior. In front of the government shack, horses await the messengers who gallop back and forth bringing advice and taking decrees. No trimmings or medals adorn the uniform of the leader of the south.

Artigas, son of the prairie, had been a smuggler and a hunter of smugglers. He knew the meanderings of every river, the secrets of every hill, the savor of the grass of each field; and even more deeply, the diffident souls of the cowboys who only have their lives to give and give them fighting in a hallucinating whirlwind of spears.

The banners of Artigas fly over the region watered by the Uruguay and Paraná rivers, which extends to the sierras of Córdoba. Sharing this immense space are the provinces that refuse to be a colony of Buenos Aires after winning their liberation from Spain.

The port of Buenos Aires lives with its back to the land that it despises and fears. Glued to their lookout windows, the merchants await ships that bring novelties of dress, speech, and thought, but no king.

Against the avalanche of European merchandise, Artigas wants to build dikes to defend *our arts and factories*—with free passage only for machines, books, and medicines; and he diverts to the port of Montevideo the provincial trade over which Buenos Aires had long assumed a monopoly. The Artiguista federal league wants no king, but assemblies and congresses of citizens; and to top off the scandal, the leader decrees agrarian reform.

(277 and 278)

1816: East Bank Ranges
Agrarian Reform

In Buenos Aires they are crying bloody murder. East of the Uruguay River, Artigas expropriates the lands of the Belgrano and Mitre families, of the family of San Martín's father-in-law, of Bernardino Rivadavia, of Azcuénaga and Almagro and Díaz Vélez. In Montevideo they call the agrarian reform a *criminal project*. Artigas has jailed Lucas Obes, Juan María Pérez and other artists of the minuet and legerdemain.

For the owners of land, devourers of acreage eaten by grace of king, fraud, or plunder, the gaucho is cannon fodder or estancia serf— and anyone denying it should be put in the stocks or up against a wall.

Artigas wants every gaucho to own a piece of land. Poor folk invade the estancias. In the eastern ranges devastated by war, huts and tilled plots and corrals begin to sprout. The trampled peasantry starts to trample. The men who put their lives on the line in the war of independence refuse to accept further abandonment. For the Montevideo town council, Encarnación Benítez, Artigas's soldier who gallops about dividing land and cattle at the head of *a troop of villains*, is an *outlaw, pervert, vagrant, and agitator*. In the shade of his spear poor people find refuge; but this brown man, illiterate, courageous, perhaps fierce, will never be a statue, nor will any avenue or street or byroad ever bear his name.

(335)

1816: Chicote Hill

The Art of War

On Chicote Hill the royalist infantry have surrounded a handful of patriots of Upper Peru.

"*I don't give myself up to the enemy!*" yells the soldier Pedro Loayza, and throws himself over the precipice.

"*We'll die for the fatherland!*" proclaims commandant Eusebio Lira, as he too runs for the precipice.

"*We'll die if we're idiots,*" drum major José Santos Vargas says abruptly, cutting him off.

"*Let's set fire to the dry grass,*" proposes sergeant Julián Reinaga.

The tall grass blazes up and the wind fans the flames toward the enemy ranks. The fire thrusts forward in waves. Confused and terrified, the besiegers flee, throwing rifles and cartridge belts to the winds and imploring the Almighty for pity.

(347)

1816: Tarabuco

Juana Azurduy,

well versed in catechisms, born to be a nun in the Chuquisaca convent, is a lieutenant colonel in the guerrilla armies of independence. Of her four children the only survivor is the one who was born in the heat of battle, amid the thunder of horses and guns. The head of her husband is stuck high up on a Spanish pike.

Juana rides in the mountains in front of her men. Her sky-blue shawl flutters in the wind. One fist clutches the reins; the other severs necks with a sword.

Everything she eats is turned into bravery. The Indians do not call her Juana. They call her Pachamama; they call her Mother Earth.

(126)

1816: Port-au-Prince
Pétion

Haiti lies in ruins, blockaded by the French and isolated by everyone
else. No country has recognized the independence of the slaves who
defeated Napoleon.

The island is divided in two.

In the north, Henri Christophe has proclaimed himself emperor.
In the castle of Sans-Souci, the new black nobility dance the minuet—
the Duke of Marmalade, the Count of Lemonade—while black lackeys
in snowy wigs bow and scrape, and black hussars parade their plumed
bonnets through gardens copied from Versailles.

To the south, Alexandre Pétion presides over the republic. Distributing lands among the former slaves, Pétion aims to create a nation
of peasants, very poor but free and armed, on the ashes of plantations
destroyed by the war.

On Haiti's southern coast Simón Bolívar lands, in search of refuge
and aid. He comes from Jamaica, where he has sold everything down
to his watch. No one believes in his cause. His brilliant military
campaigns have been no more than a mirage. Francisco Miranda is
dying in chains in the Cadiz arsenal, and the Spaniards have recon-
quered Venezuela and Colombia, which prefer the past or still do not
believe in the future promised by the patriots.

Pétion receives Bolívar as soon as he arrives, on New Year's Day.
He gives him seven ships, two hundred and fifty men, muskets,
powder, provisions, and money. He makes only one condition. Pétion, born a slave, son of a black woman and a Frenchman, demands
of Bolívar the freedom of slaves in the lands he is going to liberate.

Bolívar shakes his hand. The war will change its course. Perhaps
America will too.

(115, 116, and 202)

1816: Mexico City
El Periquillo Sarniento

The first Latin American novel is born in a printery on Zuleta Street.
In three volumes, José Joaquín Fernández de Lizardi relates the
misfortunes of *El Periquillo Sarniento*; readers devour and celebrate

it. The viceroy bans the fourth volume when it is about to appear, but there is no way to jail the character.

El Periquillo, that American offspring of the Spanish picaresque, has won the streets of Mexico. He goes everywhere, stripping customs naked. He jumps from the cardsharp's table to the notary's office, and from the barber's chair to the prison floor. Many do not enjoy his adventures. The priest drowns him in edifying sermons. Lizardi, enlightened moralist, turns every game into a moral.

(9, 111, and 303)

1817: Santiago de Chile
The Devil at Work

Elegant youths smoke cigarettes in gold holders so as not to stain their fingers, but Santiago de Chile is bounded on all four sides by garbage. To the north, the houses look out on the Mapocho River garbage dump. To the south, trash piles up in the ravine. The sun rises on mountains of rubbish on Santa Lucía hill and its last rays light up the dumps in the San Miguel and San Pablo suburbs.

From one of these dumps sprouted the visitor who crossed the city last night, a sulphurous salvo that made the little tallow candles quiver in the street lamps, and that curiously or threateningly nosed around the Compañía temple until the night watchman's voice intoned eleven o'clock:

"Hail Mary full of gra-a-ace!"

The Devil fled hell-for-leather.

The shoe he lost is touring Santiago, house to house. A monk carries it, covered by a napkin, on a silver tray. Pious ladies cross themselves.

(256)

1817: Santiago de Chile
Manuel Rodríguez

Whoever talks of American emancipation signs his own death warrant. Whoever gets a letter from Mendoza marches to the gallows or the firing squad. The Vigilance Tribunal gives free rein to informers in Santiago de Chile.

Between Mendoza and Santiago, patriots are reorganizing the army ground to pieces by the Spaniards. Winds of resistance come and go, crossing the splendor of the cordillera's snow, without leaving a trace.

The messenger passes an order at the cockfights in Santiago, and another at a smart soiree, and at the same time picks up a report between two horseraces in the suburbs. The messenger announces himself at a big house—three taps of the doorknocker—and at the same time emerges in the mountains on the back of a mule, and gallops over prairies on horseback. The guerrilla makes an assault on Melipilla, but he is also crossing the town of San Fernando. Striking in Rancagua, the guerrilla dismounts in Pomaire and drinks a glass of wine.

The Spanish governor has put a price on the head of Manuel Rodríguez, the messenger, the guerrilla. But his head travels hidden beneath the monk's hood, the muleteer's sombrero, the street peddler's basket, or the fine gentleman's plush topper. No one can catch him because he flies without moving and goes out inward and comes in outward.

(106)

1817: Montevideo
Images for an Epic

An enormous army comes from Rio de Janeiro, by land and sea, with the mission of wiping out José Artigas, of obliterating even the shadow of a memory of his contagious example. With fire and sword, the Brazilians invade, announcing that they will clear the bandits off these plains. General Lecor promises to restore the damaged rights of property and heredity.

Lecor enters Montevideo beneath a canopy. Father Larrañaga and Francisco Javier de Viana offer the keys of the city to the redeemers of the great estates. Ladies throw flowers and little blue bows in the path of this phenomenal parade of braid, decorations, and plumes. Bored tolling for funerals, the cathedral bells ring out. Censers swing to and fro, and so do businessmen; their bowings and scrapings never end.

(195, 278, and 335)

1817: Quito

Manuela Sáenz

Quito was born between volcanoes, high, far from the sea; and between the cathedral and the palace, in the central plaza, was born Manuela. She arrived in Quito on a satin bed, on sheets from Brussels, daughter of a secret love affair of Don Simón Sáenz, killer of the Creoles who rose in rebellion here.

At fifteen, Manuela wore men's clothes, smoked, and broke in horses. She did not ride side-saddle like the ladies, but with open legs, and scorning harness. Her best friend was her black slave Jonatás, who meowed like a cat, sang like a bird, and when she walked undulated like a snake. Manuela was sixteen when they shut her up in one of this prayerful and sinful city's many convents, where monks help old nuns to die a good death and young ones to live a good life. In the Santa Catalina convent Manuela learned to embroider, to play the clavichord, to feign virtue, and to faint, rolling back her eyes. At seventeen, crazy about uniforms, she eloped with Fausto D'Elhuyar, an officer of the king.

At twenty, she sparkles. All the men want to be the oyster of this pearl. They marry her to James Thorne, a respectable English doctor. The party lasts a whole week.

(295)

1818: Colonia Camp

The War of the Underdogs

By now, Artigas's army is nothing but naked people. Those who own no more property than a horse, as well as the blacks and the Indians, know that in this war everyone's destiny is at stake. From fields and rivers groups of mounted rebels attack the well-armed Brazilians with spear and knife; and like birds they vanish in a flash.

While bugles call out slaughter in this invaded land, the Buenos Aires government spreads propaganda directed toward *those who have goods to lose*. A leaflet signed by "The Friend of Order" calls Artigas a *malevolent genie, apostle of the lie, ravenous wolf, scourge of his country, new Attila, disgrace of the century and affront to the human race.*

Someone brings the leaflets to the camp. Artigas does not take his eyes off the fire: *"My people don't know how to read,"* he says.

(277)

1818: Corrientes
Andresito

"Their rights come first," Artigas has said of the Indians; and they have suffered much death for being loyal to him.

Andrés Guacurarí, Andresito, Guaraní Indian, adopted son of Artigas, is the chief. He invaded Corrientes, a flood of men, a couple of months ago, arrows against rifles, and pulverized the allies of Buenos Aires.

Naked save for mud from the march and a rag or two, Andresito's Indians entered the city. They brought along a few Indian children whom the Corrientes people had held as slaves. They met with silence and closed shutters. The commander of the garrison buried his fortune in his garden and the notary died of fright.

The Indians had not eaten for some time, but they took nothing and asked for nothing. As soon as they arrived they put on a theater show in homage to the principal families. Huge wings of silver paper spread on cane frames turned the Indians into guardian angels. For no one, because no one came, they staged "The Temptation of Saint Ignatius," an old pantomime of the Jesuit period.

"So they don't want to come to Indian parties?" Andresito lit a big cigar, smoke emerging from his ears and eyes.

At dawn, drums beat to arms. At spear point Corrientes's most respectable gentlemen are forced to cut the grass on the plaza and to sweep the streets till they are transparent. All day long the gentlemen are kept at this noble task and that night, in the theater, they deafen the Indians with applause.

Andresito governs Corrientes until Artigas sends for him.

The Indians are moving off down the road. They wear those enormous silver wings. Toward the horizon ride the angels. The sun makes them shine and gives them the shadows of eagles in flight.

(283)

1818: Paraná River
The Patriot Pirates

Andresito's forces move down to Santa Fe, skirting the river. On the Paraná a flotilla of patriot pirates accompanies the Indians.

Canoes, launches, and a few well-armed brigantines make life impossible for the merchant ships of Brazil. Artigas's tricolor sails on the rivers and the sea, everywhere, fighting. The pirates strip enemy ships in sudden boardings and take the fruits of their raids to the far Antilles.

Pedro Campbell is the admiral of this squadron of ships and small boats. He arrived here with the English invaders years ago, deserted, and took to galloping over the prairies. The Irish gaucho with hooped earrings and a fierce expression peering from beneath a mop of red hair soon becomes famous. When Artigas makes him chief of the pirates Campbell has already been slashed in Creole duels and credited with deaths but no treachery. Everyone knows that his silver knife is a snake that never bites in the back.

(277 and 283)

1818: San Fernando de Apure
War to the Death

At the head of an army pulverized by defeats rides Bolívar. A pilgrim's hood shades his face; in the shadow, gleam eyes that devour as they look, and a melancholy smile.

Bolívar rides the horse of the late Rafael López. The saddle bears the silver initials of the dead man, a Spanish officer who took a shot at Bolívar while the patriot chief slept in a hammock.

The northern offensive has failed.

In San Fernando de Apure Bolívar reviews what remains of his forces.

"*He's crazy,*" think or murmur his barefoot, exhausted, injured soldiers as he announces that they will soon carry this sacred war, war to the death, into Colombia and Peru and to the peak of Potosí.

(53 and 116)

1819: Angostura

Abecedarium: The Constituent Assembly

Beneath the awning, on a ship sailing the Orinoco, Bolívar dictates to his secretaries his projected Constitution. He listens, corrects, and dictates it again in camp, while smoke from the fire defends him against mosquitos. Other ships bring deputies from Caracas, Barcelona, Cumaná, Barinas, Guyana, and Margarita Island. Suddenly, the winds of war have changed, perhaps in homage to Bolívar's obstinacy, and in a flash half of Venezuela has fallen into the patriots' hands.

The delegates to the congress disembark at the port of Angostura, town of little houses drawn by a child. On a toy press is printed here, week after week, *El Correo del Orinoco*. From the jungle this organ of republican thought spreads the articles of Creole doctors and announcements of the arrival of beer, penknives, harnesses, and volunteer soldiers from London.

Three salvos salute Bolívar and his general staff. The birds take off, but a macaw swaggers indifferently with tough-guy strides.

The deputies mount the stone stairway.

Francisco Antonio Zea, major of Angostura, opens the session. His speech compares this patriot township with Memphis, Thebes, Alexandria, and Rome. The congress confirms Bolívar as head of the army and president with full powers. The cabinet is named.

Afterwards Bolívar takes the rostrum. *Ignorant people*, he warns, *confuse reality with imagination and justice with vengeance* . . . He expounds his ideas on the need to create Grand Colombia and lays the foundation of his projected Constitution, drawn up on the basis of the Englishmen's Magna Carta.

(202)

1820: Boquerón Pass

Finale

The three great southern ports, Rio de Janeiro, Buenos Aires, and Montevideo, could not prevail against the rural hosts of José Artigas, chief of the interior. But death has had better luck and taken most of his people. In the bellies of birds of prey lie half the men of the eastern campaign. Andresito lies dying in jail. Lavalleja and Campbell and others are prisoners; and a few have succumbed to treachery. Fructuoso Rivera calls Artigas a *criminal* and accuses him of having put *property at the mercy of despotism and anarchy*. Francisco Ramírez of Entre Ríos proclaims that *Artigas is the cause and origin of all the evils of South America*, and Estanislao López in Santa Fe does a somersault as well.

Landowner chiefs make common cause with port merchants, as the leader of the revolution goes from disaster to disaster. The last of his Indians and blacks still follow him, as do a handful of ragged gauchos under the command of Andrés Latorre, last of his officers.

On the banks of the Paraná, Artigas chooses the best horseman. He gives him four thousand silver coins, all that remain, to take to the prisoners in Brazil.

Then he sticks his spear in the bank and crosses the river. Ruefully he marches off to Paraguay, into exile, this man who didn't want America's independence to be a trap for her poorest children.

(277)

You

Without turning your head, you bury yourself in exile. I see you, I am watching you: the Paraná slips by with the sluggishness of a lizard, and over there your flaming torn poncho fades into the distance at a horse's trot and is lost in the foliage.

You don't say goodbye to your land. She would not believe you. Or perhaps you still don't know that you're leaving for good.

The countryside turns gray. You are going, defeated, and your land is left breathless. The children to be born of her, the lovers who come to her, will they give her back her breath? Those who emerge from that land, those who enter it, will they prove themselves worthy of such deep sadness?

Your land. Our land of the south. You will be very necessary to her, Don José. Every time the greedy hurt her and humiliate her, every time that fools believe her dumb or sterile, she will miss you. Because you, Don José Artigas, general of plain folk, are the best word she has spoken.

1821: Camp Laurelty
Saint Balthazar, Black King, Greatest Sage

From nearby towns and distant regions, Paraguayans flock to see these strange beings with skin like night.

Blacks are not known in Paraguay. The slaves Artigas has freed, who have followed his tracks into exile, make a town in Laurelty.

With them is Balthazar, the black king chosen to welcome God on earth. Invoking Saint Balthazar, they work the gardens, and for him resound drums and war chants brought from Africa to the River Plata plains. Artigas's companions, the "Artigas-cué," put on red silk capes and crowns of flowers when January Sixth comes around; and, dancing, they ask the sage-king that slavery may never return, and that he give them protection against bad spirits who soften heads, and hens that crow like cocks.

(66)

1821: Carabobo
Páez

At fifteen he was born killing. He killed to defend himself; had to flee to the mountains, and became a nomad horseman on the immense prairies of Venezuela. Horseman leader of horsemen: José Antonio Páez, Páez of the plains, flies at the head of the cowpoke artists of spear and lasso, who ride bareback and charge like an avalanche. He rides a white horse, because white horses ride better. When he is not on a campaign, he learns to read and to play the cello.

The half-naked plainsmen, who in the times of Boves had served Spain, defeat Spain at the battle of Carabobo. With machetes they fight their way through the impossible brushland of the west, its marshes and thickets, take the enemy by surprise, chew him up.

Bolívar names Páez commander-in-chief of the Venezuelan armed forces. The plainsman enters Caracas by his side wearing, like him, a garland of flowers.

In Venezuela, the die is cast.

(202)

1822: Guayaquil
San Martín

Appointment in Guayaquil. Between the Caribbean Sea and the Pacific Ocean, an avenue of triumphal arches. General Bolívar appears from the north. From the south comes José de San Martín, the general who crossed the Andes cordillera in search of freedom for Chile and Peru.

Bolívar talks and talks, offers and offers.

San Martín laconically cuts him short. *"I am weary."* Bolívar does not believe him; or perhaps is mistrustful because he still does not know that glory also tires one out.

San Martín has spent thirty years in battle, from Oran to Maipú. As a soldier he fought for Spain, as a hardened general for America. For America, and never against her: when the Buenos Aires government sent him to smash the federal hosts of Artigas, San Martín disobeyed and took his army into the mountains to continue his campaign for the independence of Chile. Buenos Aires, which does not forgive, now denies him bread and salt. In Lima they don't like him either. They call him *King José*.

Disappointment in Guayaquil. San Martín, great chess player, evades the game.

"I am weary of commanding," he says, but Bolívar hears other words: *You and I. Together, we don't fit.*

Later there is a banquet and ball. Bolívar dances in the center of the room, the ladies competing for him. The noise makes San Martín dizzy. After midnight, without saying goodbye, he leaves for the docks. The baggage is already aboard the brigantine.

He gives the order to sail. He walks the deck, with slow steps, accompanied by his dog and pursued by mosquitos. The ship heads away from the coast and San Martín turns to contemplate the land of America which fades and fades.

(53 and 54)

1822: Buenos Aires
Songbird

At the edge of the village of Morón, a common grave swallows the bones of a poet who until yesterday had a guitar and a name.

It's better to travel light,
like an eagle and without sorrows . . .

Bartolomé Hidalgo, troubadour of Artigas's camps, lived only for a moment, always in a whirlwind of songs and battles, and has died in exile. The dogs of hunger chewed up his lungs. Through the streets and squares of Buenos Aires wandered Hidalgo, hawking his couplets which sing to free men and strip enemies bare. They afforded him little food but much life. His unshrouded body ends up in the earth; the couplets, also naked, also plebeian, abide in the winds.

(125)

1822: Rio de Janeiro
Traffic Gone Mad

The *Diario do Rio de Janeiro* announces novelties just arrived from London: machines to repair streets or heal lungs or squeeze manioc; lathes and stills and steam cookers; eyeglasses, telescopes, razors, combs. Also padded saddles, silver stirrups, shiny harnesses and carriage lanterns.

Still seen in the streets are lone horsemen and a few old gilded palanquins from another age; but fashion dictates late-model English carriages that draw sparks from the cobblestones. The streets of Rio de Janeiro are dangerous. Speeding accidents multiply, and the power of the coachman grows.

White gloves, top hats: from high on their perches the coachmen let fall bullying glances on other black slaves, and enjoy sowing panic among pedestrians. They are famous drunkards and pimps and good guitar players; and they are indispensable in modern life. A carriage is worth a fortune when it is sold with a fast horse and a skillful black.

(119)

1822: Quito
Twelve Nymphs Stand Guard
in the Main Plaza

and each one holds up a crown. Bands and fireworks explode and the tapping of horses' hooves on the long stone street sounds like the onset of rain. At the head of his army Bolívar enters Quito: a skinny gladiator, all nerve, his golden sword longer than his body. From the balconies rain down flowers and little embroidered kerchiefs. The balconies are altars upon which the ladies of Quito permit the erectness of their almost bare breasts to be worshipped amid lace and mantillas. Manuela Sáenz stands out like a dazzling ship's figurehead. She drops a hand, and from the hand falls a crown of laurel. Bolívar raises his head and fastens his glance on her, a spear in slow motion.

That night, they dance. They waltz until they are giddy, and the world spins round and round to the rustle of that peerless woman's thousand petticoats and the sweep of her long black hair.

(202, 249, and 295)

1823: Lima
Swollen Hands from So Much Applauding

He rides from El Callao, between two files of soldiers, on a road of flowers. Lima receives General Bolívar with a hundred-gun salute, a hundred flags, a hundred speeches and hundred-cover banquets.

The Congress grants him full powers to throw out the Spaniards, who have retaken half of Peru. The Marquess of Torre Tagle presents him with a biography of Napoleon, a set of Toledo blades and bouquets of florid phrases: *Victory awaits you on the icy peaks of the Andes to crown you with her laurels and the nymphs of the Rimac are already chanting hymns to celebrate your triumphs!* The War Minister gives orders to the goddess Fortune: *Take thy majestic flight from the foothills of Chimborazo to the peaks of our Andes and there await immortal Bolívar to crown his brow with the laurels of Peru!*

The Rimac, *the river that talks*, is the only one that keeps quiet.

(53 and 202)

1824: Lima
In Spite of Everything

He rides from El Callao, between two files of soldiers, on a road of flowers. Lima receives the chief of the Spaniards, General Monet, hoisting and cheering the king's flag. The flag flutters and speeches flutter. The Marquess of Torre Tagle melts with gratitude and implores Spain to save Peru from the menace of the accursed Bolívar, *the Colombian monster*.

Lima prefers to continue sleeping, amid rippling heraldry, the slumber of a colonial arcadia. Viceroys, saints and cavaliers, crooks and coquettes exchange sighings and bowings amid the sandy wastes of America, beneath a sky that denies rain and sun but sends angels to defend the city walls. Inside them, one breathes the aroma of jasmine; outside, solitude and danger lie in wait. Inside, hand-kissings and processions and courtings: every officer imitates the king and every monk the pope. In the palaces, stucco imitates marble; in the seventy churches of gold and silver, ritual imitates faith.

Far from Lima, Bolívar lies sick in the coast town of Pativilca. *On all sides*, he writes between fevers, *I hear the sound of disaster . . . Everything is born into life and dies before my eyes, as if split by a bolt of lightning . . . Dust, ashes, nothing.* All Peru, save for a few valleys, has fallen back into the hands of Spain. The independent governments of Buenos Aires and Chile have abandoned the cause of the freedom of this land; and not even the Peruvians themselves seem very interested.

"And now, what do you plan to do?" someone asks this battered and lonely man.

"Triumph," says Bolívar.

(53, 202, and 302)

1824: Montevideo

City Chronicles from a Barber's Chair

No breeze tinkles the tin washbasin that hangs from a wire over a hole in the door to announce that here they shave beards, pull teeth, and apply suction cups.

Out of sheer habit, or to shake off the languors of summer, the Andalusian barber makes speeches or sings while he finishes covering a customer's face with foam. Between phrases and fandangos, the razor whispers. One of the barber's eyes watches the blade, which plows through the meringue; the other watches the Montevideans who plod along the dusty street. The tongue is sharper than the razor, and no one escapes its fleecing. The customer, prisoner as long as the shave lasts, dumb, immobile, listens to this chattering chronicle of customs and events and from time to time tries to follow, from the corner of an eye, the victims passing by.

A yoke of oxen hauling a dead woman to the cemetery. Behind the cart, a monk telling his beads. The sound of a bell bidding a routine farewell to the third-class deceased reaches into the shop. The razor pauses in the air. The barber crosses himself and from his mouth come words pronounced with a change of tone: "Poor little thing. She was never happy."

The corpse of Rosalía Villagrán is crossing the city occupied by Artigas's enemies. For a long time she had believed she was someone else, and believed she was living in another time and another world, and in the charity hospital she kissed the walls and talked to the pigeons. Rosalía Villagrán, Artigas's wife, has entered the gates of death without a cent to pay for her coffin.

(315)

1824: Plain of Junín
The Silent Battle

Bolívar reorganizes his army, magic of his stubborn courage, and triumphs on the Peruvian plain of Junín. The world's best horsemen charge with sword and spear and wreak havoc. Not a shot is heard in the whole battle.

The American army is a mix of gauchos from the River Plata shores; Chilean peasants and plainsmen from Grand Colombia, who fight with reins tied to their knees; Peruvian and Ecuadoran patriots, heroes of San Lorenzo and Maipú, Carabobo, and Pichincha. The men have spears from Guayaquil and ponchos from Cajamarca; the horses, saddles from Lambayeque and shoes from Trujillo. Also following Bolívar are Englishmen, Germans, Frenchmen, and even Spaniards won over by the New World, European veterans of distant wars on the Guadiana or the Rhine or the Seine.

As the sun dies, the lives of the wounded are snuffed out. Dying in Bolívar's tent is Lieutenant Colonel Sowersby, an Englishman who was with Napoleon at Borodino; and not far away a little dog howls beside the body of a Spanish officer. That dog kept running at the side of his friend's horse throughout the entire battle of Junín. Now General Miller tries to catch it or chase it off, but there is no way.

(202)

1825: La Paz
Bolivia

The imperial standard falls in surrender at the feet of Antonio José de Sucre, general at twenty-three, grand marshal at thirty, Bolívar's favorite officer. The thunderous battle of the Ayacucho pampa finishes off Spanish power not just in Peru but on the whole continent.

When the news reaches Lima, Bolívar leaps onto the dining room table and dances, stepping on plates and breaking glasses and bottles.

   Later Bolívar and Sucre ride together beneath the triumphal arches of the city of La Paz. There, a country is born. Upper Peru, which had been absorbed into the viceroyalties of Lima and Buenos Aires, now calls itself the Bolívar Republic, and will be called Bolivia, so that its sons may perpetuate the name of their liberator.

   José Mariano Ruyloba, a monk with a great gift for oratory, a mouth full of gold, has prepared a splendid welcoming speech; but fate decrees that Ruyloba shall die before Bolívar can hear it. The speech is composed in Greek.

(202)

1825: Potosí
Abecedarium: The Hero at the Peak

In Potosí, Bolívar climbs to the peak of the silver mountain. Bolívar speaks, History will speak: *This mountain whose bosom is the wonder and envy of the world* . . . The wind seizes the flags of the new fatherlands and the bells of all the churches. *I think nothing of this opulence when I compare it* . . . Bolívar's arms embrace a thousand leagues. The valleys multiply the salvos of the guns and the echo of the words . . . *with the glory of having brought to victory the standard of liberty from the burning and distant beaches* . . . History will speak of the great man up on the heights. It will say nothing of the thousand wrinkles lining the face of this man, still unworn by years but deeply furrowed by loves and sorrows. History will not be concerned with the galloping colts in his breast when, from the skies of Potosí, he embraces the land as if it were a woman. The land as if it were *that* woman: the one who sharpens his swords; and strips him and forgives him with a glance. The one who knows how to listen to him beneath the thunder of guns and the speeches and ovations, when he says: *You will be alone, Manuela. And I will be alone, in the middle of the world. There will be no more consolation than the glory of having conquered ourselves*.

(53, 202, and 238)

1825: Potosí

England Is Owed a Potosí

The Spanish colonies that are born to independent life walk bent over. From the first day they drag a heavy stone hung from the neck, a stone that grows and overwhelms. The *English debt*, born of Britain's support in arms and soldiers, is multiplied by the grace of usurers and merchants. The moneylenders and their intermediaries, versed in the arts of alchemy, turn any old cobblestone into a golden jewel; and British traders find in these lands their most lucrative markets. The new countries, fearful of Spanish reconquest, need official recognition by England; but England recognizes no one without first signing a Treaty of Friendship and Commerce which assures freedom of invasion for its industrial merchandise.

I abhor the debts more than the Spaniards, writes Bolívar to the Colombian general Santander, and tells him that to pay those debts he has sold the Potosí mines to the English for two and a half million pesos. Furthermore, he writes, *I have indicated to the government of Peru that it should sell to England all of its mines, all of its lands and properties and all the other holdings of the government, for its national debt, which is not less than twenty million*.

The Rich Mountain of Potosí, down in the world, now belongs to a London firm, the phantom Potosí, La Paz, and Peruvian Mining Association. As happens with other delusions born of speculative fevers, the name is longer than the capital: the firm claims a million pounds sterling, but actually has fifty thousand.

(40, 172, and 134)

The Curse of the Silver Mountain

Potosí, which has yielded so much silver, is yielding little. The mountain does not want to.

For more than two centuries, Potosí heard Indians groaning in her entrails. The Indians, condemned to the tunnels, implored her to exhaust her seams. And finally the mountain cursed greed.

Since then, mysterious mule caravans have been arriving by night, diving into the mountain and secretly carrying off loads of silver. No one can see them, no one can catch them; but somehow the mountain keeps emptying herself night by night.

When a mule breaks a leg because the ore makes too heavy a
load, the dawn rises upon a beetle limping painfully down the road.

(247)

1826: Chuquisaca
Bolívar and the Indians

The laws in Spain's American colonies were never obeyed. Good or
bad, the laws never existed in reality—neither the many royal war-
rants which protected the Indians (and which confessed their own
impotence through repetition), nor the ordinances that banned the
circulation of Jews and novels. This tradition does not keep eminent
Creoles, generals, or doctors, from believing that the Constitution is
an infallible potion for public happiness.

Simón Bolívar weaves constitutions with fervor. Now he presents
to the Congress a constitutional project for the new republic bearing
his name. According to the text, Bolivia will have a president-for-life
and three legislative chambers—tribunes, senators, and censors—
which have some resemblance, says Bolívar, *to the Areopagus of Athens and the censors of Rome.*

People who cannot read will not have the right to vote; and since
almost all Bolivians speak Quechua or Aymara, know nothing of the
Castilian language, and cannot read, only a handful of select males
will have that right. As in Colombia and Peru, Bolívar has decreed
in the new country the abolition of native tribute and of forced labor
for Indians; and has arranged to divide communal lands into private
plots. And, so that the Indians, the country's immense majority, may
receive the European light of Civilization, Bolívar has brought to
Chuquisaca his old teacher, Simón Rodríguez, with orders to establish
schools.

(42 and 172)

1826: Chuquisaca
Cursed Be the Creative Imagination

Simón Rodríguez, Bolívar's teacher, has returned to America. For a
quarter of a century Simón was on the other side of the sea. There,
he was a friend of the socialists of Paris, London, and Geneva; he

worked with the printers of Rome, the chemists of Vienna, and even taught elementary lessons in a small town on the Russian steppe.

After the long embrace of welcome, Bolívar names him director of education in the newly founded country. With a model school in Chuquisaca, Simón Rodríguez begins the task of uprooting the lies and fears hallowed by tradition. Pious ladies scream, learned doctors howl, dogs bark at the scandal. Horror: the madman Rodríguez proposes to mix children of high birth with mestizos who until last night slept in the streets. What is he thinking of? Does he want the orphans to take him to heaven? Or does he corrupt them so they'll accompany him to hell? In the classrooms, neither catechism nor sacristy Latin, nor rules of grammar are heard, only a racket of saws and hammers unbearable to the ears of monks and pettifoggers schooled in the repulsiveness of manual work. *A school for whores and thieves!* Those who believe the body is shameful and woman an adornment, cry to high heaven. In Don Simón's school, boys and girls sit jammed side by side; and to top it all, their studying is playing.

The prefect of Chuquisaca heads the campaign *against the satyr who has come to corrupt the morals of youth*. Soon, Marshal Sucre, president of Bolivia, demands Simón Rodríguez's resignation, because he has not presented his accounts with due meticulousness.

(296 and 298)

The Ideas of Simón Rodríguez:
Teaching How to Think

The author is considered mad. Let him transmit his ravings to the fathers yet to be born.

Everyone must be educated without distinction of race or color. Let us not deceive ourselves: without popular education, there will be no true society.

Instruction is not education. Teach, and you will have people who know; educate, and you will have people who do.

To order recital from memory of what is not understood, is to make parrots. Do not in any case order a child to do anything that has no "why" at the foot of it. If you accustom the child always to see reason behind the orders he receives, he misses it when he does not see it, and asks for it, saying, "Why?" Teach the children to be inquisitive, so that, asking the reasons for what they are told to do, they learn to obey reason, not authority like limited people, nor custom like stupid people.

Boys and girls should study together in the schools. First, so that in this way men should learn from childhood to respect women; second, so that women should learn not to be afraid of men.

The boys should learn the three principal trades: masonry, carpentry, and smithery, because with earth, wood, and metal the most essential things are made. Instruction and a trade should be given to women, so that they will not prostitute themselves out of necessity, nor make marriage a speculation to assure subsistence.

He who knows nothing can be deceived by anyone. He who has nothing, anyone can buy.

(297)

1826: Buenos Aires
Rivadavia

On the crest of the River Plata ravines, above the muddy bank of the river, lies the port that usurps the wealth of the whole country.

In the Buenos Aires Coliseum the British consul occupies the box of the viceroy of Spain. The Creole patricians use words from France and gloves from England, and thus they slip into the life of independence.

From the Thames flows the torrent of merchandise manufactured, to Argentine specifications, in Yorkshire and Lancashire. In Birmingham they imitate to the last detail the traditional copper boiler that heats water for maté, and they produce exact replicas of the wooden stirrups, bolas, and lassos used in this country. Workshops and textile mills in the provinces have scarcely a chance of resisting the assault. A single ship brings twenty thousand pairs of boots at bargain prices and a Liverpool poncho costs five times less than one from Catamarca.

Argentine banknotes are printed in London and the National Bank, with a majority of British shareholders, monopolizes their emission. Through this bank operates the River Plate Mining Association, which pays Bernardino Rivadavia an annual salary of twelve hundred pounds.

From an armchair that will be sacred, Rivadavia multiplies the public debt and public libraries. Buenos Aires's illustrious jurist, who goes about in a four-horse carriage, claims to be president of a country he does not know and despises. Beyond the city walls of Buenos Aires, that country hates him.

(55, 271, and 342)

1826: Panama

Lonely Countries

The infant said its first words. They were its last. Of those invited to the baptism, only four reached Panama, and instead of a baptism there was extreme unction. Grief, father's grief, shrinks the face of Bolívar. The condolences sound hollow.

Bells ring out for the unity of Hispanic America.

Bolívar had called on the new countries to unite, under British protection, in one fatherland. He did not invite the United States or Haiti, because they are foreign to our American ways; but he wanted Great Britain to integrate the Hispanic American league, to defend it from the danger of Spanish reconquest.

London has no interest in the unity of its new dominions. The Congress of Panama has given birth to nothing but edifying declarations, because the old viceroyalties have birthed countries tied to a new empire overseas, and divorced among themselves. The colonial economy, mines and plantations producing for abroad, cities that prefer the bazaar to the factory, opens the way not for a great nation but for a great archipelago. The independent countries are disintegrating while Bolívar dreams of a unified fatherland. They have not signed a single trade agreement among themselves, but are flooded with European merchandise and almost all have bought the chief British export product, the doctrine of free trade.

In London, Prime Minister George Canning exhibits his trophy before the House of Commons.

(202 and 207)

1826: London

Canning

The pearl of the crown speaks. Plebeian George Canning, chief of British diplomacy, consecrates his work before the House of Commons. Canning spreads out his arms, his falcon wings: *"I called the*

New World into existence," proclaims the architect of empire, "*to redress the balance of the Old.*"

From a corner comes a mocking giggle. A long silence follows. Canning rears up in the darkness his sharp ghost's profile and then the greatest ovation ever heard in this chamber explodes.

England is the axis of the planet. Lord Castlereagh had done much for the imperial project until one evening, overwhelmed, he slit his throat with a razor. Hardly had Castlereagh's successor, Canning, come to power when he announced that the knightly era had been left behind. Military glories should give way to astute diplomacy. Smugglers had done more for England than generals; and the time had come for merchants and bankers to win the real battles for world domination.

The patience of the cat is more effective than the fury of the tiger.

(171 and 280)

1828: Bogotá
Here They Hate Her

Without lowering their voices they call her "outsider" and "Messalina," and in secret they give her worse names. They say that on her account Bolívar goes about loaded with shadows and riddled with wrinkles, and that he is burning up his talents in bed.

Manuela Sáenz has fought with a spear in Ayacucho. The mustachios she tore from an enemy were a talisman of the patriot army. When the troops in Lima mutinied against Bolívar, she disguised herself as a man and went through the barracks with a pistol and a bag of money. Here, in Bogotá, she strolls in the shade of the cherry trees, dressed as a captain and escorted by two black women in hussar uniforms. A few nights ago, at a party, she put against the wall a rag doll labeled "*Death to Francisco de Paula Santander, Traitor,*" and shot it.

Santander has grown in the shadow of Bolívar. During the war years it was Bolívar who named him vice president. Now, Santander would like to assassinate the *king without a crown* at some masked ball or in treacherous ambush.

The night watchman of Bogotá, lamp in hand, says the last word. He is answered by the church bells, which scare the Devil and call all to go home.

Shots ring out, guards fall. The assassins burst up the stairs. Thanks to Manuela, who lies to put them off, Bolívar manages to escape out the window.

(53, 202, and 295)

From Manuela Sáenz's Letter to Her Husband James Thorne

No, no, not again, man, for God's sake! Why do you make me write, breaking my resolution? Look, what good are you doing, only giving me the pain of telling you a thousand times no? Mister, you are excellent, you are inimitable. I will never say anything else about you. But, my friend, leaving you for General Bolívar is something. Leaving another husband without your qualities would be nothing.

. . . I know very well that nothing can unite me to him under the auspices of what you call honor. Do you think me less honorable for having him as my lover and not my husband? Oh, I don't live by the social concerns invented for mutual torture!

Leave me alone, my dear Englishman. Let's do something else. In heaven we'll be married again, but on earth, no . . . There, everything will be English style, because a life of monotony is reserved for your nation (in love, I mean, because in other ways . . . who are cleverer in trade and navies?). They take love without pleasure, conversation without humor, and walks without vigor; they greet with bows and curtsies, get up and sit down with caution, joke without laughing. These are divine formalities; but I, wretched mortal, who laugh at myself, at you, and at these English solemnities, how badly I would do in heaven! . . .

(238)

Bonpland

He discovered America in the course of nine thousand leagues and seventy thousand little plants. When he returned to Paris, he missed America. His nostalgia made it clear to him that he belonged to the same land as the roots and flowers he had collected. That land called him as Europe had never called him; and for it he crossed the ocean again.

He was a professor in Buenos Aires and a laborer in the maté fields of the upper Paraná. There, the soldiers of Gaspar Rodríguez de Francia, Supreme and Lifetime Dictator of Paraguay, came upon him. They beat him with sticks and took him upriver in a canoe.

For nine years he has been imprisoned in Paraguay. Dictator Francia, who rules by terror and mystery, is said to have said it was for spying. Kings, emperors, and presidents intercede for the freedom of the famous sage; but neither mediations nor missions, entreaties nor threats have any effect.

The dictator condemned him on a day of north wind, the wind that turns the soul sour. One day of south wind, he decides to free him. Since Bonpland doesn't want to leave, the dictator expels him.

Bonpland has not been shut up in a cell. He was working lands that yielded cotton, sugarcane, and oranges, and has created a rum distillery, a carpentry shop, and a hospital; he attended the deliveries of women and cows throughout the region and gave out infallible concoctions against rheumatism and fever. Paraguay loved its bare-foot prisoner with the oversized shirt, seeker of rare plants, man of bad luck who gave so much good; and now he leaves because soldiers take him out by force.

No sooner does he cross the frontier into Argentine territory than someone steals his horses.

(255)

1829: Asunción, Paraguay

Francia the Supreme

There are no thieves in Paraguay, that is, none above ground, nor beggars. At the call of a drum, not of a bell, the children go to school. Although everyone can read, no print shop or library exists, nor is any book, newspaper, or bulletin received from outside, and the post office has disappeared for lack of use.

Penned in upriver by nature and neighbors, the country lives on guard, waiting for Argentina or Brazil to lash out. So that the Paraguayans should repent of their independence, Buenos Aires has cut off their outlet to the sea, and their ships rot at the wharves; but they persist in their poverty and dignity. Dignity, national solitude: high over the vast acreage, Gaspar Rodríguez de Francia commands and keeps watch. The dictator lives alone, and alone eats the bread and salt of his land in dishes previously sampled by dogs.

All Paraguayans are spies or spied upon. Very early in the morning, while sharpening his razor, Alejandro the barber gives El Supremo the first report of the day on rumors and conspiracies. After nightfall the dictator hunts stars with his telescope; and they too tell him what his enemies are plotting.

(82 and 281)

1829: Rio de Janeiro

The Snowball of External Debt

It has been seven years since Prince Pedro proclaimed himself emperor of Brazil. The country was born into independent life knocking at the doors of English bankers. King Juan, Pedro's father, had stripped the bank bare and taken with him to Lisbon the last grams of gold and silver. The first millions of pounds sterling soon arrived from London. The customs income was mortgaged as a guarantee, and native intermediaries got two percent of every loan.

Now Brazil owes double what it received and the debt rolls on, growing like a snowball. The creditors give the orders; and every Brazilian is born in debt.

In a solemn speech Emperor Pedro reveals that the public treasury is exhausted, *in a miserable state*, and that total ruin threatens the country. However, he announces salvation: the emperor has decided to take *measures which will destroy the cause of the existing calamity at one blow*. And he explains what those radical measures are: they consist of new loans that Brazil expects to receive from the houses of Rothschild and Wilson in London, with stiff but honorable interest.

Meanwhile, the newspapers report that a thousand fiestas are being prepared to celebrate the emperor's wedding to Princess Amelia. The advertisements in the papers offer black slaves for sale or hire, cheeses and pianos newly arrived from Europe, English jackets of fine woolens, and Bordeaux wines. The Hotel do Globo on Quitanda Street seeks a *white, foreign chef who is not a drunkard or a puffer of cigars*, and at 76 Duvidor Street they need *a lady who speaks French to look after a blind person*.

(186 and 275)

1830: Magdalena River

The Boat Goes Down to the Sea

Green land, black land. In the far distance mist shrouds the mountains. The Magdalena is carrying Simón Bolívar downstream.

"No."

In the streets of Lima, the same people who gave him a diamond-studded sword are burning his Constitution. Those who called him "Father of the Country" are burning his effigy in the streets of Bogotá. In Caracas, they officially dub him "enemy of Venezuela." Over in Paris, the defamatory articles about him get stronger; and the friends who know how to praise him do not know how to defend him.

"I cannot."

Was this the history of mankind? This labyrinth, this futile game of shadows? The Venezuelan people curse the wars that have taken half their sons to remote areas and given them nothing for it. Venezuela tears itself loose from Grand Colombia and Ecuador follows suit, while Bolívar lies beneath a dirty canvas in the boat that sails down the Magdalena to the sea.

"I can no more."

Blacks are still slaves in Venezuela, despite the laws. In Colombia and Peru, the laws passed to *civilize* Indians are applied to despoil them. The tribute, the colonial tax that Indians pay for being Indians, has been reimposed in Bolivia.

Was this, was this history? All grandeur ends up dwarfed. On the neck of every promise crawls betrayal. Great men become voracious landlords. The sons of America destroy each other. Sucre, the chosen inheritor, who had saved himself from poison and dagger, falls in the forests on the way to Quito, toppled by a bullet.

"I can no more. Let us go."

Crocodiles and timber interweave in the river. Bolívar, yellow-skinned, no light in his eyes, shivering, delirious, moves down the Magdalena toward the sea, toward death.

(53 and 202)

1830: Maracaibo
The Governor Proclaims:

... *Bolívar, genius of evil, torch of anarchy, oppressor of his country,
has ceased to exist.*

(202)

1830: La Guaira
Divide et Impera

The North American consul in La Guaira, J. G. Williamson, prophet
and protagonist of the disintegration of Grand Colombia, sent the
State Department a well-informed report. A month ahead of the
event, he announced the separation of Venezuela and the end of the
customs duties that do not suit the United States.

Simón Bolívar dies on December Seventeenth. On another December Seventeenth, eleven years ago, he had founded Grand Colombia, a fusion of Colombia and Venezuela which later also embraced
Ecuador and Panama. Grand Colombia has died with him.

The North American consul in Lima, William Tudor, has helped
to weave the conspiracy against the American project of Bolívar, *the
dangerous madman of Colombia*. Tudor was upset not only by Bolívar's fight against slavery, a bad example for the southern United
States, but also and above all by *the excessive aggrandizement* of the
America liberated from Spain. With all logic at his command, the
consul has said that *England and the United States have common and
potent reasons of State* against the development of a new power. The
British Admiral Fleming, meanwhile, comes and goes between Valencia and Cartagena encouraging the division.

(207 and 280)

1830: Montevideo
Abecedarium: The Oath of the Constitution

The English government, Lord John Ponsonby had said, *will never
consent that only two states, Brazil and Argentina, should be exclusive
masters of the east coasts of South America.*

Through London's influence, and under its protection, Uruguay becomes an independent state. The most rebellious province of the River Plata, which has expelled the Brazilians from its soil, breaks off from the old trunk and takes on a life of its own. The port of Buenos Aires is free at last from the nightmare of this unfriendly prairie where Artigas rose in rebellion.

In the Mother church of Montevideo, Father Larrañaga offers a thanksgiving chant to God. Fervor illuminates the face of the priest, as in that other Te Deum he celebrated some years back, from the same pulpit, in homage to the invaders from Brazil.

The Constitution is sworn beneath the City Hall balconies. The ladies, who do not exist in the laws, accompany the juridical consecration of the new country as if it involved them. With one hand they clutch their gigantic hairdos, dangerous on windy days, and with the other hold open against their breasts fans painted with patriotic themes. High starched collars keep the gentlemen from turning their heads. The Magna Carta resounds through the plaza, clause after clause, over a sea of top hats. According to the Constitution of the new republic, there will be no citizenship for the men who offered their bodies against the bullets of Spain, Buenos Aires, and Brazil. Uruguay is not being made for poor gauchos, or Indians, or blacks, who still don't know that a law has freed them. Not permitted to vote or hold public office, says the Constitution, are servants, peons, rank-and-file soldiers, vagrants, drunkards, and illiterates.

At nightfall the Coliseum is packed. It is opening night for *The Happy Deceit; or, The Triumph of Innocence*, by Rossini, the first complete opera sung in this city.

(278)

1830: Montevideo
Fatherland or Grave

The first bard of the Uruguayan Parnassus, Francisco Acuña de Figueroa, began his career with an ode, in eight-line stanzas, to the military glory of Spain. When Artigas's gauchos took Montevideo, he fled to Rio de Janeiro. There, he dedicated his adulatory rhymes to the Portuguese prince and all of his court. Still shouldering his lyre, Don Francisco followed the Brazilian invaders back to Montevideo, and rhapsodized over the occupying troops. Years later, on the day following the ouster of the Brazilians, the muses breathed patriotic decasyllables into Don Francisco's ear, words of laurel to crown the brows of the heroes of independence; and now the reptilian poet writes the national anthem of the newborn country. We Uruguayans will be forever condemned to listen to his verses standing up.

(3)

1832: Santiago de Chile
National Industry

In Chile, too, gentlemen dance and dress in French styles, imitate Byron in knotting their ties, and, at table, obey the dictates of French chefs; à la English they take tea, and à la French they down their wine.

When Vicente Pérez Rosales set up his brandy factory, he bought the best stills in Paris and a great quantity of labels with gilded arabesques and fine lettering that said in English: *Old Champagne Cognac*. On the door of his office he had a big sign painted:

```
┌─────────────────────┐
│                     │
│     DIRECT          │
│                     │
│     IMPORTATION     │
│                     │
└─────────────────────┘
```

The taste would not be too-too, but it was nearly-nearly, and no one got stomach ulcers. The business went like a house on fire. The factory could not keep up with the demand, but Don Vicente came down with an attack of patriotism and decided he could not go on living in a state of treason.

"This good reputation belongs only to Chile."

He threw the European labels in the fire and had another sign put on his door, this time even larger:

```
┌─────────────────────┐
│                     │
│     NATIONAL        │
│                     │
│     INDUSTRY        │
│                     │
└─────────────────────┘
```

The bottles now wear a new dress: labels printed here, which say in Spanish: *Chilean Cognac*.

Not even one can be sold.

(256)

Street Cries in the Santiago
de Chile Market

"Carnations and basil for stocky little girls!"

"WA-A-FER COOKIES!"

"Pretty buttons, one penny the string!"

"Sulphur matche-e-es!"

"Belts, cinches, soft like a glove!"

"Charity, for the love of God!"

"Good beef!"

"A penny for a poor blind man?"

"BROO-OO-OOMS! LAST CHANCE FOR BROOMS!"

"Baccy, chewing baccy?"

"M i r a c l e m e d a l s, s i n g l e
o r b y t h e b o x!"

"Look at these brandy cakes!"

"Knives f'yer personal security!"

"SHA-A-ARP BLADES!"

"Who'll buy this rope?"

"Get this lovely bread!"

"L i t t l e b e l l s, o n l y o n e
l e f t!"

"WATERMELONS, DEARIE!"

"Get this lovely bread, fresh from a woman's hands!"

"WA-A-ATERMELONS!"

"Get this lovely bread! It's piping hot!"

(288)

1833: Arequipa

Llamas

"*Happy creatures*," says Flora Tristán.

Flora is travelling through Peru, her father's country, and in the mountains discovers *the only animal man has not been able to debase*.

The gentle llamas are more agile than mules and climb higher. They resist cold, exhaustion, and heavy loads. With no reward they give the mountain Indians transport, milk, meat, and the clean and brilliant wool that covers their bodies. But they never let themselves be tied up or mistreated, nor do they take orders. When they let up their queenly stride, the Indian implores them to get going again. If anyone hits them, insults them, or threatens them, llamas throw themselves on the ground, and, raising their long necks, they turn their eyes heavenward, the most beautiful eyes in Creation, and softly die.

"*Happy creatures*," says Flora Tristán.

(337)

1833: San Vicente

Aquino

The head of Aquino lies in the executioner's basket.

May he rest in war. The chief of the Indians of El Salvador had raised three thousand spears against the robbers of lands. He got the better of the muskets, which the enemy fired with glowing cigars, and stripped Saint Joseph naked on the high altar of a church. Clad in the cloak of the father of Christ, he proclaimed that Indians would never again be slaves, nor soldiers, nor famished, nor drunk. But more troops arrived, and he had to seek refuge in the mountains.

His lieutenant, named Cascabel, turned him in.

"*Now I am a jaguar without claws or fangs*," said Aquino, when they loaded him with shackles and chains; and he confessed to Fray Navarro that in all his life he had only been frightened by the anger or tears of his wife.

"*I am ready to play blindman's buff*," he said, when they put on the blindfold.

(87)

1834: Paris
Tacuabé

On the headlands of the Quequay, General Rivera's cavalry have completed the civilizing operation with good marksmanship. Now, not an Indian remains alive in Uruguay.

The government donates the four last Charrúa Indians to the Natural Sciences Academy in Paris. They are sent over in the hold of a ship, as baggage, among other packages and valises.

The French public pay admission to see the savages, rare specimens of a vanished race. The scientists note their gestures, clothing, and anthropometric measurements. From the shape of their skulls, they deduce their small intelligence and violent character.

Before two months have passed, the Indians let themselves die. Academicians fight over the cadavers. Only the warrior Tacuabé survives, and escapes with his newly born daughter, reaching the city of Lyons—who knows how—disappearing there.

Tacuabé was the one who made music. He made it in the museum after the public left. He would rub a bow with a little saliva-moistened stick and draw sweet vibrations from its horsehair strings. Frenchmen who spied on him from behind the curtains said he produced very soft, muffled, almost inaudible sounds, as if he were talking in secret.

(19)

1834: Mexico City
Loving Is Giving

A calabash filled with vinegar mounts guard behind each door. On every altar a thousand candles pray. Doctors prescribe bloodlettings and chloride fumigations. Colored flags mark houses invaded by the plague. Lugubrious chants and cries indicate the passage of carts full of the dead through streets with nobody on them.

The governor issues a proclamation banning certain foods. According to him, stuffed chilis and fruits have brought cholera to Mexico.

On Holy Ghost Street, a coachman is cutting an enormous chirimoya. He stretches out from his perch to enjoy eating it bit by bit. Someone passing by leaves him with his mouth open.

"Barbarian! Don't you see you're committing suicide? Don't you know that that fruit takes you to the grave?"

The coachman hesitates. He contemplates the milky flesh, undecided whether to bite. Finally he gets up, walks a few steps and offers the chirimoya to his wife, who is sitting at the corner.

"You eat it, my love."

(266)

1835: Galapagos Islands
Darwin

Black hills rise from the sea and mist. On the rocks, as if taking siestas, move turtles as big as cows; and between the crannies slide iguanas, dragons without wings.

"The capital of hell," comments the captain of the *Beagle*.

"Even the trees feel bad," Charles Darwin confirms, as the anchor falls.

In these islands, the Galapagos, Darwin approaches the revelation of the *mystery of mysteries*. Here, he senses the keys to the never-ending transformation of life on earth. He discovers here how chaffinches have perfected their beaks; how the beak that breaks big hard seeds has taken on the form of a nutcracker, and the one that seeks nectar from cactuses that of a pincers. The same has occurred, Darwin discovers, with the shells and necks of turtles, according to whether they eat on ground level or prefer lofty fruits.

In the Galapagos is the origin of all my opinions, Darwin will write. *I go from surprise to surprise*, he writes now, in his travel journal.

When the *Beagle* sailed four years ago from an English port, Darwin still believed every word of the Sacred Writings. He thought God had made the world the way it is now, in six days, and had ended his work, as Archbishop Usher insists, at 9 A.M. on Saturday October 12 of the year 4004 before Christ.

(4 and 88)

1835: Columbia

Texas

Fifteen years ago, a wagon train creaked across the desert prairie of Texas, and the mournful voices of owls and coyotes bid them illcome. Mexico ceded lands to these three hundred families that came from Louisiana with their slaves and plows. Five years ago, there were already twenty thousand North American colonists in Texas, and they had many slaves purchased in Cuba or in the corrals where the gentry of Virginia and Kentucky fatten up little blacks. Now, the colonists hoist their own flag, the image of a bear, and decline to pay taxes to the government of Mexico or to obey Mexican law which has abolished slavery in all the national territory.

The vice president of the United States, John Calhoun, believes that God created blacks to cut wood, pick cotton, and carry water for the chosen people. Textile factories demand more cotton and cotton demands more land and more blacks. *There are powerful reasons*, said Calhoun last year, *for Texas to form part of the United States*. At that time President Jackson, who breathes frontiers with an athlete's lungs, had already sent his friend Sam Houstcn to Texas.

The rugged Houston forces his way in with his fists, makes himself an army general, and proclaims the independence of Texas. The new state, soon to be another star on the United States flag, has more land than France.

And war breaks out against Mexico.

(128 and 207)

1836: San Jacinto

The Free World Grows

Sam Houston offers land at four cents an acre. Battalions of North American volunteers pour in by every road and weapons arrive by the shipload from New York and New Orleans.

The comet that announced calamity in the skies over Mexico was no news to anybody. Mexico has lived in a perpetual state of calamity since the murderers of Hidalgo and Morelos declared independence in order to grab the country for themselves.

The war does not last long. Mexican General Santa Anna arrives calling for a bloodbath, and makes one at the Alamo, but at San Jacinto

loses four hundred men in a quarter of an hour. Santa Anna gives up
Texas in exchange for his own life and returns to Mexico City with
his beaten army, his personal chef, his seven-thousand-dollar sword,
his countless decorations and his wagonload of fighting cocks.

General Houston celebrates his victory by naming himself president of Texas.

Texas's constitution assures the master perpetual rights over his
slaves, as legitimately acquired property. *Extend the area of liberty*
had been the slogan of the victorious troops.

(128)

1836: The Alamo
Portraits of the Frontier Hero

At the outbreak of the Texas war, when fortune still smiles on the
Mexican troops, Colonel Davy Crockett falls pierced by bayonets. He
falls in the Alamo fort, together with his band of heroic outlaws, and
the buzzards finish his story.

The United States, which fattens on the lands of Indians and
Mexicans, has lost one of its frontier heroes. Davy Crockett had a
rifle named Betsy which could kill five bears with a single bullet.

Crockett could well have been the son of Daniel Boone, the
legendary pioneer of the previous century, a very macho and lonely
killer, who hated civilization but earned a living by placing colonists
on lands robbed from his Indian friends. And he could well have been
the father of Natty Bumppo, a fictional character so famous that he
now seems flesh and blood.

Since Fenimore Cooper published *The Last of the Mohicans*,
Natty Bumppo, the crude and noble hunter, has incorporated himself
into the daily life of the United States. Nature has taught him all he
knows of morality and his energy comes from the mountains and the
woods. He is ugly, only one tooth in his enormous mouth; but without
expecting anything in return he protects beautiful white virgins, who,
thanks to him, pass invincible through thicket and desire. Natty Bumppo
praises silence with many words and tells no lie when he says that
he doesn't fear death, or when he admires the Indians while ruefully
killing them.

(149 and 218)

1836: Hartford
The Colt

Samuel Colt, engineer, registers in Hartford, Connecticut, the patent of the "revolving pistol" he has invented. It is a pistol with a revolving cylinder of five shots, which kills five times in twenty seconds.

From Texas comes the first order.

(305)

1837: Guatemala City
Morazán

A storm of cassocks explodes. Rafael Carrera is the lightning flash that instills fear, and all over Guatemala roll the thunderclaps: *"Long live religion! Death to the foreigners! Death to Morazán!"*

No candle stays unlit. Nuns pray so fast that in nine seconds they roll off nine novenas. Choirs intone salutations to Mary and curse Morazán with the same fervor.

Francisco Morazán, president of Central America, is the *heretical foreigner* who has unleashed these mystical furies. Morazán, born in Honduras, has not only unified the Central American provinces into one nation, he has also reduced counts and marquesses to the category of mere citizens, and has created public schools that teach things of this world and say nothing of Heaven. According to his laws, a cross is no longer necessary for a grave nor a priest for a wedding, and he makes no distinction between a child born in the conjugal bed and a child made, without previous contract, on the straw of a stable, the one having the same inheritance rights as the other. Gravest of all, Morazán has separated Church and State, decreed freedom to believe or not to believe, suppressed the tithes and first fruits of the Lord's officers and put their lands up for sale.

The monks blame Morazán for the plague that is devastating Guatemala. Cholera is killing people off, and from the pulpits rain fulminating accusations: Morazán has poisoned the water; the Antichrist has pacted with the Devil to sell him the souls of the dead.

The people of the mountains rise against the poisoner. Rafael Carrera, the hog farmer who leads the insurrection, is just over twenty and already has three bullets in his body. He goes about covered with scapularies and medals and with a green bough stuck in his hat.

(220 and 253)

1838: Buenos Aires

Rosas

Great tamer of ponies and people, Juan Manuel de Rosas is the boss of the River Plata ranges. Guitarist and dancer, he tells the stories that provoke the most fear or laughter around the campfire, but he is made of marble and even his children call him "master." He has the cook who ruins his chicken arrested; and he has himself whipped when he carelessly violates one of his own rules.

His estancias are the most prosperous; his meat-salting plants are the best organized. Rosas owns the best of the sea of grasslands that extend from the port of Buenos Aires to the Indian villages.

Rosas governs. He has decreed a customs law that protects Argentinian production of ponchos and mattresses, shoes, carriages, ships, wine and furniture, and he has closed the interior rivers to foreign merchants.

The *Revue des Deux Mondes* demands that France give a lesson in civilization and discipline *to the degenerate sons of the Spanish conquest*. The French squadron, under command of Admiral Leblanc, blockades Buenos Aires, the only Argentine port equipped for overseas commerce.

(166, 271, and 336)

1838: Buenos Aires

The Slaughterhouse

Esteban Echeverría writes the first story of River Plata literature. In *The Slaughterhouse*, the Rosas dictatorship is the harassment of a defenseless Buenos Aires doctor by a knife-wielding mob.

Born in the slums and hardened by street-fights, but polished in Paris, Echeverría despises "the rabble." A slaughterhouse in the south of the city offers a fantastic setting for the writer to describe dogs fighting over entrails with the black women eviscerators, and to tell of the "fuck-you's" bubbling up from vulgar throats as blood flows from the beasts' necks. The throat-cutter of the story wears a gaucho's poncho, has his face daubed with blood, buries his knife up to the handle in a steer's throat, and later corners the elegant black-tied gentleman who has refused him common courtesy.

(104)

More on Cannibalism in America

In his last cavalry charge, Colonel Juan Ramón Estomba hurls his horsemen against nobody. The war against Spain has ended, but much more atrocious is the war of Argentines against Argentines. Colonel Estomba raises his sword and howls: *Charge!* and in a whirlwind of war-cries and sword-thrusts the horses attack the empty horizon.

This torn country is mad with fury. The heroes of independence devour one another. Estanislao López receives the head of Pancho Ramírez, wrapped in a sheep's hide, puts it in an iron cage, and spends a whole night joyfully contemplating it. Gregorio Lamadrid loads the mother of Facundo Quiroga with chains and drags her through the streets, before Facundo falls in an ambush, a bullet in his eye. In a corral, on a carpet of cowshit, Juan Lavalle executes Manuel Dorrego; and ever since, the ghost of Dorrego has been following Lavalle, biting at his heels until one day he catches up to him and sews him with bullets to the nude body of his lover, so that Lavalle may have the pleasure of dying inside a woman.

(55, 103, 110)

1838: Tegucigalpa
Central America Breaks to Pieces

while Morazán fights in Guatemala against the multitude inflamed by the monks.

One after another, the feeble threads that had sewn this country together break. Costa Rica and Nicaragua nullify the federal pact and Honduras, too, declares itself independent. The city of Tegucigalpa celebrates with drums and cymbals and speeches the failure of its son who, ten years ago, launched from here his great unifying campaign. Provincial rancor, envy and greed, old poisons, prove more powerful than the passion of Morazán. The Federal Republic of Central America lies torn into four pieces, soon to be five, and then six. Poor pieces. For each other, they feel more hatred than pity.

(220)

1839: Copán
A Sacred City Is Sold for Fifty Dollars

and the buyer is John Lloyd Stephens, United States ambassador to Central America. It is the Maya city of Copán, in Honduras, invaded by jungle on the bank of a river.

In Copán the gods have turned to stone, and into stone also the men whom the gods chose or chastised. In Copán, more than a thousand years ago, lived the wise astronomers who discovered the secrets of the morning star and measured the solar year with a precision never equaled.

Time has mutilated, but not conquered, the temples of lovely friezes and carved stairs. The divinities still look out from the altars, playing hide-and-seek among the plumage of masks. Jaguar and snake still open their fangs on steles rising from the underbrush, and men and gods breathe from these stones, silent but never dumb.

(133)

1839: Havana
The Drum Talks Dangerously

The Captain General of Cuba decides to authorize drum dances on the plantations, provided that they are held on fiesta days and under the vigilance of foremen.

The foremen are to prevent the drums from transmitting voices of rebellion. Black drum, live drum, it does not sound alone. The drum converses with other drums, the macho drum calls, and talks dangerously to people and gods. When the drum calls, the gods appear and enter bodies and fly from them.

In very ancient times, the scorpion Akeké killed boredom by plunging his stinger into a human couple. Since then, the blacks come dancing out of the mother's belly, dancing, they say, love or pain or fury; and dancing they pierce the ferociousness of life.

(22, 222, and 241)

1839: Havana

Classified Ads

PARTE ECONOMICA.

Ventas de animales.

Se vende una negra criolla, jóven sana y sin tachas, muy humilde y fiel, buena cocinera, con alguna intelijencia en lavado y plancha, y escelente para manejar niños, en la cantidad de 500 pesos. En la calle de Daoiz, número 150, impondrán de lo demas.   3||11

Se vende un hermoso caballo de bonita estampa, de seis cuartas tres pulgadas de alzada, de—

● SE ALQUILAN POSESIONES para viviendas. Negras para el servicio de casa. Negros para peones y para todo trabajo, y se dan negritos para jugar con niños. De todo darán razon en la calle de Daoiz número 11.   mzo. 21

SANGUIJUELAS superiores acabadas de llegar de la península, se hallan de venta en la

(276)

ECONOMIC SECTION
Sales of Animals

For sale, a Creole negro woman, young, healthy and without blemishes, very humble and faithful, good cook, with some knowledge of washing and ironing, and excellent for managing children, for the sum of 500 pesos. Further information at 150 Daoiz Street.   3//11

For sale, a handsome horse of fine breeding, six spans and three inches . . .

DOMESTIC GOODS FOR HIRE.

Negro women for service in the home. Negroes as peons and for any work, and small negroes to play with children. Full information at 11 Daoiz Street.   Mar. 21

LEECHES superior quality just arrived from the peninsula, for sale . . .

1839: Valparaíso

The Illuminator

Up a hill, in the Rinconada barrio of the Chilean port of Valparaíso, in front of a plain house there is a sign:

> AMERICAN LIGHTS AND VIRTUES
> That is, tallow candles, patience,
> soap, resignation, strong glue,
> love of work

Inside, kitchen smoke and uproar of children. Here lives Simón Rodríguez. Bolívar's teacher has in his house a school and a small factory. He teaches the children the joy of creating. Making candles and soaps, he pays the bills.

(298)

1839: Veracruz

"For God's Sake, a Husband, Be He Old, One-Armed, or Crippled"

The Spanish ambassador treads Mexican soil for the first time. He finds in Veracruz no birds except vultures stalking corpses. Arm-in-arm with his wife, he goes out to stroll the sad streets, to learn the customs of the country.

In a church the ambassador finds a battered saint. Spinsters ask him for miracles by throwing stones at him. The young women throw stones hopefully, believing that the best marksmanship will give them the best husband; and for vengeance the dried-up ones, who no longer expect from Saint Anthony of Padua either husband or consolation, strike him, shrieking insults. They have poor Saint Anthony quite

broken up, the face destroyed, stumps for arms, and his chest nothing
but a big hole. At his feet, they leave him flowers.

(57)

1840: Mexico City

Masquerade

Mexico City's dressmakers and hairdressers have to keep running
from house to house, from lady to lady. Who will be the most elegant
at the great benefit ball for the poor? Which beauty will triumph?

Madame Calderón de la Barca, wife of the Spanish ambassador,
tries on the Mexican national dress, typical costume of the valley of
Puebla. Joy of the mirror that receives the image; white blouse with
lace trimmings, red skirt, a sparkle of sequins on the embroidered
petticoats. Madame Calderón twirls the multicolored sash a thousand
turns around her waist, and combs her hair with a part down the
middle, linking the tresses with a ring.

The whole city hears of it. The Council of Ministers meets to
avert the danger. Three ministers—Foreign Relations, State, and
War—present themselves at the ambassador's home and offer him
an official warning. The most important ladies cannot believe it:
swoonings, smelling salts, winds of fans. Such a worthy lady, so un-
worthily dressed! And in public! Friends advise, the diplomatic corps
pressures. Careful now, avoid scandal, such clothes are for women
of doubtful reputation.

Madame Calderón de la Barca abandons the national dress. She
won't go to the ball as a Mexican. She will wear the dress of an Italian
peasant woman of the Lazio. One of the dance's patronesses will
appear decked out as the queen of Scotland. Other ladies will be
French courtesans or Swiss, English, or Aragonese peasants, or will
wrap themselves in the extravagant veils of Turkey.

The music will sail on a sea of pearls and diamonds. The dancing
will be clumsy: not because of the feet but because of the shoes, so
miniscule and torturing.

(57)

Mexican High Society:
Introduction to a Visit

"How are you? Are you well?"
"At your service. And you?"
"Nothing new, at your service."
"How did you pass the night?"
"At your service."
"How happy I am! And how are you, señora?"
"At your disposition. And you?"
"Many thanks. And your husband?"
"At your service, nothing new."
"Do please sit down."
"After you, señorita."
"No, señora, you first, please."
"Oh well, to oblige you, without ceremony. I am an enemy of formalities and etiquette."

(57)

A Day of Street Cries in Mexico City

"Coal, sir?"

"Lard! Lard for a penny and a half!"

"Salt beef! Good salt beef!"

"Any old grease?"

"BUTTO-O-ONS! SHIRT BUTTO-O-ONS!"

"Crab apples for hot peppers! Fresh crab apples!"

"Bananas, oranges, pomegranates!"

"LITTLE MIRRO-O-ORS!"

"F a t l i t t l e b u n s h o t f r o m t h e o v e n !"

"Who wants Puebla mats, five-yard mats?"

"Honey cakes! Cheese and honey!"

"Candies! Coconut candies! Merr-i-i-ingues!"

"Last little lottery ticket, only one left for a halfpenny!"

"TORTIIIILLAS!"

"W h o w a n t s n u t s?"

"CURD TORTILLAS!"

"Ducks, my love! Hot ducks!"

"Tamales, little tamales!"

Hot roasted chestnu-u-uts?"

(57)

Mexican High Society:
The Doctor Says Goodbye

By the bedside:
    "Señora, I am at your service!"
    "Many thanks, señor."
At the foot of the bed:
    "Consider me, señora, your most humble servant!"
    "Good morning, señor."
Pausing by the table:
    "Señora, I kiss your feet!"
    "Señor, I kiss your hand!"
Nearing the door:
    "Señora, my poor house, and what it contains, and I myself,
although useless, and all that I have, are yours!"
    "Many thanks, doctor!"
Turns his back to open the door, but turns again after opening it.
    "Adieu, señora, your servant!"
    "Adieu, señor."
Finally leaves, but half opens the door and sticks his head in:
    "Good morning, señora!"

(57)

1840: Mexico City
A Nun Begins Convent Life

Thou hast chosen the good road
now no one can remove thee
chosen one

At sixteen she says goodbye to the world. She has passed in a carriage
through streets she will never see again. Relatives and friends who
will never see her again attend the ceremony in the Santa Teresa
convent.

no one no one nothing
can remove thee

She will eat with the other brides of Christ, from a clay bowl,
with a skull for a table centerpiece. She will do penance for sins she
did not commit, mysterious sins that others enjoy and that she will
redeem by tormenting her flesh with a belt of barbs and a crown of
thorns. She will sleep forever alone, on a bed of mortification. She
will wear cloth that sands her skin.

far from the battles of great Babylon
corruptions temptations dangers
far

She is covered with flowers and pearls and diamonds. They strip
her of every adornment, they undress her.

never

To the sound of the organ, the bishop exhorts and blesses. The
pastoral ring, an enormous amethyst, makes the sign of the cross over
the kneeling girl's head. The nuns chant:

Ancilla Christi sum . . .

They dress her in black. The nuns, kneeling, press their faces
against the floor, black wings unfurled around the circle of candles.
A curtain is drawn, like the lid on a coffin.

(57)

1842: San José, Costa Rica

Though Time Forget You, This Land Will Not

In Guatemala City, ladies and monks prepare Rafael Carrera, boss from the mountains, for a long dictatorship. They try on him the three-cornered hat, the dress coat and the ceremonial sword. They teach him to walk in patent leather boots, to write his name, and to tell time on a gold watch. Carrera, a hog breeder, will continue plying his trade by other means.

In San José, Costa Rica, Francisco Morazán prepares to die. He screws up his courage. For Morazán, lover of life, a man with so much life, it is hard to tear himself away. He spends the night with his eyes fixed on the ceiling of the cell, saying goodbye. The world has been great. The general puts off his farewell. He would have liked to govern more and fight less. He has spent many years making war, machete in hand, for the great Central American motherland, while she persisted in tearing herself to bits.

Before the military trumpet, comes the song of the trumpet bird. The song comes from high in the heavens and from deep in his childhood, as before, as always, at the end of the darkness. This time it announces the final dawn.

Morazán faces the firing squad. He uncovers his head and himself gives the order to load and aim. He corrects the aim, gives the order to fire.

The volley returns him to the earth.

(220)

1844: Mexico City

The Warrior Cocks

The Church, landlord and moneylender, possesses half of Mexico. The other half belongs to a handful of gentlemen and to Indians penned up in their communities. The proprietor of the presidency is General López de Santa Anna, who watches over public peace and the good health of his fighting cocks.

Santa Anna governs with a cock in his arms. Thus, he receives bishops and ambassadors, and to tend to a wounded cock he abandons cabinet meetings. He founds more cockfight arenas than hospitals and issues more cockfight rules than decrees on education. Cockfighting men form his personal court, along with cardsharps and widows of colonels who never were.

He is very fond of a piebald cock that pretends to be a female and flirts with the enemy, then after making a fool of him slashes him to death; but of them all he prefers the fierce Pedrito. He brought Pedrito from Veracruz with some soil too, so Pedrito could wallow in it without nostalgia. Santa Anna personally fixes the blade on the spur. He exchanges bets with muleteers and vagabonds, and chews feathers from the rival to give it bad luck. When he has no coins left, he throws medals into the cockpit.

"I'll give eight to five!"

"Eight to four if you like!"

A lightning flash pierces the whirl of feathers and Pedrito's spur tears out the eyes or opens the throat of any champion. Santa Anna dances on one leg and the killer raises his crest, beats his wings and sings.

(227 and 309)

1844: Mexico City

Santa Anna

frowns, stares off into space. He is thinking about some cock fallen in combat or about his own leg, which he lost, a venerated token of military glory.

Six years ago, during a small war against the king of France, a gun salvo tore off the leg. From his bed of pain, the mutilated president dictated to his secretaries a laconic fifteen-page message of farewell to the fatherland; but he came back to life and power, as was his habit.

An enormous cortege accompanied the leg from Veracruz to the capital. The leg arrived under a canopy, escorted by Santa Anna, who waved his white-plumed hat out of the carriage window; and behind, in full regalia, came bishops and ministers and ambassadors and an army of hussars, dragoons, and cuirassiers. The leg passed beneath a thousand rows of banners, and at its passing received prayers for the dead and speeches, odes, hymns, gun salutes, and the tolling of bells. On arriving at the cemetery, the president pronounced before the pantheon a final homage to that piece of himself death had taken by way of an advance.

Since then the missing leg hurts. Today, it hurts more than ever, hurts him excruciatingly, because the rebellious people have broken open the monument that guarded it and are dragging the leg through the streets of Mexico.

(227)

1845: Vuelta de Obligado
The Invasion of the Merchants

Three years ago, the British squadron humiliated the Celestial Empire. After the blockade of Canton and the rest of the coast, the English imposed opium consumption on the Chinese, in the name of Freedom of Commerce and Western Civilization.

After China, Argentina. The long years blockading the port of Buenos Aires have availed little or nothing. Juan Manuel de Rosas, who has his portrait worshipped and governs surrounded by buffoons dressed as kings, still refuses to open Argentina's rivers. English and French bankers and merchants have for years been demanding that this insolence be punished.

Many Argentines fall defending their land, but finally the guns of the warships of the world's most powerful countries smash the chains stretched across the Paraná River.

(271 and 336)

1847: Mexico City
The Conquest

"*Mexico sparkles before our eyes*": with these words President Adams had dazzled himself at the turn of the century.

At the first bite, Mexico lost Texas.

Now the United States has all Mexico on its plate.

General Santa Anna, master of retreat, flees to the south, leaving a trail of swords and corpses in the ditches. From defeat to defeat, he withdraws his army of bleeding, ill fed, never-paid soldiers, and beside them the ancient cannons hauled by mules, and behind them the caravan of women carrying children, rags, and tortillas in baskets. The army of General Santa Anna, with more officers than soldiers, is only good for killing poor compatriots.

In Chapultepec Castle, Mexican cadets, practically children, do not surrender. They resist the bombardment with an obstinacy not born of hope. Stones collapse over their bodies. Among the stones the victors plant the stars and stripes, which rises from the smoke over the huge valley.

The conquerors enter the capital. The city of Mexico: eight engineers, two thousand monks, two thousand five hundred lawyers, twenty thousand beggars.

The people, huddled together, growl. From the roofs, it rains stones.

(7, 127, 128, and 187)

1848: Villa of Guadalupe Hidalgo
The Conquistadors

In Washington, President Polk proclaims that his nation is now as big as all Europe. No one can halt the onslaught of this young voracious country. To the south and to the west, the United States grows, killing Indians, trampling on neighbors, or even paying. It bought Louisiana from Napoleon and now offers Spain a hundred million dollars for the island of Cuba.

But the right of conquest is more glorious and cheaper. The treaty with Mexico is signed in the Villa of Guadalupe Hidalgo. Mexico cedes to the United States, pistol at chest, half of its territory.

(128)

1848: Mexico City
The Irishmen

In the main plaza of Mexico City, the conquerors mete out punishment. They scourge the rebel Mexicans. They brand with hot irons the faces of the Irish deserters and then hang them from the gallows.

The Saint Patrick Irish battalion came in with the invaders, but fought alongside the invaded. From the north to Molino del Rey, the Irish made theirs the fate, ill fate, of the Mexicans. Many died defending the Churubusco monastery without ammunition. The prisoners, their faces burned, rock to and fro on the gallows.

(128)

1848: Ibiray

An Old Man in a White Poncho
in a House of Red Stone

He never liked cities. His heart's desire is a garden in Paraguay and his carriage, a wheelbarrow full of medicinal greens. A cane helps him to walk, and black Ansina, a minstrel of happy songs, helps him to work the ground and to receive without somber shadows the light of each day.

"José Artigas, at your service."

He offers maté and respect, but few words to the visitors that sometimes come from Uruguay.

"So my name is still heard over there."

He is past eighty years old, twenty-eight of them in exile, and he won't go back. The ideas he created and the people he loved are still beaten. Artigas well knows the weight of the world and of memory, and prefers to be silent. There is no plant to heal the wounds inside a man.

(277)

José Artigas, According to
Domingo Faustino Sarmiento

He was a highwayman, no more, no less. Thirty years of practice in murdering or robbing are indisputable qualifications for the the exercise of command over a horde of mutinous Indian peasant scum for a political revolution, and among them the fearsome name of Artigas is encrusted as bandit chief . . . Who obeyed him? The poor or savage Indians whom he led by right of being the most savage, the most cruel, the greatest enemy of whites . . . Uncouth, since he never frequented cities, foreign to all human tradition of free government; and although white, commanding natives even less educated than himself . . . Considering the antecedents and actions of Artigas, we feel a sort of revolt of reason, of the instincts of the man of white race, when someone tried to endow him with political thought and human sentiment.

(311)

1848: Buenos Aires

The Lovers (I)

Dramatis Personae:

Camila O'Gorman.   Born in Buenos Aires, in a house with three patios, twenty years ago. Educated in the odor of sanctity, to be successively virgin, wife, and mother in the strait and narrow path that leads to conjugal peace, the offices of the needle, evenings at the piano, and the rosary told with black mantilla on head. She has eloped with the parish priest of the Socorro Church. The idea was hers.

Ladislao Gutiérrez.   Minister of God. Age twenty-five. Nephew of the governor of Tucumán. He could not sleep after placing the Host on the tongue of that woman kneeling by the light of candles. Ended by dropping missal and cassock, setting loose a stampede of little angels and campanile pigeons.

Adolfo O'Gorman.   Begins each meal reciting the ten commandments, from the head of a long mahogany table. From a chaste woman, he has engendered a priest son, a policeman son, and a fugitive daughter. An exemplary father, he is the first to ask exemplary punishment for *the horrendous scandal* which shames his family. In a letter to Juan Manuel de Rosas, he pleads for a firm hand *against the most atrocious and unheard-of act in the country.*

Felipe Elortondo Y Palacio.   Secretary of the Curia. Also writes to Rosas asking the capture of the lovers and their inflexible punishment, to prevent similar crimes in the future. Explains in his letter that he had nothing to do with the appointment of the priest Gutiérrez, which was an affair of the bishop.

Juan Manuel De Rosas.   Orders the lovers hunted down. His messengers gallop from Buenos Aires. They carry a leaflet describing the fugitives. Camila: *white, black eyes, pleasant expression; tall, slim body, well distributed.* Ladislao: *dark, thin, full beard and curly hair.* Justice will be done, Rosas promises, *to satisfy religion and the laws and to prevent the consequent demoralization, libertinage, and disorder.* The whole country is on guard.

Also participating:

The Opposition Press.   From Montevideo, Valparaíso, and La Paz, Rosas's enemies invoke public morality. The daily newspaper *El Mercurio Chileno* tells its readers: *To such an extreme has come the horrible corruption of the customs under the alarming tyranny of the "River Plata Caligula," that impious and sacrilegious priests of Buenos Aires elope with the daughters of the best society, without the infamous satrap adopting any measure against these monstrous immoralities.*

The Horses.   They take the lovers to the north across open country, avoiding cities. Ladislao's had a golden hide and long legs. Camila's is grayish, fat, and bobtailed. They sleep, like their riders, outdoors. They do not tire.

Baggage.   His: a woolen poncho, some clothes, a couple of penknives and a pair of pistols, a pouch, a silk tie, and a glass inkpot. Hers: a silk shawl, several dresses, four linen petticoats, a fan, a pair of gloves, a comb, and a gold wedding ring, broken.

(166 and 219)

The Lovers (II)

They are two by an error that the night corrects.

1848: Holy Places
The Lovers (III)

In the summer they elope. They spend the autumn at the port of Goya, on the shores of the Paraná. There they go by other names. In the winter they are discovered, betrayed, and caught.

They are taken south in separate carts. The wheels leave scars on the road.

They are shut up in separate dungeons in the Holy Places prison.

If they beg pardon, they will be pardoned. Camila, pregnant, does not repent. Nor does Ladislao. Irons are fixed on their feet. A priest sprinkles the shackles with holy water.

They are shot in the patio, with their eyes blindfolded.

(219)

1848: Bacalar
Cecilio Chi

The ears of corn have spoken, warning of hunger. Huge sugar plantations are devouring the Maya communities' cornfields in the Yucatán region of Mexico. Men are purchased, as in Africa, and paid for with rum. *The Indians hear with their backs*, says the lash.

And war breaks out. Sick of contributing dead to other people's wars, the Mayas answer the call of the hollow trunk drum. They erupt from the brush, from the night, from nothing, machete in one hand, torch in the other: haciendas burn along with their owners and the sons of their owners, and the documents that make debt-slaves of Indians and sons of Indians burn too.

The Maya tornado whirls and destroys. Cecilio Chi fights with fifteen thousand Indians against guns that kill en masse, and so falls the proud city of Valladolid de Yucatán which thinks itself so noble, so Castilian; and Bacalar, and many other towns and garrisons, one after the other.

Cecilio Chi exterminates enemies invoking the old-time rebel Jacinto Canek and the even earlier prophet Chilam Balam. He proclaims that blood will flood the Mérida plaza up to the people's ankles. He offers firewater and fireworks to the patron saints of each town he occupies: If the saints refuse to change sides, and continue at the masters' service, Cecilio Chi cuts their throats with his machete and throws them on the fire.

(144 and 263)

1849: Shores of the Platte River
A Horseman Called Smallpox

Of every four Pawnee Indians, one has died this year of smallpox or cholera. The Kiowas, their eternal enemies, have saved themselves thanks to Old Uncle Saynday.

The old ruffian wandered these plains from heartache to heartache. *My world is finished*, he muttered over and over while vainly seeking deer and buffalo, and the Washita River offered him red mud instead of clear water. *Soon my Kiowa people will be surrounded like cows*.

Old Uncle Saynday was walking along buried in these sad thoughts when he saw over in the east, instead of the sun, a blackness, a great dark stain spreading across the prairie. As it drew closer, he saw that the stain was a horseman dressed in black, with a high black hat and a black horse. The horseman had ferocious scars on his face.

"My name is Smallpox," he introduced himself.

"I never heard . . ." said Saynday.

"I come from far away, the other side of the sea," the stranger explained. "I bring death."

He asked for the Kiowas. Old Uncle Saynday knew how to turn him around. He explained to him that the Kiowas weren't worth his trouble, a small and starveling people, and instead recommended the Pawnees, who are many, handsome and powerful, and showed him the rivers where they live.

(198)

1849: San Francisco
The Gold of California

From Valparaíso, Chileans stream in. They bring a pair of boots and a knife, a lamp and a shovel.

The entry to San Francisco Bay is now known as "the golden gate." Until yesterday, San Francisco was the Mexican town of Yerbas Buenas. In these lands, usurped from Mexico in the war of conquest, there are three-kilo nuggets of pure gold.

The bay has no room for so many ships. An anchor touches bottom, and adventurers scatter across the mountains. No one wastes time on hellos. The cardsharp buries his patent leather boots in the mud:

"Long live my loaded dice! Long live my jack!"

Simply landing on this soil turns the bum into a king and the beauty who had scorned him dies of remorse. Vicente Pérez Rosales, newly arrived, listens to the thoughts of his compatriots: "Now I have talent! Because in Chile, who's an ass once he has cash?" *Here losing time is losing money*. Endless thunder of hammers, a world on the boil, birth-pang screams. Out of nothing rise the awnings under which are offered tools and liquor and dried meat in exchange for leather bags filled with gold dust. Crows and men squawk, flocks of men from all lands, and night and day eddies the whirlwind of frock coats and seamen's caps, Oregon furs and Maule bonnets, French daggers, Chinese hats, Russian boots, and shiny bullets at the waists of cowboys.

Under her lace sunshade, a good-looking Chilean woman smiles as best she can, squeezed by her corset and by the multitude that sweeps her over the sea of mud paved with broken bottles. In this port she is Rosarito Améstica. She was born Rosarito Izquierdo more years ago than she'll tell, became Rosarito Villaseca in Talcahuano, Rosarito Toro in Talca, and Rosarito Montalva in Valparaíso.

From the stern of a ship, the auctioneer offers ladies to the crowd. He exhibits them and sings their praises, one by one, *look gentlemen what a waist what youth what beauty what* . . .

"Who'll give more?" says the auctioneer. "Who'll give more for this incomparable flower?"

(256)

1849: El Molino

They Were Here

Man calls and gold falls from the sands and rocks. Sparks of gold jump on the winds; gold comes docilely to the hand of man, from the bottom of California's rivers and ravines.

El Molino is one of many camps that have sprung up on these golden shores. One day the miners of El Molino notice columns of smoke rising from the distant cypress forests. At night they see a line of fires mocking the wind. Someone recognizes the signals: the telegraph of the Indians is calling for war against the intruders.

In a flash, the miners form a detail of a hundred and seventy rifles and attack by surprise. They bring in a hundred prisoners and shoot fifteen to teach them a lesson.

(256)

Ashes

Since he had the dream of the White Rabbit, the old man talked of nothing else, though he had trouble talking at all, and for a long time had been unable to stand. The years made his eyes watery and bent him irremediably. He lived in a basket, his face hidden behind his pointy knees, poised for the return to the belly of the earth. Stuck in the basket, he traveled on the back of some son or grandson and told his dream to everybody: *White Rabbit gonna devour us*, he babbled. *Gonna devour our seed, our grass, our living*. He said the

White Rabbit would come mounted on an animal bigger than a deer, an animal with round feet and hair on its neck.

The old man did not live to see the gold fever in these Californian lands. Before the miners arrived on horseback, he announced: *"Can't feed my children no more. Like old root, just ready for growing now. Speak no more."*

They burned him in his basket, on firewood that he had selected.

(229)

1849: Baltimore
Poe

At the door of a tavern in Baltimore the dying man lies face up, strangling in his vomit. Some pious hand drags him to the hospital, at dawn; and nothing more, nevermore.

Edgar Allan Poe, son of ragged itinerant comedians, vagabond poet, convicted and confessed guilty of disobedience and delirium, had been condemned by invisible tribunals and crushed by invisible pincers.

He got lost looking for himself. Not looking for gold in California; no, looking for himself.

(99 and 260) ·

1849: San Francisco
Levi's Pants

The flashes of violence and miracles do not blind Levi Strauss, who arrives from far-off Bavaria and realizes at one blink that here the beggar becomes a millionaire and the millionaire a beggar or corpse in a click of cards or triggers. In another blink he discovers that pants become tatters in these mines of California, and decides to provide a better fate for the strong cloths he has brought along. He won't sell awnings or tents. He will sell pants, tough pants for tough men in the tough work of digging up rivers and mines. So the seams won't burst, he reinforces them with copper riveting. Behind, under the waist, Levi stamps his name on a leather label.

Soon the cowboys of the whole West will claim as their own these pants of blue Nîmes twill which neither sun nor years wear out.

(113)

1850: San Francisco
The Road to Development

The Chilean Pérez Rosales is looking for luck in the mines of California. Learning that, a few miles from San Francisco, fabulous prices are paid for anything edible, he gets a few sacks of worm-eaten jerky and some jars of jam and buys a launch. Hardly has he pushed off from the pier when a customs agent points a rifle at his head: *"Hold it there."*

This launch cannot move on any United States river *because it was built abroad and its keel is not made of North American wood*.

The United States had defended its national market since the times of its first president. It supplies cotton to England, but customs barriers block English cloth and any product that could injure its own industry. The planters of the southern states want English clothing, which is much better and cheaper, and complain that the northern textile mills impose on them their ugly and costly cloth from baby's diaper to corpse's shroud.

(162 and 256)

1850: Buenos Aires
The Road to Underdevelopment: The Thought of Domingo Faustino Sarmiento

We are not industrialists or navigators and Europe will provide us for long centuries with its artifacts in exchange for our raw materials.

(310)

1850: River Plata
Buenos Aires and Montevideo at Mid-Century

From his seat in the French Academy to the River Plata docks, sails the poet Xavier Marmier.

The great European powers have reached an agreement with Rosas. The Buenos Aires blockade has been lifted. Marmier thinks he is on the Rue Vivienne as he strolls down Peru Street. In the shop windows he finds Lyons silks and the *Journal de Modes*, the novels of Dumas and Sandeau and the poems of de Musset; but in the shade of the City Hall's porticos saunter barefoot blacks in soldiers' uniforms, and the pavements ring with the trot of a gaucho's horse.

Someone explains to Marmier that no gaucho dispatches anybody without first kissing the blade of his knife and swearing by the Immaculate Virgin; and if the dead man was a friend, the killer mounts him on his steed and ties him to the saddle so that he may enter the cemetery on horseback.

Further on, in the suburban plazas, Marmier finds the carts, ships of the pampa, which bring hides and wheat from the interior and on the return trip take cloth and liquor which have arrived from Le Havre and Liverpool.

The poet crosses the river. For seven years Montevideo has been under siege from the rear, harassed by General Oribe's gaucho army, but the city survives, facing the river-ocean, thanks to French ships which pour merchandise and money onto the docks. One Montevideo newspaper is *Le Patriote Français* and the majority of the population is French. In this refuge of Rosas's enemies, Marmier notes, *the rich have gone poor and all have gone mad*. A suitor pays an ounce of gold to stick a camellia in his girl's hair and the mistress of the house offers the visitor a bouquet of honeysuckle held by a ring of silver, rubies, and emeralds. For the ladies of Montevideo, the war between vanguardists and conservatives seems more important than the war against the Uruguayan peasants, a real war that kills people. Vanguardists wear their hair very short; conservatives, luxuriantly rolled.

(196)

1850: Paris

Dumas

Alexandre Dumas rolls up his cuffs of fine batiste and with a stroke of the pen writes the epic pages of *Montevideo; or, The New Troy*.

The novelist, a man of fantasy and gluttony, has priced at five thousand francs this professional feat of the imagination. He calls Montevideo's humble hill a "mountain" and turns the war of foreign merchants against the gaucho cavalry into a Greek epic. The hosts of Giuseppe Garibaldi, which fight for Montevideo, fly not the flag of Uruguay but the classic pirate skull and crossbones on a black field;

but in the novel Dumas writes to order, only martyrs and titans take part in the defense of the almost French city.

(101)

1850: Montevideo
Lautréamont at Four

Isidoro Ducasse has been born in the port of Montevideo. A double wall of fortifications separates the countryside from the besieged city. Isidoro grows up dazed by cannon fire, with the daily spectacle of dying men hanging from their horses.

His shoes take him to the sea. Standing on the sand, face to the wind, he asks the sea where music goes after it leaves the violin, where the sun goes when night arrives, and where the dead go. Isidoro asks the sea where his mother went, that woman he cannot remember, nor should name, nor knows how to imagine. Someone has told him that the other dead people threw her out of the cemetery. The sea, which talks so much, does not answer; and the boy flees up the cliff and, weeping, embraces an enormous tree with all his strength, so it won't fall.

(181)

1850: Chan Santa Cruz
The Talking Cross

Three long years of Indian war in Yucatán. More than a hundred and fifty thousand dead, a hundred thousand fled. The population has been reduced by half.

One of the captains of the rebellion, the mestizo José María Barrera, leads the Indians to a cave deep in the jungle. There, a spring offers fresh water in the shade of a very tall mahogany tree. The tree has given birth to the little cross that talks.

Says the cross, in the Maya language: *"The time has come for Yucatán to rise. I am falling hour by hour, they are cutting me with machetes, stabbing me with knives, poking sticks into me. I go about Yucatán to redeem my beloved Indians . . ."*

The cross is the size of a finger. The Indians dress it. They put a huipil and skirt on it; they adorn it with colored threads. She will unite the dispersed.

(273)

1851: Latacunga
"I Wander at Random and Naked . . ."

Instead of thinking about Medes and Persians and Egyptians, let us think about Indians. It is more important for us to understand an Indian than Ovid. Start your school with Indians, Señor Rector.

Simón Rodríguez offers his advice to the college of the town of Latacunga, in Ecuador: that a chair be established in the Quechua language instead of in Latin, that physics be taught instead of theology; that the college build a pottery factory and a glass factory; that it offer degrees in masonry, carpentry, and smithery.

Along the Pacific shores and through the Andes, from town to town, Don Simón makes his pilgrimage. He never wanted to be a tree, but the wind. For a quarter of a century he has been raising dust on America's roads. Since Sucre ousted him from Chuquisaca, he has founded many schools and candle factories and published two books with his own hands, letter by letter, since no typographer can cope with so many brackets and synoptic charts. This old vagabond, bald and ugly and potbellied, tanned by the sun, carries on his back a trunk of manuscripts condemned by lack of money and readers. He carries no clothing. He has only what he wears.

Bolívar used to call him, *My teacher, my Socrates.* He said, *You have molded my heart for the great and the beautiful.* People clench their teeth to keep from laughing when mad Rodríguez launches into his perorations about the tragic destiny of these Hispanic-American lands.

"We are blind! Blind!"

Almost no one listens to him, no one believes him. They take him for a Jew, because he goes about sowing children wherever he passes, and does not baptize them with Saints' names, but calls them Corncob, Calabash, Carrot and other heresies. He has changed his surname three times and says he was born in Caracas, but also that he was born in Philadelphia and in Sanlúcar de Barrameda. It is rumored that one of his schools, in Concepción in Chile, was destroyed by an earthquake which God sent when he learned that Don Simón taught anatomy parading himself stark naked before the students.

Each day Don Simón grows more lonely. The most audacious, most lovable of America's thinkers, every day more lonely.

At eighty, he writes: *I wanted to make the earth a paradise for all. I made it a hell for myself.*

(298)

The Ideas of Simón Rodríguez:
"Either We Invent or We Are Lost"

Look at the way Europe invents, and look how America imitates!

Some see prosperity in having their ports full of foreign ships, and their homes turned into warehouses for foreign effects. Every day brings a shipment of ready-made clothing, even caps for the Indians. Soon we shall see little gilded packages, with the royal coat-of-arms, containing earth prepared "by a new process," for the lads accustomed to eating earth.

Women making their confessions in French! Missionarees absolveeng seens een Spaneesh!

America should not servilely imitate, but be original.

The wisdom of Europe and the prosperity of the United States are, in America, two enemies of freedom of thought. The new republics do not want to admit anything that does not carry a pass . . . To form their institutions, the statesmen of those nations consulted no one but reason; and this they found on their own soil. Imitate originality, since you try to imitate everything!

Where shall we go in search of models? We are independent, but not free; masters of our soil, but not of ourselves.

Let us open up history; and for that which is not yet written, let each read it in his own memory.

(285)

1851: La Serena
The Precursors

Misery is not being able to think or store in the mind any memory except pain, says Francisco Bilbao, and adds that the exploitation of man by man leaves man no time to be man. Society is divided into those who *can* do everything and those who *do* do everything. To revive Chile, *giant buried under weeds*, an end must be put to a system that denies shelter to those who toil to build palaces, and dresses in rags those who weave the best clothing.

The precursors of socialism in Chile are not yet thirty years old. Francisco Bilbao and Santiago Arcos, tuxedoed young men cultivated in Paris, have betrayed their class. Searching for a *society of solidarity*, they have in the course of this year set off various military rebellions and popular uprisings throughout the country, against the wig-wearers and the monks, and private property.

On the last day of the year the last revolutionary bastion falls, in the city of La Serena. Many *reds* also fall—before firing squads. Bilbao, who on another occasion escaped disguised as a woman, this time has fled over the rooftops and gone into exile with cassock and missal.

(39)

1852: Santiago de Chile
"What has independence meant to the poor?" the Chilean Santiago Arcos asks himself in jail.

Since independence the government is and has been of the rich. The poor have been soldiers, national militias, have voted as their employer told them, have worked the land, have dug ditches, have worked the mines, have carried on their backs, have cultivated the country, have kept on earning a penny and a half, have been whipped and pilloried . . . The poor have enjoyed glorious independence as much as the horses that charged against the king's troops in Chacabuco and Maipú.

(306)

The People of Chile Sing to the Glory of Paradise

Saint Peter, the patron of me and of you,
sent an acolyte out for some sausage and wine
and a nice side of bacon and pigs' feet fine
to go in the pot for a succulent stew,
with a good heady punch, the way earth folks do;

and, not to be supercilious,
a basket of tortillas
so that little angels all
could out of heavenly boredom fall
and have themselves a genuine ball.
Saint Anthony, when the hour was tardy
swayed to his feet and said "Well, sirs,
damn all the devils in hell, sirs,
isn't this quite a party!
To no one's abuse
it's time to let loose
with an innocent ruse:
I'll go up to Saint Clara
and before she's aware-a'
her plump little bottom I'm going to goose."

(182)

1852: Mendoza

The Lines of the Hand

Even the little altar angels wear red sashes in Argentina. To refuse challenges the fury of the dictator. Like many enemies of Rosas, Doctor Federico Mayer Arnold has suffered exile and prison.

Not long ago this young Buenos Aires professor published a book in Santiago de Chile. The book, adorned with French, English, and Latin quotations, began this way: *Three cities have expelled me from their bosoms and four jails have received me to theirs. I have, however, thrown my thoughts freely in the despot's face. Now again I launch my ideas into the world, and await without fear what Fate has in store for me.*

Two months later, on turning a corner, Doctor Federico Mayer Arnold falls in a spray of blood. But not by order of the tyrant: Federico's mother-in-law, Doña María, an ill-humored woman from Mendoza, has paid the knife-wielding thugs. She has ordered them to kill her son-in-law because he does not please her.

(14)

1853: La Cruz
The Treasure of the Jesuits

She knows. That's why the crow follows her, flies behind her every morning, on the way to Mass, and waits for her at the church door.

She has just had her hundredth birthday. She will tell the secret when she is ready to die. If not, Divine Providence would punish her.

"Three days hence," comes the promise.

And after three days, *"Next month."*

And after the month, *"Tomorrow we'll see."*

When people pester her, her eyes go blank and she pretends to be dazed, or explodes with laughter moving her little legs, as if being so old were something naughty.

The whole town of La Cruz knows that she knows. She was just a little girl when she helped the Jesuits bury the treasure in the Misiones woods, but she hasn't forgotten.

Once, taking advantage of her absence, the neighbors opened the old chest which she spent her days sitting on. Inside there was no bag full of gold pieces. In the chest they found only the dried navels of her eleven children.

Come the death throes, the whole town is at the foot of her bed. She opens and closes her fishlike mouth as if trying to say something.

She dies in the door of sanctity. The secret was the only one she had in her life and she goes without telling it.

(147)

1853: Paita
The Three

She no longer dresses as a captain, nor fires pistols, nor rides horseback. Her legs don't work and her whole body is distorted with fat; but she sits on her invalid's chair as if it were a throne and peels oranges and guavas with the most beautiful hands in the world.

Surrounded by clay pitchers, Manuela Sáenz reigns in the shaded portico of her house. Beyond, among mountains the color of death, extends the Bay of Paita. Exiled in this Peruvian port, Manuela lives by making sweets and fruit preserves. Ships stop to buy. Her goodies enjoy great fame on these coasts. Whalers sigh for a spoonful.

At nightfall Manuela amuses herself by throwing scraps to stray dogs, which she has baptized with the names of generals who were disloyal to Bolívar. As Santander, Páez, Córdoba, Lamar, and Santa Cruz fight over the bones, her moonface lights up, and, covering her toothless mouth with a fan, she bursts out laughing. She laughs with her whole body and her many flying laces.

Sometimes an old friend comes from the town of Amotape. The wandering Simón Rodríguez sits in a rocking chair, beside Manuela, and the two of them smoke and chat and are silent together. The persons Bolívar most loved, the teacher and the lover, change the subject if the hero's name filters into the conversation.

When Don Simón leaves, Manuela sends for the silver coffer. She opens it with the key hidden in her bosom and fondles the many letters Bolívar had written *to the one and only woman*, worn-out paper that still says: *I want to see you and see you again and touch you and feel you and taste you* . . . Then she asks for the mirror and very carefully brushes her hair, in case he might come and visit her in dreams.

(295, 298, and 343)

1854: Amotape
A Witness Describes Simón Rodríguez's Farewell to the World

As soon as he saw the Amotape priest enter, Don Simón sat up in bed, waved the priest to the only chair in the room and started making something like a speech on materialism. The priest sat there stupefied, and scarcely had the heart to pronounce a few words trying to interrupt him . . .

(298)

1855: New York
Whitman

For lack of a publisher, the poet pays out of his own pocket for the publication of *Leaves of Grass*.

Waldo Emerson, theologist of Democracy, gives the book his blessing, but the press attacks it as prosaic and obscene.

In Walt Whitman's grandiose elegy multitudes and machines
roar. The poet embraces God and sinners, he embraces the Indians
and the pioneers who wipe them out, he embraces slave and master,
victim and executioner. All crime is redeemed in the ecstasy of the
New World, America the muscular and the subjugator, with no debt
to pay to the past, winds of progess that make man the comrade of
man and unchain virility and beauty.

(358)

1855: New York
Melville

The bearded sailor is a writer without readers. Four years ago he
published the story of a captain who pursues a white whale through
the seas of the universe, bloodthirsty harpoon in pursuit of Evil, and
no one paid it much attention.

In these times of euphoria, in these North American lands in full
expansion, Herman Melville's voice sings out of tune. His books are
mistrustful of Civilization, which attributes to the savage the role of
Demon and forces him to play it—as Captain Ahab does with Moby
Dick in the immensity of the ocean. His books reject the only and
obligatory Truth that certain men, believing themselves chosen, impose on the others. His books have doubts about Vice and Virtue,
shadows of the same nothingness, and teach that the sun is the only
lamp worthy of confidence.

(211 and 328)

1855: Washington Territory
"You people will suffocate in your own waste," warns Indian Chief Seattle.

*The earth is not the white man's brother, but his enemy, and when
he has conquered it, he moves on. But all things are connected.
Whatever befalls the earth befalls the sons of the earth . . .*

The clatter of cities only seems to insult the ears . . .

*The air is precious to the red man. For all things share the same
breath—beasts, trees, man. Like a man dying for many days, he is
numb to the stench . . .*

It matters little where we pass the rest of our days; they are not

*many. A few more hours, a few more winters . . . The whites, too,
shall pass—perhaps sooner than other tribes. Continue to con-
taminate your bed, and you will one night suffocate in your own
waste . . .*

(229)

The Far West

Is anyone really listening to old Chief Seattle? The Indians are condemned, like the buffalo and the moose. The one that does not die
by the bullet dies of hunger or sorrow. From the reservation where
he languishes, old Chief Seattle talks in solitude about usurpations
and exterminations and says who knows what things about the memory of his people flowing in the sap of the trees.

The Colt barks. Like the sun, the white pioneers march westward. A diamond light from the mountains guides them. The promised land rejuvenates anyone sticking a plow in it to make it fertile.
In a flash cities and streets spring up in the solitude so recently
inhabited by cacti, Indians, and snakes. The climate, they say, is so
very healthy that the only way to inaugurate cemeteries is to shoot
someone down.

Adolescent capitalism, stampeding and gluttonous, transfigures
what it touches. The forest exists for the ax to chop down and the
desert for the train to cross; the river is worth bothering about if it
contains gold, and the mountain if it shelters coal or iron. No one
walks. All run, in a hurry, it's urgent, after the nomad shadow of
wealth and power. Space exists for time to defeat, and time for progress to sacrifice on its altars.

(218)

1856: Granada
Walker

The son of Tennessee shoots from the hip and buries without epitaph.
He has eyes of cinders. He neither laughs nor drinks. He eats as a
duty. No woman has been seen with him since his deaf and dumb
fiancée died; and God is his only friend worthy of trust. He calls
himself the Predestined. He dresses in black. He hates anyone touching him.

William Walker, Southern gentleman, proclaims himself President of Nicaragua. Red carpets cover the main square of Granada. Trumpets flash in the sun. The band plays North American military marches as Walker kneels and takes the oath with one hand on the Bible. Twenty one salutes are fired. He makes his speech in English and then raises a glass of water and toasts the president of the United States, his compatriot and esteemed colleague. The North American ambassador, John Wheeler, compares Walker with Christopher Columbus.

Walker arrived in Nicaragua a year ago, at the head of the Phalanx of Immortals. *I will order the death of anyone who opposes the imperial march of my forces*. Like a knife into meat came the adventurers recruited on the wharves of San Francisco and New Orleans.

The new president of Nicaragua restores slavery, abolished in Central America over thirty years ago, and re-implants the slave trade, serfdom, and forced labor. He decrees that English is Nicaragua's official language and offers lands and hands to any white North Americans who care to come.

(154, 253, and 314)

1856: Granada

Stood

Five or none. Nicaragua wasn't much. William Walker wanted to conquer all of Central America.

The five pieces of Morazan's fatherland, united against the pirate, chop his force to bits. The people's war kills many North Americans; morbus cholera, which turns you wrinkled and gray and suddenly finishes you off, kills more.

The Messiah of slavery, roundly defeated, crosses Lake Nicaragua. Flocks of ducks and swarms of plague-infected flies pursue him. Before returning to the United States, Walker decides to punish the city of Granada. Nothing should remain alive there. Neither its people, nor its tile-roofed houses, nor its sandy streets lined with orange trees.

Flames rise to the sky.

At the foot of the ruined wharves a lance is stuck into the ground. A strip of leather hangs from the lance like a dejected flag. In red letters it says, in English: *Here stood Granada*.

(154 and 314)

Walker: "In Defense of Slavery"

The enemies of American civilization—for such are the enemies of slavery—seem to be more on the alert than its friends.

Something is due from the South to the memory of the brave dead who repose in the soil of Nicaragua. In defense of slavery these men left their homes, met with calmness and constancy the perils of a tropical climate, and finally yielded up their lives . . .

If there, then, be yet vigor in the South—and who can doubt that there is—for the further contest with the soldiers of anti-slavery, let her cast off the lethargy which enthrals her, and prepare anew for the conflict . . . The true field for the exertion of slavery is in tropical America; there it finds the natural seat of its empire and thither it can spread if it will but make the effort . . .

(356)

1858: Source of the Gila River
The Sacred Lands of the Apaches

Here, in the valley where the river is born, among the rocky heights of Arizona, is the tree that sheltered Geronimo thirty years ago. He had just sprouted from his mother's belly and was wrapped in a cloth. They hung the cloth from a branch. The wind rocked the baby while an old voice entreated the tree: *"Let him live and grow to see you give fruit many times."*

This tree is at the center of the world. Standing in its shade, Geronimo will never confuse north with south, nor evil with good.

All around spreads the vast country of the Apaches. In these rugged lands they have lived ever since the first of them, Son of the Storm, donned the feathers of the eagle who defeated the enemies of light. Here, animals to hunt have never been lacking, nor herbs to cure the sick, nor rocky caves to lie in after death.

Some strange men have arrived on horseback, carrying long ropes and many stakes. Their skin looks as if it had been drained of blood, and they speak a language never before heard. They stick bright-colored signals into the ground and ask questions of a white medal which replies by moving a needle.

Geronimo does not know that these men have come to measure the Apaches' lands, to sell them.

(24 and 91)

1858: Kaskiyeh

Geronimo

The Apaches had gone unarmed to the market of Kaskiyeh in the southern lands betweeen Sonora and Casas Grandes to exchange buffalo and deerskins for food. Mexican soldiers demolished their camps and took their horses. Among the dead lie the mother and the wife of Geronimo, and his three children.

Geronimo says nothing while his comrades meet and sadly vote. They are surrounded, unarmed, and have no choice but to leave.

Sitting by the river, motionless, he watches his people march off behind Chief Mangas Colorado. Here the dead remain. Finally, Geronimo leaves as well, looking over his shoulder. He follows his people *at the right distance to hear the soft padding of the Apaches' feet in retreat*.

During the long trek to the north, he does not open his mouth. Upon arriving home, he burns his house of skins and his mother's house and all of his things and his wife's and his mother's things, and burns his children's toys. Then, his back to the fire, he raises his head and sings a war chant.

(24)

1858: San Borja

Let Death Die

His sore body is aching to mix itself with the American earth. Aimé Bonpland knew this was where he would end up and linger on, ever since that distant day when he landed with Humboldt on the Caribbean coast.

Bonpland dies of his death, in a mud and straw hut, serenely, knowing that the stars do not die; that ants and people will not stop being born; that there will be new cloverleaves, and new oranges or suns on the branches; and that foals, newly upright on their mosquito legs, will be stretching out their necks in search of a teat. The old man bids farewell to the world as a child does to the day at bedtime.

Afterwards, a drunk stabs the body; but this sinister imbecility of mankind is a detail of no importance.

1860: Chan Santa Cruz
The Ceremonial Center
of the Yucatán Rebels

"My father didn't put me among the rich. He didn't put me with the generals or with those who have money, or with those who claim to have it." The Mother of Crosses, she who sprouted from the mahogany tree beside the spring, had announced this in Yucatán. And when soldiers ax down the mahogany and burn the little cross dressed by the Indians, she has already had daughters. From cross to cross the word has survived: *"My father put me with the poor, because I am poor."*

Around the cross, around the crosses, has grown Chan Santa Cruz, the great sanctuary of Maya rebels in the Yucatán jungle.

The soldiers of Colonel Acereto's expedition go in without resistance. They find no Indians and are left open-mouthed. The Mayas have built an immense church of sturdy walls with a lofty dome, the House of God, the House of the Jaguar God, and in the tower hang the bells taken from Bacalar.

In the sacred city, empty of people, everything is scary. There is little water in the canteens, but Colonel Acereto forbids drinking from the wells. Six years ago other soldiers drank and vomited and died while from the thickets Indians asked them if the water was fresh.

From patience to impatience the soldiers pass the days. Meanwhile, Indians flock from a hundred villages and a thousand corn patches. They bring a rifle or a machete and a little sack of corn flour. They mass in the brush; and when Colonel Acereto decides to withdraw, they mop up his troop in one sweep.

The band, which has been captured intact, will teach music to the children and play polkas in the church, where the cross lives and talks, surrounded by Maya gods. There, in the church, the people celebrate communion with corn tortillas and honey, and once a year elect interpreters for the cross and warrior-chiefs, who wear a gold earring but work in the cornfields like anyone else.

(273 and 274)

1860: Havana

Poet in Crisis

At a cost of thirteen deaths per kilometer, Cuba has constructed the railway that takes sugar from the Güines cane fields to the port of Havana: dead Africans, Irishmen, Canary Islanders and Chinese from Macao, slaves or wretched day laborers brought by traffickers from afar—and the sugar boom demands more and more.

Ten years ago the first shipment of Maya slaves reached Cuba from Yucatán. A hundred and forty Indians, prisoners of war, were sold at twenty-five pesos a head; children, gratis. Later Mexican President Santa Anna granted a monopoly on the traffic to Colonel Manuel María Jiménez and the price rose to a hundred and sixty pesos per man, a hundred and twenty per woman and eighty per child. The Maya war has gone on and on, and with it more and more Cuban loans of money and rifles. The Yucatán government collects a tax on each slave sold, and thus pays with Indians for the war against the Indians.

The Spanish poet José Zorrilla has purchased in the port of Campeche a shipment of Indians to sell in Cuba. He was all set to embark when yellow fever killed his capitalist partner Cipriano de las Cagigas in Havana, and now the author of "Don Juan Tenorio" consoles himself writing verses on a coffee plantation.

(222 and 273)

1861: Havana

Sugar Hands

Soon the city of Havana will be staging its floral games. The intellectuals of the Literary Society propose a great central motif. They want the literary competition to be on the theme of asking Spain for sixty thousand new slaves. The poets will thus support the black importation project, which already enjoys the patronage of the newspaper *Diario de La Marina* and the legal blessing of the attorney general.

Hands are needed for sugar. Blacks smuggled in via the Mariel, Cojímar, and Batabanó beaches are scarce and expensive. Three sugar mill owners have drawn up the project, because *Cuba lies exhausted and desolate*, imploring the Spanish authorities *to hear her cries of*

woe and provide her with blacks, meek and loyal slaves to whom
Cuba owes her economic prosperity. It will be easy, they insist, to
bring them from Africa. *They will run joyfully to the Spanish ships,
when they see them arriving.*

(222 and 240)

Sugar Language

The window grills of Havana homes are adorned with iron spirals and
the columns with plaster curlicues; the doorways with lacy woodwork;
the stained-glass windows with peacock feathers. The talk of doctors
and monks gleams with arabesques. Poets reach for unheard-of rhymes
and prose writers for the most reverberant adjectives. Orators strive
to make their points, their restless and fugitive points; a point peeks
out from behind an adverb or a parenthesis and the orator throws
more and more words at it; the speech stretches out trying to catch
it, but the point keeps fleeing; and the chase continues ad infinitum.

Account books, on the other hand, speak the rough language of
reality. In sugar mills throughout Cuba, they register the birth or
purchase of every black slave as the acquisition of merchandise, calculating depreciation at three percent annually. A man's illness is
equivalent to the faultiness of a valve and the end of a life is like the
loss of a head of cattle: *The killed cattle are bulls. We lost the ceiba
sow. The Negro Domingo Mondongo has died.*

(222)

1861: Bull Run
Grays Against Blues

Near the city of Washington the first battle of the Civil War is fought.
A big audience has turned out, in carriages or on horseback, to see
the show. The blood hardly begins to flow when horses bolt and the
crowd stampedes, howling with panic. Soon the capital's streets are
filled with the mutilated and dying.

Two opposing countries had previously shared the map, the flag,
and the name of the United States. A Southern newspaper reported
the election of Abraham Lincoln in its "News from Abroad" section.
Within months the Southern states formed a separate nation and war
broke out.

Lincoln, the new president, embodies the ideals of the North. He has proclaimed in his campaign that it is impossible to continue half slave and half free, and has promised farms instead of plantations and higher tariffs against the competition of European industry.

North and South: two spaces, two periods. In the North, factories that already produce more than fields; tireless inventors creating the electric telegraph, the sewing machine, and the reaper; new cities sprouting on all sides, a million inhabitants in New York and wharves too small for the ships filled with desperate Europeans seeking a new country. In the South, pride of ancestry and nostalgia, fields of to-bacco, enormous cotton plantations: four million black slaves pro-ducing raw materials for Lancashire textile mills; gentlemen fighting duels over the tainted honor of a sister or the fair name of a family; ladies airing themselves in carriages through the flowering country-side and fainting on the verandahs of their palaces at dusk.

(70)

1862: Fredericksburg
The Pencil of War

His back against a wall, legs crossed on the ground, a young soldier looks without seeing. Several months' growth of beard flattens the open collar of his tunic. A soldier's hand strokes the head of a dog sleeping on his knees.

John Geyser, recruit from Pennsylvania, sketches himself and his comrades while the war kills. His pencil freezes them for an instant on the way to the ditch excavated by cannon fire. Soldiers load rifles, or clean them, or eat the ration of army biscuit and bacon, or stare with sad eyes. Sadly, they look without seeing, or perhaps see beyond what they look at.

(69)

1863: Mexico City
"The American Algeria"

is the new name for Mexico according to the Paris press. The army of Napoleon III attacks and conquers the capital and the chief cities.

In Rome, the pope jumps for joy. The government of Benito Juárez, dislodged by the invaders, was guilty of blasphemy against

God and his properties in Mexico. Juárez had stripped the Church naked, despoiling it of its sacred tithes, of its estates vast as the sky, and of the State's loving protection.

The Conservatives join the new conquistadors. Twenty thousand Mexican soldiers help the thirty thousand from France, who have just finished storming the Crimea, Algeria, and Senegal. Napoleon III takes over Mexico invoking the Latin spirit, Latin culture, and the Latin race, and in passing demands repayment of an immense and phantasmal loan.

Taking charge of the new colony is Maximilian of Austria, one of Europe's many unemployed princes, accompanied by his stunning wife.

(15)

1863: London
Marx

"Napoleon III will break his head on Mexico, if they don't hang him first," announces a wise and penurious prophet, who lives on what he can borrow in London.

While he corrects and polishes the drafts of a work that is going to change the world, Karl Marx does not miss a detail of what is happening in the world. In letters and articles he calls the third Napoleon *an imperial Lazarillo de Tormes** and the invasion of Mexico *an infamous enterprise.* He also denounces England and Spain, who would like to share with France the territory of Mexico as war booty, and all the nation-thieving nations, accustomed to sending thousands and thousands of people to the slaughterhouse so that usurers and traders may extend the scope of their business.

Marx no longer believes that the imperial expansion of the most developed countries is a victory for progress over backwardness. Fifteen years ago, however, he did not disagree when Engels applauded the invasion of Mexico by the United States, believing that this would turn Mexican campesinos into proletarians and bring the bishops and feudal lords down from their pedestal.

(129 and 201)

---

* Anonymous Spanish picaresque novel of the sixteenth century.

1865: La Paz
Belzu

A flood of rebellious Indians has restored Belzu to power. Manuel Isidoro Belzu, "Grandpa Belzu," avenger of the poor, scourge of doctors, returns to La Paz riding a human wave.

When he was in power a few years back, the capital of Bolivia was wherever he happened to be on the haunch of his horse; and the masters of the country, who attempted more than forty military coups, never succeeded in overthrowing him. Foreign merchants hated him, because Belzu barred the door to them and protected the Cochabamba artisans against the invasion of British-made ponchos. The pettifoggers of Chuquisaca, in whose veins run ink or water, were terrified of him. Also conspiring against him were the masters of the mines, who could never dictate a decree to him.

Belzu, lean and handsome, has come back. He enters the palace on horseback, at a gentle pace, as if steering a ship.

(172)

From a Speech by Belzu
to the Bolivian People

The time has come to ask the aristocracy to give back their titles, and private property its privileges . . . Private property is the chief source of most of the offenses and crimes in Bolivia; it is the cause of the continuing struggle between Bolivians; it is the dominant principle of that selfishness eternally condemned by universal morality. No more property, no more proprietors, no more inheritances! Down with aristocrats! Let the lands be for all! Enough of exploitation of man by man!

(213)

1865: La Paz
Melgarejo

Mariano Melgarejo, Belzu's fiercest enemy, is a Hercules who can carry a horse on his shoulder. He was born in Tarata, highland of tall grass, of a father who loved and left. He was born on an Easter Sunday.

"God has chosen me to be born while He was reviving."

Before learning to walk, he knew how to gallop horses whose heads barely peeked out above the verdure; and before the maternal teat, he got to know the chicha that makes you roll or fly, the best chicha in Bolivia, milk of Tarata, corn chewed and expectorated by old women with the most villainous saliva. Before he could even sign his name, he was unstoppable in daredevil battle charges, body to body, his tunic in rags, lifting and splitting people with dagger, spear, or sword.

He has finished off many. Eternal rebel and troublemaker, he has killed in broad daylight and on moonless nights and twice has been condemned to death. Between sprees and free-for-alls, he has known exile and power. The night before last he slept on the throne and last night in mountain furrows. Yesterday he entered this city of La Paz at the head of his army, riding on an enormous cannon, his red poncho flaming like a flag; and today he crosses the plaza somber and alone.

(85)

1865: La Paz

The Shortest Coup d'État in History

It is Belzu's hour. Melgarejo, the vanquished, comes to surrender. Melgarejo crosses the plaza through the shouts.

"Long live Belzu!"

In the huge second-floor chamber, Belzu waits. Melgarejo enters the palace. Without looking up, his black beard flattened against his bull chest, he mounts the stairs. The crowd yells in the plaza.

"Long live Belzu! Grandpa Belzu!"

Melgarejo walks toward Belzu. The president rises, opens his arms.

"I forgive you."

Through the open windows thunder the voices.

"Grandpa Belzu!"

Melgarejo lets himself be embraced, and shoots. The shot rings out, and the body crashes to the floor.

The victor goes out on the balcony. He shows the body, offers it.

"Belzu is dead! Who's next?"

(85)

1865: Appomattox

General Lee Surrenders His Ruby Sword

The Northern soldiers, in the middle of a crushing advance, await the order for the final assault. At that moment, a cloud of dust rises from the enemy lines. It grows and grows. From the hungry, shattered army of the grays, a horseman breaks away. He carries a white rag tied to a stick.

In the final battles, the Southern soldiers had their names inscribed on their backs, so that they would be recognized among the dead. The South, devastated, has lost the war long ago, and continues only out of a stubborn sense of honor.

Now the beaten general, Robert E. Lee, proffers with gloved hand his sword embellished with rubies. The victorious general, Ulysses Grant, without sword or insignias, his tunic unbuttoned, smokes, or at least chews, a cigar.

The war has ended, slavery has ended. With slavery have fallen the walls that prevented the full development of United States industry and the expansion of its national market. Six hundred thousand young men have died in battle; among them, half of all the blacks who wore the blue of the Northern battalions.

(70)

1865: Washington

Lincoln

Abe comes from Kentucky. There, his father wielded the ax and pounded the hammer, and the cabin had walls and a roof and beds of dry leaves. Every day his ax cut wood for the fire, and one day it wrested from the forest the wood needed to bury Abe's mother under the snow. Abe was a small boy when that hammer knocked in those wooden nails for the mother who would never again make white bread on Saturdays, or flutter those ever-perplexed eyes; and the ax brought in wood to make a raft so that the father could take his children down river to Indiana.

He comes from Indiana. There Abe draws his first letters with a charcoal, and becomes the best railsplitter in the district.

He comes from Illinois. In Illinois, he loves a woman named Ann and marries another named Mary, who speaks French and has started the crinoline fashion in the city of Springfield. Mary decides that Abe will be president of the United States. While she is bearing boy children, he writes speeches and a few poems in the sad island of his mind, that magic island bathed in liquid light.

He comes from the Capitol in Washington. Leaning from the window, he sees the slave market, a kind of stable where blacks are penned up like horses.

He comes from the White House. He came to it promising agrarian reform and protection for industry, and proclaiming that anyone depriving another of his freedom is not worthy of enjoying it himself. He entered the White House swearing he would govern in such a way as still to have a friend inside himself when he no longer had friends. He governs in wartime and in wartime fulfills all his promises. At dawn, he can be seen in slippers, standing at the White House door, waiting for the newspaper.

He comes unhurriedly. Abraham Lincoln is never in a hurry. He walks like a duck, setting his enormous feet down flat, and juts out like a tower from the multitude that acclaim him. He enters the theater and slowly mounts the stairs into the presidential box. In the box, over flowers and flags, his bony, long-necked head cuts a profile in the shadows, and in the shadows shine the sweetest eyes and most melancholy smile in America.

He comes from victory and from dream. Today is Good Friday and five days ago General Lee surrendered. Last night, Lincoln dreamed of a sea of mystery and a strange ship that sailed toward misty shores.

Lincoln comes from his whole life, walking unhurriedly toward this appointment in the box of the comedy theater in the city of Washington.

Now comes toward him the bullet that splits open his head.

(81 and 188)

1865: *Washington*

Homage

How many blacks have been hanged for stealing a pair of pants or looking into the eyes of a white woman? What were the names of the slaves who set fire to New York over a century ago? How many whites have followed in the footsteps of Elijah Lovejoy, whose printing press was twice thrown in the river and who was assassinated in Illinois, without anyone being sought or punished for it? The history of the abolition of slavery in the United States has had infinite protagonists, black and white. Such as:

- John Russwurm and Samuel Cornish, who made the first newspaper for blacks; and Theodore Weld, who founded the first higher education center that admitted women and blacks.
- Daniel Payne, who managed to keep open for six years his school for blacks in Charleston; and Prudence Crandall, Quaker teacher in Connecticut, who for taking a black girl into her school lost her white students and was insulted, stoned, and jailed; and where her school had stood only cinders remained.
- Gabriel Prosser, who sought freedom for his brothers in Virginia and found a gallows for himself; and David Walker, for whose head the Georgia authorities paid ten thousand dollars, and who went about announcing that killing a man who is tearing out your life is like drinking water when you are thirsty, and kept on saying it until he disappeared or was disappeared.
- Nat Turner, who during a solar eclipse saw written in the sky the sign that the last should be first and went mad with murderous fury; and John Brown, hunter's beard, eyes aflame, who attacked a Virginia armory and from a railway roundhouse launched a battle against the marines and then refused to let his lawyer plead insanity and walked with dignity to the scaffold.
- William Lloyd Garrison, fanatical enemy of the robbers of men, who was paraded through the streets of Boston with a rope around his neck; and Henry Garnet, who preached in church that the resigned slave sins against God; and Henry Ward Beecher, the Brooklyn minister who said that in certain cases a rifle can be more useful than the Bible, so that arms sent to the slaves of the South came to be called "Beecher's Bibles."
- Harriet Beecher Stowe, whose *Uncle Tom's Cabin* won many whites to the cause; and Frances Harper, the poet who found the right words to curse power and money; and Solomon Northrup, Louisiana slave who could bear witness to cotton plantation life—from the sound of the horn before sunrise to the dead of night.
- Frederick Douglass, fugitive slave from Maryland, who in New York turned the Independence Day proclamation into an indictment and declared that freedom and equality sounded like a hollow parody.

- Harriet Tubman, illiterate peasant who organized the escape of more than three hundred slaves by the Pole Star Road to Canada.

(12 and 210)

1865: Buenos Aires
Triple Infamy

While in North America history wins a war, in South America a war begins which history will lose. Buenos Aires, Rio de Janeiro, and Montevideo, the three ports that wiped out José Artigas half a century ago, get set to devastate Paraguay.

Under the successive dictatorships of Gaspar Rodríguez de Francia, Carlos Antonio López and his son Francisco Solano, wielders of very absolute power, Paraguay has become a dangerous example, offering grave risk of contagion to its neighbors. In Paraguay landlords do not govern, nor do merchants speculate, nor do usurers asphyxiate. Blockaded from outside, the country has grown inward, and continues growing, without obeying the world market or foreign capital. While the others dangle from the noose of their debts, Paraguay owes no one a centavo and walks on its own legs.

The British ambassador in Buenos Aires, Edward Thornton, is high priest of this ferocious ceremony of exorcism. Argentina, Brazil, and Uruguay will exorcise the devil by sticking bayonets in these arrogant bellies.

(47, 60, and 83)

1865: Buenos Aires
The Alliance Woven of Spider-Spittle

Like a grotesque crown on a little tree, Chacho Peñaloza's head, stuck on the pike—a mane of hair held by a headband—adorns the center of a plaza. Chacho and his horse had been one single muscle. They caught him without his horse and treacherously beheaded him. *To keep the rabble quiet* they exhibited the head of the gaucho warrior of the Rioja prairie. Domingo Faustino Sarmiento congratulated the executioners.

The war against Paraguay prolongs another war which has continued for half a century: the war of Buenos Aires, the vampire port, against the provinces. The Uruguayan Venancio Flores has collaborated with Mitre and Sarmiento in exterminating rebel gauchos. As reward he gets the presidency of Uruguay. Brazilian ships and Argentine arms impose Flores on the government. The invasion of Uruguay opens up with a bombardment of the unprotected city of Paysandú. Paysandú resists for a month, until the chief of the defense, Leandro Gómez, is executed amid the flaming ruins.

Thus the double alliance has become triple. With English blessings and English credits the governments of Argentina, Brazil, and Uruguay undertake the redemption of Paraguay. They sign a treaty. They are making war, says the treaty, in the name of peace. Paraguay will have to pay the expenses of its own extermination and the victors will provide an appropriate government. In the name of respect for Paraguay's territorial integrity, the treaty guarantees Brazil one-third of its land area and assigns to Argentina all of Misiones and the vast Chaco. The war is also waged in the name of freedom. Brazil, which has two million slaves, promises freedom to Paraguay, which has none.

(47, 244, and 291)

1865: San José
Urquiza

He kisses a woman's hand, they say, and leaves her pregnant. He collects children and acreage. Of children, he has a hundred and fifty, without counting the doubtfuls, and of lands, who knows? He adores mirrors, Brazilian medals, French porcelain, and the clink of silver coins.

Justo José de Urquiza, venerable boss of the Argentine coast, the man who years ago defeated Juan Manuel de Rosas, has his doubts about the Paraguay war. He resolves them by selling thirty thousand horses from his estancias to the Brazilian army, at an excellent price, and contracting to supply bully beef to the allied armies. Freed of his doubts, he orders the death of anyone who refuses to kill Paraguayans.

(271 and 291)

1866: *Curupaytí*

Mitre

Splinters that once were ships drift in the waters. The Paraguayan navy is dead, but the allied fleet cannot press the invasion upriver. The guns of Curupaytí and Humaitá stop it, and between the two forts floats a line of demijohns, perhaps mines, stretched from shore to shore.

Under the command of Bartolomé Mitre, Argentine president and generalissimo of the Triple Alliance, soldiers storm the ramparts of Curupaytí with naked bayonets. The bugle looses successive waves of soldiers to the assault. Few reach the moat and none the palisade. The Paraguayans take target practice against an enemy who persists in showing himself in open country, in broad daylight. The roar of cannons, rumble of drums, is followed by the rattle of rifle fire. The Paraguayan fort spits tongues of fire; and when the smoke clears, slow-drifting mist, thousands of dead, shot down like rabbits, wallow in the swamps. At a prudent distance, telescope in hand, in black frock coat and chambergo hat, Bartolomé Mitre contemplates the results of his military genius.

Lying with admirable sincerity, he had promised the invading troops that in three months they would reach Asunción.

(61 and 272)

1866: *Curupaytí*

The Paintbrush of War

Cándido López, one Mitre's soldiers, will paint this disaster of Curupaytí and the earlier battles he has fought in, and also daily life in the camps. He will paint with the left hand, because at Curupaytí a grenade blew off his right one.

He will paint without imitating anyone and no one will imitate him. During the week, he will sell shoes in a Buenos Aires shop and on Sundays will make pictures that say: *"The war was like this."* The stupid left hand will become wise, by love of memory, but no artist will pay him the slightest attention, nor will any critic take him seriously, nor will anyone be interested in buying his remembrances of a rank-and-file soldier.

"I am a paintbrush chronicler."

The solitary Cándido López will paint multitudes. In his works, there will be no foregrounds of flashing swords and dashing steeds, nor dying heroes pronouncing last words with hands on bleeding breasts, nor allegories of Glory with bared breats. Through his child-like eyes will march innumerable tin soldiers and merry-go-round horses playing in ordered formation the horrendous game of war.

(100)

1867: Catamarca Plains
Felipe Varela

The mounted hillsmen of five Argentine provinces rise in rebellion. The shearing knife tied to a spear challenges the cannon of the line regiments, seeking a hand-to-hand fight; and out of the dust storm of these encounters the cry goes up: *Long live Paraguay!*

Down from the Andes comes Felipe Varela, arousing the peas-antry of the Catamarca plains against Buenos Aires, the port that usurps Argentina and negates America. He denounces the bankruptcy of the nation, embroiled in enormous loans for the purpose of anni-hilating a sister nation. In their heads, his mountaineers carry into battle the watchword *American Union*, and in their hearts an old rage: *A provincial is a beggar without a country*.

A lanky gaucho, nothing but cheekbone and chin, born and raised on horseback, Varela is the harsh voice of the poor at the end of their tether. Provincial "volunteers" are being taken in shackles to the marshes of Paraguay, shut up in corrals, and shot when they rebel or desert.

(239)

1867: Plains of La Rioja
Torture

Colonel Pablo Irrazábal takes testimony from the rebel plainsmen of La Rioja. He takes testimony, that is, he puts them in the pillory, or makes them walk with flayed feet, or slits their throats little by little with a blunt knife.

The port of Buenos Aires uses various instruments of persuasion against the rebellious provinces. One of the most effective is called the "Colombian pillory." The prisoner is doubled up in the pillory and tied with moist leather strips between two rifles so that, when the strips dry out, the spine cracks and breaks in pieces.

(214)

1867: La Paz
On Diplomacy, the Science of International Relations

Mounted on Holofernes, his horse in war and fiesta, President Melgarejo arrives at the cathedral of La Paz. Seated under a canopy on a velvet chair, he hears the solemn Mass. He wears the uniform of a Chilean army general and on his breast gleams the grand ribbon of the Imperial Order of Brazil.

After so many comings and goings and killings, Melgarejo has learned not to trust even his own shirt. They say that sometimes he tears it off and riddles it with bullets.

"The commander commands, with his finger on the trigger."

There are two beings in the world, just two, at whom the iron general does not look askance: the horse Holofernes and the lovely Juana Sánchez. The Chilean ambassador raises his glass and joins Holofernes in a toast, when the black horse appears at the presidential table to drink beer among the ministers, bishops, and generals. The Brazilian ambassador covers the body of Juana Sánchez with such necklaces, diadems, and bracelets as Melgarejo's woman has not seen in her wildest dreams.

His breast covered with Brazilian decorations, Melgarejo cedes to Brazil sixty-five thousand square kilometers of Bolivian forest in Amazonia. Transformed into a general of the Chilean army, Melgarejo presents to Chile half of the Atacama coastal desert, very rich in nitrates. There, Chilean and British capitalists are exploiting the fertilizer most coveted by Europe's exhausted lands. With the amputation of the Atacama desert, Bolivia begins to lose its outlet to the sea.

(85, 107, and 172)

Inscriptions on a Rock in the Atacama Desert

Antonia, for you I die.
> *You know who.*

THE CHAÑARCILLO JUDGE IS STEALING.
Pay me my three ounces, Ramón.
The Administrator is a lout.
Don T.P. says he isn't a mulatto.

(256)

1867: Bogotá
A Novel Called *María*

Ladies sway in their hammocks, ringlets fluttering behind their ivory necks, rocked by gentlemen dressed like the dead with faces like boiled chickens. A caravan of blacks, baskets on heads, passes silently in the distance, as if begging pardon for existing and being a nuisance. In the plantation garden, aroma of coffee, fragrance of gardenias, Jorge Isaacs moistens his pen with tears.

All Colombia sobs. Efraín didn't arrive in time. While he plowed the seas, his cousin María, victim of a hereditary and incurable disease, drew her last breath and went to Heaven a virgin. At the grave, Efraín presses to his breast the inheritance of his love. María has left him a kerchief (embroidered by herself and wetted by herself), some white lily petals, so like herself and as withered as herself, a ring slipped from the rigid hand which had been an elegant rose of Castile, and a lock of her long hair in the locket that her lily lips managed to kiss while death was freezing them.

(167 and 208)

1867: Querétaro
Maximilian

The army of Juárez and the thousand guerrilla bands of the Mexican people run the Frenchmen out. Maximilian, the emperor, topples into the mud crying *Long live Mexico*.

At the end, Napoleon III pulls out his army, the pope hates Maximilian, and the conservatives call him *Empoorer*. Napoleon had ordered him to administer the new French colony, but Maximilian did not obey. The pope expected to get his earthly properties back, and the conservatives thought he would exorcise Mexico of the liberal demon; but Maximilian, while making war on Juárez, issued laws quite like those of Juárez.

A black carriage arrives in Querétaro in the rain. President Juárez, conqueror of the intruders, goes up to the open and flowerless coffin, where lies the prince with the languid blue eyes, who liked to stroll down the Alameda dressed as a Mexican cowboy with broad-brimmed sombrero and sequins.

(94 and 143)

1867: Paris

To Be or to Copy, That Is the Question

To Paris's Universal Exhibition come oil-on-cloth paintings sent from Ecuador. All the paintings are exact copies of the most famous works of European artists. The catalog praises the Ecuadoran artists *who, if they have no great originality, at least have the merit of reproducing, with noteworthy faithfulness, masterworks of the Italian, Spanish, French, and Flemish schools*.

Meanwhile another art flourishes in the Indian markets and poor outskirts of Ecuador. It is the despised work of hands able to create beauty out of clay and wood and straw, bird-feathers, sea shells, bread crumbs. This art, as if begging pardon, is called artisanship. Academicians don't do it, only poor folk who eat flea hearts or mosquito tripe.

(37)

Song of the Poor in Ecuador

"Hungry, ducks?"
"Yes."
"Eat the pain in your guts.
Stab a mosquito,
suck blood from the cuts,
keep the tripe for a treat or
tomorrow's cold cuts."

(65)

1869: Mexico City

Juárez

The face of this Mexican Indian, who defeated the pope of Rome and the third Napoleon, has been carved out of Oaxaca stone. Without smile or speech, always in frock coat and high collar, always in black, Benito Juárez is a rock surrounded by a chorus of doctors who whirl around him discoursing and declaiming and reciting, learned pedants blessed with golden beaks and gilded plumes.

Mexico has more priests than teachers, and the Church owns half of everything, when Juárez comes to power and the liberals prescribe their civilizing potion for a country sick from ignorance and backwardness. The therapy of modernization calls for peace and order. It is necessary to do away with wars that kill more people than malaria or tuberculosis, but the plague of war harasses Juárez without mercy. First, the war against the French invaders; and since then, the war against the military hero-bosses who decline to retire, and against Indians who decline to lose their community lands.

Mexican liberals profess blind faith in universal suffrage and freedom of expression, although the vote is the privilege of few and few express themselves. They believe in salvation by education, although the few schools are all in the cities, because liberals, after all, get along better with muses than with Indians. As big estates get bigger, they dream about pioneer farmers fertilizing uncultivated lands, and they dream about magical rails, smoke of locomotives, smoking chimneys, ideas and people and capital that will bring progress from Europe.

Juárez himself, son of Zapotec Indians, is convinced that if Mexico copies North American laws, it will grow like the United States, and if it consumes English products it will become as industrious a nation as England. By importing French ideas, thinks the defeater of France, Mexico will become an erudite nation.

(142, 143, and 316)

1869: San Cristóbal de Las Casas

Neither Earth nor Time Is Dumb

The earth vibrates from all the talk among the dead below. The graveyard hums like a plaza on market day. The Mayas who fell in the old Chiapas rebellions are celebrating the latest news. Here they have fought with spear and ax since the remote day when the first usurper, son of woman and dog, swooped down upon the community lands. The dead chat happily among themselves, and through dreams congratulate the living and tell them truths that the ear does not know.

Again the Indians hereabouts have risen in rebellion. The Indians, debt-slaves, destroy haciendas and burn prisons and defend the last of their communal lands, which they work as a community despite the Juárez government.

The gods of the mountain also celebrate. They are the ones who deflect the gale when it carries disease or greed.

(155 and 274)

1869: Mexico City
Juárez and the Indians

For being a rebel, a bandit, a rabid socialist, Julio López was shot a year ago. At the head of Indians of the Chalco region, Julio López had vowed *war on the rich* and had rebelled to reclaim the stolen lands.

They have put soldiers' uniforms on Indian prisoners in Chalco and forced them to fight against the rebel Indians of Yucatán. Those "pacified" in each war become "pacifiers" in the next, rebels defeated and made to kill rebels; and thus the government of President Juárez keeps sending troops against the Mayas of Yucatán and the Mayas of Chiapas, the Coras of Nayarit and the Tarascans of Michoacán, the Yaquis of Sonora and the Apaches of the north.

To recover the lands of their communities, the Indians turn around hacienda signposts: the first dead fall and the air becomes nothing but gunsmoke. Juárez's Constitution seeks to turn the Indians into small proprietors and free workers. Juárez's laws ban the pillory and shackles, enslavement for debt and hunger wages. Reality, meanwhile, seizes lands the Indians still possess in common and makes them slaves of big estates or beggars in the cities.

Benito Juárez was born in the mountains, amid the rocks that resemble him, on the shores of Lake Guelatao. He learned to name the world in one of the hundred Indian languages of Mexico. Later, under the patronage of a pious man, he became a man of letters.

(142 and 274)

1869: London
Lafargue

When Paul Lafargue began laying siege to Laura Marx, the founder
of scientific socialism was finishing the correction of the first volume
of *Capital*. Karl Marx took a dim view of the Cuban's ardent assaults,
and told him to court his green-eyed daughter with *quieter English
manners*. He also asked him for economic guarantees. Ousted from
Germany, France, and Belgium, Marx has gone through hard times
in London, devoured by debt, sometimes without a penny to buy a
newspaper. The miseries of exile have killed three of his children.

But he cannot scare off Lafargue. He always knew he couldn't.
Lafargue was very young when he and Marx began to fight and to
love each other. And now Marx's first grandson is born of the Cuban
mestizo, great-grandson of a Haitian mulatta and an Indian from
Jamaica.

(177 and 279)

1869: Acosta Ñú
Paraguay Falls, Trampled
Under Horses' Hooves

and, fallen, fights on. The last cannons are made of church bells and
fire stones and sand, while the Triple Alliance armies press on to the
north. The wounded tear off their bandages, because it is better to
bleed to death than serve in the enemy army or march off to Brazilian
coffee plantations with the brand of slavery.

Not even graves are spared in the sacking of Asunción. In Piri-
bebuy, the invaders overrun trenches defended by women, the mutilated, and old people, and set fire to the hospital filled with wounded.
In Acosta Ñú, the offensive is resisted by battalions of children disguised with beards of wool or grass.

And the butchery goes on. Those not killed by bullets are killed
by plague. And every death hurts. Every death seems like the last,
but is the first.

(61 and 254)

1870: Mount Corá

Solano López

This is a caravan of dead people who breathe. Paraguay's last soldiers tramp behind Marshal Francisco Solano López. No boots or harnesses are to be seen, because they have been eaten, but no sores or rags either: of mud and bone are these soldiers, wandering through the woods, masks of mud, carapaces of mud, pottery flesh that the sun has cooked with the mud of the swamps and the red dust of the deserts.

Marshal López does not surrender. Hallucinating, sword borne high, he heads this last march to nowhere. He discovers plots, or imagines them, and for the crime of treason or weakness has his brother and all his in-laws executed, and also the bishop and a minister and a general . . . For lack of powder, the executions are performed with a spear. Many die by López's order, many more from exhaustion, and they are left behind on the road. The earth recovers its own and bones mark the trail for the pursuer.

Enormous enemy hosts close the circle at Mount Corá. They bring López down on the banks of the River Aquidabán, wound him with a spear, kill him with a sword, and with one shot finish him off, because he still howls.

(291)

1870: Mount Corá

Elisa Lynch

Surrounded by the conquerors, Elisa digs with her nails a grave for Solano López.

Bugles no longer sound, nor do bullets whistle, nor grenades explode. Flies cover the marshal's face and attack his gashed body, but Elisa sees only a red mist. As her hands tear the ground open, she insults this accursed day; and the sun hesitates on the horizon because the day dares not withdraw before she finished cursing it.

This Irishwoman with golden hair, who has fought at the head of columns of women armed with hoes and sticks, has been López's most implacable adviser. Last night, after sixteen years and four children, he told her for the first time that he loved her.

(25)

Guaraní

Of annihilated Paraguay, the language survives.

Mysterious powers has Guaraní, language of Indians, language of the conquered which the conquerors made their own. In spite of bans and slights, Guaraní is still the national language of this land in ruins, and will be so although the law wills otherwise. Here the mosquito will continue to be called "Devil's fingernail" and the dragonfly, "Devil's little horse"; the stars, "fires of the moon," and dusk, "the mouth of night."

Paraguayan soldiers gave passwords and pep talks in Guaraní, while the war lasted, and in Guaraní they sang. Now the dead fall silent, in Guaraní.

(152)

1870: Buenos Aires

Sarmiento

Argentina's president, Domingo Faustino Sarmiento, receives the military communiqué of the victory in Paraguay. He orders the band to play serenades, and writes: *Providence decreed that a tyrant should cause the death of that Guaraní people. It was necessary to purge the earth of all that human excrescence.*

Sarmiento, founder of the Animal Protection Society, preaches pure unabashed racism and practices it with untrembling hand. He admires the North Americans, *free from any mixture of inferior races*, but from Mexico southward he sees only barbarism, dirt, superstitions, chaos, and madness. Those dark shadows terrify and fascinate him. He goes for them with sword in one hand and lamp in the other. As governor and president, he multiplies cemeteries and schools, and fosters the noble virtues of throat-cutting, saving, and reading. As a writer, he publishes prose works of great talent in favor of the extermination of gauchos, Indians, and blacks and their replacement by white laborers from northern Europe, and in defense of the frock coat and the English-style haircut.

(310 and 311)

1870: Rio de Janeiro

A Thousand Candelabra Proliferate in the Mirrors

and silken shoes draw waltz circles on the lustrous floor of Baron de Itamaraty's palace. Through clouds of guests pass the imperial couple, from salon to salon, endless hand-kissing and tinkling of glass, and as they go, martial trumpetings and thunderous cheers interrupt the ball. The gentlemen look like penguins and the ladies like butterflies, tightly enclosed in their crinolines, unfurling laces; and more than one wear European breasts, imported by Mademoiselle Arthémise, which ripple in perfect accompaniment to their breathing. With champagne and music in the French fashion, Brazil celebrates the devastation of Paraguay.

Carriages rolling up to the fiesta cross paths with caravans of blacks toting fetid pots and barrels. Clouds of flies pursue the procession to the beaches of Rio de Janeiro. Every evening, slaves throw the masters' shit into the waters of the lovely bay.

(204)

1870: Rio de Janeiro

Mauá

While they celebrate the annihilation of Paraguay, the conquering countries fight over who will get the biggest bite of the conquered.

In Rio de Janeiro, someone observes the effervescent celebrations with furrowed brow and shrugs his shoulders at talk of new frontiers. Irineo Evangelista de Souza, baron of Mauá by grace of Emperor Pedro II, never wanted this war. From the start he had presentiments that it would be long and bloody, and also that whoever won it would lose it. Laurels for the empire of Brazil? Peace illuminated by glory? The empire prospering as if the war had never been? Baron de Mauá, Brazilian partner of the Rothschilds of London, knows that the exterminators now owe British banks twice as much as they did before. Mauá, owner of great plantations, knows that the coffee estates have lost many thousands of black slaves on the battlefields. Accustomed to financing the victorious countries' budgets and issuing their banknotes, Mauá also knows that they have papered themselves with valueless vouchers. And perhaps he knows—who knows?—that this just-ended war is the beginning of his personal ruin, that creditors will end up seizing even his gold eyeglasses and that, in his last years, he will again be that lonesome child some sailor had abandoned on the docks of Rio.

(109)

1870: Vassouras

The Coffee Barons

The southern Paraíba River valley produces most of the coffee the world consumes, and also produces the largest number of viscounts, barons, and marquises per square foot.

From the throne of Brazil, Emperor Pedro II now rewards with new titles of nobility the coffee slavers who have contributed so much money to the war against Paraguay.

No plantation has fewer than a hundred slaves. When it is still night, at the toll of the iron bell the slaves wash in the tank, offer loud thanks to Our Lord Jesus Christ, and march to work up the mountain, inspired by the cat-o'-nine-tails.

The masters' sons are brought into the world by black midwives, and black wet nurses suckle them. Black nurses teach them songs, legends, and tastes in food. With black children they learn to play and with black girls they discover love. But from early on they know who is proprietor and who is property. Marriage to a cousin or niece will fortify family unity and perpetuate the nobility of the lineage.

(327)

1870: São Paulo

Nabuco

Everyone eats off the black slave. Not only the coffee barons and the sugar lords, but every free Brazilian, no matter how poor, has at least one slave working for him.

Joaquim Nabuco denounces this deep infection in fiery speeches. Born of landowners and professional politicians, Nabuco proclaims that Brazil will not enter the modern world as long as land and politics belong to a handful of families, and as long as the whole country rests on the backs of slaves.

The poet José Bonifácio heads up a group of abolitionists from

São Paulo University. Working with him in addition to Nabuco are other brilliant orators such as Castro Alves, Rui Barbosa, and Luis Gama, who was sold by his own father in Bahia and managed to escape slavery to denounce it.

(74)

1870: Buenos Aires
The North Barrio

A blue-bloused horseman blows the bugle that warns of danger. Clatter of hooves, hubbub of bells, stampede of pedestrians: the new streetcar comes dashing on rails at the mad speed of six miles per hour. A Buenos Aires newspaper promises to reserve a column every day for the victims.

The streetcar manages a death or two to avoid disappointment, but in a short while no one talks of its homicidal furies. Yellow fever has invaded Buenos Aires and is killing off three hundred a day.

Because there is no place to bury so many paupers, the Chacarita cemetery is born of this plague, as is the North Barrio, because the rich flee from their traditional bastion. The ten blocks south of the Plaza de Mayo have always decided the fate of all Argentina, and have always prospered at its expense. There, until now, have lived the gentlemen who make politics and business in the Cafe de Paris and the ladies who shop at the London Store. Now they are chased out by the yellow fever, which feeds cruelly on the low district surrounded by garbage dumps and swamps, cradle of mosquitos, broth of plagues; and the mansions emptied by the exodus become tenements. Where one family lived before, two hundred will crowd in as best they can.

This city scattered over river banks has grown prodigiously. A couple of centuries ago, Buenos Aires was a sad, lost village. Today a hundred and eighty thousand people live here, half of them foreigners: masons, washerwomen, shoemakers, day laborers, cooks, night watchmen, carpenters, and other newcomers whom the trade winds have blown in from the Mediterranean.

(312)

1870: Paris
Lautréamont at Twenty-Four

He had speech impediments and got tired from nothing at all. He spent nights at the piano, spinning chords and words, and at dawn his eyes were pitifully feverish.

Isidoro Ducasse, the imaginary Count of Lautréamont, has died. The child born and raised in the Montevideo war, that child who asked questions of the river-sea, has died in a hotel in Paris. His publisher dared not send his "Cantos" to the bookshops.

Lautréamont had written hymns to the louse and to the pederast. He had sung to the red light of the brothels and to the insects that prefer blood to wine. He had scolded the drunken god who created us, and proclaimed it better to be born from the womb of a female shark. He had flung himself into the abyss, human scrapmeat capable of beauty and madness, and on his way down had discovered ferocious images and astounding words. Every page he wrote screams when you tear it.

(181)

1871: Lima
Juana Sánchez

Melgarejo the destroyer has fallen. Stoned by the Indians, he has fled from Bolivia, and suffers out his exile in a hovel in the Lima slums. All the power he has left is in his blood-red poncho. The Indians killed his horse Holofernes and cut off its ears.

He spends his nights howling before the home of the Sánchez family. Melgarejo's sad, booming voice sets Lima atremble. Juana doesn't open the door.

Juana was eighteen when she arrived at the palace. Melgarejo shut himself in with her for three days and three nights. His guards heard screams, blows, snorts, groans, never a word. On the fourth day Melgarejo emerged.

"I love her as much as my army!"

The banquet table was turned into an altar. In the center, surrounded by candles, reigned a nude Juana. Ministers, bishops, and generals paid homage to her beauty, falling to their knees when Melgarejo raised a glass of flaming cognac and sang verses of devotion.

She, an erect marble statue, with no more clothes than her hair, looked down and away.

And she said nothing. Juana said nothing. When Melgarejo went on a military campaign, he left her shut up in a La Paz convent. He returned to the palace with her in his arms and she said nothing, a virgin woman every night, every night born for him. Juana said nothing when Melgarejo seized the Indians' communal lands and gave her eighty properties and an entire province for her family.

Now, too, Juana says nothing. With the door of her mansion in Lima stoutly barricaded, she does not show herself or answer the desperate roarings of Melgarejo. She does not even say to him, *"You never had me. I wasn't there."*

Melgarejo weeps and bellows, his fists thundering on the door. In this shadow, shouting the name of this woman, he dies of two bullets.

(85)

1873: Camp Tempú

The Mambises

The blacks, lustrous from torches and other lights, undulate and spin and jump and talk to the gods howling with pain and pleasure. For the *New York Herald* correspondent this commotion is as incomprehensible as the seasons, which in Cuba come all at once within an endless summer. The journalist blinks hard when he discovers that the same tree has at the same time one branch bursting in full verdure and another yellowing in its death throes.

This is the land of the Mambí, in the forest of eastern Cuba. Mambí meant "bandit" or "rebel" back there in the Congo, but on this island Mambí is the slave who fights to become a person again.

Before joining the patriot army, the Mambises had been fugitive slaves in the mountains. The *Herald* correspondent calculates that in five years the colonial war has taken eighty thousand Spanish lives. Many soldiers have been felled by disease or bullet; and many more by Mambí machete. The war has turned sugar mills into fortresses armed against attacks by blacks from the outside and escapes by blacks inside.

In this camp of ragged, almost naked Mambises, everything is shared. The journalist drinks water with molasses for lack of coffee, and after a few days swears eternal hatred for sweet potatoes and hutia—a small animal that provides food for anyone who can catch it in the crannies of a tree or rock. This war could last forever, writes the journalist. Here, lianas give water when there is no nearby river, and the trees provide fruit, hammocks, sandals, and good shade for those who need to sit down and swap jokes and stories while their wounds heal.

(237)

1875: Mexico City
Martí

Recently his pointed mustache got a blunting in Havana when he started two short-lived newspapers, *The Lame Devil* and *Free Fatherland*; and for wanting independence for Cuba, a Spanish colony, he was sentenced to prison and forced labor. Earlier, when he was still a very young child, he had wanted to translate Shakespeare, and had set fire to words, and sworn vengeance before a black slave hanging from the gallows. He had guessed, in his earliest verses, that he would die in and for Cuba.

From prison they sent him into exile. The marks of the shackles have not disappeared from his ankles. No more patriotic Cuban than this son of a Spanish colonial sergeant; none more childlike than this inquisitive exile, so astonished and indignant at the world.

José Martí is twenty-two when he attends in Mexico his first joint demonstration of students and workers. The hat makers have gone on strike. They have the solidarity of the Fraternal and Constancy Society of Hairdressers, the Fraternal Society of Bookbinders, the typographers, the tailors, and the intellectuals, "workers of the Idea." At the same time, the first university strike erupts, against the expulsion of three medical students.

Martí organizes benefit recitals for the hat makers, and in his articles describes students marching with workers through the streets of Mexico City, arm-in-arm, all in their Sunday best. *These enthusiastic young people*, he observes, *are right. But even if they were wrong, we would love them.*

(129, 200, and 354)

1875: Fort Sill

The Last Buffalos of the South

The southern plains were carpeted with buffalos, which multiplied like the tall grasses, when the white man arrived from Kansas. Now the wind smells of decay. Skinned buffalos lie on the prairie. Millions of skins have gone to eastern Europe. The extermination of the buffalo not only brings in money, but, as General Sheridan explains, *it is the only way to bring lasting peace and allow civilization to advance.*

The Kiowa and Comanche Indians now find no buffalos within the Fort Sill reservation. In vain they invoke good hunting with dances to the sun god. On their federal government rations, pitiful rations, they cannot survive.

The Indians escape to far-off Palo Duro canyon, the last place with buffalos in the southern plains. There, they find food and all the rest: they use the skins for shelter, blankets, and clothing; the horns and bones for spoons, knives, and arrowheads; the nerves and tendons for ropes and nets, the bladders for water pitchers.

Soon the soldiers arrive, amid clouds of dust and gunpowder. They burn huts and provisions, kill a thousand horses and herd the Indians back into their enclosure.

A few Kiowas manage to escape. They wander the prairie until hunger defeats them. They surrender at Fort Sill. There the soldiers put them in a corral and every day throw them bits of raw meat.

(51 and 229)

Into the Beyond

The buffalos of the last southern herd hold a meeting. The discussion does not last long. Everything has been said and night continues. The buffalos know they are no longer able to protect the Indians.

When dawn rises from the river, a Kiowa woman sees the last herd passing through the mist. The leader walks with slow tread, followed by the females, the calves, and the few surviving males. Reaching the foot of Mount Scott, they pause, motionless, with their heads down. Then the mountain opens its mouth and the buffalos enter. There, inside, the world is green and fresh.

The buffalos have passed. The mountain closes.

(198)

1876: Little Big Horn
Sitting Bull

When he speaks, no word tires or falls.

No more lies, he says. Eight years ago, the United States government guaranteed to the Sioux, by solemn treaty, that they would forever be owners of the Black Hills, the center of their world, the place where warriors talk with the gods. Two years ago, gold was discovered in these lands. Last year, the government ordered the Sioux to leave the hunting grounds where miners were seeking gold in rocks and streams.

I have said enough. No more lies. Sitting Bull, chief of chiefs, has assembled thousands of warriors of the plains, Sioux, Cheyennes, Arapahos. He has danced for three days and three nights. He has fixed his eyes on the sun. He knows.

He wakes before dawn. He wets his bare feet in the dew and receives the heartbeat of the earth.

At dawn he raises his eyes beyond the hills. There comes General Custer. There comes the Seventh Cavalry.

(51 and 206)

1876: Little Big Horn
Black Elk

At the age of nine he heard the voices. He knew that all of us who have legs, wings, or roots are children of the same father sun and of the same mother earth, whose breasts we suck. The voices told him that he would make flowers bloom on the sacred cane, the tree of life planted in the center of the land of the Sioux, and that mounted on a storm cloud he would kill drought. They also announced wars and sufferings.

At ten, he met a white man for the first time. He thought the fellow must be ill.

At thirteen, Black Elk is bathing in Little Big Horn River when shouts warn him that soldiers are coming. He climbs a hill and from there sees an immense dust cloud full of hooves and yells, and from the cloud many horses stampeding with empty saddles.

(51 and 230)

1876: *Little Big Horn*

Custer

Black Kettle, the Cheyenne chief, had warned him of it when they smoked the peace pipe together. Custer would die if he betrayed his promises, and no Indian would dirty his hands scalping him. Afterwards Custer burned down that camp and Chief Black Kettle was riddled with bullets amid the flames.

Now, General George Armstrong Custer is just one more of the dead of the Seventh Cavalry, which the Indians have wiped out on the banks of the Little Big Horn River. Custer had had his golden hair shaved off the night before. His smooth cranium seems intact, and he still wears that rather stupid expression of men who have never been defeated.

(51, 91, and 198)

1876: *War Bonnet Creek*

Buffalo Bill

Shortly after the defeat at Little Big Horn, some soldiers descend upon the Cheyenne Indians camped on the banks of a brook, and in the shoot-out Chief Yellow Hand falls.

Buffalo Bill is first on the scene. At one slash he scalps the Cheyenne chief, and at one gallop flies to the footlights of distant cities. The history of the West is becoming a theatrical spectacle as it unfolds. The battle is not yet over and the scalper is already selling his epic feat in the theaters of Philadelphia, Baltimore, Washington, and New York. In memory and vengeance of General Custer, Buffalo Bill raises his arms before the packed auditorium: in one hand appears the knife and from the other, which clutches a scalp dyed with blood, hangs a cascade of multicolored feathers. The hero wears a heavily ornamented Mexican suit, with a pair of revolvers in his belt and his fifteen-shot Winchester slung from his shoulder. Soon the scene will adorn the covers of cowboy dime novels selling throughout the country.

Buffalo Bill, most famous of cowboys, has never herded a cow in his life. The living symbol of the winning of the West, the immortal superman, has earned his fame exterminating Indians and buffalos and talking endlessly about his own courage and marksmanship. They baptized him Buffalo Bill when he was working for the Kansas Pacific

Railroad: he says that in a year and a half he fired 4,280 shots and killed 4,280 buffalos although women prevented him from going all out.

(157)

1876: Mexico City
Departure

Eleven times General Santa Anna had been president of Mexico. He bought his generals' loyalty by selling bits of the country and imposing taxes on dogs, horses, and windows; but he often had to flee from the palace disguised as a pauper. Although he specialized in losing wars, he had many statues of himself erected galloping in bronze, sword on high, and by decree he turned his birthday into a national holiday.

When he returned from exile, all his friends had died, and all his enemies too. Buried deep in an armchair, always with a fighting cock in his arms, Santa Anna rubbed old medals or scratched his cork leg. He was blind, but thought he saw carriage-loads of princes and presidents drawing up at his door. He was deaf, but thought he heard supplicatory multitudes coming to plead for an audience, clemency, or a job.

"*You wait!*" Santa Anna would yell. "*Shut up!*"—while the last of his lackeys changed his wetted trousers.

Now from his house on Vergara Street, mortgaged, always empty, they take him out to the cemetery. The cocks march ahead of the coffin, confronting people and looking for a fight.

(227 and 266)

1877: Guatemala City
The Civilizer

Justo Rufino Barrios, president of Guatemala, closes his eyes and hears a din of railroads and steam engines violating the silence of the monasteries.

There is no stopping synthetic dyes in the world's markets, and no one buys the cochineal and indigo that Guatemala sells. It's time for coffee. The markets demand coffee and coffee demands lands and hands, trains and ports. *To modernize the country*, Barrios expels the parasitic monks, seizes from the Church its immense properties and gives them to his closest friends. He also expropriates the lands of Indian communities. Collective property is abolished by decree and compulsory peonage is imposed. *To integrate the Indian into the nation*, the liberal government makes him a serf of the new coffee plantations. The colonial system of forced labor returns.

Soldiers tour the plantations distributing Indians.

(59)

1879: Mexico City

The Socialists and the Indians

It is painful to say so, but we must. Colonel Alberto Santa Fe says it from Tlatelolco prison: the Indians were happier under Spanish rule. *Today they are pompously called free and they are slaves.*

According to the socialist Santa Fe, who has set off an Indian insurrection in the valley of Texmelucan, the ills of Mexico stem from the poverty of the people, which in turn stems from the concentration of land in a few hands and the lack of industry, *because everything comes from abroad when we could make it ourselves.* And he asks himself: *would we do better to lose independence and become a North American colony, or to change the social organization that has ruined us?*

In the newspaper *The Socialist*, Juan de Mata Rivera also proclaims that the Indians were better off in the colony, and demands that their lands be returned to them. There is no law granting rights to thieves over the fruits of violence and infamy.

At the same time, campesinos of Sierra Gorda publish their "Socialist Plan." They call the rapacious big estates and governments that have put the Indians at the landowners' service the root of all misfortune. They propose that haciendas become "townships," that community property in farmlands, waters, woods, and pastures be restored.

(129 and 274)

1879: Choele-Choel Island

The Remington Method

Argentine soldiers conquer twenty thousand leagues of Indian land.

The London market demands a multiplication of cattle; and the frontier explodes. For the southward and westward growth of the great estates of the pampas, repeating rifles empty out "empty spaces." Clearing savages out of Patagonia, burning villages, using Indians and ostriches for target practice, General Julio Argentino Roca winds up the brilliant military career which he began in the wars against gauchos and Paraguayans.

On the island of Choele-Choel in the Negro River, four thousand dusty soldiers attend Mass. They offer their victory to God. The desert campaign is over.

The survivors—Indian men, Indian women, frontier booty—are divided among estancias, forts, stables, kitchens, and beds. More than ten thousand of them, calculates Lieutenant Colonel Federico Barbará. Thanks to the generosity of Argentine ladies, says Barbará, the savage children change their chiripás for pants and come to look like human beings.

(353)

1879: Buenos Aires

Martín Fierro and the
Twilight of the Gaucho

José Hernández publishes in Buenos Aires the final part of "Martín Fierro," a song of the death-throes of the gaucho who made this country and ended up without a country. For some time the other half of this splendid poem has been circulating throughout the River Plata countryside, its stanzas basic necessities of life like meat, maté, and tobacco.

Sadly reciting couplets around the campfires, serfs on the big estates and conscripts in the forts evoke the ways of that wild brother, the man without ruler or rules, and thus resurrect the memory of their lost freedom.

(158)

1879: Port-au-Prince

Maceo

The exiled Antonio Maceo reaches the heights of Belle Air on the road to Santo Domingo when five assassins fall upon him. It is a night of full moon, but Maceo escapes from the shoot-out and at a gallop, buries himself in the brush. The Spanish consul in Haiti had promised the killers twenty thousand pesos in gold. Maceo is the most popular and dangerous of the fighters for the independence of Cuba.

He has lost his father and fourteen brothers in the war, and to the war he will return. In the thunder of cavalry, as clashing machetes advance into the mouths of cannons, Maceo charges ahead. He has won his promotions in combat, and certain white officers are not at all happy about a near-black being a major general.

Maceo fights for a real revolution. *It's not a matter of replacing the Spaniards*, he says. Independence is not the final goal, but the first one. After that, Cuba has to be changed. As long as the people don't command, the colony will not become a fatherland. The big Creole landowners are mistrustful, for good reasons, of this man who says there is nothing sacred about the right of property.

(262)

1879: Chinchas Islands

Guano

Pure shit were the hills that rose on these islands. For millennia, millions of birds had concluded their digestive process on the coast of southern Peru.

The Incas knew that this guano could revive any land, however dead it seemed; but Europe did not know the magical powers of the Peruvian fertilizer until Humboldt brought back the first samples.

Peru, which had gained worldwide prestige for silver and gold, perpetuated its glory thanks to the goodwill of the birds. Europeward sailed ships laden with malodorous guano, and returned bringing statues of pure Carrara marble to decorate Lima's boulevards. Their holds were also filled with English clothing, which ruined the textile mills of the southern sierra, and Bordeaux wines which bankrupted the national vineyards of Moquequa. Entire houses arrived at Callao from London. From Paris were imported whole luxury hotels complete with chefs.

After forty years, the islands are exhausted. Peru has sold twelve million tons of guano, has spent twice as much, and now owes a candle to every saint.

(43, 44, and 289)

1879: Atacama and Tarapacá Deserts

Saltpeter

No war breaks out over guano, of which little remains. It is saltpeter that throws the Chilean army into the conquest of the deserts, against the allied forces of Peru and Bolivia.

From the sterile Atacama and Tarapacá deserts comes the secret of the verdure of Europe's valleys. In these solitudes there are only lizards hiding under stones and herds of mules carting to Pacific ports loads of saltpeter, a lumpy snow which will restore enthusiasm to weary European lands. Nothing throws a shadow in this world of nothing, unless it be the sparkling mountains of saltpeter drying forsakenly in the sun or the wretched workers, desert warriors with ragged flour sacks for uniforms, pickaxes for spears, and shovels for swords.

The saltpeter, or nitrate, turns out to be indispensable for the businesses of life and of death. Not only is it the most coveted of fertilizers, mixed with carbon and sulphur it becomes gunpowder. Agriculture and the prosperous industry of war need it.

(35 and 268)

1880: Lima

The Chinese

Chile invades and devastates. With English uniforms and English weapons, the Chilean army levels the Lima beach towns of Chorrillos, Barranco, and Miraflores, leaving no stone on another. Peruvian officers send Indians into the slaughter and run off yelling, *"Long live the fatherland!"*

There are many Chinese, Chinese from Peru, fighting on the Chilean side. They are Chinese fugitives from the big estates, who now enter Lima singing the praises of the invading general Patricio Lynch, the Red Prince, the Savior.

Those Chinese were shanghaied a few years ago from the ports of Macao and Canton by English, Portuguese, and French merchants. Of every three, two reached Peru alive. In the port of Callao they were put up for sale. Lima newspapers advertised them *fresh off the boat*. Many were branded with hot irons. Railroads, cotton, sugar, guano, and coffee needed slave hands. On the guano islands the guards never took their eyes off them, because with the smallest negligence some Chinese kills himself by jumping into the sea.

The fall of Lima sets off chaos in all Peru. In the Cañete valley, blacks rise in rebellion. At the end of an Ash Wednesday carnival the hatred of centuries explodes. Ritual of humiliations: blacks, slaves until recently and still treated as such, avenge old scores killing Chinese, also slaves, with sticks and machetes.

(45 and 329)

1880: London

In Defense of Indolence

Run out by the French police and mortified by the English winter, which makes one piss stalactites, Paul Lafargue writes in London a new indictment of *the criminal system that makes man a miserable servant of the machine*.

Capitalist ethics, a pitiful parody of Christian ethics, writes Marx's Cuban son-in-law. Like the monks, capitalism teaches workers that they were born into this vale of tears to toil and suffer; and induces them to deliver up their wives and children to the factories, which grind them up for twelve hours a day. Lafargue refuses to join in *nauseating songs in honor of the god Progress, the eldest son of Work*, and claims the right to indolence and a full enjoyment of human passions. Indolence is a gift of the gods. Even Christ preached it in the Sermon on the Mount. Some day, announces Lafargue, there will come an end to the torments of hunger and forced labor, more numerous than the locusts of the Bible, and then the earth will tremble with joy.

(177)

1881: Lincoln City

Billy the Kid

"I'm gonna give you a tip, doc."

Until a minute ago, Billy the Kid was awaiting the gallows in a cell. Now he aims at the sheriff from the top of the stairs.

"I'm gettin' tired, doc."

The sheriff throws him the key to the handcuffs and when Billy bends down there is a burst of revolver fire. The sheriff topples with a bullet in his eye and his silver star in smithereens.

Billy is twenty-one and has twenty-one notches in the butt of his Colt, not counting a score of Apaches and Mexicans, who died unrecorded.

"I wouldn't do that if I was you, stranger."

He began his career at twelve, when a bum insulted his mother, and he took off at full gallop, brandishing a razor that dripped blood.

(131 and 292)

1882: Saint Joseph

Jesse James

Jesse and his lads, the "James Boys," had fought with the slaver army of the South and later were the avenging angels of that conquered land. To satisfy their sense of honor they have plucked clean eleven banks, seven mail trains, and three stage coaches. Full of braggadocio, reluctantly, without taking the trouble to draw his gun, Jesse has sent sixteen fellowmen to the other world.

One Saturday night, in Saint Joseph, Missouri, his best friend shoots him in the back.

"You, baby, dry them tears and set 'em up all around. And see if they can get that garbage out of the way. I'll tell you what he was. Know what he was? Stubbornest damn mule in Arizona."

(292)

1882: Prairies of Oklahoma

Twilight of the Cowboy

Half a century ago, the legendary wild horse of Oklahoma, amazed Washington Irving and inspired his pen. That untameable prince of the prairies, that long-maned white arrow, is now a meek beast of burden.

The cowboy, too, champion of the winning of the West, angel of justice or vengeful bandit, becomes a soldier or a peon observing regular hours. Barbed wire advances at a thousand kilometers a day and refrigerator trains cross the great prairies of the United States. Ballads and dime novels evoke the howls of coyotes and Indians, the good times of covered-wagon caravans, their creaking wooden axles greased with bacon; and Buffalo Bill is demonstrating that nostalgia can be turned into a very lucrative business. But the cowboy is another machine among the many that gin the cotton, thresh the wheat, or bale the hay.

(224 and 292)

1882: New York

You Too Can Succeed in Life

The happiness road no longer leads only to the prairies of the West. Now, it is also the day of the big cities. The whistle of the train, magic flute, awakens youth from its rustic drowsiness and invites it to join the new paradises of cement and steel. Any ragged orphan, promise the siren voices, can become a prosperous businessman if he works hard and lives virtuously in the offices and factories of the giant buildings.

A writer, Horatio Alger, sells these illusions by the millions of copies. Alger is more famous than Shakespeare and his novels have a bigger circulation than the Bible. His readers and his characters, tame wage earners, have not stopped running since they got off the trains or transatlantic ships. In reality, the track is reserved for a handful of business athletes, but North American society massively consumes the fantasy of free competition, and even cripples dream of winning races.

(282)

1882: New York

The Creation According to John D. Rockefeller

In the beginning I made light with a kerosene lamp. And the shadows, which mocked tallow or sperm candles, retreated. And the evening and the morning were the first day.

And on the second day God put me to the test and allowed the Devil to tempt me, offering me friends and lovers and other extravagances.

And I said: "Let petroleum come to me." And I founded Standard Oil. And I saw that it was good and the evening and the morning were the third day.

And on the fourth I followed God's example. Like Him, I threatened and cursed anyone refusing me obedience; and like Him I applied extortion and punishment. As God has crushed his competitors, so I pitilessly pulverized my rivals in Pittsburgh and Philadelphia. And to the repentant I promised forgiveness and eternal peace.

And I put an end to the disorder of the Universe. And where there was chaos, I made organization. And on a scale never before known I calculated costs, imposed prices, and conquered markets. And I distributed the force of millions of hands so that time would never again be wasted, nor energy, nor materials. And I banished chance and fate from the history of men. And in the space created by me I reserved no place for the weak or the inefficient. And the evening and the morning were the fifth day.

And to give my work a name I coined the word "trust." And I saw that it was good. And I confirmed that the world turned around my watchful eyes, while the evening and the morning were the sixth day.

And on the seventh day I did charity. I added up the money God had given me for having continued His perfect work and gave twenty-five cents to the poor. And then I rested.

(231 and 282)

1883: Bismarck City
The Last Buffalos of the North

The buffalo has become a curiosity in Montana and the Blackfeet Indians gnaw old bones and tree bark.

Sitting Bull heads the last hunt of the Sioux on the northern prairies. After traveling far they meet a few animals. For each one they kill, the Sioux ask forgiveness of the Great Invisible Buffalo, as tradition requires, and promise him they will not waste one hair of the body.

Soon afterwards, the Northern Pacific Railroad celebrates the completion of its coast-to-coast line. This is the fourth line to cross North American territory. Coal locomotives, with pneumatic brakes and Pullman coaches, advance behind the pioneers toward the prairies that belonged to the Indians. On all sides new cities spring up. The giant national market grows and coheres.

The Northern Pacific authorities invite Chief Sitting Bull to make a speech at the great inauguration party. Sitting Bull arrives from the reservation where the Sioux survive on charity. He mounts the rostrum covered with flowers and flags, and addresses himself to the president of the United States, the officials and personalities present, and to the general public: *"I hate all the white people,"* he says. *"You are thieves and liars . . ."*

The interpreter, a young officer, translates: "My red and gentle heart bids you welcome . . ."

Sitting Bull interrupts the clamorous applause of the audience: *"You have taken away our land and made us outcasts . . ."*

The audience gives the feather-headdressed warrior a standing ovation; and the interpreter sweats ice.

(224)

1884: Santiago de Chile
The Wizard of Finance
Eats Soldier Meat

"Our rights are born of victory, the supreme law of nations," says the victorious governor.

The War of the Pacific, the nitrates war, has ended. By sea and by land Chile has crushed its enemies. The immense deserts of Atacama and Tarapacá become part of the map of Chile. Peru loses its nitrates and the exhausted guano islands. Bolivia loses its outlet to the sea and is bottled up in the heart of South America.

In Santiago de Chile they celebrate the victory. In London they collect on it. Without firing a shot or spending a penny, John Thomas North has become the nitrates king. With money borrowed from Chilean banks, North has bought for a song the bonds that the Peruvian State had given to the deposits' old proprietors. North bought them when the war was just beginning; and before it was over, the Chilean State had the kindness to recognize the bonds as legitimate property titles.

(268 and 269)

1884: Huancayo
The Fatherland Pays

Against the Chilean invaders of Peru, Marshal Andrés Avelino Cáceres and his Indian guerrillas have fought over two hundred mountain leagues without letup for three years.

The Indians of the communities call their marshal, a man with

fierce whiskers, "Grandpa"; and many have lost their lives following
him, shouting "vivas" for a fatherland that despises them. In Lima,
too, Indians were cannon fodder, and the social chronicler Ricardo
Palma blames the defeat on *that abject and degraded race*.

In contrast, Marshal Cáceres was saying until recently that Peru
was defeated by its own merchants and bureaucrats. Until recently
he also rejected the peace treaty that amputated a good piece of Peru.
Now Cáceres has changed his mind. He wants to be president. He
has to earn merits. He must demobilize the armed Indians, who have
fought against the Chileans, but have also invaded haciendas and are
threatening the sacred order of great estates.

The marshal summons Tomás Laimes, chief of the Colca guerrilla
fighters. Laimes comes to Huancayo with fifteen hundred Indians.
He comes to say, *"At your orders, my Grandpa."*

But no sooner does Laimes arrive than his troop is disarmed.
When he has barely crossed the barracks threshold, he is felled by a
rifle butt. Later they shoot him, blindfolded and sitting down.

(194)

1885: Lima
"The trouble comes from the top,"
says Manuel González Prada.

*Peru groans under the domination of a few privileged beings. Those
men would roll us flat between the crushers of a sugar mill, they
would distill us in an alembic, they would burn us to a crisp in a
smelting oven, if they could extract from our residuum just one mil-
ligram of gold . . . Like land with a curse on it, they receive the seed
and drink the water without ever producing fruit . . .*

*In the war against Chile they proved their cowardice, not even
having the guts to defend the guano and nitrate deposits . . .We were
insulted, trodden on, and bloodied as no nation ever was; but the
war with Chile has taught us nothing, nor corrected us of any vice.*

(145)

1885: Mexico City
"All belongs to all,"

says Teodoro Flores, Mixtec Indian, hero of three wars.
"Repeat that!"
And the sons repeat: *"All belongs to all."*

Teodoro Flores has defended Mexico against North Americans, conservatives, and the French. President Juárez gave him three farms with good soil as a reward. He didn't accept.

"*Land, water, woods, houses, oxen, harvests. To all. Repeat that!*"

And the sons repeat it.

Open to the sky, the roof is almost immune to the smell of shit and frying, and it is almost quiet. Here, one can take the air and talk, while in the patio below, men fight with knives over a woman, someone calls loudly upon the Virgin, and dogs howl omens of death.

"*Tell us about the Sierra,*" asks the youngest son.

And the father tells how people live in Teotitlán del Camino. There, those who can work do so and everyone gets what he needs. No one is allowed to take more than he needs. That is a serious crime. In the sierra, crimes are punished with silence, scorn, or expulsion. It was President Juárez who brought the jail, something that wasn't known there. Juárez brought judges and property titles and ordered the communal lands divided up. "*But we paid no attention to the papers he gave us.*"

Teodoro Flores was fifteen when he learned the Spanish language. Now he wants his sons to become lawyers to defend the Indians from the tricks of the doctors. For that purpose he brought them to the capital, that deafening pigsty, to squeak by, crammed among rowdies and beggars.

"*What God created and what man creates. All belongs to all. Repeat that!*"

Night after night, the children listen to him until sleep overcomes them.

"*We are all born equal, stark naked. We are all brothers. Repeat that!*"

(287)

1885: Colón
Prestán

The city of Colón was born thirty years ago, because a terminal station was needed for the train that crosses Panama from sea to sea. The city came to birth on the Caribbean Sea swamps, and offered fevers and mosquitos, seedy hotels, gambling dens, and brothels to adventurers who streamed through in pursuit of the gold of California, and miserable hovels for the Chinese workers who maintained the tracks and died of plague or sadness.

This year, Colón burned. The fire devoured wooden arcades, houses, and markets, and Pedro Prestán took the blame. Prestán, teacher and doctor, almost black, always wearing a derby hat and bow tie, always impeccable in the mud streets, had led a popular insurrection. A thousand U.S. Marines went into action on Panamanian territory, purportedly to protect the railroad and other North American properties. Prestán, who defended the humiliated people with life and soul and derby, hangs on the gallows.

The crime puts a curse on Colón. For expiation, the city will burn every twenty years from now on and forever.

(102, 151, and 324)

1886: Chivilcoy
The Circus

At dawn a circus trailer appears out of the mist, amid the leafy groves of Chivilcoy.

By afternoon, colored banners flutter over the tent.

A triumphal parade around the city. The Podesta Brothers' *Equestrian, Gymnastic, Acrobatic, and Creole Drama Company* has a Japanese juggler and a talking dog, trained doves, a child prodigy, and four clowns. The program claims that the harlequin, Pepino the 88th, and the trapeze team *have earned the admiration of audiences in London, Paris, Vienna, Philadelphia, and Rome.*

But the main dish the circus offers is *Juan Moreira*, the first Creole drama in Argentine history, a pantomime with duels of couplets and knives, which tells the misfortunes of a gaucho harassed by an officer, a judge, a mayor, and the grocer.

(34)

1886: Atlanta
Coca-Cola

John Pemberton, pharmacist, has won some prestige for his love potions and baldness cures.

Now he invents a medicine that relieves headaches and alleviates nausea. His new product is made from a base of coca leaves, brought from the Andes, and cola nuts, stimulant seeds that come from Africa. Water, sugar, caramel, and certain secrets complete the formula.

Soon Pemberton will sell his invention for two thousand three hundred dollars. He is convinced that it is a good remedy; and he would burst with laughter, not with pride, if some fortuneteller revealed to him that he had just created the symbol of the coming century.

(184)

1887: Chicago

Every May First, They Will Live Again

The gallows awaits them. They were five, but Lingg got death up early by exploding a dynamite capsule between his teeth. Fischer dresses himself unhurriedly, humming "La Marseillaise." Parsons, the agitator, who used words like a whip or knife, grips his comrades' hands before the guards tie them behind their backs. Engel, famous for his marksmanship, asks for port wine and makes everyone laugh with a joke. Spies, who has written so much *portraying anarchy as the entrance to life*, prepares in silence for the entrance to death.

The spectators, in theater seats, fasten their eyes on the scaffold. *A signal, a noise, the trap is sprung . . . There, in a horrible dance, they died spinning in the air*.

José Martí writes reportage of the anarchists' execution in Chicago. The world's working class will revive them every First of May. That is still not known, but Martí always writes as if hearing, where it is least expected, the cry of a newborn child.

(199)

1889: London

North

Twenty years ago, he jumped onto the pier at Valparaíso, eyes of blue stone, fuzzy red whiskers. He had ten pounds sterling in his pockets and a bundle of clothing on his back. In his first job he got to know saltpeter the hard way, in the cauldron of a small deposit in Tarapacá, and later he was a merchant in the port of Iquique. During the War of the Pacific, while Chileans, Peruvians, and Bolivians were disemboweling each other with bayonets, John Thomas North performed conjuring tricks that made him owner of the battlefields.

Now North, the nitrates king, makes beer in France and cement in Belgium, owns streetcars in Egypt and sawmills in black Africa, and exploits gold in Australia and diamonds in Brazil. In England, this Midas of plebeian stock and quick fingers has bought the rank of colonel in Her Majesty's army, heads the Masonic lodge of Kent county and is a prominent member of the Conservative Party; dukes, lords and ministers sit at his table. He lived in a palace whose big iron doors were, they say, lifted from the Cathedral in Lima by Chilean soldiers.

On the eve of a voyage to Chile, North gives a farewell ball in the Hotel Metropole. A thousand English people attend. The Metropole's salons gleam like suns, and so do the dishes and drinks. The letter *N* blazes in the center of immense chrysanthemum coats-of-arms. An ovation greets the almighty host as he descends the stairs disguised as Henry VIII. On his arm is his wife dressed as a duchess; and behind comes the daughter, as a Persian princess, and the son in Cardinal Richelieu costume.

The war correspondent of the *Times* is one of the great retinue that will accompany North to his Chilean kingdom. Turbulent days await him. There, in the deserts conquered with bullets, North is the master of saltpeter and coal and water and banks and newspapers and railroads; but in the city of Santiago there is a president who has the bad taste to refuse his gifts. His name is José Manuel Balmaceda. North is heading there to overthrow him.

(269 and 270)

1889: Montevideo
Football

In London, it is Queen Victoria's seventieth birthday. On the banks of the River Plata, they celebrate it with their feet.

The Buenos Aires and Montevideo teams vie for the ball on the little Blanqueada field under the disdainful scrutiny of the queen. At the center of the grandstand, between flags, hangs a portrait of this mistress of the world's seas and a good part of its lands.

Buenos Aires wins, 3-0. There are no dead to mourn, although the penalty has not yet been invented and anyone approaching the enemy goal risks his life. To get a close shot at the goal, one must penetrate an avalanche of legs that shoot out like axes; and every match is a battle requiring bones of steel.

Football is an Englishman's game. It is played by officials of the railway, the gas companies, and the Bank of London, and by visiting sailors; but already a few Creoles, infiltrators among the blond-mustachioed marksmen, are showing that craftiness can be an efficient weapon for bringing down goalkeepers.

(221)

1890: River Plata

Comrades

More than fifty thousand workers come each year to the River Plata, Europeans washed up by desperation on these coasts. Italian flags greet the visit of Edmundo de Amicis to the Piedmontese colonies of the Argentine coast, and at workers' meetings in Buenos Aires or Montevideo speeches are heard in Spanish, Italian, French, or German.

Eight of every ten workers or artisans are foreigners, and among them are Italian socialists and anarchists, Frenchmen of the Commune, Spaniards of the first republic, and revolutionaries from Germany and Central Europe.

Strikes break out on both banks of the river. In Montevideo, streetcar conductors work eighteen hours a day; mill and noodle-factory workers, fifteen. There are no Sundays, and a member of the government in Buenos Aires has published his discovery that idleness is the mother of all vice.

In Buenos Aires, Latin America's first May First is celebrated. The chief speaker, Joseph Winiger, salutes the Chicago martyrs in German and announces that the hour of socialism is approaching, while men of the gown, pen, sword or cassock clamor for the expulsion of alien enemies of order. The inspired writer Miguel Cané drafts a law to expel foreign agitators from Argentina.

(140 and 290)

1890: Buenos Aires

Tenements

Poor and rich pay the same price at the Colón theater at carnival time, but once past the door Hands go to their place and Brains to theirs, and no one commits the sacrilege of sitting in the wrong place. The lower-downs dance in the parterre, the higher-ups in boxes and lounges.

Buenos Aires is like its theater. High-class people sleep in two-or-three-story French palaces in the North barrio, and alone sleep the spinsters who would rather die as virgins than mix their blood with some foreigner of indeterminate hue. The top people decorate their lineage, or manufacture it, with torrents of pearls and initials engraved on silver tea sets, and show off Saxony or Sèvres or Limoges porcelains, Waterford crystal, Lyons tapestries, and Brussels table-cloths. From the secluded life of the Big Village they have moved on to the frenetic exhibitionism of the Paris of America.

In the south are huddled the beaten-down of the earth. In abandoned three-patioed colonial mansions, or in specially built tenements, the workers newly arrived from Naples or Vigo or Bessarabia sleep by turns. Never cold are the scarce beds in the nonspace invaded by braziers and washbasins and chests which serve as cradles. Fights are frequent in the long queues at the door to the only latrine, and silence is an impossible luxury. But sometimes, on party nights, the accordion or mandolin or bagpipes bring back lost voices to these washerwomen and dressmakers, servants of rich bosses and husbands, and ease the loneliness of these men who from sun to sun tan hides, pack meat, saw wood, sweep streets, tote loads, raise and paint walls, roll cigarettes, grind wheat, and bake bread while their children shine shoes and call out the crime of the day.

(236 and 312)

Man Alone

One fire less, they say in the villages of Galicia when someone emigrates.

Over there, he was excess population; and here, he doesn't want to exceed. Like a mule, he works and resists and keeps quiet, a man of few words, and in the foreign city he takes up less room than a dog.

Here, they make fun of him and treat him with contempt, because he can't even sign his name, and manual labor is for inferior species. On the other hand, here they worship anyone with a lot of arrogance and applaud the slicker who can deflate the most boastful swollen head with a stroke of cunning and luck.

He gets little sleep, the lonely immigrant, but no sooner does he close his eyes than some fairy or witch comes to love him on green mountains and snowy precipices. Sometimes he has nightmares. Then, he drowns in the river. Not in just any river, but a particular river over there. Whoever crosses it, they say, loses his memory.

Tangoing

The tango, wistful offspring of the gay milonga, has been born in the corrals at the city's edge and in tenement courtyards.

On the two banks of the River Plata, it is music of ill repute. Workers and malefactors dance it on earth floors, men of the hammer or the knife, male with male if the woman is not able to follow the very daring and broken step, or if such a body-to-body embrace seems more suitable for whores: the couple slides, rocks, stretches, and flowers in coupés and filigrees.

The tango comes from gaucho tunes of the interior and comes from the sea, the chanteys of sailors. It comes from the slaves of Africa and the gypsies of Andalusia. Spain contributes its guitar, Germany its concertina, Italy its mandolin. The driver of the horse-drawn streetcar contributed his trumpet, and the immigrant worker his harmonica, comrade of lonely moments. With hesitant step the tango spans barracks and dives, midways of traveling circuses and the patios of slum brothels. Now organ grinders parade it through shore streets on the outskirts of Buenos Aires and Montevideo, heading downtown; and ships take it to drive Paris wild.

(257, 293, and 350)

1890: Hartford

Mark Twain

The novelist's hands whisk Hank Morgan, an offical of the Colt arms factory, into the distant court of King Arthur. The telephone, the bicycle, and dynamite journey to the times of Merlin the magician

and Sir Galahad in the vale of Camelot; there Hank Morgan publishes
and sells a newspaper at the modest price of two cents, founds a West
Point military academy and reveals that the world is not a dish supported on columns. Although he comes from a society that already
knows monopolies, Hank brings to the feudal castles the good news
of free competition, free trade, and the free ballot. In vain, he tries
to replace mounted duels with baseball, hereditary monarchy with
democracy, and the code of honor with the calculation of costs; and
finally he burns up thirty thousand armor-and-lance English horsemen with electric wires already tried out against the Indians of the
United States. The adventure speeds to a deadly climax and Hank
falls, asphyxiated by the miasma of putrefaction from his victims.

Mark Twain finishes writing *A Connecticut Yankee in King Arthur's Court* at his home in Hartford. "It is my swan song," he announces. He has always lived by leaps and bounds, pursuing a fugitive
million dollars. He has been journalist and explorer, publicity agent,
miner of gold, ship's pilot, speculator, inventor of gadgets, director
of an insurance company, and unsuccessful entrepreneur. Between
bankruptcy and bankruptcy he managed to invent or recall Tom Saw-
yer and Huck Finn, and found a way to invite us all to float on a raft
down the waters of the Mississippi. And he did it for the pure joy of
going, not for the urgency of arriving.

(149 and 341)

1890: Wounded Knee
Wind of Snow

The Creator did not make the Indians: he sang them, he danced
them.

Through songs and dances the Creator is now announcing that
this old and dying earth will soon be demolished by the greenish
whirlwind of a new earth. The prophet Wovoka brought word of it
from the other world. In the new earth, buffalos will be revived,
dead Indians will be reborn, and a ferocious flood will drown the
whites. Not one of the usurpers will survive.

The prophet Wovoka's dances and songs come out of the West,
cross the Rocky Mountains, and spread throughout the prairies. The
Sioux, who were the most numerous and powerful of the tribes in
these regions, celebrate the annunciation of paradise, the end of

hunger and exile. They dance and sing from dawn to the depth of every night.

Four days after Christmas, the thunder of gunfire interrupts the ceremonies in the Sioux camp at Wounded Knee. The soldiers riddle women, children, and the few men with bullets like so many buffalos. The blizzard strikes the dead and freezes them on the smow.

(51, 91, and 230)

Prophetic Song of the Sioux

A thunder-being nation I am, I have said.
A thunder-being nation I am, I have said.
You shall live.
You shall live.
You shall live.
You shall live.

(38)

1891: Santiago de Chile
Balmaceda

José Manuel Balmaceda wanted to promote national industry, *to live and dress by ourselves*, intuiting that the nitrate era would pass leaving Chile nothing but remorse. He wanted to apply stimulants and protections similar to those that the United States, England, France, and Germany had practiced in their industrial infancy. He raised the workers' wages and sowed the country with public schools. He gave Chile's long body a spine of railways and roads. In his years as president, sacred British capital ran a grave risk of profanation. Balmaceda wanted to nationalize the railways and put an end to the usury of banks and the voracity of the nitrate companies.

Balmaceda wanted much and could do plenty; but the enormous budget that John Thomas North devoted to buying consciences and twisting justice could do more. The press let loose its thunder against *the Caesar drunk with power, despotic enemy of freedom, hostile to foreign enterprises*, and the clamor of bishops and parliamentarians was no less deafening. A military rising broke out like an echo, and then the blood of the people flowed.

The South American Journal announces the triumph of the coup d'état: *Chile will return to the good times of yesterday*. The banker Eduardo Matte also celebrates it: *We are the masters of Chile, we owners of the capital and of the soil. All else is an influenceable and saleable mass*.

Balmaceda shoots himself.

(270)

1891: Washington

The Other America

For ten years José Martí has been living in the United States. There is much that he admires in this multifarious and vigorous country, where no one is afraid of anything new; but he also denounces in his articles the imperial ambitions of the young nation, the glorification of avarice into a divine right, and the atrocious racism that exterminates Indians, humiliates blacks, and looks down on Latins.

South of the Rio Grande, says Martí, there is *another* America, *our America, land that stammers*, that does not recognize its full likeness either in the European or in the North American mirror. It is the Hispanic American fatherland, he says, which reclaims Cuba to complete itself, while in the north they claim it to devour it. One America's interests don't coincide with the other's. *Does political and economic union with the United States suit Hispanic America?* Martí asks. And he replies: *Two condors, or two lambs, unite without so much danger as a condor and a lamb*. Last year the first Pan-American conference was held in Washington and now Martí sits in on the continuation of the dialog as delegate of Uruguay. *Whoever says economic union, says political union. The people that buys gives the orders. The people that sells, serves . . . The people that wants to die sells to one people alone, and the people that wants to save itself, sells to more than one . . . The people that wants to be free distributes its business among equally strong peoples. If either is to be given preference, prefer the one that needs less to the one that is less disdainful . . .*

Martí has dedicated his life to that *other* America: he wants to revive everything in it that has been killed from the conquest onward, and wants to reveal it and make it rebel, because its hidden and betrayed identity will not be revealed until it loosens its bonds.

What fault can my great mother America throw in my face?

Son of Europeans but son of America, Cuban patriot of the great fatherland, Martí feels flowing in his veins the blood of the sorely wounded peoples who were born of palm or corn seeds and who called the Milky Way *road of the soul* and the moon *sun of night* or *sun asleep*. So he writes, replying to Sarmiento, who is enamored of what is foreign: *This is no battle between civilization and barbarism, but between false learning and nature*.

(112 and 354)

1891: New York

The Thinking Begins to Be Ours, Believes José Martí

. . . To know is to resolve. Knowing the country, and governing it according to our knowledge, is the only way to free it from tyrannies. The European university must yield to the American university. The history of America, from the Incas till now, must be put at our fingertips, even though that of the Greek Archons is not taught. Our Greece is preferable to the Greece that is not ours. It is more necessary for us. National politicians must replace exotic politicians. Let the world be grafted onto our republics; but the trunk must be that of our republics. And let the defeated pedant keep quiet; for there is no fatherland in which man can take more pride than our wounded American republics . . .

We were a mask, with trousers from England, Parisian vest, jacket from North America, and cap from Spain . . . We were epaulettes and togas, in countries that came into the world with sandaled feet and banded hair . . . Neither the European book, nor the Yanqui book, has provided the key to the Hispanic American enigma . . .

The peoples stand and greet one another. "What are we like?" they ask; and they tell one another what they are like. When a problem arises in Cojímar, they don't go to Danzig for the solution. The frock coats are still French, but the thinking begins to be American . . .

(199)

1891: Guanajuato

34 Cantarranas Street. Instant Photography

The hooded gunner bends and takes aim. The victim, a highborn gentleman of Guanajuato, does not smile or blink or breathe. There is no escape. Behind him the curtain has fallen, leafy landscape of painted plaster, and the stage-prop staircase leads nowhere. Surrounded by paper flowers and cardboard columns and balustrades, the solemn personage rests his hand on the arm of a chair and with dignity confronts the cannon-mouth of the bellows camera.

All Guanajuato has itself shot in the studio at 34 Cantarranas Street. Romualdo García photographs gentlemen of the uppermost crust and their wives and children, boys who look like dwarves wrapped in large vests with pocket watches, and girls austere as grandmothers crushed by beribboned silken bonnets. He photographs plump friars and soldiers in full dress uniform, the first-communioned and the newly wed; and also some poor people who come from afar and give what they don't have just to pose, bountifully hairdressed and ironed, wearing their best clothes, before the camera of the Mexican artist who won a prize in Paris.

The magician Romualdo García turns persons into statues and sells eternity to mortals.

(158)

1891: Purísima del Rincón
Lives

He learned from no one; he paints for the love of it. Hermenegildo Bustos is paid in kind or at four pennies a portrait. The people of Purísima del Rincón have no photographer, but they have a painter.

Forty years ago Hermenegildo did a portrait of Leocadia López, the belle of the town, and it was very much her. Since then, the town of Purísima has seen successful burials and weddings, many serenades, and one or another disembowelment in the bars; some girl eloped with the clown of a traveling circus, the earth trembled more than once, and more than once a new political boss was sent from Mexico City; and as the slow days passed with their suns and downpours, Hermenegildo Bustos kept painting the live people he saw and the dead ones he remembered.

He is also a market gardener, an ice cream man, and a dozen more things. He plants corn and beans on his own land or by commission, and he keeps busy deworming crops. He makes ices with the frost he collects from maguey leaves; and when the cold spell lets up he makes orange preserves. He also embroiders national flags, fixes leaky roofs, directs the drumming during Holy Week, decorates screens, beds, and coffins, and with a very delicate touch paints Doña

Pomposa López giving thanks to the Most Holy Virgin, who pulled her from her deathbed, and Doña Refugio Segovia, highlighting her charms, not omitting a hair of the curls on her forehead and copying the gold brooch at her throat which says "Refugito."

He paints, and paints himself: freshly shaved and barbered, prominent cheekbones and frowning eyebrows, military uniform. And on the back of his image he writes: *Hermenegildo Bustos, Indian of this town of Purísima del Rincón, I was born on 13 April 1832 and I painted my portrait to see if I could on 19 June 1891.*

(333)

1892: Paris
The Canal Scandal

A French court has decreed the bankruptcy of the Panama Canal Company. Work is suspended and scandal explodes. Suddenly, the savings of thousands of French peasants and petty bourgeois disappear. The enterprise that was to open a swathe between the oceans, that passage the conquistadors sought and dreamed about, has been a colossal swindle. The multi-million-dollar squanderings to bribe politicians and silence journalists are published. From London, Friedrich Engels writes: *The Panama business could well become for the bourgeois republic a Pandora's box, this grand National Steeplechase of Scandals. The miracle has been performed of transforming a canal which has* not *been dug out, into an unfathomable abyss . . .*

No one mentions the Antillean, Chinese, and East Indian workers whom yellow fever and malaria have exterminated at the rate of seven hundred dead per kilometer of canal opened through the mountains.

(102, 201, and 324)

1892: San José, Costa Rica
Prophesy of a Young Nicaraguan Poet
Named Rubén Darío

The coming century will see the greatest of the revolutions that have bloodied the earth. Big fish eat little fish? So be it, but soon we will have our own back. Pauperism reigns, and the worker carries on his

*shoulders a mountainous curse. Nothing matters now but miserable
gold. The disinherited are the eternal flock for the eternal slaughterhouse . . .*

*No force will be able to contain the torrent of fatal vengeance.
We will have to sing a new Marseillaise which, like the trumpets of
Jericho, will bring down the dwellings of the wicked . . .The heavens
will see with fearful joy, amid the thunder of the redemptive catastrophe, the castigation of arrogant evildoers, the supreme and terrible
vengeance of drunken poverty.*

(308)

1893: Canudos
Antonio Conselheiro

For a long time prophets have roamed the burning lands of northeast
Brazil. They announce that King Sebastian will return from the island
of Las Brumas and punish the rich and turn blacks into whites and
old into young. When the century ends, they say, the desert will be
sea and the sea, desert; and fire will destroy the coastal cities, frenetic
worshipers of money and sin. On the ashes of Recife, Bahia, Rio, and
São Paulo will rise a new Jerusalem and in it Christ will reign for a
thousand years. The hour of the poor is approaching, announce the
prophets. In seven years' time the heavens will descend to earth.
Then there will be no disease or death; and in the new terrestrial
and celestial reign every injustice will be corrected.

The pious Antonio Conselheiro wanders from town to town, squalid
and dusty phantom, followed by a chorus of litanies. His skin is a
jaded armor of leather; his beard, a thicket of brambles; his tunic, a
ragged shroud. He does not eat or sleep. He distributes among the
unfortunate the alms he receives. He talks to women with his back
turned. He refuses obedience to the impious government of the republic and in the plaza of the town of Bom Conselho throws the tax
edicts on a fire.

Pursued by the police, he flees into the desert. With two hundred
pilgrims he founds the community of Canudos beside the bed of an
ephemeral river. Here, heat does not permit rain to touch the soil.
From bald hillsides rise the first huts of mud and straw. In the middle
of this sullen land, promised land, first stair up to heaven, Antonio
Conselheiro triumphantly raises the image of Christ and announces
the apocalypse: *The rich, the unbelieving, and the fickle will be wiped*

*out. The waters will be dyed with blood. There will be only one
shepherd and one flock. Many hats and few heads . . .*

(80 and 252)

1895: Key West
Freedom Travels in a Cigar

He never sleeps, eats little. José Martí collects people and money,
writes articles and letters, gives speeches, poetry readings, and lectures; discusses, organizes, buys weapons. More than twenty years
of exile have not been able to put out his light.

He always knew that Cuba could not be itself without a revolution. Three years ago he founded the Cuban Revolutionary Party
on three Florida coasts. The party was born in the tobacco workshops
of Tampa and Key West, under the aegis of exiled Cuban workers
who have heard Martí in person and from the printed page.

The workshops are like labor universities. It is the tradition that
someone reads books or articles while the others work in silence, and
thus the tobacco workers daily receive ideas and news, and daily
travel through the world and history and the wonderful regions of
the imagination. Through the mouth of the "reader" the human word
shoots out and penetrates the women who strip tobacco and the men
who twist the leaves and shape cigars on thigh or table.

By agreement with generals Máximo Gómez and Antonio Maceo,
Martí gives the order to rise. The order travels from these Florida
workshops and reaches Cuba concealed within a Havana cigar.

(165, 200, and 242)

1895: Playitas
The Landing

Forty years from now, Marcos del Rosario will recall: *"General Gómez
didn't like me at first sight. He asked me, 'What are you going to
Cuba for? Did you lose something there?' "*

Marcos will clap his hands, knocking the dirt off them. *"General
Gómez was a fabulous little old guy, strong, strong, and very agile,
and talked very loud and sometimes would rear up and try to swallow
you. . ."*

He will cross the orchard looking for shade. *"Finally we found a ship that put us close to the coast of Cuba."*

He will show off the iron rings of his hammock. *"These are from that ship."*

Lying in the hammock, he will light a cigar. *"The ship left us in the sea and there was a terrific swell . . . "*

Two Dominicans and four Cubans in a boat. The storm plays with them. They have sworn that Cuba will be free.

"A dark night, you couldn't see a thing . . ."

A red moon rises, fights with the clouds. The boat fights with the hungry sea.

"The old guy was up in the prow. He was holding the wheel and Martí had the boat's compass. A big wave tore the wheel from the general . . . We were fighting the sea that wanted to swallow us and didn't want to let us reach land in Cuba . . ."

By some magic the boat does not shatter against the cliffs. The boat flies and plunges and surges back. Suddenly, it tacks about, the waves open up, and a little beach appears, a tiny horseshoe of sand.

"And General Gómez jumped onto the beach and when he stood on terra firma, he kissed the ground straight off and crowed like a rooster."

(258 and 286)

1895: Arroyo Hondo

In the Sierra

Not sadly but radiantly, festively, Marcos del Rosario will speak of Martí. *"When I saw him, I thought he was too weak. And then I saw he was a little live wire, who would jump here and land over there . . ."*

Martí teaches him to write. Martí puts his hand on Marcos's while he draws the letter A. *"He had gone to school and was a superb man."*

Marcos looks after Martí. He makes him good mattresses of dry leaves; he brings him coconut water to drink. The six men who landed at Playitas become a hundred, a thousand . . . Martí marches, knapsack on back, rifle over shoulder, climbing the sierra and stirring up people.

"When we were climbing the mountains, all loaded up, sometimes he'd fall. And I'd go to pick him up and right away he'd say, 'No,

thanks, no.' He had a ring made out of the shackles the Spaniards put on him when he was still a child."

(286)

1895: Dos Rios Camp

Martí's Testament

In the camp, in his shirtsleeves, Martí writes a letter to the Mexican Manuel Mercado, his intimate friend. He tells him that his life is in danger every day, and that it is well worthwhile to give it for his country, *and for my duty to prevent, in time, with the independence of Cuba, the United States from extending itself into the Antilles and from falling, with that extra force, upon our American lands. All I have done until now, and all I will do, is for that. It has had to be done in silence* . . . Shedding blood, writes Martí, the Cubans are preventing *the annexation of the peoples of our America by the turbulent and brutal North which despises them . . . I lived within the monster and I know its entrails—and my sling is the sling of David.* And further on: *This is death or life, and there is no room for error.*

Later his tone changes. He has other things to tell about. *And now, I will talk to you about myself.* But the night stops him, or maybe modesty, as soon as he starts to offer his friend those depths of his soul. *There is an affection of such delicate honesty* . . . he writes, and that is the last thing he writes.

At noon the next day, a bullet tumbles him from his horse.

(199)

1895: Niquinohomo

His Name Will Be Sandino

At the doors of this adobe house people gather, drawn by the cry. Like an upside-down spider the newborn baby moves his arms and legs. No Magi Kings come from afar to welcome him, but a farm laborer, a carpenter, and a passing market woman leave gifts.

The godmother offers lavender water to the mother and to the child a pinch of honey, which is his first taste of the world.

Later the godmother buries the placenta, which looks so like a root, in a corner of the garden. She buries it in a good spot, where there is plenty of sun, so that it will become soil here in Niquinohomo.

Within a few years, the child that just came from that placenta
will become soil too, the rebellious soil of all Nicaragua.

(8 and 317)

1896: Port-au-Prince
Disguises

According to the Constitution of Haiti, the republic of free blacks
speaks French and professes the Christian religion. The doctors are
mortified because, despite laws and punishments, "Creole" continues
as the language of nearly all Haitians and nearly all continue believing
in the voodoo gods who wander at large through woods and bodies.

The government demands that peasants publicly swear an oath:
"*I swear to destroy all fetishes and objects of superstition, if I carry
them with me or have them in my house or on my land. I swear never
to lower myself to any superstitious practice . . .*"

(68)

1896: Boca de Dos Rios
Requiem

"*Was it here?*"

A year has passed, and Máximo Gómez is telling the story to
Calixto García. The old warriors for Cuba's independence lead the
way from the Contramaestre River. Behind come their armies. General Gómez tells, that midday, how Martí had eaten with a good
appetite and afterwards recited some verses, as was his custom, and
how they then heard some shots. Everyone ran looking for a horse.

"*Was it here?*"

They come to a thicket, at the entrance to the road to Palo Picado.

"*Here,*" someone says.

Machete wielders clear the little patch of ground.

"*I never heard him complain or saw him give in,*" says Gómez.
Grumbling and getting angry, he adds, "*I ordered him . . . I advised
him to stay behind.*"

A patch of ground the size of his body.

General Máximo Gómez drops a stone. General Calixto García
another stone. And officers and soldiers keep filing past, and one after
another stones fall with a sharp click, stones on top of stones, as

Martí's memorial mound rears toward the sky, and only those clicks can be heard in the immense silence of Cuba.

(105)

1896: Papeete
Flora Tristán

The canvas, bare and immense, offers itself challengingly. Paul Gauguin paints, hunts around, throws on color as if bidding farewell to the world; and his desperate hand writes: *Where do we come from, what are we, where are we going?*

Over half a century ago, Gauguin's grandmother asked the same question in one of her books, and died finding out. The Peruvian family of Flora Tristán never mentioned it, as if it were bad luck or as if she were crazy or a ghost. When Paul asked about his grandmother, in the remote years of his childhood in Lima, they answered him:

"Time to go to bed, it's late."

Flora Tristán had burned up her short life preaching revolution, the proletarian revolution and the revolution of women enslaved by father, employer, and husband. Illness and the police finished her off. She died in France. The workers of Bordeaux paid for her coffin and carried her on a bier to the cemetery.

(21)

1896: Bogotá
José Asunción Silva

He loves his sister Elvira, aroma of lavender, balsam incense, furtive kisses of the palest sylph in Bogotá, and for her he writes his best verses. Night after night he goes to visit her in the cemetery. At the foot of her grave he feels better than in literary coteries.

José Asunción Silva had been born dressed in black, with a flower in his buttonhole. Thus has he lived for thirty years, through blow after blow, this languid founder of modernism in Colombia. The bankruptcy of his father, a silk and perfume merchant, has taken the bread from his mouth; and his complete works have been lost at sea in a shipwreck.

Far into the night he discusses, for the last time, the cadence of an alexandrine verse. From the door, lamp in hand, he bids goodnight to his guests. Then he smokes his last Turkish cigarette and for the last time pities himself before the mirror. No letter arrives from Paris to save him. Tormented by his creditors and by the spiteful who call him Chaste Susan, the poet unbuttons his shirt and presses the revolver against the ink cross that a doctor friend has drawn over his heart.

(319)

1896: Manaos

The Tree That Weeps Milk

The Indians call it "caucho." They slash it and the milk flows. In plantain leaves folded like bowls, the milk is collected and hardens in the heat of sun or smoke, while the human hand gives it shape. Since very ancient times the Indians have made from this wild milk long-lasting torches, pots that don't break, roofs that laugh at the rain, and balls that bounce and fly.

Over a century ago, the king of Portugal received from Brazil syringes without plungers and waterproof clothing; and before that the French sage La Condamine had studied the virtues of the scandalous gum that paid no attention to the law of gravity.

Thousands and thousands of shoes traveled from the Amazonian jungle to the port of Boston, until Charles Goodyear and Thomas Hancock, half a century ago, discovered how to keep the gum from breaking and softening. Then the United States started producing five million shoes a year, shoes invulnerable to cold, damp, and snow; and great factories arose in England, Germany, and France.

And not only shoes. The gum multiplies products and creates needs. Modern life turns giddily about the immense tree that weeps milk when you wound it. Eight years ago, in Belfast, the son of John Dunlop won a tricycle race using the pneumatic tires his father had invented to replace solid wheels; and last year Michelin created removable pneumatic tires for automobiles racing from Paris to Bordeaux.

Amazonia, fantastic jungle that seemed to be a reserve for monkeys, Indians, and lunatics, is now a game preserve for the United States Rubber Company, the Amazon Rubber Company, and other distant enterprises that suck its milk.

(334)

1896: Manaos

The Golden Age of Rubber

The curtain rises, parsimoniously, as the first chords of Ponchielli's opera *La Gioconda* are struck up. It is a night of great pomp and gala and mosquitos in the city of Manaos. Italian opera stars are inaugurating the Amazonas Theater, an immense nave of marble brought, like them, from Europe to the heart of the jungle.

Manaos and Belem do Parí are the rubber capitals of Brazil. Along with Iquitos in the Peruvian thickets, the three Amazonian cities lay out their streets with European paving stones and enliven their nights with horizontal girls from Paris, Budapest, Baghdad, or the local jungle. Gold batons conduct orchestras and ingots serve as paperweights; a hen's egg costs an arm and a leg. Extremely important people drink extremely imported drinks, recuperate in the thermal baths of Vichy, and send their children to study in Lisbon or Geneva on Booth Line ships which ply the muddy waters of the Amazon.

Who does the work in the rubber forests? In Brazil, victims of the droughts in the northeast. From those deserts peasants come to these swamps where one would be better off as a fish. This green prison shuts them in under contract; and soon death comes to rescue them from slavery and appalling solitude. In Peru, the hands are Indian. Many tribes are annihilated in this age of rubber which seems so eternal.

(299, 325, and 334)

1897: Canudos

Euclides da Cunha

During the day the earth smokes, flames, expands. When night falls, ax of ice, the earth shivers and contracts; by dawn, it has split apart.

Debris of earthquakes, Euclides da Cunha writes in his notebook. *Landscape that seems made to run away*, he notes. He observes the wrinkles of the earth and the curves of the river, a twisting strip of dried mud that the Indians call "Red Honey," and vainly seeks shade among the rachitic bushes. Here, the air turns all it touches to stone. A soldier lies face up with arms outstretched. A black scab disfigures his forehead. They killed him three months ago in hand-to-hand fighting, and now he is his own statue.

From afar, from the sacred village of Canudos, shots ring out. The monotonous staccato lasts for days, months, varied at times by cannon fire and machine-gun bursts, and Euclides would like to understand what kind of strength enables these mystical peasants to resist so fearlessly the assault of thirty battalions. Many thousands of them are letting themselves be killed out of devotion to the Messiah Antonio Conselheiro. The chronicler of this holy war asks himself how they can confuse these barren plains with heaven and this visionary, who only escaped the madhouse because it had no room for him, with Jesus Christ.

Hesitating between disgust and admiration, Euclides da Cunha describes what he sees, from bewilderment to bewilderment, for the readers of a São Paulo newspaper. A European-style socialist, mestizo who despises mestizos, Brazilian ashamed of Brazil, Euclides is among the most brilliant intellectuals of the republic that displays on its newly born flag the motto "Order and Progress." While the slaughter lasts, he strives to comprehend the mystery of the northeastern hinterland, land of fanatics where animosities and loyalties are inherited, where the "melancholia" of squalid cattle is cured with prayers and the deaths of children are celebrated with guitars.

(80)

1897: Canudos
The Dead Contain More Bullets Than Bones

but the last defenders of Canudos sing behind an enormous wooden cross, still expecting the arrival of archangels.

The commander of the first column has the horrifying corpse of Antonio Conselheiro photographed, *so that his death may be confirmed*. He too needs to be sure. Out of the corner of his eye the commander glances at that handful of rags and little bones.

Wretched peasants of all ages and colors had raised a rampart of bodies around this battered Methuselah, enemy of the republic and of the sinful cities. Five military expeditions have been necessary: five thousand soldiers surrounding Canudos, twenty cannons bombarding from the hillsides, incredible war of blunderbuss against Nordenfeldt machine gun.

The trenches have been reduced to graves of dust, and still the Canudos community does not surrender, this utopia without property or law where the poor shared the miserly land, the paltry bread, and faith in the immensity of heaven.

They fight house by house, inch by inch.
The four last survivors fall. Three men, one child.

(80)

1897: Rio de Janeiro
Machado de Assís

Brazilian writers, divided into sects that loathe each other, celebrate communions and consecrations at the Colombo and other cafes and bookshops. There they bid farewell, in the odor of sanctity, to colleagues journeying to lay flowers on Maupassant's grave in Paris; and in those temples, to the clink of glasses blessed by sacred liquors, is born the Brazilian Academy of Letters. Its first president is Machado de Assís.

He is the great Latin American novelist of this century. His books lovingly and humorously unmask the high society of drones that he, son of a mulatto father, has conquered and knows better than anyone. Machado de Assís tears off the fancy wrapping, false frames of false windows with a European view, and winks at the reader as he strips the mud wall.

(62 and 190)

1898: Coasts of Cuba
This Fruit Is Ready to Fall

The three hundred and twenty-five pounds of General William Shafter land on the eastern coast of Cuba. They come from cold northern climes where the general was busy killing Indians, and here they melt inside his overpowering wool uniform. Shafter sends his body up some steps to the back of a horse, and from there scans the horizon with a telescope.

He has come to command. As one of his officers, General Young, puts it, *the insurgents are a lot of degenerates, no more capable of self-government than the savages of Africa*. When the Spanish army begins to collapse before the patriots' implacable assault, the United States decides to take charge of the freedom of Cuba. If they come in, no one will be able to get them out, Martí and Maceo had warned. And they come in.

Spain had declined to sell this island *for a reasonable price*, and the North American intervention found its pretext in the opportune explosion of the battleship *Maine*, sunk in Havana harbor with its many guns and crewmen.

The invading army invokes the protection of North American citizens and the rescue of their interests threatened by devastating war and economic disaster. But in private, the officers explain that they must prevent the emergence of a black republic off the coasts of Florida.

(114)

1898: Washington
Ten Thousand Lynchings

In the name of the Negroes of the United States, Ida Wells protests to President McKinley that ten thousand lynchings have occurred in the past twenty years. If the government does not protect North American citizens within its borders, asks Ida Wells, by what right does it invoke that protection to invade other countries? Are not Negroes citizens? Or does the Constitution only guarantee them the right to be burned to death?

Mobs of fanatics, stirred up by press and pulpit, drag blacks from jails, tie them to trees, and burn them alive. Then the executioners celebrate in bars and broadcast their feats through the streets.

As a pretext, nigger-hunters use the rape of white women, in a country where a black woman's violation by a white is considered normal, but in the great majority of cases the burned blacks are guilty of no greater crime than a bad reputation, suspicion of robbery, or insolence.

President McKinley promises to look into the matter

(12)

1898: San Juan Hill
Teddy Roosevelt

Brandishing his Stetson, Teddy Roosevelt gallops at the head of his "Rough Riders"; and when he descends San Juan Hill he carries, crumpled in his hand, a Spanish flag. He will take all the glory for this battle which opens the way to Santiago de Cuba. Of the Cubans who also fought, no journalist will write a word.

Teddy believes in the grandeur of imperial destiny and in the power of his fists. He learned to box in New York, to save himself from beatings and humiliations he suffered as a sickly, asthmatic, and very myopic child. As an adult, he puts on the gloves with champions, hunts lions, lassos bulls, writes books, and roars speeches. On the printed page and from platforms he exalts the virtues of the strong races, born to rule, warlike races like his own, and proclaims that in nine out of ten cases there is no better Indian than a dead Indian (and the tenth, he says, must be more closely examined). A volunteer in all wars, he adores the supreme qualities of the soldier, who in the euphoria of battle feels himself in his heart to be a wolf, and despises soft generals who anguish over the loss of a couple of thousand men.

To make a quick end to the Cuban war, Teddy has proposed that a North American squadron should flatten Cadiz and Barcelona with its guns; but Spain, exhausted from so much warfare against the Cubans, surrenders in less than four months. From San Juan Hill, the victorious Teddy Roosevelt gallops at top speed to the governor-ship of New York State and on to the presidency of the United States. This fanatical devotee of a God who prefers gunpowder to incense takes a deep breath and writes: *No triumph of peace is quite so great as the supreme triumph of war.*

Within a few years, he will receive the Nobel Peace Prize.

(114 and 161)

1898: *Coasts of Puerto Rico*
This Fruit Is Falling

Ramón Emeterio Betances, long white beard, eyes of melancholy, is dying in Paris, in exile.

"*I do not want a colony,*" he says. "*Not with Spain, nor with the United States.*"

While the patriarch of Puerto Rico's independence approaches death, General Miles's soldiers sing as they land on the Guánica coast. With guns slung from shoulders and toothbrushes stuck in hats, the soldiers march before the impassive gaze of the peasants of sugarcane and coffee.

And Eugenio María de Hostos, who also wanted a fatherland, contemplates the hills of Puerto Rico from the deck of a ship, and feels sad and ashamed to see them pass from one master to another.

(141 and 192)

1898: Washington

President McKinley Explains
That the United States Should Keep
the Philippines by Direct Order of God

I walked the floor of the White House night after night until midnight; and I am not ashamed to tell you, gentlemen, that I went down on my knees and prayed Almighty God for light and guidance more than one night. And one night late it came to me this way—I don't know how it was but it came; first, that we could not give [the Philippines] back to Spain—that would be cowardly and dishonorable; second, that we could not turn them over to France or Germany—our commercial rivals in the Orient—that would be bad business and discreditable; third, we could not leave them to themselves—they were unfit for self-government, and they would soon have anarchy and misrule over there worse than Spain's was; and fourth, that there was nothing left for us to do but to take them all, and to educate the Filipinos, and uplift and civilize and Christianize them, and by God's grace do the very best we could by them, as our fellow men for whom Christ also died. And then I went to bed, and went to sleep and slept soundly.

(168)

1899: New York

Mark Twain Proposes Changing the Flag

I lift my lamp beside the golden door. The Statue of Liberty welcomes innumerable pilgrims, Europeans in search of the Promised Land, while it is announced that the center of the world, which took millennia to shift from the Euphrates to the Thames, is now the Hudson River.

In full imperial euphoria, the United States celebrates the conquest of the Hawaiian islands, Samoa and the Philippines, Cuba, Puerto Rico, and some little islands eloquently named the Ladrones (Thieves).* Now the Pacific and Caribbean are North American lakes, and the United Fruit Company is coming to birth; but novelist Mark Twain, the old spoilsport, proposes changing the national flag: the

---

* Former name of the Marianas in the Western Pacific.

white stripes should be black, he says, and the stars should be skulls and crossbones.

Trade union leader Samuel Gompers demands recognition of Cuba's independence and denounces those who throw freedom to the dogs at the moment of choosing between freedom and profit. For the great newspapers, on the other hand, the Cubans wanting independence are ingrates. Cuba is an occupied country. The United States flag, without black bars or skulls, flies in place of the Spanish flag. The invading forces have doubled in a year. The schools are teaching English; and the new history books speak of Washington and Jefferson and do not mention Maceo or Martí. There is no slavery any more; but in Havana cafes signs appear that warn: "Whites Only." The market is opened without conditions to capital hungry for sugar and tobacco.

(114 and 224)

1899: Rome

Calamity Jane

They say she sleeps with her revolvers hung from the bedpost and that she still beats the men at poker, drinking, and blasphemy. She has felled many men, they say, with a hook to the jaw, since the time when she is said to have fought with General Custer in Wyoming, and killed Indians to protect miners in the Black Hills of the Sioux. They say that they say that she rode a bull down the main street of Rapid City, and that she held up trains, and that in Fort Laramie she got the handsome sheriff Wild Bill Hickok to fall for her, and that he gave her a daughter and a horse named Satan that knelt to help her dismount. She always wore pants, they say, and often took them off, and there was no more generous woman in the saloons, nor more barefaced in loving and lying.

They say. Maybe she never was. Maybe, tonight, she isn't really in the arena of the Wild West Show, and old Buffalo Bill is having us on again. If it were not for the applause of the audience, not even the real Calamity Jane would be sure that she is this woman of forty-four, overweight and plain, who sends her Stetson flying and turns it into a colander.

(169)

1899: Rome

The Nascent Empire Flexes Its Muscles

In an ostentatious ceremony Buffalo Bill receives a gold watch encrusted with diamonds from the hands of the king of Italy. The Wild West Show is touring Europe. The conquest of the West has ended and the conquest of the world has begun. Buffalo Bill has under his orders a multinational army of five hundred men. Not only cowboys work in his circus; but also authentic lancers of the Prince of Wales, light cavalrymen of the French republican guard, cuirassiers of the emperor of Germany, Russian Cossacks, Arab horsemen, Mexican charros, and gauchos from the River Plata. Soldiers of the Fifth Cavalry act out their role as conquerors and conquered Indians, torn from the reservations, appear as extras repeating their defeats on the sands of the arena. A herd of buffalos, rare museum pieces, add realism to the blue uniforms and plumed helmets. Teddy Roosevelt's Rough Riders dramatize for the audience their recent conquest of Cuba and squads of Cubans, Hawaiians, and Filipinos pay servile homage to the victorious flag.

The program of the spectacle explains the winning of the West with Darwin's words: *It is the inevitable law of survival of the fittest.* In epic phrases, Buffalo Bill exalts the civic and military virtues of his nation, which has digested half of Mexico and numerous islands and now enters the twentieth century striding the world with the strut of a great power.

(157)

1899: Saint Louis

Far Away

Fire sprouts from mouths and rabbits from top hats; from the magic horn come little glass horses. A car runs over a prostrate woman, who gets up with one jump; another dances with a sword stuck in her belly. An enormous bear obeys complicated orders given in English.

Geronimo is invited to enter a little house with four windows. Suddenly the house moves and rises into the air. Startled, Geronimo leans out: down there the people look the size of ants. The keepers laugh. They give him some binoculars, like those he took from officers fallen in battle. Through the binoculars the far away comes close.

Geronimo aims at the sun and the violent light hurts his eyes. The keepers laugh; and since they laugh, he laughs too.

Geronimo, prisoner of war of the United States, is one of the attractions at the Saint Louis fair. Crowds come to see the tamed beast. The chief of the Apaches of Arizona sells bows and arrows, and for a few cents poses for snapshots, or prints as best he can the letters of his name.

(24)

1899: Rio de Janeiro
How to Cure by Killing

Sorcerous hands play with the price of coffee, and Brazil cannot pay the London and River Plate Bank and other very important creditors.

It is the hour of sacrifice, announces Finance Minister Joaquim Murtinho. The minister believes in the *natural laws* of economics, which by *natural selection* condemn the weak, that is to say the poor, that is to say almost everyone. Should the State take the coffee business out of the speculators' hands? That, says an indignant Murtinho, would be a violation of *natural laws* and a dangerous step toward socialism, that fearsome plague that European workers are bringing to Brazil: socialism, he says, denies freedom and turns man into an ant.

National industry, Murtinho believes, is not *natural*. Small as it is, national industry is taking labor from the plantations and raising the price of hands. Murtinho, guardian angel of the great-estate order, will see to it that the crisis is not paid for by the owners of men and lands, who have survived intact the abolition of slavery and the proclamation of the republic. To pay off the English banks and balance the books, the minister burns in an oven any banknote that comes his way, suppresses any public service that is handy, and lets loose a hail of taxes on the poor.

Economist by vocation and physician by profession, Murtinho also makes interesting experiments in the field of physiology. In his laboratory he extracts the encephalic mass of rats and rabbits and decapitates frogs to study the convulsions of the body, which continues moving as if it had a head.

(75)

1900: Huanuni
Patiño

The horseman comes from desolation and rides across desolation, through icy winds, at a slow gait over the nakedness of the planet. A mule loaded with rocks follows him.

The horseman has spent much time boring into rocks and opening up caves with dynamite charges. He has never seen the sea, nor known even the city of La Paz, but suspects that the world is living an industrial era and that industry eats hitherto disdained minerals. He has not gone into the mountains after silver, as so many have. Searching for tin, as no one else is, he has penetrated to the heart of the mountain, to its very soul, and has found it.

Simón Patiño, the horseman stung through with cold, the miner mortified by solitude and debt, reaches the town of Huanuni. In his mule's saddlebags he has pieces of the world's richest vein of tin. These rocks will make him king of Bolivia.

(132)

1900: Mexico City
Posada

He illustrates verses and news. His broadsheets sell in the markets and at the doors of churches and wherever a balladeer sings the prophesies of Nostradamus, the horrifying details of the train derailment at Temamatla, the last appearance of the Virgin of Guadalupe, or the tragedy of the woman who gave birth to four lizards in a barrio of this city.

By the magical hand of José Guadalupe Posada, *corrido* ballads never lose their spontaneity, topicality, and popularity. In his drawings, the knives of loudmouths and tongues of gossips will always be sharp, the Devil will keep dancing and flaming, Death laughing, pulque moistening mustaches, *the unhappy Eleuterio Mirafuentes crushing with an enormous stone the cranium of the ancient author of his days*. This year, a Posada drawing celebrated the appearance of the first electric streetcar in the streets of Mexico. Now, another shows the streetcar crashing into a funeral procession in front of the cemetery, with a tremendous scattering of skeletons. They sell for one centavo a copy, printed on brown paper, with verses for anyone who knows how to read and weep.

His workshop is a mess of rolls and receptacles and zinc plates and wooden wedges, all piled around the press and beneath a rain of newly printed papers hung up to dry. Posada works from morning till night, engraving marvels. "Little drawings," he says. From time to time he goes to the door to smoke a restful cigar, not forgetting to cover his head with a derby and his great belly with a dark woolen vest.

Every day, past Posada's workshop door go the professors of the neighboring Fine Arts Academy. They never look in or greet him.

(263 and 357)

1900: Mexico City
Porfirio Díaz

He grew up in the shadow of Juárez. *The man who weeps as he kills*, Juárez called him.

"*Weeping, weeping, he'll kill me if I'm not careful.*"

Porfirio Díaz has been ruling Mexico for a quarter of a century. The official biographers record for posterity his yawns and his aphorisms. They do not note it down when he says:

"*The best Indian is six feet underground.*"

"*Kill them on the spot.*"

"*Don't stir up the herd on me.*"

"The herd" are the legislators, who vote Yes when their heads nod from sleepiness, and who call Don Porfirio *the Unique, the Indispensable, the Irreplaceable*. The people call him "Don Perfidy" and make fun of his courtiers:

"*What time is it?*"

"*Whatever you say, Señor President.*"

He displays his little finger and says: "*Tlaxcala hurts me.*" He points to his heart and says: "*Oaxaca hurts me.*" With his hand on his liver, he says: "*Michoacán hurts me.*" In a flash he has three governors trembling before him.

The shot-while-trying-to-escape law is applied to the rebellious and the curious. At the height of Pax Porfiriana, Mexico makes progress. Messages that previously went by mule, horse, or pigeon now fly over seventy thousand kilometers of telegraph wires. Where stagecoaches used to go, there are fifteen thousand kilometers of railway. The nation pays its debts punctually and supplies minerals and food to the world market. On every big estate a fortress rises. From the battlements guards keep watch over the Indians, who may not even

change masters. There are no schools of economics but Don Porfirio
rules surrounded by "scientists" specializing in the purchase of lands
precisely where the next railway will pass. Capital comes from the
United States and ideas and fashions are bought secondhand in France.
Mexico City likes to call itself "the Paris of the Americas," although
more white peasant pants than trousers are seen in the streets; and
the frock-coated minority inhabit Second Empire–style palaces. The
poets have baptized its evenings as "the green hour," not because of
the light through the trees, but in memory of De Musset's absinthe.

(33 and 142)

1900: Mexico City
The Flores Magón Brothers

The people sail on rivers of pulque as bells ring out and rockets boom
and knives glint under the Bengal lights. The crowd invades the
Alameda and other prohibited streets, the zone sacred to corseted
ladies and jacketed gentlemen, with the Virgin on a portable platform.
From that lofty ship of lights, the Virgin's wings protect and guide.

This is the day of Our Lady of the Angels, which in Mexico lasts
for a week of balls; and on the margin of the violent joy of people,
as if wishing to merit it, a new newspaper is born. It is called *Re-
generation*. It inherits the enthusiasms and debts of *The Democrat*,
closed down by the dictatorship. Jesús, Ricardo, and Enrique Flores
Magón write it, publish it, and sell it.

The Flores Magón brothers grow with punishment. Since their
father died, they have taken turns between jail, law studies, occasional
small jobs, combative journalism, and stones-against-bullets street
demonstrations.

All belongs to all, they had been told by their father, the Indian
Teodoro Flores, that bony face now up among the stars. A thousand
times he had told them: *Repeat that!*

(287)

1900: Merida, Yucatán
Henequén

One of every three Mayas in Yucatán is a slave, hostage of henequén,
and their children, who inherit their debts, will be slaves too. Lands
are sold complete with Indians, but the great henequén plantations

use scientific methods and modern machinery, receive orders by telegraph and are financed by New York banks. Steam-driven scraping machines separate the fibers; and International Harvester trains run them to a port called Progress. Meanwhile guards shut the Indians into barracks when night falls, and at dawn mount horses to herd them back to the rows of spiny plants.

With sisal yarn, henequén yarn, everything on earth can be tied up, and every ship on the ocean uses henequén ropes. Henequén brings prosperity to Yucatán, one of Mexico's richest regions: in Mérida, the capital, golden grilles keep mules and Indians from trampling gardens badly copied from Versailles. The bishop's carriage is almost identical to the one the pope uses in Rome, and from Paris come architects who imitate French medieval castles, although today's heroes venture forth not for captive princesses but for free Indians.

General Ignacio Bravo, eyes like knives, white moustache, mouth clamped tight, has arrived in Mérida to exterminate the Mayas who still beat the drums of war. The guns of San Benito salute the redeemer of henequén. In the Plaza de Armas, beneath leafy laurels, the masters of Yucatán offer General Bravo the silver sword that awaits the conqueror of Chan Santa Cruz, the rebels' sacred city in the jungle.

And then falls the slow lid of night.

(273)

From the Mexican Corrido of the Twenty-Eighth Battalion

I'm on my way, on my way,
on my way with great delight,
because the Maya Indians
are dying, they say, of fright.

I'm on my way, on my way,
to the other side of the sea,
for the Indians no longer
have any way to flee.

I'm on my way, on my way,
God keep you warm, my jewel,
because the Maya Indians
will make a lovely fuel.

I'm on my way, on my way,
for the winter there to dwell,
because the Maya Indians
are going straight to hell.

(212)

1900: Tabi
The Iron Serpent

In the forefront the cannons thunder, overturning barricades and crushing the dying. Behind the cannons the soldiers, almost all Indians, set fire to the communities' cornfields and fire repeating Mausers against old weapons loaded by the barrel. Behind the soldiers, peons, almost all Indians, lay tracks for the railway and raise posts for the telegraph and the gallows.

The railway, snake without scales, has its tail in Mérida and its long body grows toward Chan Santa Cruz. The head reaches Santa María and jumps to Hobompich and from Hobompich to Tabi, double tongue of iron, swift, voracious. Breaking jungle, cutting earth, it pursues, attacks, and bites. On its gleaming march it swallows free Indians and shits slaves.

The Chan Santa Cruz sanctuary is doomed. It had come into being half a century ago, born of that little mahogany cross that appeared in the thicket and said, "*My father has sent me to speak with you, who are earth.*"

(273)

The Prophet

Here it came to pass, more than four centuries ago. Lying on his mat, on his back, the priest-jaguar of Yucatán heard the message of the gods. They spoke to him through the roof, squatting on his house, in a language no one understood any more.

Chilam Balam, he who was the mouth of the gods, remembered what had not yet happened and announced what would be:

"*Stick and stone will rise up for the struggle . . . Dogs will bite their masters . . . Those with borrowed thrones must throw up what they swallowed. Very sweet, very tasty was what they swallowed, but they will vomit it up. The usurpers will depart to the limits of the waters . . . Then there will be no more devourers of man . . . When greed comes to an end, the face of the world will be set free, its hands will be set free, its feet will be set free."*

(23)

(End of the second volume of
Memory of Fire)

The Sources

1. Abreu y Gómez, Ermilo. *Canek. Historia y leyenda de un héroe maya*. Mexico City: Oasis, 1982.
2. Acevedo, Edberto Oscar. *El ciclo histórico de la revolución de mayo*. Seville: Escuela de Estudios Hispanoamericanos, 1957.
3. Acuña de Figueroa, Francisco. *Nuevo mosaico poético*, (prologue by Gustavo Gallinal). Montevideo: Claudio García, 1944.
4. Adoum, Jorge Enrique. "Las Galápagos: el origen de *El origen* . . ." (and articles by Asimov, Pyke, and others) in *Darwin*, El Correo de la Unesco, Paris, May 1982.
5. Aguirre, Nataniel. *Juan de la Rosa*. La Paz: Gisbert, 1973.
6. Ajofrín, Francisco de. *Diaro de viaje*. Madrid: Real Academia de la Historia, 1958.
7. Alcáraz, Ramón, *et al. Apuntes para la historia de la guerra entre México y los Estados Unidos*. Mexico City: Siglo XXI, 1970.
8. Alemán Bolaños, Gustavo. *Sandino, el libertador*. Mexico City and Guatemala: Ed. del Caribe, 1951.
9. Anderson Imbert, Enrique. *Historia de la literatura hispanoamericana*. Mexico City: FCE, 1974.
10. Anson, George, *Voyage autour du monde*, Amsterdam and Leipzig, 1751.
11. Antonil, André João. *Cultura e opulencia do Brasil por suas drogas e minas*, (annotated by A. Mansuy). Paris: Université, 1968.
12. Aptheker, Herbert (ed.). *A Documentary History of the Negro People in the United States*. New York: Citadel, 1969.
13. Arciniegas, Germán, *Los comuneros*. Mexico City: Guarania, 1951.
14. Arnold, Mayer. *Del Plata a los Andes. Viaje por las provincias en la época de Rosas*. Buenos Aires: Huarpes, 1944.
15. Arriaga, Antonio. *La patria recobrada*. Mexico City: FCE, 1967.
16. Arzáns de Orsúa y Vela, Bartolomé. *Historia de la Villa Imperial de Potosí* (Lewis Hanke and Gunnar Mendoza, eds.). Providence: Brown University Press, 1965.
17. Astuto, Philip Louis. *Eugenio Espejo, reformador ecuatoriano de la Ilustración*. Mexico City: FCE, 1969.
18. Atl, Dr. *Las artes populares en México*. Mexico City: Instituto Nacional Indigenista, 1980.
19. Aubry, Octave. *Vie privée de Napoléon*. Paris: Tallandier, 1977.
20. Ayestarán, Lauro. *La música en el Uruguay*. Montevideo: SODRE, 1953.
21. Baelen, Jean. *Flora Tristán: Feminismo y socialismo en el siglo XIX*. Madrid: Taurus, 1974.
22. Barnet, Miguel. *Akeké y la jutía*. Havana: Unión, 1978.

23. Barrera Vásquez, Alfredo, and Silvia Rendón (eds.). *El libro de los libros de Chilam Balam*. Mexico City: FCE, 1978.
24. Barrett, S. M. (ed.). *Gerónimo, historia de su vida* (notes by Manuel Sacristán). Barcelona: Grijalbo, 1975.
25. Barrett, William E. *La amazona*. Barcelona: Grijalbo, 1982.
26. Basadre, Jorge. *La multitud, la ciudad y el campo en la historia del Perú*. Lima: Treintaetrés y Mosca Azul, 1980.
27. Bastide, Roger. *Les religions africaines au Brésil*. Paris: Presses Universitaires, 1960.
28. ———. *Les Amériques noires*. Paris: Payot, 1967.
29. Bazin, Germain. *Aleijadinho et la sculpture baroque au Brésil*. Paris: Du Temps, 1963.
30. Beck, Hanno. *Alexander von Humboldt*. Mexico City: FCE, 1971.
31. Benítez, Fernando. *Los indios de México* (Vol. 2). Mexico City: Era, 1968.
32. ———. *Los indios de México* (Vol. 4). Mexico City: Era, 1972.
33. ———. *El porfirismo*. *Lázaro Cárdenas y la revolución mexicana*. Mexico City: FCE, 1977.
34. Benítez, Rubén A. *Una histórica función de circo*. Buenos Aires: Universidad, 1956.
35. Bermúdez, Oscar. *Historia del salitre, desde sus orígenes hasta la guerra del Pacífico*. Santiago de Chile: Universidad, 1963.
36. Bermúdez Bermúdez, Arturo. *Materiales para la historia de Santa Marta*. Bogotá: Banco Central Hipotecario, 1981.
37. Beyhaut, Gustavo. *American centrale e meridionale. Dall'indipendenza alla crisis attuale*. Roma: Feltrinelli, 1968.
38. Bierhorst, John. *In the Trail of the Wind. American Indian Poems and Ritual Orations*. New York: Farrar, Straus and Giroux, 1973.
39. Bilbao, Francisco. *La revolución en Chile y los mensajes del proscripto*. Lima: Imprenta del Comercio, 1853.
40. Bolívar, Simón. *Documentos*. (Selected by Manuel Galich.) Havana: Casa de las Américas, 1975.
41. Boorstin, Daniel J. *The Lost World of Thomas Jefferson*. Chicago: University of Chicago Press, 1981.
42. Bonilla, Heraclio, *et el*. *La independencia del Perú*. Lima: Instituto de Estudios Peruanos, 1981.
43. ———. *et al*. *Nueva historia general del Perú*. Lima: Mosca Azul, 1980.
44. ———. *Guano y burguesía en el Perú*. Lima: Instituto de Estudios Peruanos, 1974.
45. ———. *Un siglo a la deriva. Ensayos sobre el Perú, Bolivia y la guerra*. Lima: Instituto de Estudios Peruanos, 1980.
46. Botting, Douglas. *Humboldt and the Cosmos*. London: Sphere, 1973.
47. Box, Pelham Horton. *Los orígenes de la guerra de la Triple Alianza*. Buenos Aires and Asunción: Nizza, 1958.

48. Boxer, C. R. *The Golden Age of Brazil (1695–1750)*. Berkeley: University of California Press, 1969.

49. Brading, D. A., *Mineros y comerciantes en el México borbónico (1763–1810)*. Mexico City: FCE, 1975.

50. Brooke, Frances. *The History of Emily Montague*. Toronto: McClelland and Stewart, 1961.

51. Brown, Dee. *Bury My Heart at Wounded Knee. An Indian History of The American West*. New York: Holt, Rinehart and Winston, 1971.

52. Brunet, Michel. *Les canadiens après la conquête (1759–1775)*. Montreal: Fides, 1980.

53. Busaniche, José Luis. *Bolívar visto por sus contemporáneos*. Mexico City: FCE, 1981.

54. ———. *San Martín vivo*. Buenos Aires: Emecé, 1950.

55. ———. *Historia argentina*. Buenos Aires: Solar/Hachette, 1973.

56. Cabrera, Lydia. *El monte*. Havana: CR, 1954.

57. Calderón de la Barca, Frances Erskine de. *La vida en México durante una residencia de dos años en ese pas*. Mexico City: Porrúa, 1959.

58. Canales, Claudia. *Romualdo García. Un fotógrafo, una ciudad, una época*. Guanajuato: Gobierno del Estado, 1980.

59. Cardoza y Aragón, Luis. *Guatemala: las líneas de su mano*. Mexico City: FCE, 1965.

60. Cardozo, Efraím. *Breve historia del Paraguay*. Buenos Aires: EUDEBA, 1965.

61. ———. *Hace cien años. Crónicas de la guerra de 1864–1870*, Asunción, Emasa, 1967/1976.

62. Carlos, Lasinha Luis. *A Colombo na vida do Rio*. Rio de Janeiro: n.p., 1970.

63. Carpentier, Alejo. *El reino de este mundo*. Barcelona: Seix Barral, 1975.

64. Carrera Damas, Germán. *Bolívar*. Montevideo: Marcha, 1974.

65. Carvalho-Neto, Paulo de. *El folklore de las luchas sociales*. Mexico City: Siglo XXI, 1973.

66. ———. "Contribución al estudio de los negros paraguayos de Acampamento Loma," in *América Latina*, Rio de Janeiro, Centro Latinoamericano de Pesquisas em Ciencias Sociais, January/June 1962.

67. Casarrubias, Vicente. *Rebeliones indígenas en la Nueva España*. Mexico City: Secretaría de Educación Pública, 1945.

68. Casimir, Jean. *La cultura oprimida*. Mexico City: Nueva Imagen, 1980.

69. Catton, Bruce. *Reflections on the Civil War*. New York: Berkley, 1982.

70. ———. *Short History of the Civil War*. New York: Dell, 1976.

71. Césaire, Aimé. *Toussaint Louverture*. Havana: Instituto del Libro, 1967.

72. Clastres, Hélène. *La terre sans mal. Le prophetisme tupi-guarani*. Paris: Seuil, 1975.

73. Clavijero, Francisco Javier. *Historia antigua de México*. Mexico City: Editora México, 1958.

74. Conrad, Robert. *Os últimos anos da escravatura no Brasil*. Rio de Janeiro: Civilização Brasileira, 1975.

75. Corrêa Filho, Virgilio. *Joaquim Murtinho*. Rio de Janeiro: Imprensa Nacional, 1951.

76. Cortesão, Jaime. *Do Tratado de Madri à conquista dos Sete Povos*. Rio de Janeiro: Biblioteca Nacional, 1969.

77. Coughtry, Jay. *The Notorious Triangle. Rhode Island and the African Slave Trade, 1700–1807*. Philadelphia: Temple University Press, 1981.

78. Craton, Michael. *Testing the Chains. Resistance to Slavery in the British West Indies*. Ithaca: Cornell University Press, 1982.

79. Crowther, J. G. *Benjamin Franklin y J. Willard Gibbs*. Buenos Aires: Espasa-Calpe, 1946.

80. Cunha, Euclides da. *Os sertões*. São Paulo: Alves, 1936.

81. Current, Richard N. *The Lincoln Nobody Knows*. New York: Hill and Wang, 1981.

82. Cháves, Julio César. *El Supremo Dictador*. Buenos Aires: Difusam, 1942.

83. ———. *El presidente López. Vida y govierno de don Carlos*. Buenos Aires: Ayacucho, 1955.

84. ———. *Castelli, el adalid de Mayo*. Buenos Aires: Ayacucho, 1944.

85. Daireaux, Max. *Melgarejo*. Buenos Aires: Andina, 1966.

86. Dallas, Robert Charles. *Historia de los cimarrones*. Havana: Casa de las Américas, 1980.

87. Dalton, Roque. *Las historias prohibidas del Pulgarcito*. Mexico City: Siglo XXI, 1974.

88. Darwin, Charles. *Mi viaje alrededor del mundo*. Valencia: Sampere, n.d.

89. Davidson, Basil. *Black Mother: Africa and the Atlantic Slave Trade*. London: Pelican, 1980.

90. Debien, Gabriel. "Le marronage aux Antilles Français au XVIIIe. siècle," in *Caribbean Studies*, Vol. 6, No. 3, Río Piedras, Institute of Caribbean Studies, October 1966.

91. Debo, Angie. *A History of the Indians of the United States*. Oklahoma: University of Oklahoma Press, 1979.

92. Defoe, Daniel. *Aventuras de Robinsón Crusoe*. Mexico City: Porrúa, 1975.

93. Descola, Jean. *La vida cotidiana en el Perú en tiempos de los españoles (1710–1820)*. Buenos Aires: Hachette, 1962.

94. Díaz, Lilia. "El liberalismo militante," in *Historia general de México*. Mexico City: El Colegio de México, 1977.

95. Doucet, Louis. *Quand les français cherchaient fortune aux Caraïbes*. Paris: Fayard, 1981.

96. Douville, Raymond, and Jacques-Donat Casanova. *La vie quotidienne en Nouvelle-France. Le Canada, de Champlain a Montcalm*. Paris: Hachette, 1964.

97. ———. *Des indiens du Canada a l'époque de la colonisation française*. Paris: Hachette, 1967.

98. Duchet, Michèle. *Antropología e historia en el Siglo de las Luces*. Mexico City: Siglo XXI, 1975.

99. Dugran, J. H. *Edgar A. Poe*. Buenos Aires: Lautaro, 1944.

100. Dujovne, Marta (with Augusto Roa Bastos *et al*.). *Cándido López*. Parma: Ricci, 1976.

101. Dumas, Alejandro. *Montevideo o una nueva Troya*. Montevideo: Claudio García, 1941.

102. Duval, Miles P., Jr. *De Cádiz a Catay*. Panama: Editorial Universitaria, 1973.

103. Echagüe, J. P. *Tradiciones, leyendas y cuentos argentinos*. Buenos Aires: Espasa-Calpe, 1960.

104. Echeverría, Esteban. *La cautiva/El matadero*. (Prologue by Juan Carlos Pellegrini.) Buenos Aires: Huemul, 1964.

105. Escalante Beatón, Aníbal. *Calixto García. Su campaña en el 95*. Havana: Ciencias Sociales, 1978.

106. Eyzaguirre, Jaime. *Historia de Chile*. Santiago de Chile: Zig-Zag, 1977.

107. ———. *Chile y Bolivia. Esquema de un proceso diplomático*. Santiago de Chile: Zig-Zag, 1963.

108. Fals Borda, Orlando. *Historia doble de la costa*. Bogotá: Carlos Valencia, 1980/1981.

109. Faria, Alberto de. *Irenêo Evangelista de Souza, barão e visconde de Mauá 1813–1889*. São Paulo: Editora Nacional, 1946.

110. Felce, Emma, and León Benarós. *Los caudillos del año 20*. Buenos Aires: Nova, 1944.

111. Fernández de Lizardi, José Joaquín. *El Periquillo Sarniento*. Buenos Aires: Maucci, n.d.

112. Fernández Retamar, Roberto. *Introducción a José Martí*. Havana: Casa de las Américas, 1978.

113. Fohlen, Claude. *La vie quotidienne au Far West*. Paris: Hachette, 1974.

114. Foner, Philip S. *La guerra hispano-cubano-norteamericana y el surgimiento del imperialismo yanqui*. Havana: Ciencias Sociales, 1978.

115. Franco, José Luciano. *Historia de la revolución de Haití*. Havana: Academia de Ciencias, 1966.

116. Frank, Waldo. *Nacimiento de un mundo. Bolívar dentro del marco de sus propios pueblos*. Havana: Instituto del Libro, 1967.

117. Freitas, Décio. *O socialismo missioneiro*. Porto Alegre: Movimento, 1982.

118. Freitas, Newton. *El Aleijadinho*. Buenos Aires: Nova, 1944.

119. Freyre, Gilberto. *Sobrados e mucambos*. Rio de Janeiro: José Olympio, 1951.

120. Friedemann, Nina S. de (with Richard Cross). *Ma Ngombe: Guerreros y ganaderos en Palenque*. Bogotá: Carlos Valencia, 1979.

121. ———. (with Jaime Arocha). *Herederos del jaguar y la anaconda*. Bogotá: Carlos Valencia, 1982.

122. Frieiro, Eduardo. *Feijão, agua e couve*. Belo Horizonte: Itatiaia, 1982.

123. Frota, Lélia Coelho. *Ataíde*. Rio de Janeiro: Nova Fronteira, 1982.

124. Furst, Peter T., and Salomón Nahmad. *Mitos y arte huicholes*. Mexico City: SEP/Setentas, 1972.

125. Fusco Sansone, Nicolás. *Vida y obras de Bartolomé Hidalgo*. Buenos Aires: n.p., 1952.

126. Gantier, Joaquín, *Doña Juana Azurduy de Padilla*. La Paz: Icthus, 1973.

127. García Cantú, Gastón. *Utopías mexcianas*. Mexico City: FCE, 1978.

128. ———. *Las invasiones norteamericanas en México*. Mexico City: Era, 1974.

129. ———. *El socialismo en México, siglo XIX*. Mexico City: Era, 1974.

130. Garraty, John A., and Peter Gay. *Columbia History of the World*. New York: Harper and Row, 1972.

131. Garrett, Pat. *La verdadera historia de Billy the Kid*. Mexico City: Premiá, 1981.

132. Geddes, Charles F. *Patiño, the Tin King*. London: Hale, 1972.

133. Gendrop, Paul. "La escultura clásica maya," in *Artes de México*, No. 167, Mexico.

134. Gerbi, Antonello. *La disputa del Neuvo Mundo*. Mexico City: FCE, 1960.

135. Gibson, Charles. *Los aztecas bajo el dominio español (1519–1810)*. Mexico City: Siglo XXI, 1977.

136. Girod, François. *La vie quotidienne de la société créole (Saint-Domingue au 18e. siècle)*. Paris: Hachette, 1972.

137. Gisbert, Teresa. *Iconografía y mitos indígenas en el arte*. La Paz: Gisbert, 1980.

138. ——— (with José de Mesa). *Historia de la pintura cuzqueña*. Lima: Banco Wiese, 1982.

139. Gisler, Antoine. *L'esclavage aux Antilles français (XVIIe.–XIXe. siècle)*. Paris: Karthala, 1981.

140. Godio, Julio. *Historia del movimiento obrero latinoamericano*. Mexico City: Nueva Imagen, 1980.

141. González, José Luis. *La llegada*. San Juan: Mortiz/Huracán, 1980.

142. González, Luis. "El liberalismo triunfante," in *Historia General de México*. Mexico City: El Colegio de México, 1977.

143. ——— et al. *La economía mexicana en la época de Juárez*. Mexico City: Secretaría de Industria y Comercio, 1972.

144. González Navarro, Moisés. *Raza y tierra. La guerra de castas y el henequén*. Mexico City: El Colegio de México, 1979.

145. González Prada, Manuel. *Horas de lucha*. Lima: Universo, 1972.

146. González Sánchez, Isabel. "Sistemas de trabajo, salarios, y situación de los trabajadores agrícolas (1750–1810)," in *Las clase obrera en la historia de México. 1. De la colonia al imperio*. Mexico City: Siglo XXI, 1980.

147. Granada, Daniel. *Supersticiones del río de la Plata*. Buenos Aires: Kraft, 1947.

148. Gredilla, A. Federico. *Biografía de José Celestino Mutis y sus observaciones sobre las viglias y sueños de algunas plantas*. Bogotá: Plaza y Janés, 1982.

149. Green, Martin. *Dreams of Adventure, Deeds of Empire*. New York: Basic Books, 1979.

150. Grigulévich, José. *Francisco de Mirana y la lucha por la liberación de la América Latina*. Havana: Casa de las Américas, 1978.

151. Griswold, D. C. *El istmo de Panamá y lo que vi en él*. Panama: Ed. Universitaria, 1974.

152. Guasch, Antonio. *Diccionario castellano-guaraní y guaraní-castellano*. Seville: Loyola, 1961.

153. Guerrero Guerrero, Raúl. *El pulque*. Mexico City: Instituto Nacional de Antropología e Historia, 1980.

154. Guier, Enrique. *William Walker*. San José, Costa Rica: n.p., 1971.

155. Guiteras Holmes, Cali. *Los peligros del alma. Visión del mundo de un tzotzil*. Mexico City: FCE 1965.

156. Guy, Christian. *Almanach historique de la gastronomie française*. Paris: Hachette, 1981.

157. Hassrick, Peter H., *et al. Buffalo Bill and the Wild West*. New York: The Brooklyn Museum, 1981.

158. Hernández, José. *Martín Fierro*. Buenos Aires: EUDEBA, 1963.

159. Hernández Matos, Román. *Micaela Bastidas, la precursora*. Lima: Atlas, 1981.

160. Herrera Luque, Francisco. *Boves, el Urogallo*. Caracas: Fuentes, 1973.

161. Hofstadter, Richard. *The American Political Tradition*. New York: Knopf, 1948.

162. Huberman, Leo. *We, the People. The Drama of America*. New York: Monthly Review Press, 1970.

163. Humboldt, Alejandro de. *Ensayo político sobre el reino del la Nueva España*. Mexico City: Porrúa, 1973.

164. Ibañez Fonseca, Rodrigo, *et al. Literatura de Colombia aborigen*. Bogotá: Instituto Colombiano de Cultura, 1978.

165. Ibarra, Jorge. *José Martí, dirigente político e ideólogo revolucionario*. Havana: Ciencias Sociales, 1980.

166. Irazusta, Julio. *Ensayo sobre Rosas*. Buenos Aires: Tor, 1935.

167. Isaacs, Jorge. *María* (introduction by Germán Arciniegas). Barcelona: Círculo de Lectores, 1975.

168. Jacobs, Paul (with Saul Landau and Eve Pell). *To Serve the Devil. A*

Documentary Analysis of America's Racial History and Why It Has Been Kept Hidden. New York: Random House, 1971.

169. Jane, Calamity. *Cartas a la hija (1877–1902)*. Barcelona: Anagrama, 1982.

170. Juan, Jorge, and Antonio de Ulloa. *Noticias secretas de América*. Caracas: Ayacucho, 1979.

171. Kaufmann, William W. *British Policy and the Independence of Latin American (1804–1828)*. Hamden, Connecticut: Shoe String Press, 1967.

172. Klein, Herbert S. *Bolivia. The Evolution of a Multiethnic Society*. New York and Oxford: Oxford University Press, 1982.

173. Kom, Anton de. *Nosotros, esclavos de Surinam*. Havana: Casa de las Américas, 1981.

174. Konetzke, Richard. *Colección de documentos para la historia de la formación social de Hispanoamérica*. Madrid: Consejo Superior de Investigaciones Científicas, 1962.

175. Kossok, Manfred. *El virreynato del río de la Plata. Su estructura económico-social*. Buenos Aires: Futuro, 1959.

176. Lacoursière, J. (with J. Provencher and D. Vaugeois). *Canada/Quebec. Synthése historique*. Montreal: Renouveau Pedagogique, 1978.

177. Lafargue, Pablo (Paul). *Textos escogidos*. (Selection and introduction by Salvador Morales.) Havana: Ciencias Sociales, 1976.

178. Lafaye, Jacques. *Quetzalcóatl y Guadalupe. La formación de la conciencia nacional en México*. Mexico City: FCE, 1977.

179. Lanuza, José Luis. *Coplas y cantares argentinos*. Buenos Aires: Emecé, 1952.

180. Lara, Oruno. *La Guadeloupe dans l'histoire*. Paris: L'Harmattan, 1979.

181. Lautréamont, Conde de. *Oeuvres complètes*. (Prologue by Maurice Saillet.) Paris, Librairie Générale Française, 1963. Spanish trans: *Obras completas*. (Prologue by Aldo Pellegrini.) Buenos Aires: Argonauta, 1964.

182. Laval, Ramon. *Oraciones, ensalmos y conjuros del pueblo chileno*. Santiago de Chile: n.p., 1910.

183. Lewin, Boleslao. *La rebelión de Túpac Amaru y los orígenes de la emancipación americana*. Buenos Aires: Hachette, 1957.

184. Liedtke, Klaus. "Coca-Cola über alles," in the newspaper *El País*. Madrid, 30 July 1978.

185. Liévano Aguirre, Indalecio. *Los orandes conflictos sociales y económicos de nuestra historia*. Bogotá: Tercer Mundo, 1964.

186. Lima, Heitor Ferreira. "Os primeiros empréstimos externos," in *Ensaios de Opinião*, No. 2/1, Rio de Janeiro, 1975.

187. López Cámara, Francisco. *La estructura económica y social de México en la época de la Reforma*. Mexico City: Siglo XXI, 1967.

188. Ludwig, Emil. *Lincoln*. Barcelona: Juventud, 1969.

189. Lugon, Clovis. *A república "comunista" cristã dos quaranis (1610–1768)*. Rio de Janeiro: Paz e Terra, 1977.

190. Machado de Assís. *Obras completas*. Rio de Janeiro: Jackson, 1961.

191. Madariaga, Salvador de. *El auge y el ocaso del imperio español en América*. Madrid: Espasa-Calpa, 1979.

192. Maldonado Denis, Manuel. *Puerto Rico: una interpretación histórico-social*. Mexico City: Siglo XXI, 1978.

193. Mannix, Daniel P., and M. Cowley. *Historia de la trata de negros*. Madrid: Alianza, 1970.

194. Manrique, Nelson. *Las guerrillas indígenas en la guerra con Chile*. Lima: CIC, 1981.

195. Maria, Isidoro de. *Montevideo antiguo. Tradiciones y recuerdos*. Montevideo: Ministerio de Educación y Cultura, 1976.

196. Marmier, Xavier. *Buenos Aires y Montevideo en 1850*. Buenos Aires: El Ateneo, 1948.

197. Marmolejo, Lucio. *Efemérides guanajuatenses*. Guanajuato: Universidad, 1973.

198. Marriott, Alice, and Carol K. Rachlin. *American Indian Mythology*. New York: Mentor, 1972.

199. Martí, José. *Letras fieras*. (Selection and prologue by Roberto Fernández Retamar.) Havana: Letras Cubanas, 1981.

200. Martínez Estrada, Ezequiel. *Martí: el heroe y su acción revolucionaria*. Mexico City: Siglo XXI, 1972.

201. Marx, Karl, and Friedrich Engels. *Materiales para la historia de América Latina*. (Selection and commentaries by Pedro Scarón.) Mexico City: Pasado y Presente, 1979.

202. Masur, Gerhard. *Simón Bolívar*. Mexico City: Grijalbo, 1960.

203. Matute, Álvaro. *México en el siglo XIX. Fuentes e interpretaciones históricas* (anthology). Mexico City: UNAM, 1973.

204. Mauro, Frédéric. *La vie quotidienne au Brésil au temps de Pedro Segundo (1831–1889)*. Paris: Hachette, 1980.

205. Maxwell, Kenneth. *A devassa da devassa. A Inconfidência Mineira, Brasil-Portugal, 1750–1808*. Rio de Janeiro: Paz e Terra, 1978.

206. McLuhan, T. C. (ed.). *Touch the Earth. A Self-Portrait of Indian Existence*. New York: Simon and Schuster, 1971.

207. Medina Castro, Manuel. *Estados Unidos y América Latina, siglo XIX*. Havana: Casa de las Américas, 1968.

208. Mejía Duque, Jaime. *Isaacs y María*. Bogota: La Carreta, 1979.

209. Mello e Souza, Laura de. *Declassificados do ouro: a pobreza mineira no século XVIII*. Rio de Janeiro: Graal, 1982.

210. Meltzer, Milton (ed.). *In Their Own Words. A History of the American Negro (1619–1865)*. New York: Crowell, 1964.

211. Melville, Herman. *Moby Dick*. (Trans. by José María Valverde.) Barcelona: Bruguera, 1982

212. Mendoza, Vicente T. *El corrido mexicano*. Mexico City: FCE, 1976.
213. Mercader, Martha. *Juanamanuela, mucha mujer*. Buenos Aires: Sudamericana, 1982.
214. Mercado Luna, Ricardo. *Los coroneles de Mitre*. Buenos Aires: Plus Ultra, 1974.
215. Mesa, José de, (with Teresa Gisbert). *Holguín y la pintura virreinal en Bolivia*. La Paz: Juventud, 1977.
216. Mir, Pedro. *El gran incendio*. Santo Domingo: Taller, 1974.
217. Miranda, José. *Humboldt y México*. Mexico City: UNAM, 1962.
218. Mitchell, Lee Clark. *Witnesses to a Vanishing America. The Nineteenth-Century Response*. Princeton: Princeton University Press, 1981.
219. Molina, Enrique. *Una sombra donde sueña Camila O'Gorman*. Barcelona: Seix-Barral, 1982.
220. Montes, Arturo Humberto. *Morazán y la federación centroamericana*. Mexico: Libro Mex, 1958.
221. Morales, Franklin. "Los albores del futbol uruguayo," in *Cien años de futbol*. No. 1, Montevideo, Editores Reunidos, November 1969.
222. Moreno Fraginals, Manuel. *El ingenio*. Havana: Ciencias Sociales, 1978.
223. Morin, Claude. *Michoacán en la Nueva España del siglo XVIII. Crecimiento y desigualdad en una economía colonial*. Mexico City: FCE, 1979.
224. Morison, Samuel Eliot, (with Henry Steele Commager and W. E. Leuchtenburg). *Breve historia de los Estados Unidos*. Mexico City: FCE, 1980.
225. Mörner, Magnus. *La mezcla de razas en la historia de América Latina*. Buenos Aires: Paidós, 1969.
226. Mousnier, Roland, and Ernest Labrousse. *Historia general de las civilizaciones. El siglo XVIII*. Barcelona: Destino, 1967.
227. Muñoz, Rafael F. *Santa Anna. El que todo lo oanó y todo lo perdió*. Madrid: Espasa-Calpe, 1936.
228. Museo Nacional de Culturas Populares. *El maíz, fundamento de la cultura popular mexicana*; and *Nuestro maíz. Treinta monografías populares*. Mexico City: SEP, 1982.
229. Nabokov, Peter. *Native American Testimony. An Anthology of Indian and White Relations: First Encounter to Dispossession*. New York: Harper and Row, 1978.
230. Neilhardt, John G. *Black Elk Speaks*. New York: Washington Square, 1972.
231. Nevins, Allan. *John D. Rockefeller: The Heroic Age of American Business*. New York: Scribner's, 1940.
232. Nimuendajú, Curt. *Los mitos de creación y de destrucción del mundo*. Lima: Centro Amazónico de Antropología, 1978.
233. Nino, Bernadino de. *Etnografía chiriguana*. La Paz: Argote, 1912.
234. Núñez, Jorge. *El mito de la independencia*. Quito: Universidad, 1976.

235. Ocampo López, Javier, *et al. Manual de historia de Colombia*. Bogotá: Instituto Colombiano de Cultura, 1982.

236. Oddone, Juan Antonio. *La formación del Uruguay moderno. La inmigración y el desarrollo económico-social*. Buenos Aires: EUDEBA, 1966.

237. O'Kelly, James J. *La tierra del mambí*. Havana: Instituto del Libro, 1968.

238. O'Leary, Daniel Florencio. *Memorias*. Madrid: América, 1919.

239. Ortega Peña, Rodolfo, and Eduardo Duhalde. *Felipe Varela contra el Imperio británico*. Buenos Aires: Peña Lillo, 1966.

240. Ortiz, Fernando. *Los negros esclavos*. Havana: Ciencias Sociales, 1975.

241. ———. *Los bailes y el teatro de los negros en el folklore de Cuba*. Havana: Letras Cubanas, 1981.

242. ———. *Contrapunteo cubano del tabaco y el azúcar*. Havana: Consejo Nacional de Cultura, 1963.

243. Paine, Thomas. *Complete Writings*. New York: Citadel, 1945.

244. Palacio, Ernesto. *Historia de la Argentina (1515–1943)*. Buenos Aires: Peña Lillo, 1975.

245. Palma, Ricardo. *Tradiciones peruanas*. Lima: Peisa, 1969.

246. Palma de Feuillet, Milagros. *El cóndor: dimensión mítica del ave sagrada*. Bogotá: Caja Agraria, 1982.

247. Paredes, M. Rigoberto. *Mitos, supersticiones y supervivencias populares de Bolivia*. La Paz: Burgos, 1973.

248. Paredes-Candia, Antonio. *Leyendas de Bolivia*. La Paz and Cochabamba: Amigos del Libro, 1975.

249. Pareja Diezcanseco, Alfredo. *Historia del Ecuador*. Quito: Casa de la Cultura Ecuatoriana, 1958.

250. Parienté, Henriette, and Geneviève de Ternant. *La fabuleuse histoire de la cuisine française*. Paris: Odil, 1981.

251. Pereda Valdes, Ildefonso. *El negro en el Uruguay. Pasado y presente*. Montevideo: Instituto Histórico y Geográfico, 1965.

252. Pereira de Queiroz, Maria Isaura. *Historia y etnología de los movimientos mesiánicos*. Mexico City: Siglo XXI, 1978.

253. Pereyra, Carlos. *Historia de América española*. Madrid: Calleja, 1924.

254. ———. *Solano López y su drama*. Buenos Aires: Patria Grande, 1962.

255. Pérez Acosta, Juan F. *Francia y Bonpland*. Buenos Aires: Peuser, 1942.

256. Pérez Rosales, Vicente. *Recuerdos del pasado*. Havana: Casa de las Américas, 1972.

257. Petit de Murat, Ulyses. *Presencia viva del tango*. Buenos Aires: Reader's Digest. 1968.

258. Pichardo, Hortensia. *Documentos para la historia de Cuba*. Havana: Ciencias Sociales, 1973.

259. Plath, Oreste. *Geografía del mito y la leyenda chilenos*. Santiago de Chile: Nascimiento, 1973.

260. Poe, Edgar Allan. *Selected Prose and Poetry*. (Prologue by W. H. Auden.) New York: Rinehart, 1950.

261. Ponce de León, Salvador. *Guanajuato en el arte, en la historia y en la leyenda*. Guanajuato: Universidad, 1973.

262. Portuondo, Jose A. (ed.) *El pensamiento vivo de Maceo*. Havana: Ciencias Sociales, 1971.

263. Posada, Jose Guadalupe. *La vida mexicana*. Mexico City: Fondo Editorial de la Plástica Mexicana, 1963.

264. Price, Richard (ed.). *Sociedades cimarronas*. Mexico City: Siglo XXI, 1981.

265. Price-Mars, Jean. *Así habló el Tío*. Havana: Casa de las Américas, 1968.

266. Prieto, Guillermo. *Memorias de mis tiempos*. Mexico City: Patria, 1964.

267. Puiggros, Rodolfo. *La época de Mariano Moreno*. Buenos Aires: Partenon, 1949.

268. Querejazu Calvo, Roberto. *Guano, salitre, sangre. Historia de la guerra del Pacífico*. La Paz and Cochabamba: Amigos del Libro, 1979.

269. Ramírez Necochea, Hernan. *Historia del imperialismo en Chile*. Havana: Revolucionaria, 1966.

270. ———. *Balmaceda y la contrarrevolución de 1891*. Santiago de Chile: Universitaria, 1958.

271. Ramos, Jorge Abelardo. *Revolución y contrarrevolución en la Argentina*. Buenos Aires: Plus Ultra, 1965.

272. Ramos, Juan P. *Historia de la instrucción primaria en la Argentina*. Buenos Aires: Peuser, 1910.

273. Reed, Nelson. *La Guerra de Castas de Yucatán*. Mexico City: Era, 1971.

274. Reina, Leticia. *Las rebeliones campesinas en México (1819–1906)*. Mexico City: Siglo XXI, 1980.

275. Renault, Delso. *O Rio antigo nos anúncios de jornais*. Rio de Janeiro: José Olympio, 1969.

276. Revista *Signos*, Santa Clara, Cuba, July/December, 1979.

277. Reyes Abadie, W. (with Oscar H. Bruschera and Tabaré Melogno). *El ciclo artiquista*. Montevideo: Universidad, 1968.

278. ——— (with A. Vásquez Romero). *Crónica general del Uruguay*. Montevideo: Banda Oriental, 1979–1981.

279. Riazanov, David. *Karl Marx and Friedrich Engels. An Introduction to their Lives and Work*. New York: Monthly Review Press, 1973.

280. Rippy, J. Fred. *La rivalidad entre Estados Unidos y Gran Bretaña por América Latina (1808–1830)*. Buenos Aires: EUDEBA, 1967.

281. Roa Bastos, Augusto. *Yo el Supremo*. Buenos Aires: Siglo XXI, 1974.

282. Robertson, James Oliver. *American Myth, American Reality*. New York: Hill and Wang, 1980.

283. Robertson, J. P., and G. P. Robertson. *Cartas de Sud-América*. (Prologue by Jose Luis Busaniche.) Buenos Aires: Emecé, 1950.

284. Rodrigues, Nina. *Os africanos no Brasil*. São Paulo: Editora Nacional, 1977.

285. Rodríguez, Simón. *Sociedades americanas*. (Facsimile edition with prologues by Germán Carrera Damas and J. A. Cora.) Caracas: Catalá/ Centauro, 1975.

286. Rodríguez, Demorizi, Emilio. *Martí en Santo Domingo*. Havana: Ucar Garcia, 1953.

287. Roeder, Ralph. *Hacia el México moderno: Porfirio Díaz*. Mexico City: FCE, 1973.

288. Rojas-Mix, Miguel. *La Plaza Mayor. El urbanismo, instrumento de dominio colonial*. Barcelona: Muchnik, 1978.

289. Romero, Emilio. *Historia económica del Perú*. Lima: Universo, 1949.

290. Romero, José Luis. *Las ideas políticas en Argentina*. Mexico City and Buenos Aires: FCE, 1956.

291. Rosa, José María. *La guerra del Paraguay y las montoneras argentinas*. Buenos Aires: Huemul, 1965.

292. Rosenberg, Bruce A. *The Code of the West*. Bloomington, Indiana: Indiana University Press, 1982.

293. Rossi, Vicente. *Cosas de negros*. Buenos Aires: Hachette, 1958.

294. Rubin de la Barbolla, Daniel F. *Arte popular mexicano*. Mexico City: FCE, 1974.

295. Rumazo González, Alfonso. *Manuela Sáenz. La libertadora del Libertador*. Caracas and Madrid, Mediterráneo, 1979.

296. ———. *Sucre*. Caracas: Presidencia de la República, 1980.

297. ———. *Ideario de Simón Rodríguez*. Caracas: Centauro, 1980.

298. ———.*Simón Rodríguez*. Caracas: Centauro, 1976.

299. Rumrrill, Roger, and Pierre de Zutter. *Amazonia y capitalismo. Los condenados de la selva*. Lima: Horizonte, 1976.

300. Sabogal, José. *El desván de la imaginería peruana*. Lima: Mejía Baca y Villanueva, 1956.

301. Salazar, Sonia (compiler). "Testimonio sobre el origen de la leyenda del Señor de Ccoyllorithi," in *Sur*, No. 52, Cuzco, July 1982.

302. Salazar Bondy, Sebastian. *Lima la horrible*. Havana: Casa de las Américas, 1967.

303. Salomon, Noel. "Introducción a José Joaquín Fernández de Lizardi," in *Casa del Tiempo*, Vol. 2, No. 16, Mexico City, December 1981.

304. Sánchez, Luis Alberto. *La Perricholi*. Lima: Nuevo Mundo, 1964.

305. Sanford, John. *A More Godly Country. A Personal History of America*. New York: Horizon Press, 1975.

306. Sanhueza, Gabriel. *Santiago Arcos, comunista, millonario y calavera*. Santiago de Chile: Pacífico, 1956.

307. Santos, Joaquim Felício dos. *Memórias do Distrito Diamantino*. Belo Horizonte: Itatiaia, 1976.

308. Santos Rivera, José (compiler). *Rubén Darío y su tiempo*. Managua: Nueva Nicaragua, 1981.

309. Sarabia Viejo, María Justina. *El juego de gallos en Neuva España*. Seville: Escuela de Estudios Hispano-Americanos, 1972.

310. Sarmiento, Domingo Faustino. *Vida de Juan Facundo Quiroga*. Barcelona: Bruguera, 1970.

311. ———. *Conflicto y armonías de las razas en América*. Buenos Aires: La Cultura Argentina, 1915.

312. Scobie, James R. *Buenos Aires del centro a los barrios (1870–1910)*. Buenos Aires: Hachette, 1977.

313. Scott, Anne Firor. "Self-Portraits," in *Women's America*. Linda Kerber and Jane Mathews, eds. New York: Oxford University Press, 1982.

314. Scroggs, William O. *Filibusteros y financieros. La historia de William Walker y sus asociados*. Managua: Banco de America, 1974.

315. Schinca, Milton. *Boulevard Sarandí. 250 años de Montevideo; anécdotas, gentes, sucesos*. Montevideo: Banda Oriental, 1976.

316. Scholas, Walter V. *Política mexicana durante el régimen de Juárez (1855–1872)*. Mexico City: FCE, 1972.

317. Selser, Gregorio. *Sandino, general de hombres libres*. Buenos Aires: Triangulo, 1959.

318. Servando, Fray (Servando Teresa de Mier). *Memorias*. (Prologue by Alfonso Reyes.) Madrid: América, n.d.

319. Silva, José Asunción. *Prosas y versos*. (Prologue by Carlos García Prada.) Madrid: Eisa, 1960.

320. Silva Santisteban, Fernando. *Los obrajes en el Virreinato del Perú*. Lima: Museo Nacional de Historia, 1964.

321. Simpson, Lesley Byrd. *Muchos Méxicos*. Mexico City: FCE, 1977.

322. Solano, Francisco de. *Los mayas del siglo XVIII*. Madrid: Cultura Hispánica, 1974.

323. Soler, Ricaurte. "Formas ideológicas de la nación panameña," in *Tareas*, Panama City, October/November 1963.

324. Sosa, Juan B., and Enrique J. Arce. *Compendio de historia de Panamá*. Panama City: Editorial Universitaria, 1977.

325. Souza, Márcio. *Gálvez, Imperador do Acre*. Rio de Janeiro: Civilização Brasileira, 1981.

326. Sozina, S. A. *En el horizonte está El Dorado*. Havana: Casa de las Américas, 1982.

327. Stein, Stanley J. *Grandeza e decadência do café no vale do Paraíba*. São Paulo: Brasiliense, 1961.

328. Stern, Milton R. *the Fine Hammered Steel of Herman Melville*. Urban: University of Illinois Press, 1968.

329. Stewart, Watt. *La servidumbre china en el Peru*. Lima: Mosca Azul, 1976.

330. Syme, Ronald. *Fur Trader of the North*. New York: Morrow, 1973.

331. Taylor, William B. *Drinking, Homicide and Rebellion in Colonial Mexican Villages*. Stanford: Stanford University Press, 1979.
332. Teja Zabre, Alfonso. *Morelos*. Buenos Aires: Espasa-Calpe, 1946.
333. Tibol, Raquel. *Hermenegildo Bustos, pintor de pueblo*. Guanajuato: Gobierno del Estado, 1981.
334. Tocantins, Leandro. *Formação histórica do Acre*. Rio de Janeiro: Civilização Brasileira, 1979.
335. Touron, Lucía Sala de (with Nelson de la Torre and Julio C. Rodríguez). *Artigas y su revolución agraria (1811–1820)*. Mexico City: Siglo XXI, 1978.
336. Trías, Vivian. *Juan Manuel de Rosas*. Montevideo: Banda Oriental, 1970.
337. Tristán, Flora. *Les pérégrinations d'une paria*. Paris: Maspero, 1979.
338. Tulard, Jean (compiler). *L'Amérique espagnole en 1800 vue par un savant allemand: Humboldt*. Paris: Calmann-Lévy, 1965.
339. Tuñón de Lara, Manuel. *La España del siglo XIX*. Barcelona: Laia, 1973.
340. Turner, Frederick W., III. *The Portable North American Indian Reader*. London: Penguin, 1977.
341. Twain, Mark. *Un yanqui en la corte del rey Arturo*. Barcelona: Bruguera, 1981.
342. Un inglés ("An Englishman"). *Cinco años en Buenos Aires (1820–1825)*. Buenos Aires: Solar/Hachette, 1962.
343. Uslar, Pietri, Arturo. *La isla de Robinson*. Barcelona: Seix Barral, 1981.
344. Valcarcel, Carlos Daniel. *La rebelión de Túpac Amaru*. Mexico City: FCE, 1973.
345. ———, (ed.). *Colección documental de la independencia del Perú*, Book II, Vol. 2. Lima: Comisión Nacional del Sesquicentenario, 1971.
346. Valle-Arizpe, Artemio de. *Fray Servando*. Buenos Aires: Espasa-Calpe, 1951.
347. Vargas, José Santos. *Diario de un comandante de la independencia americana (1814–1825)*. Mexico City: Siglo XXI, 1982.
348. Vargas Martínez, Ubaldo. *Morelos, siervo de la nación*. Mexico City: Porrúa, 1966.
349. Velasco, Cuauhtemoc. "Los trabajadores mineros en la Nueva España (1750–1810)," in *La clase obrera en la historia de Mexico. 1. De la colonia al imperio*. Mexico City: Siglo XXI, 1980.
350. Vidart, Daniel. *El tango y su mundo*. Montevideo: Tauro, 1967.
351. Vieira, Antonio. *Obras várias*. Lisbon: Sá da Costa, 1951/1953.
352. Villarroel, Hipólito. *Enfermedades políticas que padece la capital de esta Nueva España*. Mexico City: Porrúa, 1979.
353. Viñas, David. *Indios, ejército y frontera*. Mexico City: Siglo XXI, 1983.
354. Vitier, Cintio. *Temas martianos*. Havana: Centro de Estudios Martianos, 1969 and 1982.

355. Von Hagen, Víctor W. *Culturas preincaicas*. Madrid: Guadarrama, 1976.

356. Walker, William. *La guerra de Nicaragua*. San José, Costa Rica: Educa, 1975.

357. Westheim, Paul, *et al*. *José Guadalupe Posada*. Mexico City: Instituto Nacional de Bellas Artes, 1963.

358. Whitman, Walt. *Hojas de hierba*. (Translation by Jorge Luis Borges.) Barcelona: Lumen, 1972.

359. Williams García, Roberto. *Mitos tepehuas*. Mexico City: SEP/Setentas, 1972.

360. Wissler, Clark. *Indians of the United States*. New York: Doubleday, 1967.

361. Ziegler, Jean. *Les vivants et la mort*. Paris: Seuil, 1975.

Century of the Wind

Contents

Preface

This Book

is the last volume of the trilogy *Memory of Fire*. It is not an anthology but a literary creation, based on solid documentation but moving with complete freedom. The author does not know to what literary form the book belongs: narrative, essay, epic poem, chronicle, testimony . . . Perhaps it belongs to all or to none. The author relates what has happened, the history of America, and above all, the history of Latin America; and he has sought to do it in such a way that the reader should feel that what has happened happens again when the author tells it.

At the head of each text is given the year and place of each episode, except in certain texts which cannot be situated in any specific moment or place. At the foot, the numbers show the chief works the author has consulted in search of information and reference points. The absence of numbers shows that in that particular case the author has consulted no written source, or that he obtained his raw material from general information in periodicals or from the mouths of protagonists or witnesses. The sources consulted are listed at the end of the book.

Literal transcriptions are italicized.

Acknowledgments

To Helena Villagra, who helped so much at each stage of the work. Without her, *Memory of Fire* would not have been possible;

To the friends whose contributions were gratefully acknowledged in the previous volumes, and who also helped here with sources, trails, and suggestions;

To Alfredo Ahuerma, Susan Bergholz, Leonardo Cáceres, Rafael Cartay, Alfredo Cedeño, Rosa del Olmo, Enrique Fierro, César Galeano, Horacio García, Sergius Gonzaga, Berta and Fernanda Navarro, Eric Nepomuceno, David Sánchez-Juliao, Andrés Soliz Rada, and Julio Valle-Castillo, who provided access to the necessary bibliography;

To Jorge Enrique Adoum, Pepe Barrientos, Álvaro Barros-Lémez, Jean-

Paul Borel, Rogelio García Lupo, Mauricio Gatti, Juan Gelman, Santiago Kovadloff, Ole Østergaard, Rami Rodríguez, Miguel Rojas-Mix, Nicole Rouan, Pilar Royo, José María Valverde, and Daniel Vidart, who read the drafts with Chinese patience.

This book

is dedicated to Mariana, the Little Flea.

and clawing ourselves out of the wind with our fingernails

—Juan Rulfo

1900: San José de Gracia

The World Goes On

There were some who spent the savings of several generations on one last spree. Many insulted those they couldn't afford to insult and kissed those they shouldn't have kissed. No one wanted to end up without confession. The parish priest gave preference to the pregnant and to new mothers. This self-denying cleric lasted three days and three nights in the confessional before fainting from an indigestion of sins.

When midnight came on the last day of the century, all the inhabitants of San José de Gracia prepared to die clean. God had accumulated much wrath since the creation of the world, and no one doubted that the time had come for the final blowout. Breath held, eyes closed, teeth clenched, the people listened to the twelve chimes of the church clock, one after the other, deeply convinced that there would be no afterwards.

But there was. For quite a while the twentieth century has been on its way; it forges ahead as if nothing had happened. The inhabitants of San José de Gracia continue in the same houses, living and surviving among the same mountains of central Mexico—to the disenchantment of the devout who were expecting Paradise, and to the relief of sinners, who find that this little village isn't so bad after all, if one makes comparisons.

(200)*

1900: West Orange, New Jersey

Edison

Through his inventions the new century receives light and music.

Everyday life bears the seal of Thomas Alva Edison. His electric lamp illumines the nights and his phonograph preserves and diffuses the voices of the world, no longer to be lost. People talk by telephone thanks to the microphone he has added to Bell's invention, and pictures move by virtue of the projecting apparatus with which he completed the work of the Lumière brothers.

* The numbers at the foot of each item refer to the documentary sources consulted by the author, listed on pages 281–301.

In the patent office they clutch their heads when they see him coming. Not for a single moment has this multiplier of human powers stopped inventing, a tireless creator ever since that distant time when he sold newspapers on trains, and one fine day decided he could make them as well as sell them—then set his hand to the task.

(99 and 148)

1900: Montevideo
Rodó

The Master, the talking statue, sends forth his sermon to the youth of America.

José Enrique Rodó vindicates ethereal Ariel, the pure spirit against savage Caliban, the brute who wants to eat. The century being born is the time of anybodies. The people want democracy and trade unions; and Rodó warns that the barbarous multitude can scale the heights of the kingdom of the spirit where superior beings dwell. The intellectual chosen by the gods, the great immortal man, fights in defense of private property in culture.

Rodó also attacks North American civilization, rooted in vulgarity and utilitarianism. To it he opposes the Spanish aristocratic tradition which scorns practical sense, manual labor, technology, and other mediocrities.

(273, 360, and 386)

1901: New York
This is America,
to the South There's Nothing

For 250 million dollars Andrew Carnegie sells the steel monopoly to banker John Pierpont Morgan, master of General Electric, who thereupon founds the United States Steel Corporation. A fever of consumption, a vertigo of money cascading from the tops of skyscrapers: the United States belongs to the monopolies, and the monopolies to a handful of men; but multitudes of workers flock here from Europe, year after year, lured by the factory sirens, and sleeping on deck they dream of becoming millionaires as soon as they jump onto the New

York piers. In the industrial era, El Dorado is the United States; and the United States is America.

To the south, the other America hasn't yet managed to mumble its own name. A recently published report states that *all* the countries of this sub-America have commercial treaties with the United States, England, France, and Germany—but *none* has any with its neighbors. Latin America is an archipelago of idiot countries, organized for separation, and trained to dislike each other.

(113 and 289)

1901: In All Latin America
Processions Greet the Birth of the Century

In the villages and cities south of the Rio Grande, Jesus Christ marches to the cemeteries, a dying beast lustrous with blood, and behind him with torches and hymns comes the crowd, tattered, battered people afflicted with a thousand ills that no doctor or faith-healer would know how to cure, but deserving a fate that no prophet or fortuneteller could possibly divine.

1901: Amiens
Verne

Twenty years ago Alberto Santos Dumont read Jules Verne. Reading him, he had fled from his house, from Brazil, and from the world, until, sailing through the sky from cloud to cloud, he decided to live entirely on air.

Now Santos Dumont defies wind and the law of gravity. The Brazilian aeronaut invents a dirigible balloon, master of its own course, that does not drift, that will not get lost in the high seas or over the Russian Steppe or at the North Pole. Equipped with motor, propeller, and rudder, Santos Dumont rises into the air, makes a complete circuit of the Eiffel Tower, and lands at the announced spot, against the wind, before an applauding crowd.

Then he journeys to Amiens, to shake the hand of the man who taught him to fly.

Settled in his rocking chair, Jules Verne smooths his big white beard. He takes a shine to this child badly disguised as a gentleman, who calls him *my Captain* and looks at him without blinking.

(144 and 424)

1902: Quetzaltenango
The Government Decides That Reality Doesn't Exist

Drums and trumpets blast in the main plaza of Quetzaltenango, calling the citizenry; but all anyone can hear is the terrifying thunder of the Santa María volcano in full eruption.

At the top of his voice the town crier reads the proclamation of the sovereign government. More than a hundred towns in this section of Guatemala are being destroyed by avalanches of lava and mud and an endless rain of ashes while the town crier, protecting himself as best he can, performs his duty. The Santa María volcano shakes the ground beneath his feet and bombards his head with stones. At noon there is total night. In the blackout nothing can be seen but the volcano's vomit of fire. The town crier yells desperately, reading the proclamation by the shaky light of a lantern.

The proclamation, signed by President Manuel Estrada Cabrera, informs the populace that the Santa María volcano is quiet, that all of Guatemala's volcanos are quiet, that the earthquake is occurring far from here in some part of Mexico, and that, the situation being normal, there is no reason not to celebrate the feast of the goddess Minerva, which will take place today in the capital despite the nasty rumors being spread by the enemies of order.

(28)

1902: Guatemala City
Estrada Cabrera

In the city of Quetzaltenango, Manuel Estrada Cabrera had for many years exercised *the august priesthood of the Law in the majestic temple of Justice upon the immovable rock of Truth*. When he got through stripping the province, the doctor came to the capital, where he brought his political career to a happy culmination, pistol in hand, assaulting the presidency of Guatemala.

Since then he has reestablished throughout the country the use of stocks, whips, and gallows. Now Indians pick plantations' coffee for nothing, and for nothing bricklayers build jails and barracks.

Almost daily, in a solemn ceremony, President Estrada Cabrera lays the foundation stone of a new school that will never be built. He has conferred on himself the title Educator of Peoples and Protector of Studious Youth, and in homage to himself celebrates each year the colossal feast of the goddess Minerva. In his Parthenon here, a full-scale replica of the Greek original, poets pluck their lyres as they announce that Guatemala City, the Athens of the New World, has a Pericles.

(28)

1902: Saint Pierre
Only the Condemned Is Saved

On the island of Martinique, too, a volcano explodes. As if splitting the world in two, the mountain Pelée coughs up a huge red cloud that covers the sky and falls, glowing, over the earth. In a wink the city of Saint Pierre is annihilated. Its thirty-four thousand inhabitants disappear—except one.

The survivor is Ludger Sylbaris, the only prisoner in the city. The walls of the jail had been made escape-proof.

(188)

1903: Panama City
The Panama Canal

The passage between the oceans had obsessed the conquistadors. Furiously they sought and finally found it, too far south, down by remote, glacial Tierra del Fuego. But when someone suggested opening the narrow waist of Central America, King Philip II quickly squelched it: he forbade excavation of a canal on pain of death, because *what God hath joined let no man put asunder*.

Three centuries later a French concern, the Universal Inter-Oceanic Canal Company, began the work in Panama, but after thirty-three kilometers crashed noisily into bankruptcy.

Now the United States has decided to complete the canal, and hang on to it, too. There is one hitch: Colombia doesn't agree, and Panama is a province of Colombia. In Washington, Senator Hanna advises waiting it out, *due to the nature of the beast we are dealing with*, but President Teddy Roosevelt doesn't believe in patience. He sends in the Marines. And so, by grace of the United States and its warships, the province becomes an independent state.

(240 and 423)

1903: Panama City
Casualties of This War:
One Chinese, One Burro,

victims of the broadsides of a Colombian gunboat. There are no further misfortunes to lament. Manuel Amador, Panama's brand-new president, parades between U.S. flags, seated in an armchair that the crowd carries on a platform. As he passes, Amador shouts vivas for his colleague Roosevelt.

Two weeks later, in Washington, in the Blue Room of the White House, a treaty is signed granting the United States in perpetuity the half-finished canal and more than fourteen hundred square kilometers of Panamanian territory. Representing the newborn republic is Philippe Bunau-Varilla, commercial magician, political acrobat, French citizen.

(240 and 423)

1903: La Paz
Huilka

The Bolivian liberals have won the war against the conservatives. More accurately, it has been won for them by the Indian army of Pablo Zárate Huilka. The feats claimed by the mustachioed generals were performed by Indians.

Colonel José Manuel Pando, leader of the liberals, had promised Huilka's soldiers freedom from serfdom and recovery of their lands. From battle to battle, as he passed through the villages, Huilka returned stolen lands to the communities and cut the throat of anyone wearing trousers.

With the conservatives defeated, Colonel Pando appoints himself general and president, and, dotting all the *i*'s, proclaims: *"The Indians are inferior beings. Their elimination is not a crime."*

Then he gets on with it. Many are shot. Huilka, yesterday's indispensable ally, he kills several times, by bullet, blade, and rope. Still, on rainy nights, Huilka awaits the president at the gate of the government palace and stares at him, saying nothing, until Pando turns away.

(110 and 475)

1904: Rio de Janeiro
Vaccine

With the slaughter of rats and mosquitos, bubonic plague and yellow fever have been vanquished. Now Oswaldo Cruz declares war on smallpox.

By the thousands Brazilians die of the disease, while doctors bleed the moribund and healers scare off the plague with the smoke of smoldering cowshit. Oswaldo Cruz, in charge of public health, makes vaccination obligatory.

Senator Rui Barbosa, pigeon-chested and smooth-tongued orator, attacks vaccination using juridical weapons flowery with adjectives. In the name of liberty Rui Barbosa defends the right of every individual to be contaminated if he so desires. Torrential applause, thunderous ovations interrupt him from phrase to phrase.

The politicians oppose vaccination. And the doctors. And the journalists. Every newspaper carries choleric editorials and cruel caricatures victimizing Oswaldo Cruz. He cannot show his face on any street without drawing insults and stones.

The whole country closes ranks against vaccination. On all sides, "Down with vaccination!" is heard. Against vaccination the cadets of the military school rise in arms, and just miss overthrowing the president.

(158, 272, 378, and 425)

1905: Montevideo

The Automobile,

that roaring beast, makes its first kill in Montevideo. An innocent pedestrian crossing a downtown street falls and is crushed.

Few automobiles have reached these streets, but as they pass, old ladies cross themselves and people scamper into doorways for protection.

Until not very long ago, the man who thought he was a streetcar still trotted through this motorless city. Going uphill, he would crack his invisible whip, and downhill pull reins that no one could see. At intersections he tooted a horn as imaginary as his horses, as imaginary as his passengers climbing aboard at each stop, as imaginary as the tickets he sold them and the change he received. When the man-streetcar stopped coming, never to pass again, the city found that it missed this endearing lunatic.

(413)

1905: Montevideo

The Decadent Poets

Roberto de las Carreras climbs to the balcony. Pressed to his breast, a bouquet of roses and an incandescent sonnet; awaiting him, not a lovely odalisque, but a gentleman of evil character who fires five shots. Two hit the target. Roberto closes his eyes and muses: *"Tonight I'll sup with the gods."*

He sups not with the gods but with the nurses in the hospital. And a few days later this handsome Satan reappears perfidiously strolling down Sarandí Street, he who has vowed to corrupt all the married and engaged women in Montevideo. His red vest looks very chic decorated with two bulletholes. And on the title page of his latest book, *Funereal Diadem*, appears a drop of blood.

Another son of Byron and Aphrodite is Julio Herrera y Reissig, who calls the foul attic in which he writes and recites the Tower of Panoramas. The two have long been at odds over the theft of a metaphor, but both fight the same war against hypocritical, pre-Columbian Monte-idioto, which in the department of aphrodisiacs has progressed no further than egg yolks mixed with grape wine, and in the department of literature—the less said the better.

(284 and 389)

1905: Ilopango
Miguel at One Week

Señorita Santos Mármol, unrespectably pregnant, refuses to name the author of her dishonor. Her mother, Doña Tomasa, beats her out of the house. Doña Tomasa, widow of a man who was poor but white, suspects the worst.

When the baby is born, the spurned señorita brings it in her arms: *"This is your grandson, Mama."*

Doña Tomasa lets out a fearful scream at the sight of the baby, a blue spider, a thick-lipped Indian, such an ugly little thing as to arouse anger more than pity, and slams the door, boom, in her daughter's face.

On the doorstep Señorita Santos falls in a heap. Beneath his unconscious mother the baby seems dead. But when the neighbors haul him out, the squashed newcomer raises a tremendous howl.

And so occurs the second birth of Miguel Mármol, age one week.

(126)

1906: Paris
Santos Dumont

Five years after creating his dirigible balloon, the Brazilian Santos Dumont invents the airplane.

He has spent these five years shut up in hangars, assembling and dismantling enormous iron and bamboo Things which are born and unborn at top speed around the clock: at night they go to bed equipped with seagull wings and fish fins, and wake up transformed into dragonflies or wild ducks. On these Things Santos Dumont wants to get off the earth, which tenaciously holds him back; he collides and crashes; he has fires, tailspins, and shipwrecks; he survives by sheer stubbornness. But he fights and fights until at last he makes one of the Things into an airplane or magic carpet that soars high into the sky.

The whole world wants to meet the hero of this immense feat, king of the air, master of the winds, who is four feet tall, talks in a whisper, and weighs no more than a fly.

(144 and 424)

1907: Sagua la Grande
Lam

In the first heat of this warm morning, the little boy wakes and sees. The world is on its back and whirling; and in that vertigo a desperate bat circles, chasing its own shadow. The black shadow retreats to the wall as the bat approaches, beating at it with a wing.

The little boy jumps up, covering his head with his hands, and collides with a big mirror. In the mirror he sees nobody, or someone else. Turning, he recognizes in the open closet the decapitated clothes of his Chinese father and his black grandfather.

Somewhere in the morning a blank sheet of paper awaits him. But this Cuban boy, this frenzy called Wilfredo Lam, still cannot draw his own lost shadow, which revolves crazily in the hallucinating world above him, having not yet discovered his dazzling way of exorcising fear.

(319)

1907: Iquique
The Flags of Many Countries

head the march of the striking nitrate workers across the gravelly desert of northern Chile—thousands of them and their thousands of women and children—marching on the port of Iquique, chanting slogans and songs. When the workers occupy Iquique the Interior Minister sends an order to kill. The workers decide to stick it out. Not a stone is to be thrown.

José Briggs, leader of the strike, is the son of a North American, but refuses to seek protection from the U.S. consul. The consul of Peru tries to save the Peruvian workers, but they won't abandon their Chilean comrades. The consul of Bolivia tries to lure away the Bolivian workers. The Bolivian workers say: *"With the Chileans we live, and with the Chileans we die."*

General Roberto Silva Renard's machineguns and rifles cut down the unarmed strikers and leave a blanket of bodies. Interior Minister Rafael Sotomayor justifies the carnage in the name of *the most sacred things*, which are, in order of importance, *property, public order, and life*.

(64 and 326)

1907: Rio Batalha
Nimuendajú

Curt Unkel was not born Indian, he became one, or discovered that he was one. Years ago he left Germany for Brazil, and in Brazil, in the deepest depths of Brazil, he recognized his people. Now he accompanies the Guaraní Indians as they wander the jungle as pilgrims seeking paradise. He shares their food and shares the joy of sharing food.

High aloft rise their chants. In the dead of night a sacred ceremony is performed. They perforate the lower lip of Curt Unkel, who comes to be known as Nimuendajú: *He who creates his house*.

(316, 374, and 411)

1908: Asunción
Barrett

Perhaps he once lived in Paraguay, centuries or millennia ago—who knows when—and has forgotten it. Certainly four years ago, when by chance or curiosity Rafael Barrett landed here, he felt he had finally reached the place that was waiting for him: this godforsaken place was his place in the world.

Ever since then, on street corners, mounted on a soapbox, he has harangued the people, while publishing articles of revelation and denunciation. In response, the government throws him out. Bayonets shove the young anarchist to the border—deported as a *foreign agitator*.

Most Paraguayan of all Paraguayans, true weed of this soil, true saliva of this mouth, he was born in Asturias, of a Spanish mother and English father, and was educated in Paris.

Barrett's gravest sin, unforgivable violation of a taboo, is to denounce slavery on the maté plantations.

Forty years ago, when the war of extermination against Paraguay ended, the victorious countries in the name of Civilization and Liberty legalized the enslavement of the survivors and the children of the survivors. Since then Argentine and Brazilian landowners count their Paraguayan peons by the head as if they were cows.

(37)

1908: San Andrés de Sotavento
The Government Decides That Indians Don't Exist

The governor, General Miguel Marino Torralvo, issues the order for the oil companies operating on the Colombian coast. *The Indians do not exist*, the governor certifies before a notary and witnesses. Three years ago, Law No. 1905/55, approved in Bogotá by the National Congress, established that Indians did not exist in San Andrés de Sotavento and other Indian communities where oil had suddenly spurted from the ground. Now the governor merely confirms the law. If the Indians existed, they would be illegal. Thus they are consigned to the cemetery or exile.

(160)

1908: San Andrés de Sotavento
Portrait of a Master of Lives and Estates

General Miguel Marino Torralvo, glutton of lands, who tramples on Indians and women, governs these Colombian coastal regions from the back of a horse. With the butt of his whip he strikes faces and doors, and shapes destinies. Those who cross his path kiss his hand. In an impeccable white habit he canters along the roads, always followed by a page on a burro. The page carries his brandy, his boiled water, his shaving kit, and the book in which the general notes the names of the girls he devours.

His properties increase as he rides by. He started out with one cattle farm and now has six. A believer in progress, but not to the exclusion of tradition, he uses barbed wire to set limits to his lands, the stocks to set limits for his people.

(160)

1908: Guanape
Portrait of Another Master of Lives
and Estates

He orders: *"Tell him he'd better carry his shroud on the back of his horse."*

He punishes with five shots, for nonperformance of duty, the serf who is late with the bushels of corn he owes, or who makes trouble about delivering a daughter or a plot of land.

"Don't hurry it," he orders. *"Only the last shot should kill."*

Not even his family is spared the wrath of Deogracias Itriago, supreme boss of the Venezuelan valley of Guanape. One night a relative borrows his best horse to go to a dance in style. The next morning Don Deogracias has him tied face down to four stakes, and skins the soles of his feet and his buttocks with a cassava grater to cure him of the urge to dance and show off on someone else's horse.

When in an unguarded moment he is finally killed by some peons he himself had condemned to death, for nine nights the family chants the novena for the dead, and for nine nights the people of Guanape go wild celebrating. No one tires of making merry and no musician wants payment for the marathon.

(410)

1908: Mérida, Yucatán
Curtain Time and After

The train is already disappearing, and the president of Mexico with it. Porfirio Díaz has examined the henequén plantations in Yucatán and is taking away a most favorable impression.

"A beautiful spectacle," he said, as he supped with the bishop and the owners of millions of hectares and thousands of Indians who produce cheap fibers for the International Harvester Company. *"Here one breathes an atmosphere of general happiness."*

The locomotive smoke is scarcely dissipated when the houses of painted cardboard, with their elegant windows, collapse with the slap of a hand. Garlands and pennants become litter, swept up and burned, and the wind undoes with a puff the arches of flowers that spanned the roads. The lightning visit over, the merchants of Mérida repossess the sewing machines, the North American furniture, and the brand-new clothes the slaves have worn while the show lasted.

The slaves are Mayan Indians who until recently lived free in the kingdom of the little talking cross, and Yaqui Indians from the plains of the north, purchased for four hundred pesos a head. They sleep piled up in fortresses of stone and work to the rhythm of a moistened whip. When one of them gets surly, they bury him up to his ears and turn the horses loose on him.

(40, 44, 245, and 451)

1908: Ciudad Juárez
Wanted

A few years ago, at the request of Porfirio Díaz, North American Rangers crossed the border here to crush the striking copper miners of Sonora. Later, the strike in the Veracruz textile plants ended in arrests and executions. Still, strikes have broken out again this year in Coahuila, Chihuahua, and Yucatán.

Striking, which disturbs order, is a crime. Whoever does it commits a crime. The Flores Magón brothers, agitators of the working class, are criminals of the highest order. Their faces are plastered on the wall of the railroad station in Ciudad Juárez as in all stations on both sides of the border. The Furlong detective agency offers a forty-thousand-dollar reward for each of them.

For years, the Flores Magón brothers have flouted the authority of eternal president Porfirio Díaz. In journals and pamphlets they have taught the people to lose respect for him. With respect once lost, the people begin to lose their fear.

(40, 44, and 245)

1908: Caracas

Castro

He shakes hands with just the index finger, because no one is worthy of the other four. Cipriano Castro reigns in Venezuela, his crown a cap with hanging tassel. A fanfare of trumpets, a thunder of applause, and a rustle of bowing shoulders announce his appearance, followed by his retinue of bullies and court jesters. Like Bolívar, Castro is short, quick-tempered, and addicted to dancing and women; and he plays Bolívar when posing for immortality; but Bolívar lost some battles and Castro, Semper Victorious, never.

His dungeons are crammed. He trusts no one, with the exception of Juan Vicente Gómez, his right hand in war and government, who calls him the Greatest Man of Modern Times. Least of all does Castro trust the local medics, who cure leprosy and insanity with a broth of boiled buzzard. Instead he decides to put his ailments in the hands of learned German physicians.

At the port of La Guaira he embarks for Europe. Hardly has the ship cast off when Gómez seizes power.

(193 and 344)

1908: Caracas

Dolls

Every Venezuelan male is a Cipriano Castro to the women who come his way.

A proper señorita serves her father and her brothers as she will serve her husband, and neither does nor says anything without asking permission. If she has money or comes from a good family, she attends early morning Mass, then spends the day learning to give orders to the black staff—cooks, maids, wet nurses, nannies, laundrywomen—and working with needle or bobbin. At times she receives friends, and even goes so far as to recommend some outrageous novel, whispering: "You should have seen how I cried . . ."

Twice a week, in the early evening, seated on a sofa under an aunt's attentive gaze, she spends a few hours listening to her fiancé without looking at him or letting him near. Every night, before bed, she repeats her Ave Marias and, by moonlight, applies to her skin an infusion of jasmine petals steeped in rainwater.

If her fiancé deserts her, she becomes an aunt, condemned forever to clothe saints, corpses, and new babies, watch engaged couples, tend the sick, teach catechism, and spend the night in her solitary bed, sighing over the portrait of her disdainful lover.

(117)

1909: Paris

A Theory of National Impotence

The Bolivian Alcides Arguedas, sent to Paris on a scholarship by Simón Patiño, publishes a new book entitled *Sick People*. The tin king feeds Arguedas so that Arguedas may reveal that the Bolivian people are not just ailing, but incurable.

A while ago another Bolivian thinker, Gabriel René Moreno, discovered that the native and mestizo brains are *cellularly incapable*, and that they weigh from five to seven or even ten ounces less than the brain of the white man. Now Arguedas proclaims that mestizos inherit the worst characteristics of their forebears and this is why the Bolivian people do not want to wash or learn, can't read, only drink, are two-faced, egoistic, lazy, and altogether deplorable. Their thousand and one miseries thus spring from their own nature, not the voracity of their masters. Here is a people condemned by biology and reduced to zoology. Theirs is the bestial fate of the ox: incapable of making his own history, he can only fulfill his destiny. And that destiny, that hopeless disaster, is written not in the stars, but in the blood.

(29 and 473)

1909: New York

Charlotte

What would happen if a woman woke up one morning changed into a man? What if the family were not a training camp where boys learn to command and girls to obey? What if there were daycare for babies, and husbands shared the cleaning and cooking? What if innocence turned into dignity and reason and emotion went arm in arm? What if preachers and newspapers told the truth? And if no one were anyone's property?

So Charlotte Perkins Gilman raves, while the press attacks her, calling her an *unnatural mother*. Yet the fantasies that inhabit her soul and bite at her guts attack her far more fiercely. It is they, those terrible enemies inside, that sometimes bring her down. She falls but recovers, falls and recovers again, some impulse to go forward never abandoning her entirely. This stubborn wayfarer travels tirelessly around the United States, announcing a world upside down.

(195 and 196)

1909: *Managua*
Inter-American Relations at Work

Philander Knox is a lawyer and a shareholder in the Rosario and Light Mines Company. He is also secretary of state of the United States. The president of Nicaragua, José Santos Zelaya, does not treat the company with due respect. He wants Rosario and Light to pay taxes. Nor does he respect the Church enough. The Holy Mother has judged him to be in sin ever since he expropriated her lands and suppressed tithes and first-fruits and profaned the sacrament of matrimony with a divorce law. So the Church applauds when the United States breaks relations with Nicaragua and Secretary of State Knox sends down some Marines who overthrow President Zelaya and put in his place the accountant of the Rosario and Light Mines Company.

(10 and 56)

1910: *Amazon Jungle*
The People Eaters

Overnight the price of rubber collapses, and the Amazonian dream of prosperity comes to nothing. With a rude slap the world market abruptly awakens Belém do Pará, Manaos, Iquitos, all the sleeping beauties who lie in the jungle in the shade of the rubber tree. From one day to the next the so-called Land of Tomorrow turns into Never-Never Land, or the Land of Yesterday, abandoned by the merchants who have extracted its sap. The big rubber money flees the Amazon jungle for new Asian plantations which produce better rubber at cheaper prices.

This has been a cannibalistic business. *People eaters* the Indians called the slave hunters who cruised the rivers in search of labor. All that is left of substantial villages is the scraps. The people eaters sent the Indians, bound, to the rubber companies. They sent them in the holds of ships along with other merchandise, appropriately invoiced for sales commissions and freight charges.

(92, 119, and 462)

1910: Rio de Janeiro
The Black Admiral

On board, the order for silence. An officer reads out the sentence. Drums beat furiously as a sailor is flogged for a breach of discipline. On his knees, bound to the deck balustrade, the condemned man receives his punishment before the whole crew. The last of the lashes—two hundred and forty-eight, two hundred and forty-nine, two hundred and fifty—fall upon a flayed body, bathed in blood, unconscious or dead.

Then the mutiny breaks out. In the waters of Guanabara Bay, the sailors rise up. Three officers fall, knifed to death. The warships fly the red ensign. An ordinary seaman is the squadron's new commander. João Cándido, the Black Admiral, leans into the wind on the command tower of his flagship, and the rebel pariahs present arms to him.

At dawn two booming guns wake Rio de Janeiro. The Black Admiral issues a warning: the city is at his mercy. Unless flogging—the custom of the Brazilian fleet—is prohibited and an amnesty granted, he will bombard Rio, leaving no stone upon stone. The mouths of the warships' cannons are pointed at Rio's most important buildings.

"We want an answer now, right now."

The city, in panic, obeys. The government declares the abolition of corporal punishment in the fleet and an amnesty for the rebels. João Cándido removes the red kerchief from his neck and surrenders his sword. The admiral transforms himself back into a sailor.

(303)

1910: Rio de Janeiro

Portrait of Brazil's Most Expensive Lawyer

Six years ago he opposed smallpox vaccination in the name of Liberty. An individual's skin is as inviolable as his conscience, said Rui Barbosa. The State has no right to violate thought or body, not even in the name of public hygiene. Now, he condemns *with all severity the violence and barbarity* of the sailors' rebellion. This illustrious jurist and preeminent legislator opposes flogging but denounces the methods of the flogged. The sailors, he says, did not make their just demand in a civilized way, *by constitutional means, using the proper channels within the framework of prevailing juridical norms.*

Rui Barbosa believes in the law, and bases his belief on erudite quotations from imperial Romans and English liberals. But he doesn't believe in reality. The doctor shows a certain realism only when, at the end of the month, he collects his salary as lawyer for Light and Power, that foreign enterprise which in Brazil exercises more power than God.

(272 and 303)

1910: Rio de Janeiro

Reality and the Law Seldom Meet

in this country of legally free slaves, and when they do they don't shake hands. The ink is still fresh on the laws that put an end to the sailors' revolt when the officers resume flogging and kill the recently amnestied rebels. Many sailors are shot on the high seas; others are buried alive in the catacombs of Cobra Island, called the Isle of Despair, where they are thrown quicklimed water when they complain of thirst.

The Black Admiral ends up in a lunatic asylum.

(303)

1910: Mauricio Colony

Tolstoy

Exiled for being poor and a Jew, Isaac Zimmerman ends up in Argentina. The first time he sees a maté cup he takes it for an inkpot, the straw for a pen, and that pen burns his hand. On this pampa he built his hut, not far from the huts of other pilgrims, exiles like him from the valleys of the Dniester River; and here he produces children and crops.

Isaac and his wife have very little, almost nothing, and the little they have they possess graciously. Some vegetable crates serve as a table, but the tablecloth is always starched and very white, and on it flowers lend color, and apples perfume.

One night the children come upon Isaac collapsed at this table, his head buried in his hands. By the candle's light they see his face glistening with tears. And he tells them. By sheer accident, he says, he has just learned that over there, on the far side of the world, Leo Tolstoy has died. And he explains who this old friend of the peasants was, this man who knew how to portray his time so grandly and to foretell another.

(155)

1910: Havana

The Cinema

Ladder on shoulder, the lamplighter goes on his way. With his long pole he lights the wicks, so that people can walk without tripping through the streets of Havana.

The messenger goes by bicycle. Under his arm he carries rolls of film from one cinema to another, so that people may walk without tripping through other worlds and other times and float high in the sky with a girl seated on a star.

This city has two halls consecrated to the greatest marvel of modern life. Both offer the same films. When the messenger dawdles with the rolls, the pianist will entertain the audience with waltzes and dance tunes, or the usher will recite selected fragments from *Don Juan Tenorio*. But the audience bites its nails waiting for the femme fatale with the bedroom circles under her eyes to dazzle in the darkness, or for the knights in coats of mail to gallop at epileptic speed toward the castle wreathed in mist.

The cinema robs the public of the circus. No longer does the crowd queue up to see the mustachioed lion-tamer or Lovely Geraldine, sheathed in sequins, glittering erect on the horse with enormous haunches. The puppeteers, too, abandon Havana to wander the beaches and villages, and the gypsies who read fortunes depart along with the sad bear that dances to the rhythm of the tambourine, with the goat that gyrates on a stool, with the gaunt acrobats in their checkered costumes. All quit Havana because people no longer throw them pennies of admiration, but only of pity.

No one can compete with the cinema. The cinema is more miraculous than the water of Lourdes. Stomach chills are cured by Ceylon cinnamon; colds by parsley; everything else by the cinema.

(292)

1910: Mexico City
The Centennial and Love

Celebrating a hundred years of Mexico's independence, all of the capital's whorehouses display the portrait of President Porfirio Díaz.

In Mexico City, out of every ten young women, two engage in prostitution. Peace and Order, Order and Progress: the law regulates the practice of this crowded profession. The brothel law, promulgated by Don Porfirio himself, prohibits carnal commerce without the proper façade, or in the proximity of schools and churches. It also prohibits the mixing of social classes—*In the brothels there shall only be women of the class to which the customers belong*—while it imposes all sorts of sanitary controls and penalties, and even obliges the madams *to prevent their pupils from going into the streets in groups that might attract attention*. They are allowed to go out singly: condemned to exist between bed, hospital, and jail, the whores at least have the right to an occasional stroll through the city. In this sense, they are better off than the Indians. By order of the almost pure Mixtec Indian president, Indians may not walk on the principal avenues or sit in public plazas.

(300)

1910: Mexico City

The Centennial and Food

The Centennial is inaugurated with a banquet of French *haute cuisine* in the salons of the National Palace. Three hundred and fifty waiters serve dishes prepared by forty chefs and sixty assistants under the direction of the renowned Sylvain Daumont.

Elegant Mexicans eat in French. They prefer the *crêpe* to its poor relation of native birth, the corn tortilla; *oeufs en cocotte* to the humble rancheros. They find *béchamel* sauce more worthy than guacamole, that delicious but excessively indigenous mixture of avocados, tomatoes, and chili. Faced with foreign peppers or Mexican chilies, the gentry reject the chili, although later they sneak back to the family kitchen and devour it secretly, ground or whole, side dish or main dish, stuffed or plain, unpeeled or naked.

(318)

1910: Mexico City

The Centennial and Art

Mexico celebrates its national fiesta with a great exhibition of Spanish art, brought from Madrid. To give these Spanish artists the presentation they deserve, Don Porfirio has built a special pavilion for them in the city center.

In Mexico, even the stones for building the post office come from Europe, like all that is considered worthwhile. From Italy, France, Spain, or England come construction materials and architects, or when money is lacking for imported architects, native architects undertake to put up houses just like those of Rome, Paris, Madrid, or London. Meanwhile, Mexican artists paint ecstatic Virgins, plump Cupids, and high-society ladies in the European mode of half a century ago, and sculptors entitle their monumental marbles and bronzes *Malgré Tout, Désespoir, Après l'Orgie.*

Beyond the boundaries of official art, far removed from its star performers, the genius engraver José Guadalupe Posada strips naked his country and his time. No critic takes him seriously. He has no pupils, although two young artists have been following him since they were children. José Clemente Orozco and Diego Rivera haunt Posada's little workshop and watch him labor, with devotion as if at a Mass, as the metal shavings fall to the floor at the passage of the burin over the plates.

(44 and 47)

1910: Mexico City
The Centennial and the Dictator

At the height of the Centennial celebrations, Don Porfirio opens a mental asylum. Soon afterward he lays the foundation stone for a new jail.

Don Porfirio is decorated from his paunch up to his plumed head, which reigns above a cloud of top-hats and imperial helmets. His courtiers, rheumatic antiques in frock coats and gaiters, with flowers in their buttonholes, dance to the strains of "Long Live My Misery," the latest hit waltz. An orchestra of a hundred and fifty musicians plays beneath thirty thousand electric stars in the National Palace's grand ballroom.

The festivities last a whole month. Don Porfirio, eight times reelected by himself, makes one of these balls the occasion for announcing the imminence of his ninth term, while conferring ninety-nine-year concessions of copper, oil, and land on Morgan, Guggenheim, Rockefeller, and Hearst. For more than thirty years the deaf, rigid dictator has administered the largest tropical territory of the United States.

On one of these nights, at the peak of this patriotic binge, Halley's Comet bursts into the sky. Panic spreads. The press announces that the comet will stick its tail into Mexico and set everything on fire.

(40, 44, and 391)

1911: Anenecuilco
Zapata

He was born in the saddle, a rider and breaker-in of horses. He navigates the countryside on horseback, careful not to disturb the deep sleep of the earth. Emiliano Zapata is a man of silences, someone who talks by keeping quiet.

The campesinos of his village Anenecuilco, little palm-thatched adobe houses peppered over a hill, have made Zapata their leader, entrusting him with papers from the time of the viceroys. The bundle of documents proves that this community, rooted here from the beginning, is no intruder on its own land.

Anenecuilco is being strangled, like all the other communities in the Mexican region of Morelos. There are ever fewer islands of corn in an ocean of sugar. Of the village of Tequesquitengo, condemned to die because its free Indians refused to become a gang of peons, nothing remains but the church-tower cross. The immense plantations advance, swallowing up land, water, and woods. They leave no room even to bury the dead.

"If they want to plant, let them plant in pots."

Gunmen and conmen see to the actual plundering while the consumers of communities hold concerts in their gardens and breed polo ponies and pedigreed dogs.

Zapata, leader of the enslaved villagers, buries the viceregal land titles under the Anenecuilco church floor and throws himself into the struggle. His troops of Indians, well turned out and well mounted, if badly armed, grows as it goes.

(468)

1911: Mexico City
Madero

Meanwhile, the whole of the north is rising behind Francisco Madero; and after thirty continuous years on the throne, Porfirio Díaz collapses in a few months.

Madero, the new president, is a virtuous son of the liberal Constitution. He wants to save Mexico by judicial reform, while Zapata demands agrarian reform. Confronting the clamor of the campesinos, the new deputies promise to study their misery.

(44 and 194)

1911: The Fields of Chihuahua
Pancho Villa

Of all the northern leaders who have raised Madero to the presidency, Pancho Villa is the most loved and loving.

He likes to get married and keeps on doing it. Pistol to head, there is no priest who balks nor girl who resists. He also likes to dance the *tanatío* to the strains of the marimba, and to get into shoot-outs. Bullets bounce off his sombrero like raindrops.

He took to the desert early on: *"For me the war began when I was born."* He was little more than a child when he avenged his sister. Of the many deaths notched up since, the first was that of his boss, leaving him little choice but to become a horse thief.

He was born as Doroteo Arango. Pancho Villa was someone else entirely—a gang compañero, a friend, the best of friends. When the Rural Guards killed the real Pancho Villa, Doroteo Arango took his name and kept it. Against death and forgetting, he began calling himself Pancho Villa, so that his friend should continue to be.

(206)

1911: Machu Picchu
The Last Sanctuary of the Incas

isn't dead; it only sleeps. For centuries the Urubamba River, foaming and roaring, has exhaled its potent breath against these sacred stones, covering them with a blanket of dense jungle to guard their sleep. Thus has the last bastion of the Incas, the last foothold of the Indian kings of Peru, been kept secret.

Among snow mountains which appear on no maps, a North American archeologist, Hiram Bingham, stumbles upon Machu Picchu. A child of the region leads him by the hand over precipices to the lofty throne veiled by clouds and greenery. There, Bingham finds the white stones still alive beneath the verdure, and reveals them, awakened, to the world.

(53 and 453)

1912: Quito
Alfaro

A tall woman, dressed all in black, curses President Alfaro as she plunges a dagger into his corpse. Then she raises, on the point of a stick, a flaming banner, the bloody rag of his shirt.

Behind the woman in black march the avengers of Holy Mother Church. With ropes tied to his feet they drag away the nude body. Flowers rain from windows. Saint-eating, host-swallowing, gossipy old women cry *"Long live religion!"* The cobbled streets run with blood which the dogs can never lick away nor the rain wash off. The butchery ends in flames. A great bonfire is lit, and on it they throw what remains of old Alfaro. Then gunmen and thugs, hired by the landed gentry, stamp on his ashes.

Eloy Alfaro had dared to expropriate the lands of the Church, owner of much of Ecuador, and used the rents to create schools and hospitals. A friend of God but not of the Pope, he had legalized divorce and freed Indians jailed for debt. No one was so hated by the surpliced, nor so feared by the frock-coated.

Night falls. The air of Quito reeks of burned flesh. As on every Sunday, the military band plays waltzes and *pasillos* in the Grand Plaza bandstand.

(12, 24, 265, and 332)

Sad Verses from the Ecuadoran Songbook

Don't come near, anyone,
Stand aside or go.
My disease is contagious,
I'm full of woe.

I'm alone, born alone,
Of a mother forlorn,
All alone I stay,
A feather in a storm.

Why should a painted house
Make a blind man sing?
What are balconies to the street,
If he can't see a thing?

(294)

1912: Cantón Santa Ana
Chronicle of the Customs of Manabí

Eloy Alfaro was born on the coast of Ecuador, in the province of Manabí. In that hot land, region of insolence and violence, no one paid the least attention to his recent divorce law, pushed through against wind and tide. Here, it's simpler to become a widower than to get caught up in red tape. On the bed where two go to sleep, sometimes only one wakes up. Manabís are famous for short tempers, no money, and big hearts.

Martín Vera was a rare Manabí. His knife had rusted from remaining so long in its sheath. When the neighbors' hog invaded his little garden and ate his manioc plants, Martín went to talk to them, the Rosados, and asked them nicely to shut the creature in. On the second occasion, Martín offered to repair the rickety walls of the Rosados' pigsty for nothing. But the third time, as the hog romped about in his garden, Martín took a shot at it with his gun. Round as it was, the baneful animal fell flat. The Rosados hauled it back to their property to give it a porcine burial.

The Veras and the Rosados stopped greeting each other. Some days later, the executioner of the hog was crossing the Calvo cliffs, holding on to the mane of his mule, when a bullet left him hanging from one stirrup. The mule dragged Martín Vera home, too late for any kneeling woman to help him to a decent death.

The Rosados fled. When Martín's children hunted them down in an empty convent near Colimas, they lit a fire around the place. The Rosados, thirty in all, had to choose death. Some expired by fire, burnt to a crisp; others by bullet, riddled like colanders.

This happened a year ago. Now, the jungle has devoured the gardens of both families, leaving only a no-man's-land.

(226)

1912: Pajeú de Flores
Family Wars

In the deserts of northeast Brazil the elite inherit land and hatred: sad land, land dying of thirst; and hatred, which relatives perpetuate from generation to generation, vengeance to vengeance, forever and a day. In Ceará there is eternal war between the Cunha family and the Pataca family, and the Monteses and the Faitosas practice mutual extermination. In Paraíba it is the Dantases and the Nóbregases who kill each other. In Pernambuco, in the Pajeú River region, every newly born Pereira receives from his parents and godparents the order to hunt down his Carvalho; and every Carvalho comes into the world prepared to liquidate his Pereira.

Today, Virgulino da Silva Pereira, known as Lampião, fires his first shots at a Carvalho. Though still a child, he automatically becomes an outlaw, a *cangaceiro*. Life is not worth much around here, where the only hospital is the cemetery. If Lampião were the child of the rich, he would not have to kill on others' account; he would have it done for him.

(343)

1912: Daiquirí
Daily Life in the Caribbean: An Invasion

The Platt Amendment, handiwork of Senator Platt of Connecticut, is the passkey that the United States uses to enter Cuba at any hour. The amendment, part of the Cuban Constitution, authorizes the United States to invade and stand fast, and gives it the power to decide who is or is not a proper president for Cuba.

The current proper president, Mario García Menocal, who also presides over the Cuban American Sugar Company, applies the Platt Amendment, calling in the Marines to put unrest to rest. Too many blacks are in revolt, and none of them has a high enough opinion of private property. Two warships steam in and the Marines land on the beach at Daiquirí to protect the iron and copper mines of the Spanish American and Cuban Copper companies, threatened by black wrath, and the sugar mills all along the Guantánamo and Western Railroad tracks.

(208 and 241)

1912: Niquinohomo
Daily Life in Central America: Another Invasion

Nicaragua pays the United States a colossal indemnity for *moral damages*, inflicted by fallen president Zelaya when he committed the grave offense of trying to impose taxes on North American companies.

As Nicaragua lacks funds, U.S. bankers lend the necessary monies to pay the indemnity, and since Nicaragua lacks guarantees, U.S. Secretary of State Philander Knox sends back the Marines to take charge of customs houses, national banks, and railroads.

Benjamin Zeledón heads the resistance. The chief of the patriots has a fresh-looking face and startled eyes. The invaders cannot bribe him because Zeledón spits on money, so they defeat him by treachery.

Augusto César Sandino, a no-account peon from a no-account village, sees Zeledón's corpse pass by, dragged through the dust, hands and feet bound to the saddle of a drunken invader.

(10 and 56)

1912: Mexico City

Huerta

looks like a malignant corpse. His shiny dark glasses are all that seem alive in his face.

Veteran bodyguard of Porfirio Díaz, Victoriano Huerta converted to democracy on the day the dictatorship fell. Now he is President Madero's right-hand man, and has dedicated himself to hunting down revolutionaries. In the north he catches Pancho Villa, in the south Zapata's lieutenant, Gildardo Magaña, and orders them shot. The firing squad are stroking their triggers when the presidential pardon interrupts the ceremony. *"Death came for me,"* sighs Villa, *"but missed the appointment."*

The resuscitated pair end up in the same cell in Tlatelolco prison. They pass days, months, chatting. Magaña talks of Zapata, of his plan for agrarian reform, and of Madero, who turns a deaf ear, so eager is he to offend neither campesinos nor landlords, *riding two horses at once.*

A small blackboard and a few books arrive. Pancho Villa knows how to read people, but not letters. Magaña teaches him, and together they enter, word by word, sword-thrust by sword-thrust, the castles of *The Three Musketeers*. Then they start the journey through *Don Quixote de la Mancha*, crazy roads of old Spain; and Pancho Villa, fierce warrior of the desert, strokes the pages with the hand of a lover.

Magaña tells him: *"This book . . . You know? A jailbird wrote it. One of us."*

(194 and 206)

1913: Mexico City

An Eighteen-Cent Rope

President Madero imposes a tax, a tiny tax, on the heretofore untouched oil companies, and North American ambassador Henry Lane Wilson threatens invasion. Several warships are heading for the ports of Mexico, announces the ambassador, while General Huerta rebels and his troops bombard the National Palace.

The fate of Mexico is discussed in the smoking lounge of the U.S. embassy. It is decided to invoke the shot-while-trying-to-escape law, so they put Madero in a car, order him to get out of town, and riddle him with bullets when he tries to.

General Huerta, the new president, attends a banquet at the Jockey Club. There he announces that he has a good remedy, an eighteen-cent rope, for Emiliano Zapata and Pancho Villa and the other enemies of order.

(194 and 246)

1913: Jonacatepec

The Hordes Are Not Destroyed

Huerta's officers, old hands at massacring rebellious Indians, propose to clean up the southern areas—burning villages and hunting down campesinos. Anyone they meet falls dead or prisoner, for in the south, who is not with Zapata?

Zapata's forces are hungry and sick, frayed, but the leader of the landless knows what he wants, and his people believe in what he does; neither fire nor deceit can prevail against that. While the capital's newspapers report that *the Zapata hordes have been totally destroyed*, Zapata blows up trains, surprises garrisons and annihilates them, occupies villages, attacks cities, and moves wherever he wants across impenetrable mountains, through impassable ravines, fighting and loving as though it's all in a day's work.

Zapata sleeps where he likes with anyone he likes, but of them all he prefers two who are one.

(468)

Zapata and Those Two

We were twins. We were both named Luz for the day of our baptism and Gregoria for the day we were born. They called her Luz and me Gregoria and there we were, two young girls in the house, when Zapata's boys came along, and then their chief, trying to persuade my sister to go with him.

"Look, come with me."

And precisely one September 15 he came by and took her.

Afterward, in this continuous moving around, my sister died in Huautla of a disease that they call—what do they call it?—Saint Vitus, the Saint Vitus disease.

Three days and three nights chief Zapata was there with us, not eating or drinking a thing. We had only just lit the candles for my sister when ay, ay, ay, he took me by force. He said I belonged to him, because my sister and I were one . . .

(244)

1913: The Plains of Chihuahua
The North of Mexico Celebrates
War and Fiesta

The cocks crow whenever they feel like it. This land has caught fire, gone crazy. Everyone is in rebellion.

"We're off to the war, woman."

"But why me?"

"Do you want me to die of starvation in the war? Who'll make my tortillas?"

Flocks of vultures follow the armed peons over plains and mountains. If life is worth nothing, what can death be worth? Men roll themselves like dice into the tumult, and find vengeance or oblivion, land to feed them or to cover them.

"Here comes Pancho Villa!" the peons exult.

"Here comes Pancho Villa!" cry the overseers, crossing themselves.

"Where, where is he?" asks General Huerta.

"In the north, south, east, and west, and also nowhere," replies the Chihuahua garrison commander.

Confronting the enemy, Pancho Villa is always the first to charge, right into the smoking jaws of the guns. When the battle gets hot, he just horse-laughs. His heart thumps like a fish out of water.

"*There's nothing wrong with the general. He's just a bit emotional,*" his officers explain.

And so he is. With a single shot, for pure fun, he has been known to disembowel the messenger who gallops up with good news from the front.

(206 and 260)

1913: Culiacán
Bullets

There are bullets with imagination, Martín Luis Guzmán discovers. Bullets which amuse themselves in afflicting the flesh. He has known serious bullets, which serve human fury, but not these bullets that play with human pain.

For being a bad marksman with a good heart, the young novelist is assigned to direct one of Pancho Villa's hospitals. The wounded pile up in the dirt with no recourse but to clench their teeth, if they have any.

Checking the jammed wards, Guzmán confirms the improbable trajectories of these fanciful bullets, capable of emptying an eye-socket while leaving a body alive, or of sticking a piece of ear into the neck and a piece of neck into the foot. And he witnesses the sinister joy of bullets, which, having been ordered to kill a soldier, condemn him never again to sit down or never again to eat with his mouth.

(216)

1913: The Fields of Chihuahua
One of These Mornings I Murdered Myself,

on some dusty Mexican road, and the event left a deep impression on me.

This wasn't the first crime I committed. From the time I was born in Ohio seventy-one years ago and received the name Ambrose Bierce, until my recent death, I have played havoc with the lives of my parents and various relatives, friends, and colleagues. These touching episodes have splashed blood over my days—or my stories, which is all the same to me: the difference between the life I lived and the life I wrote is a matter for the jokers who execute human law, literary criticism, and the will of God in this world.

To put an end to my days, I joined the troops of Pancho Villa and chose one of those many stray bullets zooming through the Mexican sky these days. This method proved more practical than hanging, cheaper than poison, more convenient than firing with my own finger, and more dignified than waiting for disease or old age.

1914: Montevideo
Batlle

He writes articles slandering the saints and makes speeches attacking the company that sells real estate in the Great Beyond. When he assumed the presidency of Uruguay, he had no alternative but to swear before God and the Holy Evangels, but explained immediately that he didn't believe in any of that.

José Batlle y Ordoñez governs in defiance of the powers of heaven and earth. The Church has promised him a nice place in hell; companies he nationalized, or forced to respect their workers' unions and the eight-hour work day, will feed the fire; and the Devil will avenge his offenses against male-supremacists.

"He is legalizing licentiousness," say his enemies when he approves a law permitting women to sue for divorce.

"He is dissolving the family," they say, when he extends inheritance rights to illegitimate children.

"The female brain is inferior," they say, when he creates a women's university and announces that women will soon have the vote so that Uruguayan democracy need not walk on just one leg, and so that women will not forever be children passing from the hands of the father to those of the husband.

(35 and 271)

1914: San Ignacio
Quiroga

From the Paraná River jungle where he lives in voluntary exile, Horacio Quiroga applauds Batlle's reforms and *that ardent faith in noble things*.

But Quiroga is indeed far from Uruguay. He left the country some years ago, fleeing the shadow of death. A curse has darkened his life since he killed his best friend while trying to defend him; or perhaps he was cursed from the beginning.

In the jungle, a step away from the ruins of the Jesuit missions, Quiroga lives surrounded by bugs and palm trees. He writes stories without detours, just as he opens paths through the thicket with his machete. He works the word with the same rugged love as he does the soil, and wood, and iron.

What Quiroga seeks he could never find away from here. Here, yes, though only very occasionally. In this house which his hands built by the river, Quiroga has at times the joy of hearing voices more powerful than the call of death: rare and fleeting certainties of life, which while they last are as absolute as the sun.

(20, 357, 358, and 390)

1914: Montevideo

Delmira

In this rented room she had an appointment with the man who had been her husband. Wanting to possess her, wanting to stay with her, he made love to her, killed her, then killed himself.

The Uruguayan papers publish a photo of the body lying beside the bed: Delmira struck down by two bullets, naked like her poems, all unclothed in red.

Let's go further in the night, let's . . .

Delmira Agustini wrote in a trance. She sang to the fevers of love without shame, and was condemned by those who punish women for what they applaud in men, because chastity is a feminine duty, and desire, like reason, a male privilege. In Uruguay the laws march ahead of the people, who still separate soul from body as if they were Beauty and the Beast. Before the corpse of Delmira flow tears and phrases about this irreplaceable loss to national letters, but deep down the mourners feel some relief: the woman is dead, and better so.

But is she dead? Will not all the lovers burning in the nights of the world be the shadows of her voice and the echoes of her body? In the nights of the world won't they make a small place where her unfettered voice can sing and her radiant feet can dance?

(49 and 426)

1914: Ciudad Jiménez
Chronicler of Angry Peoples

From shock to shock, from marvel to marvel, John Reed travels the roads of northern Mexico. He is looking for Pancho Villa and finds him at every step.

Reed, chronicler of revolution, sleeps wherever night catches up with him. No one ever steals from him, or ever lets him pay for anything except dance music; and there's always someone to offer him a piece of tortilla or a place on his horse.

"Where do you come from?"

"From New York."

"Well, I don't know anything about New York, but I'll bet you don't see such fine cattle going through the streets as you see in the streets of Jiménez."

A woman carries a pitcher on her head. Another, squatting, suckles her baby. Another, on her knees, grinds corn. Enveloped in faded serapes, the men sit in a circle, drinking and smoking.

"Listen, Juanito, why is it your people don't like Mexicans? Why do they call us 'greasers'?"

Everyone has something to ask this thin, bespectacled, blond man who looks as if he were here by mistake.

"Listen, Juanito, how do you say 'mula' in English?"

"Goddamn stubborn—fathead mule . . ."

(368)

1914: Salt Lake City
Songster of Angry Peoples

They condemn him for singing red ballads that make fun of God, that wake up the worker, that curse money. The sentence doesn't say that Joe Hill is a proletarian troubadour, or worse, a foreigner seeking to subvert the good order of business. The sentence speaks of assault and crime. There is no proof, the witnesses change their stories each time they testify, and the defense lawyers act as if they were the prosecutors. But these details lack importance for the judges and for all who make decisions in Salt Lake City. Joe Hill will be bound to a chair with a cardboard circle pinned over his heart as a target for the firing squad.

Joe Hill came from Sweden. In the United States he wandered the roads. In the cities he cleaned spittoons and built walls; in the countryside he stacked wheat and picked fruit, dug copper in the mines, toted sacks on the piers, slept under bridges and in barns, sang anywhere at any hour, and never stopped singing. He bids his comrades farewell singing, now that he's off to Mars to disturb its social peace.

(167)

1914: Torreón

By Rail They March to Battle

In the red car, which displays his name in big gilt letters, General Pancho Villa receives John Reed. He receives him in his underpants, pours him coffee, and studies him for a long moment. Deciding that this gringo deserves the truth, he begins to talk.

"The chocolate politicians want to win without dirtying their hands. Those perfumed . . ."

Then he takes him to visit the field hospital, a train with a surgery and doctors to heal their own men and others: and he shows him the cars that take corn, sugar, coffee, and tobacco to the front. He also shows him the platform on which traitors are shot.

The railroads were the work of Porfirio Díaz, the key to peace and order, masterkey to the progress of a country without rivers or roads. They had been created not to transport an armed people but cheap raw materials, docile workers, and the executioners of rebellions. But General Villa makes war by train. From Camargo he turns loose a locomotive at full speed and smashes a trainful of soldiers. Villa's men enter Ciudad Juárez crouching in innocent coal cars, and after firing a few shots occupy it, more out of fun than necessity. By train the Villista troops roll to the front lines of the war. The locomotive gasps, painfully climbing the bare northern slopes. From behind a plume of black smoke come creaking shaking cars filled with soldiers and horses. On their roofs sprout rifles, sombreros, and stoves. Up there, among soldiers singing *mañanitas* and shooting into the air, children bawl and women cook—the women, the *soldaderas*, dressed in bridal gowns and silk shoes from the last looting.

(246 and 368)

1914: The Fields of Morelos
It's Time to Get Moving and Fight,

and the roars and rifle shots echo like mountain landslides. The army of Zapata—*down with the haciendas, up with the villages*—opens the way to Mexico City.

Around chief Zapata, General Genovevo de la O meditates and cleans his rifle, his face like a mustachioed sun, while Otilio Montaño, anarchist, discusses a manifesto with Antonio Díaz Soto y Gama, socialist.

Among Zapata's officers and advisers there is but one woman. Colonel Rosa Bobadilla, who won her rank in battle, commands a troop of cavalrymen and maintains a ban on drinking so much as a drop of tequila. They obey her, mysteriously, although they remain convinced that women are only good for adorning the world, making children, and cooking corn, chili, beans, or whatever God provides and permits.

(296 and 468)

1914: Mexico City
Huerta Flees

on the same ship that took Porfirio Díaz from Mexico.

Rags are winning the war against lace. A campesino tide beats against the capital. Zapata, *the Attila of Morelos*, and Pancho Villa, *the orangutan who eats raw meat and gnaws bones*, attack from north and south, avenging wrongs. Just before Christmas, the front pages of Mexico City's newspapers appear with black borders, mourning the arrival of the outlaws, barbarian violators of young ladies and locks.

Turbulent years. Now nobody knows who is who. The city trembles in panic and sighs with nostalgia. Only yesterday at the hub of the world were the masters in their big houses with their lackeys and pianos, candelabra and Carrara marble baths; and all around, serfs, the poor of the barrios, dizzy with *pulque*, drowning in garbage, condemned to the wages or tips which barely bought some occasional watered milk or *frijol* coffee or burro meat.

(194 and 246)

1915: Mexico City
Power Ungrasped

A timid knock, somewhere between wanting and not wanting. A door that half opens. An uncovered head, enormous sombrero clutched in hands pleading, for the love of God, for water or tortillas. Zapata's men, Indians in white pants, cartridge belts crossed on chests, wander the streets of the city that scorns and fears them. Nowhere are they invited in. In no time they run into Villa's men, also foreigners lost, blind.

Soft click of sandals, chas-ches, chas-ches, on the marble stairways, feet that are frightened by the pleasure of carpets, faces staring bewildered at themselves in the mirrors of waxed floors: Zapata's and Villa's men enter the National Palace as if begging pardon. Pancho Villa sits on the gilt armchair that was Porfirio Díaz's throne *to see how it feels*, while at his side Zapata, in a very embroidered suit, with an expression of being there without being there, murmurs answers to the reporters' questions.

The campesino generals have triumphed, but they don't know what to do with their victory: *"This shack is pretty big for us."*

Power is something for doctors, a threatening mystery that can only be deciphered by the cultured, those who understand the high art of politics, *those who sleep on downy pillows*.

When night falls, Zapata goes to a seedy hotel just a step away from the railway that leads to his country, and Villa to a military train. After a few days, they bid farewell to Mexico City.

The hacienda peons, the Indians of the communities, the pariahs of the countryside, have discovered the center of power and occupied it for a moment, as if on a visit, on tiptoe, anxious to end as soon as possible this trip to the moon. Strangers to the glory of victory, they end up going home to the lands where they know how to move around without getting lost.

No better news could be imagined by Huerta's successor, General Venustiano Carranza, whose battered troops are recovering with the aid of the United States.

(47, 194, 246, and 260)

1915: Tlaltizapán
Agrarian Reform

In an old mill in the village of Tlaltizapán, Zapata installs his headquarters. Here, in his native district, far from the sideburned lords and their feathered ladies, far from the flashy, deceitful city, the Morelos rebel chief liquidates the great estates, nationalizes sugarmills and distilleries without paying a centavo, and restores to the communities lands stolen through the centuries. Free villages are reborn, the conscience and memory of Indian traditions, and with them local democracy. Here neither bureaucrats nor generals make the decisions, but the assembled community in open forum. Selling or renting land is forbidden. Covetousness is forbidden.

In the shade of the laurels, in the village plaza, the talk is of more than fighting cocks, horses, and rain. Zapata's army, a league of armed communities, watches over the recovered land; they oil their guns and reload them with old Mauser and .30-.30 cartridges.

Young technicians are arriving in Morelos with tripods and other strange instruments to help the agrarian reform. The campesinos receive these budding engineers from Cuernavaca with a rain of flowers; but the dogs bark at the mounted messengers who gallop in from the north with the grim news that Pancho Villa's army is being wiped out.

(468)

1915: El Paso
Azuela

Exiled in Texas, a medic from Pancho Villa's army treats the Mexican revolution as a pointless outburst. According to Mariano Azuela's novel *The Underdogs*, this is a tale of drunken blind men who shoot without knowing why or against whom, who lash out like animals

seeking things to steal or women to tumble on the ground in a land
that stinks of gunpowder and frying grease.

(33)

1916: Tlaltizapán
Carranza

The clink of Villa's horsemen's spurs can still be heard in the mountains, but it is no longer an army. From trenches defended by barbed
wire, machineguns have made a clean sweep in four long battles of
Villa's fiery cavalry, ground to dust in stubbornly repeated suicide
charges.

Venustiano Carranza, president in spite of Villa and Zapata,
launches the war in the south: *"This business of dividing up the land
is crazy,"* he says. One decree announces that lands distributed by
Zapata will be returned to their old owners; another promises to shoot
anyone who is, or looks like, a Zapatista.

Shooting and burning with rifles and torches, government forces
swoop down on the flourishing fields of Morelos. They kill five hundred
people in Tlaltizapán, and many more elsewhere. The prisoners are
sold in Yucatán as slave labor for the henequén plantations, as in the
days of Porfirio Díaz; and crops, herds, all war booty is taken to the
markets of the capital.

In the mountains, Zapata resists. When the rainy season approaches, the revolution is suspended for planting; but later, stubbornly, incredibly, it goes on.

(246, 260, and 468)

1916: Buenos Aires
Isadora

Barefoot, naked, scantily draped in the Argentine flag, Isadora Duncan dances to the national anthem in a students' café in Buenos Aires,
and the next morning the whole world knows of it. The impresario
breaks his contract, good families cancel their reservations at the
Colón Theater, and the press demands the immediate expulsion of

this disgraceful North American who has come to Argentina to sully patriotic symbols.

Isadora cannot understand it. No Frenchman protested when she danced the Marseillaise in nothing but a red shawl. If one can dance an emotion, if one can dance an idea, why not an anthem?

Liberty offends. This woman with shining eyes is the declared enemy of schools, matrimony, classical dance, and everything that cages the wind. She dances for the joy of dancing; dances what she wants, when she wants, how she wants; and orchestras hush before the music that is born of her body.

(145)

1916: New Orleans

Jazz

From the slaves comes the freest of all music, jazz, which flies without asking permission. Its grandparents are the blacks who sang at their work on their owners' plantations in the southern United States, and its parents are the musicians of black New Orleans brothels. The whorehouse bands play all night without stopping, on balconies that keep them safe above the brawling in the street. From their improvisations is born the new music.

With his savings from delivering newspapers, milk, and coal, a short, timid lad has just bought his own trumpet for ten dollars. He blows and the music stretches out, out, greeting the day. Louis Armstrong, like jazz, is the grandson of slaves, and has been raised, like jazz, in the whorehouse.

(105)

1916: Columbus

Latin America Invades the United States

Rain falls upward. Hen bites fox and hare shoots hunter. For the first and only time in history, Mexican soldiers invade the United States.

With the tattered force remaining, five hundred men out of the many thousands he once had, Pancho Villa crosses the border and, crying *Viva Mexico!* showers bullets on the city of Columbus, Texas.

(206 and 260)

1916: León

Darío

In Nicaragua, occupied land, humiliated land, Rubén Darío dies.

The doctor kills him, fatally puncturing his liver. The embalmer, the hairdresser, the makeup man, and the tailor torment his remains.

A sumptuous funeral is inflicted upon him. The warm February air in the city of León smells of incense and myrrh. The most distinguished señoritas, festooned in lilies and heron feathers, serve as Canephoras and Virgins of Minerva strewing flowers along the route of the funeral procession.

Surrounded by candles and admirers, the corpse of Darío wears a Greek tunic and laurel crown by day, by night a formal black frock coat and gloves to match. For a whole week, day and night, night and day, he is scourged with never-ending recitals of shoddy verses, and regaled with speeches proclaiming him Immortal Swan, Messiah of the Spanish Lyre, and Samson of the Metaphor.

Guns roar. The government contributes to the martyrdom by piling War Ministry honors on the poet who preached peace. Bishops brandish crosses; steeple bells ring out. In the culminating moment of this flagellation, the poet who believed in divorce and lay education is dropped into the hole converted, a prince of the Church.

(129, 229, and 454)

1917: The Fields of Chihuahua and Durango

Eagles into Hens

A punitive expedition, ten thousand soldiers with plentiful artillery enter Mexico to make Pancho Villa pay for his impudent attack on the North American city of Columbus.

"We'll bring back that assassin in an iron cage," proclaims General John Pershing, and the thunder of his guns echoes the words.

Across the drought-stricken immensities of northern Mexico, General Pershing finds various graves—*Here lies Pancho Villa*—

without a Villa in any of them. He finds snakes and lizards and silent stones, and campesinos who murmur false leads when beaten, threatened, or offered all the gold in the world.

After some months, almost a year, Pershing returns to the United States. He brings back a long caravan of soldiers fed up with breathing dust, with the people throwing stones, with the lies in each little village in that gravelly desert. Two young lieutenants march at the head of the humbled procession. Both have had in Mexico their baptism of fire. For Dwight Eisenhower, newly graduated from West Point, it is an unlucky start on the road to military glory. George Patton spits as he leaves *this ignorant and half-savage country*.

From the crest of a hill, Pancho Villa looks down and comments: *"They came like eagles and they leave like wet hens."*

(206 and 260)

1918: Córdoba
Moldy Scholars

At the Argentine university of Córdoba degrees are no longer denied to those unable to prove their white lineage as was the case a few years ago, but *Duties toward Servants* is still a subject studied in the Philosophy of Law course, and students of medicine still graduate without having set eyes on a sick person.

The professors, venerable specters, copy a Europe several centuries gone, a lost world of gentlemen and pious ladies, the sinister beauty of a colonial past. The merits of the parrot and the virtues of the monkey are rewarded with trimmings and tassels.

The Córdoba students, fed up, explode with disgust. They go on strike against these jailers of the spirit, calling on students and workers throughout Latin America to fight for a culture of their own. From Mexico to Chile come mighty echoes.

(164)

1918: Córdoba

"The Pains That Linger Are the Liberties We Lack," Proclaims the Student Manifesto

. . . We have resolved to call all things by their right names. Córdoba is redeeming itself. From today we count for our country one shame less and one freedom more. The pains that linger are the liberties we lack. We believe we are not wrong, the resonances of the heart tell us so: we are treading on the skirts of the revolution, we are living an American hour . . .

The unversities have till now been a secular refuge for the mediocre, income of the ignorant, secure hospital for the invalid, and —which is even worse—the place where all forms of tyranny and insensitivity have found a professor to teach them. The universities thus faithfully reflect those decadent societies which offer the sad spectacle of senile immobility. For that reason, science, confronting these mute and shut-in establishments, passes by in silence or enters into bureaucratic service, mutilated and grotesque . . .

(164)

1918: Ilopango

Miguel at Thirteen

He arrives at the Ilopango barracks driven by a hunger that has sunk his eyes into the depths of his head.

In the barracks, in exchange for food, Miguel begins running errands and shining lieutenants' boots. He learns fast to split coconuts with one blow of the machete as if they were necks, and to fire a carbine without wasting cartridges. Thus he becomes a soldier.

At the end of a year of barracks life, the wretched boy gives out. After putting up for so long with drunken officers who beat him for no reason, Miguel escapes. And that night, the night of his flight, is the night of the Ilopango earthquake. Miguel hears it from far away.

For a whole day and the next day too, the earth shakes El Salvador, this little country of warm people, until between tremor and tremor the real quake comes, the super-earthquake that bursts and shatters everything. It brings down the barracks to the last stone, crushing officers and soldiers alike—but not Miguel.

And so occurs the third birth of Miguel Mármol, at thirteen years of age.

(126)

1918: *The Mountains of Morelos*
Ravaged Land, Living Land

The hogs, the cows, the chickens, are they Zapatistas? And the jugs, the pans, the stewpots, what of them? Government troops have exterminated half the population of Morelos in these years of stubborn peasant war, and taken away everything. Only stones and charred stalks remain in the fields; the wreckage of a house, a woman heaving a plow. Of the men, any not dead or exiled have become outlaws.

But the war continues. The war will continue as long as corn sprouts in secret mountain crannies, as long as Zapata's eyes flash.

(468)

1918: *Mexico City*
The New Bourgeoisie Is Born Lying

"We fight for the land," says Zapata, *"and not for illusions that give us nothing to eat . . . With or without elections, the people are chewing the cud of bitterness."*

While taking the land from the campesinos of Morelos and wrecking their villages, President Carranza talks about agrarian reform. While applying state terror against the poor, he grants them the right to vote for the rich and offers illiterates freedom of the press.

The new Mexican bourgeoisie, voracious child of war and plunder, sings hymns of praise to the Revolution while gobbling it down with knife and fork from an embroidered tablecloth.

(468)

1919: Cuautla

This Man Taught Them That Life Is Not Only Fear of Suffering and Hope for Death

It had to be done by treachery. Shamming friendship, a government officer leads him into the trap. A thousand soldiers are waiting, a thousand rifles tumble him from his horse.

Afterward they haul him to Cuautla and exhibit him face up.

Campesinos from everywhere flock there for the silent march-past, which lasts several days. Approaching the body, they remove their sombreros, look attentively, and shake their heads. No one believes it. There's a wart missing, a scar too many; that suit isn't his; this face swollen by so many bullets could be anybody's.

The campesinos talk in slow whispers, peeling off words like grains of corn:

"They say he went with a compadre to Arabia."

"Hell, Zapata doesn't chicken out."

"He's been seen on the Quilamula heights."

"I know he's sleeping in a cave in Cerro Prieto."

"Last night his horse was drinking in the river."

The Morelos campesinos don't now believe, nor will they ever believe, that Emiliano Zapata could have committed the infamy of dying and leaving them all alone.

(468)

Ballad of the Death of Zapata

Little star in the night
that rides the sky like a witch,
where is our chief Zapata
who was the scourge of the rich?

Little flower of the fields
and valleys of Morelos,
if they ask for Zapata,
say he's gone to try on halos.

Little bubbling brook,
what did that carnation say to you?
It says our chief didn't die.
that Zapata's on his way to you.

(293)

1919: Hollywood
Chaplin

In the beginning were rags.

From the rag bag of the Keystone studios, Charles Chaplin chose the most useless garments, the too big, too small, too ugly, and put them together, as if picking through a garbage can. Some outsized pants, a dwarf's jacket, a bowler hat, and some huge dilapidated shoes. To that he added a prop mustache and cane. Then this little heap of rejected rags stood up, saluted its author with a ridiculous bow, and set off walking like a duck. After a few steps he collided with a tree and asked its pardon, doffing his hat.

And so came to life Charlie the Tramp, outcast and poet.

(121 and 383)

1919: Hollywood
Keaton

The man who never laughs creates laughter.

Like Chaplin, Buster Keaton is a Hollywood magician. His outcast hero—straw hat, stone face, cat's body—in no way resembles Charlie the Tramp, but is caught in the same absurd war with cops, bullies, and machines. Always impassive, icy outside, burning inside, he walks with great dignity on walls, on air, on the bottom of the sea.

Keaton is not as popular as Chaplin. His films entertain, but with too much mystery, too much melancholy.

(128 and 382)

1919: Memphis

Thousands of People Flock to the Show,

and many are women with babies in their arms. The family performance reaches its high point when Ell Persons, tied to a stake, is
baptized with gasoline and the flames draw his first howls.

Not long afterward, the audience departs in an orderly fashion,
complaining of the brevity of these things. Some stir the cinders
seeking a bone as a souvenir.

Ell Persons is one of the seventy-seven blacks who have been
roasted alive or hanged by white crowds this year in the southern
United States for committing a murder or a rape—that is to say, for
looking at a white woman, possibly with a lascivious gleam; or for
saying "Yes" instead of "Yes, ma'am"; or for not removing his hat
before speaking.

Among these lynched "niggers," some have worn the military
uniform of the United States of America and hunted Pancho Villa
through Mexico's northern deserts, or are newly returned from the
world war.

(51, 113, and 242)

1921: Rio de Janeiro

Rice Powder

President Epitácio Pessoa makes a recommendation to the managers
of Brazilian football. For reasons of patriotic prestige, he suggests
that no player with black skin be sent to the coming South American
soccer championships.

It happens, however, that Brazil won last year thanks to the
mulatto Artur Friedenreich, who scored the winning goal and whose
boots, grimed with mud, are still on display in a jeweler's window.
Friedenreich, born of a German and a black, is Brazil's best player.
He always arrives on the field last. It takes him at least half an hour
in the dressingroom to iron out his frizz, so that during the game not
a hair will move, even when he heads the ball.

Football, that elegant after-Mass diversion, is something for whites.
"Rice powder! Rice powder!" yell the fans at Carlos Alberto,

another mulatto player on the Fluminense club who whitens his face with it.

(279)

1921: Rio de Janeiro
Pixinguinha

It is announced that the Batons will soon be appearing on the Paris stage, and indignation mounts in the Brazilian press. What will Europeans think? Will they imagine Brazil is an African colony? The Batons' repertory contains no operatic arias or waltzes, only *maxixes*, *lundús*, *cortajacas*, *batuques*, *cateretês*, *modinhas*, and the newborn *samba*. It is an orchestra of blacks who play black music. Articles exhort the government to head off the disgrace. The foreign ministry promptly explains that the Batons are not on an official mission.

Pixinguinha, one of the blacks in the ensemble, is the best musician in Brazil. He doesn't know it, nor does it interest him. He is too busy seeking on his flute, with devilish joy, sounds stolen from the birds.

(75)

1921: Rio de Janeiro
Brazil's Fashionable Author

inaugurates a swimming pool in a sports club. Coelho Neto's speech exalting the virtues of the pool draws tears and applause. Coelho Neto invokes the powers of sea, sky, and earth *on this solemn occasion of such magnitude that we cannot evaluate it without tracing, through the Shadows of Time, its projection into the Future.*

Sweets for the rich, denounces Lima Barreto, an author not in vogue and accursed both as a mulatto and a rebel, who, cursing back, dies in some godforsaken hospital.

Lima Barreto mocks the pomposities of writers who parrot the literature of ornamental culture. They sing the glories of a happy Brazil, without blacks, workers, or the poor; a Brazil populated with sage economists whose most original idea is to impose more taxes on the people, a Brazil with two hundred and sixty-two generals whose job is to design new uniforms for next year's parade.

(36)

1922: Toronto
This Reprieve

saves thousands condemned to early death. Neither royal nor presidential, it has been extended by a Canadian doctor who a week ago, with seven cents in his pocket, was looking for a job.

On a hunch that deprived him of sleep, and after much error and discouragement, Fred Banting discovers that insulin, secreted by the pancreas, reduces sugar in the blood; and thus he commutes the many death sentences imposed by diabetes.

(54)

1922: Leavenworth
For Continuing to Believe That
All Belongs to All

Ricardo, most talented and dangerous of the Flores Magón brothers, has been absent from the revolution he did so much to start. While Mexico's fate was played out on its battlefields, he was breaking stones, shackled in a North American prison.

A United States court had sentenced him to twenty years' hard labor for signing an anarchist manifesto against private property. He was many times offered a pardon, if only he would ask for it. He never asked.

"When I die, perhaps my friends will write on my grave: 'Here Lies a Dreamer,' and my enemies: 'Here Lies a Madman.' But no one will dare write: 'Here Lies a Coward and Traitor to his Ideas.' "

In his cell, far from his land, they strangle him. *Heart failure*, says the medical report.

(44 and 391)

1922: *The Fields of Patagonia*
The Worker-Shoot

Three years ago young aristocrats of the Argentine Patriotic League went hunting in the barrios of Buenos Aires. The safari was a success. The rich kids killed workers and Jews for a whole week without a license, and no one went to jail.

Now it's the army that is using workers for target practice in the frozen lands of the south. The boys of the Tenth Cavalry under Lieutenant Colonel Héctor Benigno Varela roam the great estates of Patagonia shooting peons on strike. Fervent Patriotic League volunteers accompany them. No one is executed without a trial. Each trial lasts less time than it takes to smoke a cigarette.

Estancia owners and officers act as judges. The condemned are buried by the heap in common graves they dig themselves.

President Hipólito Yrigoyen in general doesn't approve of this method of finishing off anarchists and reds, but lifts not a finger against the murderers.

(38 and 365)

1923: *Guayas River*
Crosses Float in the River,

hundreds of crosses crowned with mountain blossoms, flowery squadrons of tiny ships cruising on the swell of waves and memory. Each cross recalls a murdered worker. People have thrown these floating crosses into the water so that the workers lying in the riverbed may rest in peace.

It happened a year ago, in the port of Guayaquil, which for several hours was in the hands of the workers. Fed up with eating hunger, they had called the first general strike in Ecuador's history—not even government officials were able to circulate without a pass from the unions. The women—washerwomen, tobacco workers, cooks, peddlers—had formed the Rosa Luxemburg Committee; they were the most defiant.

"*Today the rabble got up laughing. Tomorrow they'll go to bed crying,*" announced Carlos Arroyo, president of the Chamber of Deputies. And the president of the republic, José Luis Tamayo, ordered

General Enrique Barriga to take care of the matter: *"At any cost."*

At the first shots, many workers tried to escape, scattering like ants from an anthill squashed by a foot. These were the first to fall.

No one knows how many were thrown into the Guayas river to sink, their bellies slashed with bayonets.

(192, 332, and 472)

1923: Acapulco

The Function of the Forces of Order in the Democratic Process

As soon as the Tom Mix film ends, Juan Escudero surprises the audience by stepping in front of the screen of Acapulco's only cinema and delivering a harangue against bloodsucking merchants. By the time the boys in uniform pile on him, the Workers' Party of Acapulco has already been born, baptized by acclamation.

In no time at all, the Workers' Party has grown and won the elections and stuck its black-and-red flag over city hall. Juan Escudero—tall, thick sideburns, pointed mustache—is the new mayor, the socialist mayor. In the blink of an eye he turns the palace into a headquarters for cooperatives and unions, launches a literacy campaign, and defies the power of the three companies that own the water, air, ground, and grime of this filthy Mexican port abandoned by God and the federal government. Then the owners of everything organize new elections, so that the people may correct their error, but the Workers' Party of Acapulco wins again. So there's no way out but to call in the army, which promptly normalizes the situation. The victorious Juan Escudero receives two bullets, one in the arm and the other in the forehead, a mercy-shot from close range, while the soldiers set fire to city hall.

But Escudero survives, and continues winning elections. In a wheelchair, mutilated, hardly able to talk, Escudero conducts a victorious new campaign for deputy by dictating speeches to a youngster who deciphers his mumblings and repeats them aloud on campaign platforms.

The owners of Acapulco decide to pay thirty thousand pesos so that this time the military patrol will shoot properly. In the company ledgers these outlays are duly entered, but not their purpose. And finally Juan Escudero falls, very much shot, dead of total death you might say, thank you, gentlemen.

(441)

1923: Azángaro
Urviola

His family wanted him to be a doctor. Instead he became an Indian, as if his double-humped back and dwarf stature were not curse enough. Ezequiel Urviola quit his law career in Puno vowing to follow in the footsteps of Túpac Amaru. Since then he speaks Quechua, wears sandals, chews coca, and plays the *quena* flute. Day and night he comes and goes, inciting revolt in the Peruvian sierra, where the Indians have proprietors like the mules and the trees.

The police dream of catching the hunchback Urviola; the landlords pledge it; but the little shrimp turns into an eagle flying over the mountains.

(370)

1923: Callao
Mariátegui

A ship brings José Carlos Mariátegui back to Peru after some years in Europe. When he left he was a bohemian nighthawk from Lima who wrote about horses, a mystical poet who felt deeply and understood little. Over in Europe he discovered America. Mariátegui found Marxism and found Mariátegui, and this was how he learned to see from afar the Peru he couldn't see close up.

Mariátegui believes that Marxism means human progress as indisputably as smallpox vaccine or the theory of relativity, but to Peruvianize Peru one has to start by Peruvianizing Marxism, which is not a catechism or the tracing of some master plan, but a key to enter deep into this country. And the clues to the depths of his country are in the Indian communities, dispossessed by the sterile landowner system but unconquered in their socialist traditions of work and life.

(321, 277, and 355)

1923: Buenos Aires
Snapshot of a Worker-Hunter

He peruses the firearms catalogs lasciviously, as if they were pornography. For him the uniform of the Argentine army is as beautiful as the smoothest of human skin. He likes skinning alive the foxes that fall into his traps, but prefers making target practice of fleeing workers, the more so if they are reds, and more yet if they are foreign reds.

Jorge Ernesto Pérez Millán Temperley enlisted as a volunteer in the troop of Lieutenant Colonel Varela, and last year marched to Patagonia for the sport of liquidating any strikers who came within range. Later, when the German anarchist Kurt Wilckens threw the bomb that blew up Lieutenant Colonel Varela, this hunter of workers swore loudly to avenge his superior.

And avenge him he does. In the name of the Argentine Patriotic League, Jorge Ernesto Pérez Millán Temperley fires a Mauser bullet into the chest of Wilckens as he sleeps in his cell, then has himself immediately photographed for posterity, gun in hand, striking a martial pose of duty done.

(38)

1923: Tampico
Traven

A phantom ship, an old hulk destined to be wrecked, arrives off the coast of Mexico. Among its crew, vagabonds without name or nation, is a survivor of the suppressed revolution in Germany.

This comrade of Rosa Luxemburg, fugitive from hunger and the police, writes his first novel in Tampico and signs it B. Traven. With that name he will become famous without anyone ever knowing which face or voice or footstep is his. Traven decides to be a mystery, so that no bureaucracy can label him. All the better to mock a world where the marriage contract and inheritance matter more than love and death.

(398)

1923: The Fields of Durango

Pancho Villa Reads the
Thousand and One Nights,

deciphering the words out loud by candlelight, because this is the book that gives him the best dreams; and afterward, he awakens early to pasture the cows with his old battle comrades.

Villa is still the most popular man in the fields of northern Mexico, and officialdom doesn't like it a bit. Today it is three years since his men turned the Canutillo hacienda into a cooperative, which now has a hospital and a school, and a world of people have come to celebrate.

Villa is listening to his favorite *corridos* when Don Fernando, a pilgrim from Granada, mentions that John Reed has just died in Moscow.

Pancho Villa orders the party stopped. Even the flies pause in flight.

"So old Juan died? My old pal, Juan?"

"Himself."

Villa half believes and half not.

"I saw it in the papers," Don Fernando says, excusing himself. "He's buried over there with the heroes of the revolution."

Nobody breathes. Nobody disturbs the silence. Don Fernando murmurs: "It was typhus, not a bullet."

And Villa nods his head: "So old Juan died."

Then repeats: "So old Juan's dead."

He falls silent. Looking into the distance, he finally says: "I never even heard the word 'socialism' until he explained it to me."

All at once he rises, and extending his arms, rebukes the silent guitar-players: "And the music? What happened to the music? Play!"

(206)

1923: Mexico City/Parral

The People Donated a Million Dead to the
Mexican Revolution

in ten years of war so that military chieftains could finally take possession of the best lands and the most profitable businesses. These officers of the revolution share power and glory with Indian-fleecing doctors and the politicos-for-hire, brilliant banquet orators who call Obregón *the Mexican Lenin*.

On this road to national reconciliation there is no problem that can't be overcome by a public-works contract, a land concession, or the sort of favor that flows out of an open purse. Álvaro Obregón, the president, defines his style of government with a phrase soon to become a classic in Mexico: *"There's no general who can resist a salvo of fifty thousand pesos."*

But Obregón gets it wrong with General Villa.

Nothing can be done with him except to shoot him down.

Villa arrives in Parral by car in the early morning. At the sight of him someone signals with a red scarf. Twelve men respond by squeezing triggers.

Parral was his favorite city. *"I like Parral so much, so much . . ."* And the day when the women and children of Parral chased out the gringo invaders with stones, the horses inside Pancho broke free, and he let out a tremendous yell of joy: *"I just love Parral to death!"*

(206, 246, and 260)

1924: Mérida, Yucatán
More on the Function of the Forces of Order in the Democratic Process

Felipe Carrillo Puerto, also invulnerable to the gun from which Obregón fires pesos, faces a firing squad one damp January morning.

"Do you want a confessor?"

"I'm not a Catholic."

"How about a notary?"

"I've nothing to leave."

He had been a colonel in Zapata's army in Morelos before founding the Socialist Workers' Party in Yucatán. There Carrillo Puerto delivered his speeches in Mayan, explaining that Marx was a brother of Jacinto Canek and Cecilio Chi and that socialism, the inheritor of the communitarian tradition, gave a future dimension to the glorious Indian past.

Until yesterday he headed the socialist government of Yucatán. Innumerable frauds and private interests had not been able to keep the socialists from an easy electoral victory, nor afterward keep them from fulfilling their promises. Their sacrileges against the hallowed big estates, the slave labor system and various imperial monopolies aroused the rage of those who ran the henequén plantations, not to speak of the International Harvester Company. The archbishop went into convulsions over lay education, free love, and red baptisms—so called because children received their names on a mattress of red flowers, and along with those names, wishes for a long life of socialist militancy. So what could be done, but call in the army to bring the scandal to an end?

The shooting of Felipe Carrillo Puerto repeats the history of Juan Escudero in Acapulco. The government of the humiliated has lasted a couple of years in Yucatán. The humiliated govern with the weapons of reason. The humiliators don't have the government, but they do have the reason of weapons. And as in all of Mexico, death rides the dice of destiny.

(330)

1924: Mexico City
Nationalizing the Walls

Easel art invites confinement. The mural, on the other hand, offers itself to the passing multitude. The people may be illiterate but they are not blind; so Rivera, Orozco, and Siqueiros assault the walls of Mexico. They paint something new and different. On moist lime is born a truly national art, child of the Mexican revolution and of these days of births and funerals.

Mexican muralism crashes head on into the dwarfed, castrated art of a country trained to deny itself. All of a sudden, still lifes and defunct landscapes spring dizzily to life, and the wretched of the earth become subjects of art and history rather than objects of use, scorn, or pity.

Complaints pelt down on the muralists, but praise, not a drop. Still, mounted on their scaffoldings, they stick to their jobs. Sixteen hours without a break is the working day for Rivera, eyes and belly of a toad, teeth like a fish. He keeps a pistol at his waist.

"To set a line for the critics," he says.

(80 and 387)

1924: Mexico City

Diego Rivera

resurrects Felipe Carrillo Puerto, redeemer of Yucatán, with a bullet wound in his chest but uninformed of his own death, and paints Emiliano Zapata arousing his people, and paints the people, all the peoples of Mexico, united in an epic of work and war and fiesta, on sixteen hundred square meters of wall in the Ministry of Education. While he washes the world with colors, Diego amuses himself by lying. To anyone who wants to listen he tells lies as colossal as his belly, as his passion for creating, and as his woman-devouring insatiability.

Barely three years ago he returned from Europe. Over there in Paris, Diego was a vanguard painter who got tired of the "isms"; and just as his star was fading, and he was painting just from boredom, he returned to Mexico and the lights of his country hit him in the face, setting his eyes aflame.

(82)

1924: Mexico City

Orozco

Diego Rivera rounds out, José Clemente Orozco sharpens. Rivera paints sensualities: bodies of corn flesh, voluptuous fruits. Orozco paints desperations: skin-and-bone bodies, a maguey mutilated and bleeding. What is happiness in Rivera is tragedy in Orozco. In Rivera there is tenderness and radiant serenity; in Orozco, severity and contortion. Orozco's Mexican revolution has grandeur, like Rivera's; but where Rivera speaks to us of hope, Orozco seems to say that whoever steals the sacred fire from the gods will deny it to his fellow men.

(83 and 323)

1924: Mexico City
Siqueiros

Surly, withdrawn, turbulent inside—that's Orozco. Spectacular, bombastic, turbulent on the outside—that's David Alfaro Siqueiros. Orozco practices painting as a ceremony of solitude. For Siqueiros it is an act of militant solidarity. *"There is no other way except ours,"* says Siqueiros. To European culture, which he considers sick, he opposes his own muscular energy. Orozco doubts, lacks faith in what he does. Siqueiros bulls ahead, sure that his patriotic brashness is no bad medicine for a country with a severe inferiority complex.

(27)

The People Are the Hero of Mexican Mural Painting, Says Diego Rivera

The true novelty of Mexican painting, in the sense that we initiated it with Orozco and Siqueiros, was to make the people the hero of mural painting. Until then the heroes of mural painting had been gods, angels, archangels, saints, war heroes, kings and emperors, prelates, and great military and political chiefs, the people appearing as the chorus around the star personalities of the tragedy . . .

(79)

1924: Regla
Lenin

The mayor of the Cuban community of Regla calls everybody together. From the neighboring city of Havana has come news of the death of Lenin in the Soviet Union. The mayor issues a proclamation of mourning. The proclamation says that *the aforementioned Lenin won well-deserved sympathy among the proletarian and intellectual elements of this municipal district. Accordingly, at 5:00 P.M. Sunday next its residents will observe two minutes of silence and meditation, during which persons and vehicles will maintain absolute stillness.*

At precisely five o'clock on Sunday afternoon, the mayor of Regla climbs up Fortín hill. Despite a heavy downpour, over a thousand people accompany him to observe the two minutes of silence and meditation. Afterward, the mayor plants an olive tree on top of the hill in homage to the man who was always planting the red flag over there, in the middle of the snow.

(215)

1926: San Albino
Sandino

is short and thin as a rake. A stray wind would blow him away were he not so firmly planted in the soil of Nicaragua.

In this land, his land, Augusto César Sandino stands tall and speaks of what the land has said to him, for when Sandino stretches out to sleep, his land whispers sorrow and sweetness to him.

Sandino speaks of the secrets of his invaded and humiliated land, and asks, *How many of you love it as much as I do?*

Twenty-nine San Albino miners step forward.

These are the first soldiers in Nicaragua's army of liberation. Illiterate, they toil fifteen hours a day hacking gold out of the ground for a North American firm and sleep piled up in a shed. They blow up the mine with dynamite and follow Sandino into the mountains.

Sandino goes on a small white burro.

(118 and 361)

1926: Puerto Cabezas
The Most Admirable Women on Earth

are the whores of Puerto Cabezas. From pillow talk they know the exact spot under water where U.S. Marines have buried forty rifles and seven thousand cartridges. Thanks to these women, who risk their lives in defiance of the foreign occupation troops, Sandino and his men rescue from the waters, by torchlight, their first weapons and first ammunition.

(361)

1926: Juazeiro do Norte
Father Cicero

Once Juazeiro was a nothing of a hamlet—four shacks God seemed to have spat into the void when, one fine day, He pointed a finger at this garbage heap and decided it was to be a Holy City. Since then, the afflicted flock here by the thousands. Every road of martyrdom and miracle leads here. Squalid pilgrims from all Brazil, long lines of rags and stumps of limbs, have turned Juazeiro into the richest city of the northeastern hinterland. In this faith-restoring new Jerusalem, memorials to the forgotten, polestar of the lost, the modest Salgadinho stream is now known as the River Jordan. Surrounded by pious women brandishing their bleeding bronze crucifixes, Father Cicero announces that Jesus Christ is on his way.

Father Cicero Romão Baptista is the master of the lands and souls. This savior of the shipwrecked in the desert, tamer of madmen and criminals, gives children to sterile women, rain to dry ground, light to the blind, and, to the poor, some crumbs from the bread he eats.

(133)

1926: Juazeiro do Norte
By Divine Miracle a Bandit Becomes a Captain

Lampião's warriors fire off bullets and sing songs. Tolling bells and fireworks welcome them to the city of Juazeiro. The *cangaceiros* display a complete arsenal and a luxuriance of medals on their leather armor.

At the foot of the statue of Father Cicero, Father Cicero blesses the chief of the gang. It is well known that the bandit Lampião never touches a house containing an image of Father Cicero, or kills any devotee of the miracle-working saint.

In the name of the government of Brazil, Father Cicero confers on Lampião the rank of captain, three blue stripes on either shoulder, and hands out to his men impeccable Mausers in exchange for their old Winchester rifles. In return, Captain Lampião promises to defeat the rebels under Lieutenant Luis Carlos Prestes, who roam Brazil preaching democracy and other devilish ideas; but he has hardly left this city before he forgets about the Prestes Column and returns to his old routine.

(120, 133, and 263)

1926: New York

Valentino

Last night, in an Italian bar, Rudolph Valentino collapsed, struck down by a pasta banquet.

Millions of women on five continents have been widowed. They adored the elegant, feline Latin on the screen-altar of the movie theater, itself a temple for all peoples in all cities. With him they galloped to the oasis, spurred by the wind of the desert, and with him participated in tragic bullfights, entered mysterious palaces, danced on mirrored floors, and undressed in the bedrooms of Indian Prince and Son of the Sheik. Pierced by the languid gimlet of his eyes and crushed by his arms, they swooned into deep silken beds.

He didn't even realize. Valentino, the Hollywood god who casually smoked while kissing and annihilated with a glance, he who daily received a thousand love letters, in reality slept alone and dreamed of Mother.

(443)

1927: Chicago

Louie

She lived on New Orleans' Perdido Street—the street of the lost— where the dead were laid out with a saucer on the chest for the neighbors' coins to pay for the funeral. When she dies, her son Louis takes pleasure in giving her a fine funeral—the deluxe funeral she would have dreamed of at the end of the dream in which God made her white and a millionaire.

Louis Armstrong, who grew up with no more to eat than leftovers and music, fled New Orleans for Chicago with only a trumpet for baggage and a fish sandwich for company. A few years have passed and he is getting fat. He eats to avenge himself. And if he returned to the South now, maybe he'd be welcomed in some of the places barred to blacks and out of bounds for the poor. He could probably walk down most any street in town. He's the king of jazz and no one argues it. His trumpet whispers, moans, wails, howls like a wounded beast, and laughs uproariously, celebrating with euphoria and immense power the absurdity of life.

(105)

1927: New York

Bessie

This woman sings her sufferings with the voice of glory and no one can listen and pretend he doesn't hear or he's not moved. Lungs of deep night: Bessie Smith, immensely fat, immensely black, curses the thieves of Creation. Her blues are the hymns of poor drunk black women of the slums. They announce that the whites and the supermen and the rich who humiliate the world will be dethroned.

(165)

1927: Rapallo

Pound

It is twenty years since Ezra Pound pulled out of America. Son of poets, father of poets, Pound seeks beneath the Italian sun new images, worthy accompaniments to the bison of Altamira, unknown words for talking to gods more ancient than the fish.

Along the road, he makes the wrong friends.

(261, 349, and 437)

1927: Charlestown

"Lovely day,"

says the governor of the state of Massachusetts.

At midnight on this August Monday, two Italian workers will occupy the electric chair of Charlestown prison's death house. Nicola Sacco, shoemaker, and Bartolomeo Vanzetti, fish peddler, will be executed for crimes they did not commit.

The lives of Sacco and Vanzetti are in the hands of a businessman

who has made forty million dollars selling Packard cars. Alvan Tufts
Fuller, governor of Massachusetts, a small man behind a big desk of
carved wood, declines to yield to the protests rumbling from every
direction. He honestly believes in the correctness of the trial and the
validity of the evidence. He also believes that all the damned anarchists and filthy foreigners who come to ruin this country deserve
to die.

(162 and 445)

1927: Araraquara
Mário de Andrade

challenges everything servile, saccharine, grandiloquent in official
culture. He is a creator of words, words dying of envy for music,
which nonetheless are capable of seeing and speaking everything to
Brazil, and also of savoring it, Brazil the tasty hot peanut.

On holidays, for the fun of it, Mário de Andrade transcribes the
sayings and deeds of one Macunaíma, a hero with no character, just
as he hears them from the golden beak of a parrot. According to the
parrot, Macunaíma was an ugly black man, born in the heart of the
jungle, who didn't bother saying a word until he was six—for sheer
laziness, and preoccupied as he was with decapitating ants, spitting
in his brothers' faces, and fondling his female relatives. Macunaíma's
wild adventures cover all times and all spaces in Brazil, while stripping
saints of their robes, and puppets of their heads.

Macunaíma is more real than his author. Like every flesh-and-
blood Brazilian, Mário de Andrade is a figment of the imagination.

(23)

1927: Paris
Villa-Lobos

From behind the enormous cigar floats a cloud of smoke. Enveloped
within it, happy and in love, Heitor Villa-Lobos whistles a vagabond
tune.

In Brazil, hostile critics claim he composes music to be played
by epileptics for an audience of paranoiacs, but in France he is received with ovations. The Paris press enthusiastically applauds his

audacious harmonies and his vigorous sense of nationality. They publish articles on the maestro's life. One newspaper recounts how Villa-Lobos was once bound to a grill and almost roasted alive by cannibal Indians while out strolling in the Amazon jungle with a Victrola in his arms playing Bach.

At one of the many parties they throw for him between concerts in Paris, a lady asks him if he has eaten people raw, and how he liked it.

(280)

1927: The Plains of Jalisco
Behind a Huge Cross of Sticks

charge the *Cristeros*, rebelling in Jalisco and other states of Mexico in search of martyrdom and glory. They shout *Vivas!* for a Christ the King crowned with jewels instead of thorns, and *Vivas!* for the Pope, who has not resigned himself to the loss of the few clerical privileges still remaining in Mexico.

These poor campesinos have just been dying for a revolution that promised them land. Now, condemned to a living death, they start dying for a Church that promises them heaven.

(297)

1927: San Gabriel de Jalisco
A Child Looks On

The mother covers his eyes so he cannot see his grandfather hanging by the feet. And then the mother's hands prevent his seeing his father's body riddled by the bandits' bullets, or his uncle's twisting in the wind over there on the telegraph posts.

Now the mother too has died, or perhaps has just tired of defending her child's eyes. Sitting on the stone fence that snakes over the slopes, Juan Rulfo contemplates his harsh land with a naked eye. He sees horsemen—federal police or *Cristeros*, it makes no difference—emerging from smoke, and behind them, in the distance, a fire. He sees bodies hanging in a row, nothing now but ragged clothing emptied by the vultures. He sees a procession of women dressed in black.

Juan Rulfo, a child of nine, is surrounded by ghosts who look like him.

Here there is nothing alive—the only voices those of howling coyotes, the only air the black wind that rises in gusts from the plains of Jalisco, where the survivors are only dead people pretending.

(48 and 400)

1927: El Chipote
The War of Jaguars and Birds

Fifteen years ago the Marines landed in Nicaragua for a while, *to protect the lives and properties of United States citizens,* and forgot to leave. Against them now loom these northern mountains. Villages are scarce here; but anyone who hasn't actually become one of Sandino's soldiers is his spy or messenger. Since the dynamiting of the San Albino mine and the first battle, at Muy Muy, the liberating force keeps growing.

The whole Honduran army is mobilized on the border to prevent arms from reaching Sandino from across the river, but the guerrillas, unconcerned, acquire rifles from fallen enemies and carve bullets out of the trees in which they imbed themselves; nor is there any shortage of machetes for chopping off heads, or sardine-can grenades filled with glass, nails, screws, and dynamite for scattering the enemy.

U.S. airplanes bomb haphazardly, destroying villages. And Marines roam the forests, between abysses and high peaks, roasted by the sun, drowned by the rain, asphyxiated by dust, burning and killing all they find. Even the little monkeys throw things at them.

They offer Sandino a pardon and ten dollars for every day he has been in rebellion. Captain Hatfield hints at a surrender.

From his stronghold in El Chipote, a mysterious peak wreathed in mist, comes the reply: *I don't sell out or surrender.* It closes: *Your obedient servant, who desires to put you in a handsome coffin with beautiful bouquets of flowers.* And then Sandino's signature.

His soldiers bite like jaguars and flit like birds. When least expected, they lash out in a single jaguar leap, and before the enemy can even react are already striking from the rear or the flanks, only to disappear with a flap of wings.

(118 and 361)

1928: San Rafael del Norte
Crazy Little Army

Four Corsairs bombard El Chipote, already encircled and harassed by salvos from Marine artillery. For days and nights now the whole region thunders and trembles, until the invaders fix bayonets and charge the stone trenches bristling with rifles. This heroic action ends with neither dead nor wounded, because the attackers find only soldiers of straw and guns of sticks.

U.S. papers promptly report the victory without mentioning that the Marines have demolished a legion of dolls with wide-brimmed hats and black-and-red kerchiefs. They do verify, however, that Sandino himself is among the victims.

In the remote village of San Rafael del Norte, Sandino listens to his men singing by the light of campfires. There he receives word of his death.

"God and our mountains are with us. And after all is said and done, death is no more than a little moment of pain."

Over the past months thirty-six warships and six thousand more Marines have arrived as reinforcements in Nicaragua. Yet, of seventy-five big and small battles, almost all have been lost, and the quarry has slipped through their fingers, no one knows how.

Crazy little army, the Chilean poet Gabriela Mistral calls Sandino's battered warriors, these masters of daring and devilment.

(118, 361, and 419)

"It Was All Very Brotherly"

JUAN PABLO RAMÍREZ: *We made dolls of straw and stuck them there. As decoys we fixed up sticks topped by sombreros. And it was fun . . . They spent a week firing at them, bombing them, and I pissed in my pants laughing!*

ALFONSO ALEXANDER: *The invaders were like the elephant and we the snake. They were immobility, we were mobility.*

PEDRO ANTONIO ARAÚZ: *The Yanquis died sad deaths, the ingrates. They just didn't know how things work in our country's mountains.*

SINFOROSO GONZÁLEZ ZELEDÓN: *The campesinos helped us, they worked with us, they felt for us.*

COSME CASTRO ANDINO: *We weren't drawing any pay. When we got to a village and the campesinos gave us food, we shared it. It was all very brotherly.*

(236)

1928: Washington
Newsreel

In an emotional ceremony in Washington, ten Marine officers receive the Cross of Merit *for distinguished service and extraordinary heroism* in the war against Sandino.

The *Washington Herald* and other papers devote pages to the crimes of the *outlaw band* who slit Marines' throats. They also publish documents newly arrived from Mexico, with impressive numbers of spelling mistakes, proving that Mexican president Calles is sending bolshevik weapons and propaganda to Sandino through Soviet diplomats. Official State Department sources explain that Calles began revealing his communist sympathies when he raised taxes on U.S. oil companies operating in Mexico, and fully confirmed them when his government established diplomatic relations with the Soviet Union.

The U.S. government warns that it *will not permit Russian and Mexican soldiers to implant the Soviet in Nicaragua.* According to official State Department spokesmen, Mexico is *exporting bolshevism.* After Nicaragua the next target of Soviet expansion in Central America will be the Panama Canal.

Senator Shortridge declares that the citizens of the United States *deserve as much protection as those of ancient Rome,* and Senator Bingham says: *We are obliged to accept our function as international policemen.* Senator Bingham, the famous archaeologist who sixteen years ago discovered the ruins of Machu Picchu in Peru, has never concealed his admiration for the works of dead Indians.

For the opposition, Senator Borah denies his country's right to act as the censor of Central America, and Senator Wheeler suggests that the government send Marines to Chicago, not Nicaragua, if it really wants to take on bandits. The *Nation* magazine, for its part, takes the view that for the U.S. president to call Sandino a bandit is like George III of England labeling George Washington a thief.

(39 and 419)

1928: Managua
Profile of Colonial Power

North American children study geography from maps showing Nicaragua as a colored blob labeled *Protectorate of the United States of America*.

When the United States decided that Nicaragua could not govern itself, there were forty public schools in its Atlantic coast region. Now there are six. The tutelary power has not put in a railroad, opened a single highway, or founded a university. At the same time, the occupied country falls farther into debt, paying the costs of its own occupation, while the occupiers continue to occupy—to guarantee the payment of the expenses of the occupation.

The Nicaraguan customs offices are in the hands of North American creditor banks, which appoint Clifford D. Ham comptroller of customs and general tax collector. Ham is also the Nicaraguan correspondent for the United Press news agency, The vice-comptroller of customs and vice-collector of taxes, Irving Lindbergh, is the correspondent for the Associated Press. So Ham and Lindbergh not only usurp the tariffs of Nicaragua, they also usurp the information. It is they who inform international public opinion about the misdeeds of Sandino, *criminal bandit and bolshevik agent*. A North American colonel leads the Nicaraguan army—the National Guard—and a North American captain leads the Nicaraguan police.

North American General Frank McCoy administers the National Electoral Junta. Four hundred and thirty-two U.S. Marines and twelve U.S. airplanes preside over the voting tables. The Nicaraguans vote, the North Americans elect. The new president is barely chosen before he announces that the Marines will stay.

This unforgettable civic fiesta has been organized by General Logan Feland, commander of the occupation forces. General Feland, all muscle and eyebrows, crosses his feet under the desk. In the matter of Sandino, he yawns and says, *"This bird has to fall one day."*

(39 and 419)

1928: Mexico City

Obregón

At the Náinari hacienda in Mexico's Yaqui Valley, the dogs howled.

"*Shut them up!*" ordered General Álvaro Obregón.

But the dogs barked more than ever.

"*Have them fed!*" ordered the general.

But the dogs ignored the food and continued their uproar.

"*Throw them fresh meat!*"

But the fresh meat had no effect. Even when they were beaten, the din went on.

"*I know what they want,*" said Obregón with resignation.

This happened on May 17. On July 9, in Culiacán, Obregón was sipping a tamarind drink in the shade of a porch, when the cathedral bells tolled and the poet Chuy Andrade, slightly drunk, said, "*They're tolling for you, friend.*"

And the next day, in Escuinapa, after a banquet of shrimp tamales, Obregón was boarding a train when Elisa Beaven, a good friend, pressed his arm and pleaded with him in her hoarse voice, "*Don't go. They're going to kill you.*"

But Obregón entered the train anyway and rode to the capital. After all, he had known how to muscle and hustle his way ahead in the days when bullets buzzed like hornets. He was the killer of killers, the conqueror of conquerors, and had won power, and glory, and money, without losing anything but the hand that Pancho Villa blew off; so he wasn't about to back off now that he knew his days were numbered. He simply went ahead, blithely but sadly. He had, after all, lost his one innocence: the happiness of unconcern about his own death.

Today, July 17, 1928, two months after the dogs barked in Náinari, a Christ-the-King fanatic kills reelected President Álvaro Obregón in a Mexico City restaurant.

(4)

1928: Villahermosa
The Priest Eater

Obregón is hardly dead, felled by the bullets of an ultra-Catholic, when Governor Manuel Garrido of the Mexican state of Tabasco decrees vengeance. He orders the cathedral demolished to the last stone, and from the bronze of the bells erects a statue of the late lamented.

Garrido believes that Catholicism shuts workers into a cage of fear, terrorizing them with the threat of eternal fire. For freedom to come to Tabasco, says Garrido, religion must go; and he kicks it out, decapitating saints, wrecking churches, yanking crosses out of cemeteries, forcing priests to marry, and renaming all places named after saints. The state capital, San Juan Bautista, becomes Villahermosa. And in a solemn ceremony he has a stud bull called "Bishop" and an ass, "Pope."

(283)

1928: Southern Santa Marta
Bananization

They were no more than lost villages on the Colombian coast, a strip of dust between river and cemetery, a yawn between two siestas, when the yellow train of the United Fruit Company pulled in. Coughing smoke, the train had crossed the swamps and penetrated the jungle and emerged here in brilliant clarity, announcing with a whistle that the age of the banana had come.

The region awoke to find itself an immense plantation. Ciénaga, Aracataca, and Fundación got telegraph and post offices and new streets with poolrooms and brothels. Campesinos, who arrived by the thousands, left their mules at the hitching posts and went to work.

For years these workers proved obedient and cheap as they hacked at the undergrowth and roots with their machetes for less than a dollar a day, and consented to live in filthy sheds and die of malaria or tuberculosis.

Then they form a union.

(186 and 464)

1928: Aracataca

The Curse

Swelter and languor and rancor. Bananas rot on the trees. Oxen sleep before empty carts. Trains stand dead on their tracks, not a single bunch of fruit reaching them. Seven ships wait anchored at the Santa Marta piers: in their fruit-less holds, the ventilators have stopped whirring.

Four hundred strikers are behind bars, but the strike goes relentlessly on.

In Aracataca, United Fruit throws a supper in honor of the regional Civil and Military Chief. Over dessert, General Carlos Cortés Vargas curses the workers, *armed evildoers*, and their *bolshevik agitators*, and announces that tomorrow he'll march to Ciénaga at the head of the forces of order, to get on with the job.

(93 and 464)

1928: Ciénaga

Carnage

On the shores of Ciénaga, a high tide of banners. Men with machetes at their waists, women toting pots and children wait here amid the campfires. The company has promised that tonight it will sign an agreement ending the strike.

Instead of the manager of United Fruit comes General Cortés Vargas. Instead of an agreement he reads them an ultimatum.

No one moves. Three times the warning bugle blares. And then, in an instant, the world explodes, sudden thunder of thunders, as machineguns and rifles empty. The plaza is carpeted with dead.

The soldiers sweep and wash all night long, while corpses are thrown into the sea. In the morning there is nothing.

"In Macondo nothing has happened, nor is happening, nor ever will happen."

(93 and 464)

1928: Aracataca

García Márquez

The roundup is on for the wounded and hiding strikers. They are hunted like rabbits, with broadsides from a moving train, and in the stations netted like fish. One hundred and twenty are captured in Aracataca in a single night. The soldiers awaken the priest and grab the key to the cemetery. Trembling in his underwear, the priest listens as the shootings begin.

Not far away, a little boy bawls in his crib.

The years will pass and this child will reveal to the world the secrets of a region so attacked by a plague of forgetfulness that it lost the names of things. He will discover the documents that tell how the workers were shot in the plaza, and how Big Mamma is the owner of lives and haciendas and of the rain that has fallen and will fall, and how between rain and rain Remedios the Beautiful goes to heaven, and in the air passes a little old plucked angel who is falling into a henhouse.

(187 and 464)

1928: Bogotá

Newsreel

The press reports on recent events in the banana zone. According to official sources, the excesses of the strikers have left a total of forty plantations burned, thirty-five thousand meters of telegraph wires destroyed, and eight workers killed when they tried to attack the army.

The president of the republic charges the strikers with treason and felony. *With their poisoned dagger they have pierced the loving heart of the Fatherland*, he declares. By decree, the president appoints General Cortés Vargas head of the National Police, and announces promotions and rewards for the other officers who participated in the events.

In a spectacular speech, the young liberal legislator Jorge Eliécer Gaitán contradicts the official story. He accuses the Colombian army of committing butchery under the orders of a foreign company. The United Fruit Company, which directed the massacre, according to

Gaitán, has subsequently reduced the daily wage that it pays in coupons, not money. The legislator stresses that the company exploits lands donated by the Colombian state, which are not subject to taxes.

(174 and 464)

1929: Mexico City
Mella

The dictator of Cuba, Gerardo Machado, orders him killed. Julio Antonio Mella is just another expatriate student in Mexico, intensely busy chasing around and publishing articles—for very few readers—against racism and the hidden face of colonialism; but the dictator is not mistaken in thinking him his most dangerous enemy. He has been a marked man ever since his fiery speeches rocked Havana's students. Mella blazed as he denounced the dictatorship and mocked the decrepitude of the Cuban university, a factory of professionals with the mentality of a colonial convent.

One night Mella is strolling arm in arm with his friend Tina Modotti, when the murderers shoot him down.

Tina screams, but doesn't cry. Not until she returns home at dawn and sees Mella's empty shoes waiting for her under the bed.

Until a few hours ago, this woman was so happy she was jealous of herself.

(290)

1929: Mexico City
Tina Modotti

The Cuban government has nothing to do with it, insist the right-wing Mexican papers. Mella was the victim of a crime of passion, *whatever the Muscovite bolshevik yids may say*. The press reveals that Tina Modotti, *a woman of dubious decency*, reacted coldly to the tragic episode and subsequently, in her statements to the police, fell into suspicious contradictions.

Modotti, an Italian photographer, has dug her feet deeply into Mexico in the few years she has been here. Her photographs mirror a grandeur in everyday things, and in people who work with their hands.

But she is guilty of freedom. She was living alone when she found Mella mixed up in a crowd demonstrating for Sacco and Vanzetti and for Sandino, and she hitched up with him unceremoniously. Previously she had been a Hollywood actress, a model, and a lover of artists; and she makes every man who sees her nervous. In short, she is a harlot—and to top it off, a foreigner and a communist. The police circulate photos showing her unforgivable beauty in the nude, while proceedings begin to expel her from Mexico.

(112)

1929: Mexico City
Frida

Tina Modotti is not alone before her inquisitors. Accompanying her, one on each arm, are Diego Rivera and Frida Kahlo: the immense painter-Buddha and his little Frida, also a painter, Tina's best friend, who looks like a mysterious oriental princess but swears and drinks tequila like a Jalisco mariachi.

Kahlo has a wild laugh, and has painted splendid canvases in oils ever since the day she was condemned to pain without end. She had known other pain from infancy, when her parents dressed her up with straw wings. But constant and crippling agony has come only since her accident, when a shard from a shattered street car pierced her body, like a lance, tearing at her bones.

Now she is a pain that survives as a person. They have operated in vain several times; and it was in her hospital bed that she started painting self-portraits, desperate homage to the life that remains for her.

(224 and 444)

1929: Capela
Lampião

The most famous gang in northeast Brazil attacks the town of Capela. Its chief, Lampião, who never smiles, fixes a reasonable sum as ransom, then offers a reduction, because we are in the drought season. While the town notables drum up the money, he strolls the streets.

The whole town follows him. His horrifying crimes have won him general admiration.

Lampião, the one-eyed king, master of the open spaces, sparkles in the sun. His glittering gold-wire glasses give him the look of an absent-minded professor; his gleaming dagger is as long as a sword. On each finger shimmers a diamond ring, and to the hairband around his forehead are sewn English pound notes.

Lampião wanders into the cinema, where they are showing a Janet Gaynor film. That night he dines at the hotel. The town telegraph operator, seated beside him, tastes the first mouthful of each dish. Then Lampião has a few drinks while reading Ellen G. White's *Life of Jesus*. He ends the day in the whorehouse. He picks the plumpest one, a certain Enedina. With her he spends the whole night. By dawn, Enedina is famous. For years men will line up outside her door.

(120 and 348)

1929: Atlantic City
The Crime Trust

Organized crime in the United States holds its first national convention, in the salons of the President Hotel. Attending are the qualified representatives of mobs operating in each of the major cities.

Olive branch, white flag: The convention resolves that rival gangs will stop killing one another and decrees a general amnesty. To guarantee peace, the executives of the crime industry follow the example of the oil industry. As Standard Oil and Shell have just done, the powerful gangsters divide markets, fix prices, and agree to eliminate the competition of small and middle fry.

In recent years, crime's impresarios have diversified their activities and modernized their methods. Now they not only engage in extortion, murder, pimping, and smuggling, but also own distilleries, hotels, casinos, banks, and supermarkets. They use the latest-model machineguns and accounting machines. Engineers, economists, and publicity experts direct the teams of technicians that avoid waste of resources and ensure a constant rise in profits.

Al Capone chairs the board of the most lucrative company in the game. He earns a hundred million dollars a year.

(335)

1929: Chicago

Al Capone

Ten thousand students chant the name of Al Capone on the sports field of Northwestern University. The popular Capone greets the multitude with a two-handed wave. Twelve bodyguards escort him. At the gate an armored Cadillac awaits him. Capone sports a rose in his lapel and a diamond stickpin in his tie, but underneath he wears a steel vest, and his heart beats against a .45.

He is an idol. No one provides as much business for funeral parlors, flower shops, and tailors who do invisible mending on small holes; and he pays generous salaries to policemen, judges, legislators, and mayors. Exemplary family man, Capone abominates short skirts and cosmetics. He believes woman's place is in the kitchen. Fervent patriot, he exhibits portraits of George Washington and Abraham Lincoln on his desk. Influential professional, he offers the best available service for breaking strikes, beating up workers, and sending rebels to the other world. He is ever alert to the red menace.

(335)

Al Capone Calls for Defense Against the Communist Danger

Bolshevism is knocking at our door. We must not let it in. We have to remain united and defend ourselves against it with full decisiveness. America must remain safe and uncorrupted. We must protect the workers from the red press and from red perfidy, and ensure that their minds stay healthy . . .

(153)

1929: New York

Euphoria

Millions are reading *The Man Nobody Knows*, the book by Bruce Barton that places heaven on Wall Street. According to the author, Jesus of Nazareth founded the modern world of business. Jesus, it turns out, was a market-conquering entrepreneur gifted with a genius for publicity, professionally assisted by twelve salesmen in his image and likeness.

With a faith bordering on the religious, capitalism believes in its own eternity. What North American citizen does not feel himself one of the elect? The Stock Exchange is a casino where everybody plays and no one loses. God has made them prosperous. The entrepreneur Henry Ford wishes he never had to sleep, so he could make more money.

(2 and 304)

From the Capitalist Manifesto of Henry Ford, Automobile Manufacturer

Bolshevism failed because it was both unnatural and immoral. Our system stands . . .

There can be no greater absurdity and no greater disservice to humanity in general, than to insist that all men are equal . . .

Money comes naturally as the result of service. And it is absolutely necessary to have money. But we do not want to forget that the end of money is not ease but the opportunity to perform more service. In my mind nothing is more abhorrent than a life of ease. None of us has any right to ease. There is no place in civilization for the idler . . .

In our first advertisement we showed that a motor car was a utility. We said: "We often hear quoted the old proverb, 'Time is money'—and yet how few business and professional men act as if they really believed its truth . . ."

(168)

1929: New York
The Crisis

Speculation grows faster than production and production faster than consumption, and everything grows at a giddy rhythm until, all of a sudden, in a single day, the collapse of the New York Stock Exchange reduces to ashes the profits of years. The most prized stocks become mere scraps of paper, useless even for wrapping fish.

Prices and salaries plummet along with stock quotations, and more than one businessman from his tower. Factories and banks close; farmers are ruined. Workers without jobs chafe their hands at burning garbage heaps and chew gum to pacify their stomachs. The largest enterprises collapse; and even Al Capone takes a fall.

(2 and 304)

1930: La Paz

A Touching Adventure of the Prince of Wales Among the Savages

The New York Stock Exchange pulls many governments down into the abyss. International prices crumble, and with them, one after another, the civilian presidents of Latin America—feathers plucked from the wings of the eagle—and new dictatorships are born, to make hunger hungrier.

In Bolivia, the collapse of the price of tin brings down President Hernando Siles and puts in his place a general on the payroll of Patiño, the tin king. A mob accompanying the military rises, attacks the government palace, is granted permission to loot it. Out of control, they make off with furniture, carpets, paintings, everything. Everything. They take whole bathrooms, including toilets, tubs, and drain-pipes.

Just then the Prince of Wales visits Bolivia. The people expect a prince to arrive in the style God intended, riding on a white steed, a sword at his waist and golden locks streaming in the wind. They are disappointed by a gentleman with top hat and cane who gets off the train looking exhausted.

That evening the new president offers the prince a banquet in the stripped-down palace. At dessert, just when speeches are due to begin, His Highness whispers dramatic words into the ear of his interpreter, who transmits them to the aide-de-camp, who transmits them to the president. The president turns pale. The prince's foot nervously taps the floor. His wishes are commands; but in the palace there's no place, no way. Without hesitation the president appoints a committee, headed by the Foreign Minister and the Chief of the Armed Forces.

Impressively top-hatted and plumed, the retinue accompanies the prince at a dignified but brisk pace, almost a hop, across the Plaza de Armas. Arriving at the corner, they all enter the Paris Hotel. The

Foreign Minister opens the door marked GENTLEMEN and points the way for the heir to the imperial British crown.

(34)

1930: Buenos Aires

Yrigoyen

The world crisis also leaves Argentine president Hipólito Yrigoyen teetering at the edge of a precipice, doomed by the collapse of meat and wheat prices.

Silent and alone, a stubborn old hangover from another time, another world, Yrigoyen still refuses to use the telephone, has never entered a movie theater, distrusts automobiles, and doesn't believe in airplanes. He has conquered the people just by chatting, convincing them one by one, little by little, without speeches. Now the same people who yesterday unyoked the horses from his carriage and pulled him with their hands, revile him. The crowd actually throws his furniture into the street.

The military coup that overthrows him has been cooked up at the Jockey Club and the Círculo de Armas on the flames of this sudden crisis. The ailing patriarch, creaking with rheumatism, sealed his own fate when he refused to hand over Argentine petroleum to Standard Oil and Shell. Worse, he wanted to alleviate the price catastrophe by doing business with the Soviet Union.

Once more, for the good of the world, the hour of the sword has struck, writes the poet Leopoldo Lugones, ushering in the military era in Argentina.

At the height of the coup, a young captain, Juan Domingo Perón, observes some enthusiast dashing at top speed from the government palace, yelling, *"Long live the Fatherland! Long live the Revolution!"*

The enthusiast carries an Argentine flag rolled up under his arm. Inside the flag is a stolen typewriter.

(178, 341, and 365)

1930: Paris

Ortiz Echagüe, Journalist, Comments on the Fallen Price of Meat

Every time I return from Buenos Aires, the Argentines in Paris ask me: "How are the cows?"

One must come to Paris to appreciate the importance of the Argentine cow. Last night at El Garrón—a Montmartre cabaret where young Argentines experience the tough apprenticeship of life—some guys at a neighboring table asked me, with that small-hours familiarity, "Say, chum, how are the cows back home making out?"

"Pretty down and out," I said.

"And they can't get up?"

"Doesn't look good."

"You don't have any cows?"

I felt my pockets and said no.

"You don't know, old pal, how lucky you are." At that point three concertinas broke into sobs of nostalgia and cut the dialogue short.

"How are the cows?" I have been asked by maître d's and musicians, flower girls and waiters, pallid ballerinas, gold-braided porters, diligent grooms, and above all, by painted women, those poor baggy-eyed anemic women . . .

(325)

1930: Avellaneda

The Cow, the Sword, and the Cross

form the holy trinity of power in Argentina. Conservative Party toughs guard the altar.

In the heart of Buenos Aires, white-gloved gunmen use laws and decrees like machineguns in their holdups. Experts in double accounting and double morality, they needn't trouble themselves picking locks. They don't have doctorates for nothing. They know precisely what secret combinations will open the country's cashboxes.

Across the river, in Avellaneda, the Conservative Party sticks to honest shooting for its politics and business. Don Alberto Barceló, senator, makes and breaks lives from his throne there. Outcasts line up to receive from Don Alberto some small gratuity, fatherly advice, a chummy embrace. His brother, One-Arm Enrique, takes care of the brothel department. Don Alberto's responsibilities are lotteries and social peace. He smokes with a holder, spies on the world from beneath swollen lids. His henchmen break strikes, burn libraries, wreck printshops, and make short work of trade unionists, Jews, and all who forget to pay up and obey in this hour of crisis so conducive to disorder. Afterward, the good Don Alberto will give a hundred pesos to the orphans.

(166 and 176)

1930: Castex

The Last Rebel Gaucho

on the Argentine pampa is called Bairoletto, the son of peasants from Italy. He became an outlaw quite young, after shooting in the forehead a policeman who had humiliated him, and now he has no choice but to sleep outdoors. In the desert, beaten by the wind, he appears and disappears, lightning or mirage, riding an inky-black stallion that jumps seven-strand wire fences without effort. The poor protect him, and he avenges them against the powerful who abuse them and then swallow up their land. At the end of each raid, he engraves a B with bullets into the wings of the estancia's windmill, and seeds the wind with anarchist pamphlets foretelling revolution.

(123)

1930: Santo Domingo

The Hurricane

beats down with a roar, smashing ships against piers, shredding bridges, uprooting trees and whirling them through the air. Tin roofs, flying like crazy hatchets, decapitate people. This island is being leveled by winds, raked by lightning, drowned by rain and sea. The hurricane strikes as if revenging itself, or executing some fantastic curse. One might think that the Dominican Republic had been condemned, alone, to pay a debt due from the entire planet.

Later, when the hurricane moves on, the burning begins. Corpses and ruins have to be incinerated or plagues will finish off whatever remains alive and standing. For a week a vast cloud of black smoke hangs over the city of Santo Domingo.

So go the first days of the government of General Rafael Leónidas Trujillo, who has come to power on the eve of the cyclone, borne by a no less catastrophic fall in the international price of sugar.

(60 and 101)

1930: Ilopango
Miguel at Twenty-Five

The crisis also knocks the price of coffee for a loop. Beans spoil on the trees; a sickly odor of rotten coffee hangs in the air. Throughout Central America, growers put their workers out on the road. The few who still have work get the same rations as hogs.

In the worst of the crisis the Communist Party is born in El Salvador. Miguel, now a master shoemaker who works wherever he finds himself, is one of the founders. He stirs people up, wins recruits, hides and flees, the police always on his heels.

One morning Miguel, in disguise, approaches his house. It seems not to be watched. He hears his little boy crying and he enters. The child is alone, screaming his lungs out. Miguel has begun changing his diapers when he looks up and through the window sees police surrounding the place.

"*Pardon me,*" he says to his shitty little half-changed boy, and springs up like a cat, slipping through a hole between some broken roof tiles just as the first shots ring out.

And so occurs the fourth birth of Miguel Mármol, at twenty-five years of age.

(126 and 404)

1930: New York
Daily Life in the Crisis

Unpleasantly, like a series of rude slaps in the face, the crisis wakes up North Americans. The disaster at the New York Stock Exchange has pricked the Great Dream, which promised to fill every pocket with money, every sky with planes, every inch of land with automobiles and skyscrapers.

Nobody is selling optimism in the market. Fashions sadden. Long faces, long dresses, long hair. The roaring twenties come to an end, and with them, the exposed leg and bobbed hair.

All consumption drops vertically. Sales are up only for cigarettes, horoscopes, and twenty-five-watt bulbs, which don't give much light, but don't draw much current. Hollywood prepares films about giant monsters on the loose: King Kong, Frankenstein, as inexplicable as the economy, as unstoppable as the crisis that sows terror in the streets of the city.

(15 and 331)

1930: Achuapa
Shrinking the Rainbow

Nicaragua, a country condemned to produce cheap desserts—bananas, coffee, and sugar—keeps on ruining the digestion of its customers.

The Sandinista chief Miguel Ángel Ortez celebrates the new year by wiping out a Marine patrol in the muddy ravines of Achuapa, and on the same day another patrol falls over a precipice in the vicinity of Ocotal.

In vain, the invaders seek victory through hunger, by burning huts and crops. Many families are forced to take to the mountains, wandering and unprotected. Behind them they leave pillars of smoke and bayonetted animals.

The campesinos believe that Sandino knows how to lure the rainbow to him; and as it comes it shrinks until he can pick it up with just two fingers.

(118 and 361)

1931: Bocay
The Trumpets Will Sound

By the light of aromatic pitch-pine chips, Sandino writes letters, orders, and reports to be read aloud in the camp on the military and political situation in Nicaragua (*Like a firecracker, the enemy will soon burn himself out . . .*), manifestos condemning traitors (*They will find no place to live, unless under seven spans of earth . . .*), and prophesies announcing that soon war trumpets will sound against oppressors everywhere, and sooner than later the Last Judgment will destroy injustice so that the world may at last be what it wanted to be when there was was still nothing.

(237)

Sandino Writes to One of His Officers: "We won't be able to walk for all the flowers . . ."

If sleep, hunger, or petty fears overtake you, ask God to comfort you . . . God will give us this other triumph, which will be the definitive one, because I am sure that after this battle they won't come back to get their change, and you will be covered with glory! When we enter Managua, we won't be able to walk for all the flowers . . .

(361)

1931: Bocay
Santos López

Whoever joins the liberating army gets no pay, no pay ever, only the right to be called *brother*. He has to find a rifle on his own, in battle, and maybe a uniform stripped from some dead Marine, to wear once the pants have been properly shortened.

Santos López has been with Sandino from day one. He had worked for the farmers who owned him since he was eight. He was twelve at the time of the San Albino mine rebellion, and became a water boy and messenger in Sandino's army, a spy among drunken or distracted enemies, and along with his other buddies, specialized in setting ambushes and creating diversions with cans and whatever noisy odds and ends he could lay his hands on to make a few people seem like a crowd.

Santos López turns seventeen on the day Sandino promotes him to colonel.

(236, 267, and 361)

1931: Bocay

Tranquilino

In Sandino's rickety arsenal the finest weapon is a Browning machine-gun of the latest model, rescued from a North American plane downed by rifle fire.

In the hands of Tranquilino Jarquín, this Browning shoots and sings.

Tranquilino is the cook. He shows one tooth when he smiles, sticks an orchid in his hat, and as he stirs the big steaming pot, meat-poor but rich in aroma, he tosses down a good swig of rum.

In Sandino's army drinking is forbidden, Tranquilino excepted. It took a lot to win that privilege. But without his little swigs this artist of wooden spoon and trigger doesn't function. When they put him on a water diet, his dishes are flat, his shots twisted and off-key.

(236 and 393)

1931: Bocay

Little Cabrera

Tranquilino makes music with the machinegun, Pedro Cabrera with the trumpet. For Tranquilino's Browning it's bursts of tangos, marches, and ballads, while Little Cabrera's trumpet moans protests of love and proclaims brave deeds.

To kiss his celestial trumpet each morning, Little Cabrera must freeze his body and shut his eyes. Before dawn he wakens the soldiers, and at night lulls them to sleep, blowing low, low, lingering notes.

Musician and poet, warm heart and itchy feet, Little Cabrera has been Sandino's assistant since the war began. Nature has given him a yard and a half of stature and seven women.

(393)

1931: Hanwell

The Winner

Charlie the Tramp visits Hanwell School. He walks on one leg, as if skating. He twists his ear and out spurts a stream of water. Hundreds of children, orphaned, poor, or abandoned, scream with laughter. Thirty-five years ago, Charlie Chaplin was one of these children. Now he recognizes the chair he used to sit on and the corner of the dismal gym where he was birched.

Later he had escaped to London. In those days, shop windows displayed sizzling pork chops and golden potatoes steeped in gravy; Chaplin's nose still remembers the smell that filtered through the glass to mock him. And still engraved in his memory are the prices of other unattainable treats: a cup of tea, one halfpenny; a bit of herring, one penny; a tart, twopence.

Twenty years ago he left England in a cattle boat. Now he returns, the most famous man in the world. A cloud of journalists follows him like his shadow, and wherever he goes crowds jostle to see him, touch him. He can do whatever he wants. At the height of the talkie euphoria, his silent films have a devastating success. And he can spend whatever he wants—although he never wants. On the screen, Charlie the Tramp, poor leaf in the wind, knows nothing of money; in reality, Charles Chaplin, who perspires millions, watches the pennies and is incapable of looking at a painting without calculating its price. He will never share the fate of Buster Keaton, a man with open pockets, from whom everything flies away as soon as he earns it.

(121 and 383)

1932: Hollywood

The Loser

Buster Keaton arrives at the Metro studios hours late, dragging the hangover of last night's drinking spree: feverish eyes, coppery tongue, dishrag muscles. Who knows how he manages to execute the clownish pirouettes and recite the idiotic jokes ordered by the script.

Now his films are talkies and Keaton is not allowed to improvise; nor may he do retakes in search of that elusive instant when poetry discovers imprisoned laughter and unchains it. Keaton, genius of liberty and silence, must follow to the letter the charlatan scenarios written by others. In this way costs are halved and talent eliminated, according to the production norms of the movie factories of the sound-film era. Left behind forever are the days when Hollywood was a mad adventure.

Every day Keaton feels more at home with dogs and cows. Every night he opens a bottle of bourbon and implores his own memory to drink and be still.

(128 and 382)

1932: Mexico City
Eisenstein

While in Mexico they accuse him of being a *bolshevik, homosexual, and libertine*; in Hollywood they call him a *red dog and friend of murderers*.

Sergei Eisenstein has come to Mexico to film an indigenous epic. Before it is half-produced, the guts are ripped out. The Mexican censor bans some scenes because the truth is all very well, but not so much of it, thank you. The North American producer leaves the filmed footage in the hands of whoever may want to cut it to pieces.

Eisenstein's film *Que Viva México* ends up as nothing but a pile of grandiose scraps, images lacking articulation put together inco-herently or with deceit, dazzling letters torn loose from a word that was never before spoken about this country, this delirium sprung from the place where the bottom of the sea meets the center of the earth: pyramids that are volcanoes about to erupt, creepers inter-woven like hungry bodies, stones that breathe . . .

(151 and 305)

1932: The Roads of Santa Fe
The Puppeteer

didn't know he was one until the evening when, high on a balcony in Buenos Aires with a friend, he noticed a haycart passing down the street. On the hay lay a young boy smoking, face to the sky, hands behind his neck, legs crossed. Both he and his friend felt an irre-pressible urge to get away. The friend took off with a woman toward the mysterious frozen lands to the South of the South; and the puppeteer discovered puppeteering, craft of the free, and hit the road on a cart pulled by two horses.

From town to town along the banks of the River Paraná, the cart's wooden wheels leave long scars. The name of the puppeteer, conjurer of happiness, is Javier Villafañe. Javier travels with his children whose flesh is paper and paste. The best beloved of them is Master Globetrotter: long sad nose, black cape, flying necktie. During the show he is an extension of Javier's hand, and afterward, he sleeps and dreams at his feet, in a shoebox.

1932: Izalco

The Right to Vote and Its Painful Consequences

General Maximiliano Hernández Martínez, president by coup d'état, convokes the people of El Salvador to elect deputies and mayors. Despite a thousand traps, the tiny Communist Party wins the elections. The general takes umbrage. Scrutiny of ballots is suspended *sine die*.

Swindled, the Communists rebel. Salvadorans erupt on the same day that the Izalco volcano erupts. As boiling lava runs down the slopes and clouds of ashes blot out the sky, red campesinos attack the barracks with machetes in Izalco, Nahuizalco, Tacuba, Juayúa, and other towns. For three days America's first soviets come to power.

Three days. Three months of slaughter follow. Farabundo Martí and other Communist leaders face firing squads. Soldiers beat to death the Indian chief José Feliciano Ama, leader of the revolution in Izalco. They hang Ama's corpse in the main plaza and force schoolchildren to watch the show. Thirty thousand campesinos, denounced by their employers, or condemned on mere suspicion or old wives' tales, dig their own graves with their hands. Children die too, for Communists, like snakes, need to be killed young. Wherever a dog or pig scratches up the earth, remains of people appear. One of the firing-squad victims is the shoemaker Miguel Mármol.

(9, 21, and 404)

1932: Soyapango

Miguel at Twenty-Six

As they take them away bound in a truck, Miguel recognizes his childhood haunts.

"What luck," he thinks, *"I'm going to die where my umbilical cord was buried."*

They beat them to the ground with rifle butts, then shoot them in pairs. The truck's headlights and the moon give more than enough light.

After a few volleys, it's the turn of Miguel and a man who sells engravings, condemned for being Russian. The Russian and Miguel, standing before the firing squad, grip each other's hands, which are bound behind their backs. Miguel itches all over and desperately needs to scratch; this fills his mind as he hears: *"Ready! Aim! Fire!"*

Miguel regains consciousness under a pile of bodies dripping blood. He feels his head throbbing and bleeding, and the pain of the bullets in his body, soul, and clothes. He hears the click of a rifle reloading. A coup de grâce.

Another. Another. His eyes misted with blood, Miguel awaits the final shot, but feels a machete chopping at him instead.

The soldiers kick the bodies into a ditch and throw dirt over them. Hearing the trucks drive off, Miguel, wounded and cut, tries to move. It takes him centuries to crawl out from under so much death and earth. Finally, managing to walk at a ferociously slow pace, more falling than standing, he very gradually gets out, wearing the sombrero of a comrade whose name was Serafín.

And so occurs the fifth birth of Miguel Mármol, at twenty-six years of age.

(126)

1932: Managua

Sandino Is Advancing

in a great sweep that reaches the banks of Lake Managua. The occupation troops fall back in disarray. Meanwhile, two photographs appear in the world's newspapers. One shows Lieutenant Pensington of the United States Navy holding up a trophy, a head chopped from a Nicaraguan campesino. From the other smiles the entire general staff of the Nicaraguan National Guard, officers wearing high boots and safari headgear. At their center is seated the director of the Guard, Colonel Calvin B. Matthews. Behind them is the jungle. At the feet of the group, sprawled on the ground, is a dog. The jungle and the dog are the only Nicaraguans.

(118 and 361)

1932: San Salvador
Miguel at Twenty-Seven

Of those who saved Miguel, no one is left. Soldiers have riddled with bullets the comrades who found him in a ditch, those who carried him across the river on a chair of hands, those who hid him in a cave, and those who managed to bring him to his sister's home in San Salvador. When his sister saw the specter of Miguel stitched with bullets and crisscrossed with machete cuts, she had to be revived with a fan. Praying, she began a novena for his eternal rest.

The funeral service proceeds. Miguel begins to recover as best he can, hidden behind the altar set up in his memory, with nothing but the chichipince-juice ointment his sister applies with saintly patience to his purulent wounds. Lying behind the curtain, burning with fever, Miguel spends his birthday listening to disconsolate relatives and neighbors awash in oceans of tears, extolling his memory with nonstop prayers.

On one of these nights a military patrol stops at the door.

"Who are you praying for?"

"For the soul of my brother, the departed."

The soldiers enter, approach the altar, wrinkle their noses.

Miguel's sister clutches her rosary. The candles flicker before the image of our Lord Jesus Christ. Miguel has the sudden urge to cough. The soldiers cross themselves. "May he rest in peace," they say, and continue on their way.

And so occurs the sixth birth of Miguel Mármol, at twenty-seven.

(126)

1933: Managua

The First U.S. Military Defeat
in Latin America

On the first day of the year the Marines leave Nicaragua with all their ships and planes. The scraggy general, the little man who looks like a capital T with his wide-brimmed sombrero, has humbled an empire.

The U.S. press deplores the many dead in so many years of occupation, but stresses the value of the training of their aviators. Thanks to the war against Sandino, the United States has for the first time been able to experiment with aerial bombing from Fokker and Curtiss planes specially designed to fight in Nicaragua.

The departing Colonel Matthews is replaced by a sympathetic and faithful native officer, Anastasio Tacho Somoza, as head of the National Guard, now called the Guardia Nacional.

As soon as he reaches Managua, the triumphant Sandino says: *"Now we're free. I won't fire another shot."*

The president of Nicaragua, Juan Bautista Sacasa, greets him with an embrace. General Somoza embraces him too.

(118 and 361)

1933: Camp Jordán

The Chaco War

Bolivia and Paraguay are at war. The two poorest countries in South America, the two with no ocean, the two most thoroughly conquered and looted, annihilate each other for a bit of map. Concealed in the folds of both flags, Standard Oil and Royal Dutch Shell are disputing the oil of the Chaco.

In this war, Paraguayans and Bolivians are compelled to hate each other in the name of a land they do not love, that nobody loves. The Chaco is a gray desert inhabited by thorns and snakes; not a songbird or a person in sight. Everything is thirsty in this world of horror. Butterflies form desperate clots on the few drops of water. For Bolivians, it is going from freezer to oven: They are hauled down from the heights of the Andes and dumped into these roasting scrublands. Here some die of bullets, but more die of thirst.

Clouds of flies and mosquitos pursue the soldiers, who charge through thickets, heads lowered, on forced marches against enemy lines. On both sides barefoot people are the down payment on the errors of their officers. The slaves of feudal landlord and rural priest die in different uniforms, at the service of imperial avarice.

One of the Bolivian soldiers marching to death speaks. He says nothing about glory, nothing about the Fatherland. He says, ! reathing heavily, *"A curse on the hour that I was born a man."*

(354 and 402)

Céspedes

On the Bolivian side, this pitiful epic will be related by Augusto Céspedes:

A squadron of soldiers in search of water start digging a well with picks and shovels. The little rain that has fallen has already evaporated, and there is no water anywhere. At twelve meters the water hunters come upon liquid mud. But at thirty meters, at forty-five, the pulley brings up bucketfuls of sand, each one drier than the last. The soldiers keep on digging, day after day, into that well of sand, ever deeper, ever more silent. And when the Paraguayans, likewise hounded by thirst, launch an attack, the Bolivians die defending the well as if it contained water.

(96)

Roa Bastos

From the Paraguayan side, Augusto Roa Bastos will tell the story. He too will speak of wells that become graves, and of the multitude of dead, and of the living who are only distinguishable from them by the fact that they move, though like drunkards who have forgotten the way home. He will accompany the lost soldiers, who haven't a drop of water, not even to shed as tears.

(380)

1934: Managua

Horror Film: Scenario for Two Actors
and a Few Extras

Somoza leaves the house of Arthur Bliss Lane, ambassador of the United States.

Sandino arrives at the house of Sacasa, president of Nicaragua.

While Somoza sits down to work with his officers, Sandino sits down to supper with the president.

Somoza tells his officers that the ambassador has just given his unconditional support to the killing of Sandino.

Sandino tells the president about the problems of the Wiwilí cooperative, where he and his soldiers have been working the land for over a year.

Somoza explains to his officers that Sandino is a communistic enemy of order, who has many more weapons concealed than those he has turned in.

Sandino explains to the president that Somoza won't let him work in peace.

Somoza discusses with his officers whether Sandino should die by poison, shooting, airplane accident, or ambush in the mountains.

Sandino discusses with the president the growing power of the Guardia Nacional, led by Somoza, and warns that Somoza will soon blow him away to sit in the presidential chair himself.

Somoza finishes settling some practical details and leaves his officers.

Sandino finishes his coffee and takes leave of the president.

Somoza goes off to a poetry reading and Sandino goes off to his death.

While Somoza listens to the sonnets of Zoila Rosa Cárdenas, young luminary of Peruvian letters who honors this country by her visit, Sandino is shot in a place called The Skull, on Lonesome Road.

(339 and 405)

1934: Managua

The Government Decides That Crime Does Not Exist

That night, Colonel Santos López escapes the trap in Managua. On a bleeding leg, his seventh bullet wound in these years of war, he climbs over roofs, drops to the ground, jumps walls, and finally begins a nightmare crawl northward along the railroad tracks.

The next day, while Santos López is still dragging his wounded leg along the lake shore, a wholesale massacre takes place in the mountains. Somoza orders the Wiwilí cooperative destroyed, and the new Guardia Nacional strikes with total surprise, wiping out Sandino's former soldiers, who were sowing tobacco and bananas and had a hospital half built. The mules are saved, but not the children.

Soon after, banquets in homage to Somoza are given by the United States embassy in Managua and by the most exclusive clubs of León and Granada.

The government issues orders to forget. An amnesty wipes out all crimes committed since the eve of Sandino's death.

(267 and 405)

1934: San Salvador

Miguel at Twenty-Nine

Hunted as ever by the Salvadoran police, Miguel finds refuge in the house of the Spanish consul's lover.

One night a storm sweeps in. From the window, Miguel sees that, far over there where the river bends, the rising waters are threatening the mud-and-cane hut of his wife and children. Leaving his hideout in defiance of both gale and night patrol, Miguel hurries to his family.

They spend the night huddled together inside the fragile walls, listening to the roar of wind and river. At dawn, when winds and waters subside, the little hut is slightly askew and very damp, but still standing. And so Miguel says goodbye to his family and returns to his refuge.

But it is nowhere to be found. Of that solidly built house not a brick remains. The fury of the river has undermined the ravine, torn away the foundations, and carried off to the devil the house, the consul's lover, and the servant girl.

And so occurs the seventh birth of Miguel Mármol, at twenty-nine years of age.

(126)

1935: The Villamontes-Boyuibe Road
After Ninety Thousand Deaths

the Chaco War ends. It is three years since the first Paraguayan and Bolivian bullets were exchanged in a hamlet called Masamaclay, which in the Indian language means *place where two brothers fought*.

At noon the news reaches the front. The guns fall silent. The soldiers stand up, very slowly, and even more slowly emerge from the trenches. Ragged ghosts, blinded by the sun, they lurch across the no-man's-land between Bolivia's Santa Cruz regiment and Paraguay's Toledo regiment—the scraps, the shreds. Newly received orders prohibit fraternization with those who just now were enemies. Only the military salute is allowed; and so they salute each other. But someone lets loose a great howl, and then there is no stopping it. The soldiers break ranks, throw caps, weapons, anything, everything into the air and run in mad confusion, Paraguayans to Bolivians, Bolivians to Paraguayans, shouting, singing, weeping, embracing one another as they roll in the hot sand.

(354 and 402)

1935: Maracay
Gómez

The dictator of Venezuela, Juan Vicente Gómez, dies and keeps on ruling. For twenty-seven years no one has been able to budge him, and now no one dares crack a joke about his corpse. When the coffin of the terrible old man is unquestionably buried beneath a heap of earth, the prisoners finally break down the jail doors, and only then does the cheering and looting begin.

Gómez died a bachelor. He has sired mountains of children, loving as if relieving himself, but has never spent a whole night in a woman's arms. The dawn light always found him alone in his iron bed beneath the image of the Virgin Mary and alongside his chests filled with money.

He never spent a penny, paying for everything with oil. He distributed oil in gushers, to Gulf, Standard, Texaco, Shell, and with oil wells paid for the doctor who probed his bladder, for the poets whose sonnets hymned his glory, and for the executioners whose secret tasks kept his order.

(114, 333, and 366)

1935: Buenos Aires

Borges

Everything that brings people together, like football or politics, and everything that multiples them, like a mirror or the act of love, gives him the horrors. He recognizes no other reality than what exists in the past, in the past of his forefathers, and in books written by those who knew how to expound that reality. The rest is smoke.

With great delicacy and sharp wit, Jorge Luis Borges tells the *Universal History of Infamy.* About the national infamy that surrounds him, he doesn't even inquire.

(25 and 59)

1935: Buenos Aires

These Infamous Years

In London, the Argentine government signs a commercial treaty selling the country for halfpence. In the opulent estates north of Buenos Aires, the cattlocracy dance the waltz in shady arbors; but if the entire country is worth only halfpence, how much are its poorest children worth? Working hands go at bargain prices and you can find any number of girls who will strip for a cup of coffee. New factories sprout, and around them tin-can barrios, harried by police and tuberculosis, where yesterday's maté, dried in the sun, stifles hunger. The Argentine police invent the electric prod to convince those in doubt and straighten out those who buckle.

In the Buenos Aires night, the pimp seeks a girl wanting a good time, and the girl seeks a man who'll give her one; the racetrack gambler seeks a hot tip; the con man, a sucker; the jobless, a job in the early editions. Coming and going in the streets are the bohemian, the roué, and the cardsharp, all solitary in their solitude, while Discepolín's last tango sings that the world was and will continue to be a dirty joke.

(176, 365, and 412)

1935: Buenos Aires
Discepolín

He is one long bone with a nose, so thin that injections are put through his overcoat, the somber poet of Buenos Aires in the infamous years.

Enrique Santos Discépolo creates his first tangos, *sad thoughts that can be danced,* as a touring-company comedian lost in the provinces. In ramshackle dressing rooms he makes the acquaintance of huge, almost human-size fleas, and for them he hums tangos that speak of those with neither money nor faith.

(379)

1935: Buenos Aires
Evita

To look at, she's just a run-of-the-mill stick of a girl, pale, washed-out, not ugly, not pretty, who wears secondhand clothes and solemnly repeats the daily routines of poverty. Like the others, she lives hanging on to each episode of the radio soaps, dreams every Sunday of being Norma Shearer, and every evening goes to the railway station to see the Buenos Aires train pass by. But Eva Duarte has turned fifteen and she's fed up; she climbs aboard the train and takes off.

This little creature has nothing at all. No father, no money, no memories to hold on to. Since she was born in the town of Los Toldos, of an unmarried mother, she has been condemned to humiliation, and now she is a nobody among the thousands of nobodies the trains pour into Buenos Aires every day, a multitude of tousle-haired dark-skinned provincials, workers and servant girls who are sucked into the city's mouth and are promptly devoured. During the week Buenos Aires chews them up; on Sundays it spits out the pieces.

At the feet of the arrogant Moloch, great peaks of cement, Evita is paralyzed by a panic that only lets her clasp her hands, red and cold, and weep. Then she dries her tears, clenches her teeth, takes a firm grip of her cardboard valise, and buries herself in the city.

(311 and 417)

1935: Buenos Aires
Alfonsina

The ovaries of a woman who thinks dry up. Woman is born to produce milk and tears, not ideas; not to live life but to spy on it through slatted venetian blinds. A thousand times they have explained it to her but Alfonsina Storni never believed them, and her best-known verses protest against the macho jailer.

When she came to Buenos Aires from the provinces, all Alfonsina had were some down-at-heel shoes and, in her belly, a child with no legal father. In this city she worked at whatever she could get and stole blank telegram forms to write her sorrows. As she polished her words, verse by verse, night by night, she crossed her fingers and kissed the cards that announced journeys, inheritances, and loves.

Time has passed, almost a quarter of a century, and fate has given her no presents. But somehow Alfonsina has made her way in the male world. Her face, like a mischievous mouse, is never missing from group photos of Argentina's most illustrious writers.

This year, this summer, she finds she has cancer. So now she writes of the embrace of the sea and of the home that awaits her in the depths, on the avenue of Corals.

(310)

1935: Medellín
Gardel

Each time he sings, in that voice of many colors, he sings as never before. He makes dark notes, his opaque lyrics shine. He's the Magician, the Greatest, Carlos Gardel.

The shadow of a sombrero over his eyes, a perpetual and perfect smile forever young, he looks like a winner who has never been defeated. His origin is a mystery; his life, an enigma. Tragedy had no choice but to save him from explanation and decay. His worshippers would not have forgiven him for old age. The plane in which he is traveling takes off from Medellín airport and blows up in flight.

1936: Buenos Aires
Patoruzú

For ten years the Patoruzú comic strip, the work of Dante Quintero, has been published in the Buenos Aires dailies. Now, a monthly magazine appears wholly devoted to the character. Patoruzú is a big landlord, the owner of half of Patagonia, who lives in five-star hotels in Buenos Aires, squanders millions with both hands, and passionately believes in private property and the consumer civilization. Dante Quintero explains that Patoruzú is a typical Argentine Indian.

(446 and 456)

1936: Rio de Janeiro
Olga and He

With his rebel army Luis Carlos Prestes has crossed the immensity of Brazil on foot, end to end, there and back, southern prairies to northeastern deserts, the whole breadth of the Amazon jungle. In three years the Prestes Column has battled the coffee and sugar barons to a standstill, without a single defeat. So that Olga Benário imagined him as some devastating giant of a man, and is amazed when he turns out to be a fragile little fellow who blushes when she looks him in the eye.

She, toughened in the revolutionary struggles of Germany, a militant without frontiers, loves and sustains this rebel who has never known a woman. In time, both are taken prisoner. They are taken to different prisons.

From Germany, Hitler demands Olga, that Jew and Communist—vile blood, vile ideas—and Brazilian president Getulio Vargas turns her over. When soldiers come for her the prisoners riot. Olga stops them, seeing no point in useless slaughter, and lets herself be taken. Through the bars of his cell the novelist Graciliano Ramos sees her pass, handcuffed, with her pregnant belly.

At the docks a ship flying the swastika sits waiting for her; the captain has orders to head straight for Hamburg. There, Olga will be deposited in a concentration camp, asphyxiated in a gas chamber, carbonized in an oven.

(263, 302, and 364)

1936: Madrid
The Spanish War

The rising against the Spanish republic has been incubated in barracks, sacristies, and palaces. Generals, monks, lackeys of the king, and feudal lords of the gallows and the knife are its murky protagonists. The Chilean poet Pablo Neruda curses them, invoking the bullets that will one day find a home in their hearts. In Granada the fascists have just shot his beloved brother Federico García Lorca, the poet of Andalusía, *the ever-free flash of lightning*, for being or seeming to be homosexual and red.

Neruda roams the Spanish earth so soaked in blood and is transformed. The poet, distracted by politics, asks of poetry that it make itself useful like metal or flour, that it get ready to stain its face with coal dust and fight body to body.

(313 and 314)

1936: San Salvador
Martínez

At the head of the rebellion, Francisco Franco proclaims himself Generalisimo and Spanish Chief of State. The first diplomatic recognition comes to the city of Burgos from the remote Caribbean. General Maximiliano Hernández Martínez, dictator of El Salvador, congratulates the newly born dictatorship of his colleague.

Martínez, the kindly grandfather who murdered thirty thousand Salvadorans, believes killing ants more criminal than killing people; because ants, he says, cannot be reincarnated. Every Sunday Maestro Martínez speaks to the country on the radio about the international political situation, intestinal parasites, the reincarnation of souls, and the Communist peril. He routinely cures the ills of his ministers and officials with colored waters kept in big bottles on the patio of the presidential palace, and when the smallpox epidemic strikes he scares it off by wrapping the street lights in red cellophane.

To uncover conspiracies, he hangs a clock pendulum over steaming soup. For the gravest problems he resorts to President Roosevelt, communicating directly with the White House by telepathy.

(250)

1936: San Salvador
Miguel at Thirty-One

Miguel, just released from jail—almost two years handcuffed in solitary—wanders the roads, a ragged pariah with nothing. He has no party, because his Communist Party comrades suspect he made a deal with dictator Martínez. He has no work, because dictator Martínez sees to it that he can't get any. He has no wife, because she has left him and taken the children with her; no house either, or food, or shoes, or even a name. It has been officially established that Miguel Mármol does not exist, because he was executed in 1932.

He decides to put an end to it, once and for all. Enough of these thoughts. A single machete blow will open his veins. He is just raising the machete when a boy on a burro appears in the road. The boy greets him with a sweep of his enormous straw sombrero, asks to borrow the machete to split a coconut, then offers half the split nut, water to drink, coconut meat to eat. Miguel drinks and eats as if this unknown lad had invited him to a feast, and gets up and walks away from death.

And thus occurs the eighth birth of Miguel Mármol, at thirty-one years of age.

(126)

1936: Guatemala City
Ubico

Martínez has beaten him to it by a few hours, but Ubico is the second to recognize Franco. Ten days before Hitler and Mussolini, Ubico puts a stamp of legitimacy on the rising against Spanish democracy.

General Jorge Ubico, Chief of State of Guatemala, governs surrounded by effigies of Napoleon Bonaparte, whom he resembles, he says, like a twin. But Ubico rides motorcycles and the war he is waging has nothing to do with the conquest of Europe. His is a war against bad thoughts.

Against bad thoughts, military discipline. Ubico militarizes the post office employees, the symphony orchestra musicians, and the schoolchildren. Since a full belly is the mother of bad thoughts, he has United Fruit's plantation wages cut by half. He scourges idleness, father of bad thoughts, by forcing those guilty of it to work his lands for nothing. To expel the bad thoughts from the minds of revolutionaries, he invents a steel crown that squeezes their heads in police dungeons.

Ubico has imposed on the Indians a compulsory contribution of five centavos a month to raise a great monument to Ubico. Hand in jacket, he poses for the sculptor.

(250)

1936: Trujillo City
In the Year Six of the Trujillo Era

the name of the Dominican Republic's capital is corrected. Santo Domingo, so baptized by its founders, becomes Trujillo City. The port is now called Trujillo, as are many towns, plazas, markets, and avenues. From Trujillo City, Generalísimo Rafael Leónidas Trujillo sends Generalísimo Francisco Franco his most ardent support.

Trujillo, tireless bane of reds and heretics, was, like Anastasio Somoza, born of a U.S. military occupation. His natural modesty does not prevent him from allowing his name to appear on all automobile license plates and his likeness on all postage stamps, nor does he oppose the conferring of the rank of colonel on his three-year-old son Ramfis, as an act of simple justice. His sense of responsibility obliges him to appoint personally all ministers, porters, bishops, and beauty queens. To stimulate the spirit of enterprise, Trujillo grants the salt, tobacco, oil, cement, flour, and match monopolies to Trujillo. In defense of public health, Trujillo closes down businesses that do not sell meat from the Trujillo slaughterhouses or milk from his dairy farms; and for the sake of public security he makes obligatory the purchase of insurance policies sold by Trujillo. Firmly grasping the helm of progress, Trujillo releases the Trujillo enterprises from taxes, while providing his estates with irrigation and roads and his factories with customers. By order of Trujillo, shoe manufacturer, anyone caught barefoot on the streets of town or city goes to jail.

The all-powerful has a voice like a whistle, with which there is no discussion. At supper, he clinks glasses with a governor or deputy who will be off to the cemetery after coffee. When a piece of land interests him, he doesn't buy it: he occupies it. When a woman appeals to him, he doesn't seduce her; he points at her.

(89, 101, and 177)

Procedure Against Rain

What the Dominican Republic needs when torrential rains drown crops is a proper supplicant who can walk in the rain without getting wet to send up urgent pleas to God and the Blessed Saint Barbara. Twins are especially good at leashing rain and scaring off thunder.

In the Dominican region of Salcedo they use another method. They look for two big oval stones, the kind that get polished by the river; they tie them firmly to a rope, one at each end, and hang them from the bough of a tree. Giving the stone eggs a hard squeeze and a sharp tug, they pray to God, who lets out a yell and moves on somewhere else with his black clouds.

(251)

Procedure Against Disobedience

A woman of daily Masses and continual prayer and penitence, the mother of María la O skinned her knees imploring God for the miracle of making her daughter obedient and good, and begging pardon for the brazen girl's insolences.

One Good Friday evening, María la O went down to the river. Her mother tried in vain to stop her: *"Just think, they're killing Our Lord Jesus Christ . . ."*

God's wrath leaves forever stuck together those who make love on Good Friday, and though María la O was not going to meet a lover, she did commit a sin. She swam naked in the river, and when the water tickled the prohibited recesses of her body, she trembled with pleasure.

Afterward she tried to get out of the river and couldn't because she was covered with scales and had a flipper where her feet had been.

And in the waters of Dominican rivers María la O swims to this day: she was never forgiven.

(251)

1937: Dajabón

Procedure Against the Black Menace

The condemned are Haitian blacks who work in the Dominican Republic. This military exorcism, planned to the last detail by General Trujillo, lasts a day and a half. In the sugar region, the soldiers shut up Haitian day-laborers in corrals—herds of men, women, and children—and finish them off then and there with machetes; or bind their hands and feet and drive them at bayonet point into the sea.

Trujillo, who powders his face several times a day, wants the Dominician Republic white.

(101, 177, and 286)

1937: Washington

Newsreel

Two weeks later, the government of Haiti conveys to the government of the Dominican Republic its *concern about the recent events at the border*. The government of the Dominican Republic promises *an exhaustive investigation*.

In the name of continental security, the government of the United States proposes to President Trujillo that he pay an indemnity to avoid possible friction in the zone. After prolonged negotiation Trujillo recognizes the death of eighteen thousand Haitians on Dominican territory. According to him, the figure of twenty-five thousand victims, put forward by some sources, reflects the intention to manipulate the events dishonestly. Trujillo agrees to pay the government of Haiti, by way of indemnity, $522,000, or twenty-nine dollars for every officially recognized death.

The White House congratulates itself on an agreement reached within the framework of established inter-American treaties and procedures. Secretary of State Cordell Hull declares in Washington that

President Trujillo is one of the greatest men in Central America and in most of South America.

The indemnity duly paid in cash, the presidents of the Dominican Republic and Haiti embrace each other at the border.

(101)

1937: Rio de Janeiro
Procedure Against the Red Menace

The president of Brazil, Getulio Vargas, has no alternative but to set up a dictatorship. A drumroll of press and radio reports discloses the sinister Cohen Plan, obliging Vargas to suppress Parliament and the electoral process. The Fatherland is not about to sit back and succumb to the advance of Moscow's hordes. The Cohen Plan, which the government has discovered in some cellar, gives the full details—tactics *and* strategy—of the Communist plot against Brazil.

The plan is called "Cohen" due to a stenographic error. The originator of the plan, Captain Olympio Mourão Filho, actually baptized it the Kun Plan, having based it on documents from the brief Hungarian revolution headed by Béla Kun.

But the name is secondary. Captain Mourão Filho gets a well-earned promotion to major.

(43)

1937: Cariri Valley
The Crime of Community

From planes, they bomb and machinegun them. On the ground, they cut their throats, burn them alive, crucify them. Forty years after it wiped out the community of Canudos, the Brazilian army does the same to Caldeirão, verdant island in the northeast, and for the same crime—denying the principle of private property.

In Caldeirão nothing belonged to anyone: neither textile looms, nor brick ovens, nor the sea of cornfields around the village, nor the snowy immensity of cotton fields beyond. The owners were everyone and no one, and there were no naked or hungry. The needy had formed this community at the call of the Holy Cross of the Desert, which saintly José Lourenço, desert pilgrim, had carried there on his shoulder. The Virgin Mary had chosen both the spot for the cross and the holy man to bring it. Where he stuck in the cross, water flowed continuously.

According to the newspapers of distant cities, this squalid holy man is the prosperous sultan of a harem of eleven thousand virgins; and if that were not enough, also an agent of Moscow with a concealed arsenal in his granaries.

Of the community of Caldeirão nothing and no one is left. The colt Trancelim, which only the holy man mounted, flees into the stony mountains. In vain it seeks some shrub offering shade under this infernal sun.

(3)

1937: Rio de Janeiro
Monteiro Lobato

The censors ban *The Oil Scandal* by Monteiro Lobato. The book offends the oil trust and its technicians, hired or purchased, who claim that Brazil has no oil.

The author has ruined himself trying to create a Brazilian oil company. Before that, he failed in the publishing business, when he had the crazy idea of selling books not only in bookstores, but also in pharmacies, bazaars, and newsstands.

Monteiro Lobato was born not to publish books but to write them. His forte is telling tales to children. On the Benteveo Amarillo farm a pig of small intelligence is the Marquis of Rabicó and an ear of corn becomes a distinguished viscount who can read the Bible in Latin and talk in English to Leghorn chickens. The Marquis casts a warm eye on Emilia, the rag doll, who chatters on nonstop, because she started so late in life and has so much chatter stored up.

(252)

1937: Madrid
Hemingway

The reports of Ernest Hemingway describe the war that is raging a step from his hotel in this capital besieged by Franco's soldiers and Hitler's airplanes.

Why has Hemingway gone to lonely Spain? He is not exactly a militant like the ones who have come from all parts of the world to join the International Brigades. What Hemingway reveals in his writings is something else—the desperate search for dignity among men. And dignity is the only thing that is not rationed in these trenches of the Spanish republic.

(220 and 312)

1937: Mexico City
The Bolero

Mexico's Ministry of Public Education prohibits the boleros of Agustín Lara in schools, because *their obscene, immoral, and degenerate lyrics* might corrupt children.

Lara exalts the Lost Woman, in whose eyes are seen sun-drunk palm trees; he beseeches love from the Decadent One, in whose pupils boredom spreads like a peacock's tail; he dreams of the sumptuous bed of the silky-skinned Courtesan; with sublime ecstasy he deposits roses at the feet of the Sinful One, and covers the Shameful Whore with incense and jewels in exchange for the honey of her mouth.

(299)

1937: Mexico City
Cantinflas

For laughter, the people flock into the suburban tents, poor little makeshift theaters, where all the footlights shine on Cantinflas.

"There are moments in life that are truly momentary," says Cantinflas, with his pencil mustache and baggy pants, reeling off his spiel at top speed. His fusillade of nonsense apes the rhetoric of half-baked intellectuals and politicians, doctors of verbal diarrhea who say nothing, who pursue a point with endless phrases, never catching up to it. In these lands, the economy suffers from monetary inflation; politics and culture from verbal inflation.

(205)

1937: Mexico City
Cárdenas

Mexico does not wash its hands of the war in Spain. Lázaro Cárdenas—rare president, friend of silence and enemy of verbosity—not only proclaims his solidarity, but practices it, sending arms to the republican front across the sea, and receiving orphaned children by the shipload.

Cárdenas listens as he governs. He gets around and listens. From town to town he goes, hearing complaints with infinite patience, and never promising more than is possible. A man of his word, he talks little. Until Cárdenas, the art of governing in Mexico consisted of moving the tongue; but when he says yes or no, people believe it. Last summer he announced an agrarian reform program and since then has not stopped allocating lands to native communities.

He is cordially hated by those for whom the revolution is a business. They say that Cárdenas keeps quiet because, spending so much time among the Indians, he has forgotten Spanish, and that one of these days he will appear in a loincloth and feathers.

(45, 78, and 201)

1938: Anenecuilco
Nicolás, Son of Zapata

Earlier than anyone else, harder than anyone else, the campesinos of Anenecuilco have fought for the land; but after so much time and bloodshed, little has changed in the community where Emiliano Zapata was born and rose in rebellion.

A bunch of papers, eaten by moths and centuries, lie at the heart of the struggle. These documents, with the seal of the viceroy on them, prove that this community is the owner of its own land. Emiliano Zapata left them in the hands of one of his soldiers, Pancho Franco: *"If you lose them, compadre, you'll dry up hanging from a branch."*

And, indeed, on several occasions, Pancho Franco has saved the papers and his life by a hair.

Anenecuilco's best friend is President Lázaro Cárdenas, who has visited, listened to the campesinos, and recognized and amplified their rights. Its worst enemy is deputy Nicolás Zapata, Emiliano's eldest son, who has taken possession of the richest lands and aims to get the rest too.

(468)

1938: Mexico City
The Nationalization of Oil

North of Tampico, Mexico's petroleum belongs to Standard Oil; to the south, Shell. Mexico pays dearly for its own oil, which Europe and the United States buy cheap. These companies have been looting the subsoil and robbing Mexico of taxes and salaries for thirty years—until one fine day Cárdenas decides that Mexico is the owner of Mexican oil.

Since that day, nobody can sleep a wink. The challenge wakes up the country. In never-ending demonstrations, enormous crowds stream into the streets carrying coffins for Standard and Shell on their backs. To a marimba beat and the tolling of bells, workers occupy wells and refineries. But the companies reply in kind: all the foreign technicians, those masters of mystery, are withdrawn. No one is left to tend the indecipherable instrument panels of management. The national flag flutters over silent towers. The drills are halted, the pipelines emptied, the fires extinguished. It is war: war against the Latin American tradition of impotence, the colonial custom of *don't know, no can do*.

(45, 201, 234, and 321)

1938: Mexico City
Showdown

Standard Oil demands an immediate invasion of Mexico.

If a single soldier shows up at the border, Cárdenas warns, he will order the wells set on fire. President Roosevelt whistles and looks the other way, but the British Crown, adopting the fury of Shell, announces it will not buy one more drop of Mexican oil. France concurs. Other countries join the blockade. Mexico can't find anyone to sell it a spare part, and the ships disappear from its ports.

Still, Cárdenas won't get off the mule. He looks for customers

in the prohibited areas—Red Russia, Nazi Germany, Fascist Italy—
while the abandoned installations revive bit by bit. The Mexican
workers mend, improvise, invent, getting by on pure enthusiasm,
and so the magic of creation begins to make dignity possible.

(45, 201, 234, and 321)

1938: Coyoacán

Trotsky

Every morning he is surprised to find himself alive. Although his
house has guardtowers and electrified wire fences, Leon Trotsky knows
it to be a futile fortress. The creator of the Red Army is grateful to
Mexico for giving him refuge, but even more grateful to fate. *"See,
Natasha?"* he says to his wife each morning. *"Last night they didn't
kill us, and yet you're complaining."*

Since Lenin's death, Stalin has liquidated, one after another, the
men who had made the Russian revolution—to save it, says Stalin;
to take it over, says Trotsky, a man marked for death.

Stubbornly, Trotsky continues to believe in socialism, fouled as
it is by human mud; for when all is said, who can deny that Christianity
is much more than the Inquisition?

(132)

1938: The Hinterland

The *Cangaceiros*

operate on a modest scale and never without motive. They don't rob
towns with more than two churches, and kill only by specific order
or for a vengeance sworn by kissing a dagger. They work in the burned
lands of the desert, far from the sea and the salty breath of its dragons.
They cross the lonely stretches of northeast Brazil, on horse or on
foot, their half-moon sombreros dripping with decorations. They rarely
linger anywhere. They neither raise their children nor bury their
parents. They have made a pact with Heaven and Hell not to shelter
their bodies from bullets or knives simply for the sake of dying a
natural death; and sooner or later these hazardous, hazarded lives, a
thousand times lauded in the couplets of blind singers, come to very
bad ends: *God will say, God will give, high road, long road*—the

epic of wandering bandits who go from fight to fight, without time
for their sweat to go cold.

(136, 348, and 353)

1938: Angico
The *Cangaceiro* Hunters

To throw their enemies off the scent, the *cangaceiros* imitate the
noises and tracks of animals or use trick soles with heel and toe
reversed. But those who know, know. A good tracker recognizes the
passage of humans through this dying landscape from what he sees,
a broken branch or a stone out of place, and what he smells. The
cangaceiros are crazy about perfume. They douse themselves by the
liter, and this weakness betrays them.

Following tracks and scents, the hunters reach the hideout of
Chief Lampião; and behind them the troops, so close they hear Lampião arguing with his wife. Seated on a stone at the entrance to a
cave, María Bonita curses him, while smoking one cigarette after
another; from within, he makes sad replies. The soldiers mount their
machineguns and await the command to fire.

A light drizzle falls.

(52, 348, 352, and 353)

1939: São Salvador de Bahia
The Women of the Gods

Ruth Landes, North American anthropologist, comes to Brazil to learn
about the lives of blacks in a country without racism. In Rio de Janeiro,
Minister Osvaldo Aranha receives her. He explains that the government proposes to clean up the Brazilian race, soiled as it is by black
blood, because black blood is to blame for national backwardness.

From Rio, Ruth goes to Bahia. In this city, where the sugar- and
slave-rich viceroy once had his throne, blacks are an ample majority,
and whether it's religion, music, or food, black is what is worthwhile
here. Nevertheless, all Bahians, including blacks, think white skin is
proof of good quality. No, not everyone. Ruth discovers pride of
blackness in the women of the African temples.

There it is nearly always women, black priestesses, who receive in their bodies the gods from Africa. Resplendent and round as cannonballs, they offer their capacious bodies as homes where it is pleasant to visit, to linger. While the gods enter them, dance in them, from the hands of these possessed priestesses the people get encouragement and solace, and from their mouths hear the voices of fate.

The black priestesses of Bahia accept lovers, not husbands. What matrimony gives in prestige, it takes away in freedom and happiness. None of them is interested in formal marriage before priest or judge. None wants to be a handcuffed wife, a Mrs. Someone-or-other. Heads erect, with languid swings, the priestesses move like queens of Creation, condemning their men to the incomparable torment of jealousy of the gods.

(253)

Exú

An earthquake of drums disturbs Rio de Janeiro's sleep. From the backwoods, by firelight, Exú mocks the rich, sending against them his deadly curses. Perfidious avenger of the have-nots, he lights up the night and darkens the day. If he throws a stone into a thicket, the thicket bleeds.

The god of the poor is also a devil. He has two heads: one, Jesus of Nazareth; the other, Satan of Hell. In Bahia he is a pesky messenger from the other world, a little second-class god; but in the slums of Rio he is the powerful master of midnight. Capable of caress or crime, Exú can save or kill, sometimes both at once.

He comes from the bowels of the earth, entering violently, destructively, through the soles of unshod feet. He is lent body and voice by men and women who dance with rats in shacks perilously suspended over the void, people whom Exú redeems with such craziness that they roll on the ground laughing themselves to death.

(255)

María Padilha

She is both Exú and one of his women, mirror and lover: María Padilha, the most whorish of the female devils with whom Exú likes to roll in the bonfires.

She is not hard to recognize when she enters the body. María Padilha shrieks, howls insults, laughs crudely, and at the end of a trance demands expensive drinks and imported cigarettes. She has to be treated like a great lady and passionately implored before she will deign to use her well-known influence with the most important gods and devils.

María Padilha doesn't enter just any body. To manifest herself in this world, she chooses the women of the Rio slums who make a livelihood selling themselves for small change. Thus do the despised become worthy of devotion. Hired flesh mounts to the center of the altar. The garbage of the night shines brighter than the sun.

1939: Rio de Janeiro
The Samba

Brazil is Brazilian and so is God, proclaims Ari Barroso in the very patriotic and danceable music that is becoming the heart of Rio's carnival.

But the tastier samba lyrics offered at the carnival, far from exalting the virtues of this tropical paradise, perversely eulogize the bohemian life and the misdeeds of free souls, damn poverty and the police, and scorn work. Work is for idiots, because anyone can see that the bricklayer can never enter what his hands erect.

The samba, black rhythm, offspring of the chants that convoke the black gods of the slums, now dominates the carnivals, even if in respectable homes it is still scorned. It invites distrust because it is black and poor and born in the refuges of people hunted by the police. But the samba quickens the feet and caresses the soul and there is no disregarding it once it strikes up. The universe breathes to the rhythms of the samba until Ash Wednesday in a fiesta that turns every proletarian into a king, every paralytic into an athlete, and every bore into a beautiful madman.

(74 and 285)

1939: Rio de Janeiro

The Scoundrel

most feared in Rio is called Madame Satan.

When the child was seven, the mother swapped it for a horse. Since then, it has passed from hand to hand, master to master, until it ended up in a brothel where it learned the craft of cooking and the pleasures of the bed. There it became a professional tough, protector of whores, male and female, and of all defenseless bohemians. Beaten often enough and hard enough by the police to send several men to the cemetery, this fierce black never gets past hospital or jail.

Madame Satan is a he from Monday to Friday, a panama-hatted devil who with fist and razor dominates the night in the Lapa barrio, where he strolls about whistling a samba and marking time with a box of matches; but on the weekends he is a she, the very harpy who has just won the carnival fancy-dress contest with the campiest golden-bat cape, who wears a ring on every finger and moves her hips like her friend Carmen Miranda.

(146)

1939: Rio de Janeiro

Cartola

On the Mangueira knoll, Cartola is the soul of samba, and of practically everything else.

Often he passes by in a flash, waving his pants like a flag, pursued by some intolerant husband. Between his sprees and flights, melodies and protestations of love float up inside him, to be hummed and quickly forgotten.

Cartola sells his sambas to anyone who comes along and for whatever pittance he can get. He is always amazed that there are people who will pay anything at all for them.

(428)

1939: Montserrat

Vallejo

Mortally wounded, the Spanish republic staggers its final few steps. Little breath remains to it as Franco's exterminating army pushes on.

In the abbey of Montserrat, by way of farewell, the militias publish verses that two Latin Americans have written in homage to Spain and its tragedy. The poems of the Chilean Pablo Neruda and the Peruvian Vallejo are printed on paper made from rags of uniforms, enemy flags, and bandages.

César Vallejo has just died, hurt and alone, like Spain. He died in Paris, a day he had foreseen and recorded, and his last poems, written between four menacing walls, were for Spain. Vallejo sang of the heroism of the Spanish people in arms, of Spain's independent spirit, its beloved sun, beloved shade; and Spain was the last word he spoke in his death agony, this American poet, this most American of poets.

(457)

1939: Washington

Roosevelt

When Franklin Delano Roosevelt became president, the United States had fifteen million workless workers looking around with the eyes of lost children, raising a thumb on the highways as they wandered from city to city, barefoot or with cardboard tops on leaky soles, using public urinals and railroad stations for hotels.

To save his nation, Roosevelt's first act was to put money in a cage: He closed all the banks until the way ahead was clear. Since then he has governed the economy without letting it govern him, and has consolidated a democracy threatened by the crisis.

With Latin American dictators, however, he gets along fine. Roosevelt protects them, as he protects Ford automobiles, Kelvinator refrigerators, and other products of the United States.

(276 and 304)

1939: Washington

In the Year Nine of the Trujillo Era

a twenty-one-gun salute welcomes him to West Point, where Trujillo cools himself with a perfumed ivory fan and salutes the cadets with flutters of his ostrich-plume hat. A plump delegation of bishops, generals, and courtiers accompanies him, as well as a doctor and a sorcerer, both specializing in eye problems, not to speak of Brigadier General Ramfis Trujillo, age nine, dragging a sword longer than himself.

General George Marshall offers Trujillo a banquet on board the *Mayflower* and President Roosevelt receives him in the White House. Legislators, governors, and journalists shower this exemplary statesman with praise. Trujillo, who pays cash for murders, acquires his eulogies likewise, and lists the disbursements under the heading "Birdseed" in the executive budget of the Dominican Republic.

(60 and 177)

1939: Washington

Somoza

Before the Marines made him a general and the supreme boss of Nicaragua, Anastasio Tacho Somoza had pursued a successful career forging gold coins and cheating at poker and love.

Now that all power is his, Sandino's murderer has turned the national budget into his private bank account and has personally taken over the country's richest lands. He has liquidated his lukewarm enemies by firing National Bank loans at them, while his warmer enemies have providentially ended up in accidents or ambushes.

Somoza's visit to the United States is no less triumphant than Trujillo's. President Roosevelt and several cabinet members appear at Union Station to welcome him. A military band plays the anthems of both countries, and a rumble of guns and speeches follows. Somoza announces that the main avenue of Managua, which crosses the city from lake to lake, will be renamed Roosevelt Avenue.

(102)

1939: New York

Superman

Action Comics celebrates the first anniversary of the successful launch of Superman.

This Hercules of our time guards private property in the universe. From a place called Metropolis, flying faster than the speed of light and breaking time barriers, he travels to other epochs and galaxies. Wherever he goes, in this world or others, Superman restores order more efficiently and quickly than the whole Marine Corps put together. With a glance he melts steel, with a kick he fells a forest of trees, with a punch he perforates mountain chains.

In his other personality, Superman is timid Clark Kent, as meek as any of his readers.

(147)

1941: New York

Portrait of an Opinion Maker

At first, few theaters dare to show *Citizen Kane*, the movie in which Orson Welles tells the story of a man sick with power fever, a man who too closely resembles William Randolph Hearst.

Hearst owns eighteen newspapers, nine magazines, seven castles, and quite a few people. He is expert at stirring up public opinion. In his long life he has provoked wars and bankruptcies, made and destroyed fortunes, created idols and demolished reputations. Among his best inventions are the scandal campaign and the gossip column, so good for what he likes to do best—land a solid punch well below the belt.

The most powerful fabricator of opinion in the United States thinks that the white race is the only really human race; believes in the necessary victory of the strongest; is convinced that Communists are to blame for alcohol consumption among the young; and that Japanese are born traitors.

When Japan bombs the naval base at Pearl Harbor, Hearst's newspapers have already been beating a steady warning rhythm for half a century about the Yellow Peril. The United States enters the World War.

(130 and 441)

1942: New York
The Red Cross Doesn't Accept Black Blood

U.S. soldiers embark for the war fronts. Many are black under the command of white officers.

Those who survive will return home. The blacks will enter by the back door, and, in the Southern states, continue to live, work, and die apart, and even then will lie in separate graves. Hooded Ku Klux Klansmen will still insure that blacks do not intrude into the white world, and above all into the bedrooms of white women.

The war accepts blacks, thousands and thousands of them, but not the Red Cross. The Red Cross bans black blood in the plasma banks, so as to avoid the possibility that races might mix by tranfusion.

The research of Charles Drew, inventor of life, has finally made it possible to save blood. Thanks to him, plasma banks are reviving thousands of dying men on the battlefields of Europe.

When the Red Cross decides to reject the blood of blacks, Drew, director of the Red Cross plasma service, resigns. Drew is black.

(51, 218, and 262)

1942: Oxford, Mississippi
Faulkner

Seated on a rocker, on the columned porch of a decaying mansion, William Faulkner smokes his pipe and listens to the whispered confidences of ghosts.

The plantation masters tell Faulkner of their glories and their dreads. Nothing horrifies them like miscegenation. A drop of black blood, even one tiny drop, curses a whole life and ensures, after death, the fires of hell. The old Southern dynasties, born of crime and condemned to crime, watch anxiously over the pale splendor of their own twilight, affronted by the shadow of blackness, the slightest hint of blackness. These gentlemen would love to believe that purity of lineage will not die out, though its memory may fade and the trumpets of the horsemen defeated by Lincoln echo no more.

(163 and 247)

1942: Hollywood
Brecht

Hollywood manufactures films to turn the frightful vigil of humanity, on the point of annihilation, into sweet dreams. Bertolt Brecht, exiled from Hitler's Germany, is employed in this sleeping-pill industry. Founder of a theater that sought to open eyes wide, he earns his living at the United Artists studios, just one more writer who works office hours for Hollywood, competing to produce the biggest daily ration of idiocies.

On one of these days, Brecht buys a little God of Luck for forty cents in a Chinese store and puts it on his desk. Brecht has been told that the God of Luck licks his lips each time they make him take poison.

(66)

1942: Hollywood
The Good Neighbors to the South

accompany the United States into the World War. It is the time of *democratic prices*: Latin American countries supply cheap raw materials, cheap food, and a soldier or two.

The movies glorify the common cause. Rarely missing from a film is the South American number, sung and danced in Spanish or Portuguese. Donald Duck acquires a Brazilian sidekick, the little parrot José Carioca. On Pacific islands or in the fields of Europe, Hollywood Adonises wipe out Japanese and Germans by the heap. And how many Adonises have at their sides a simpatico, indolent, somewhat stupid Latin, who admires his blond northern brother and serves as his echo and shadow, faithful henchman, merry minstrel, messenger, and cook?

(467)

1942: María Barzola Pampa
A Latin American Method for Reducing Production Costs

Bolivia—subsisting, as ever, on hunger rations—is one of the countries that pays for the World War by selling its tin at a tenth of the normal price.

The mine workers finance this bargain price. Their wages go from almost nothing to nothing at all. And when a government decree calls for forced labor at gunpoint, the strikes begin. Another decree bans the strikes, but fails to stop them. So the president, Enrique Peñaranda, orders the army to take *severe and energetic* action. Patiño, king of the mines, issues his own orders: *Proceed without vacillation*. His viceroys, Aramayo and Hochschild, approve. The machineguns spit fire for hours and leave the ground strewn with people.

Patiño Mines pays for some coffins, but saves on indemnities. Death by machinegun is not an occupational hazard.

(97 and 474)

1943: Sans-Souci
Carpentier

Alejo Carpentier discovers the kingdom of Henri Christophe. The Cuban writer roams these majestic ruins, this memorial to the delirium of a slave cook who became monarch of Haiti and killed himself with the gold bullet that always hung around his neck. Ceremonial hymns and magic drums of invocation rise up to meet Carpentier as he visits the palace that King Christophe copied from Versailles, and walks around his invulnerable fortress, an immense bulk whose stones, cemented by the blood of bulls sacrificed to the gods, have resisted lightning and earthquakes.

In Haiti, Carpentier learns that there is no magic more prodigious and delightful than the voyage that leads through experience, through the body, to the depths of America. In Europe, magicians have become bureaucrats, and wonder, exhausted, has dwindled to a conjuring trick. But in America, surrealism is as natural as rain or madness.

(85)

1943: Port-au-Prince
Hands That Don't Lie

Dewitt Peters founds an open workshop and from it suddenly explodes Haitian art. Everybody paints everything: cloth, cardboard, cans, wooden boards, walls, whatever presents itself. They paint in a great outburst of splendor, with the seven souls of the rainbow. Everyone: the shoe repairman and fisherman, river washerwoman and market-stall holder. In America's poorest country, wrung out by Europe, invaded by the United States, torn apart by wars and dictatorships, the people shout colors and no one can shut them up.

(122, 142, and 385)

1943: Mount Rouis
A Little Grain of Salt

In a bar, surrounded by kids with bloated bellies and skeletal dogs, Hector Hyppolite paints gods with a brush of hens' feathers. Saint John the Baptist turns up in the evenings and helps him.

Hyppolite portrays the gods who paint through his hand. These Haitian gods, painted and painters, live simultaneously on earth and in heaven and hell: Capable of good and evil, they offer their children vengeance and solace.

Not all have come from Africa. Some were born here, like Baron Samedi, god of solemn stride, master of poisons and graves, his blackness enhanced by top hat and cane. That poison should kill and the dead rest in peace depends upon Baron Samedi. He turns many dead into zombies and condemns them to slave labor.

Zombies—dead people who walk or live ones who have lost their souls—have a look of hopeless stupidity. But in no time they can escape and recover their lost lives, their stolen souls. One little grain of salt is enough to awaken them. And how could salt be lacking in

the home of the slaves who defeated Napoleon and founded freedom
in America?

(146, 233, and 295)

1944: New York

Learning to See

It is noon and James Baldwin is walking with a friend through the
streets of downtown Manhattan. A red light stops them.

"*Look*," says the friend, pointing at the ground.

Baldwin looks. He sees nothing.

"*Look, look.*"

Nothing. There is nothing to look at but a filthy little pool of
water against the curb.

His friend insists: "*See? Are you seeing?*"

And then Baldwin takes a good look and this time he sees, sees
a spot of oil spreading in the pool. Then, in the spot of oil, a rainbow,
and even deeper down in the pool, the street moving, and people
moving in the street: the shipwrecked, the madmen, the magicians,
the whole world moving, an astounding world full of worlds that glow
in the world. Baldwin sees. For the first time in his life, he sees.

(152)

1945: The Guatemala–El Salvador Border

Miguel at Forty

He sleeps in caves and cemeteries. Condemned by hunger to constant
hiccups, he competes with the magpies for scraps. His sister, who
meets him from time to time, says: "*God has given you many talents,
but he has punished you by making you a Communist.*"

Since Miguel recovered his party's confidence, the running and
suffering have only increased. Now the party has decided that its
most sacrificed member must go into exile in Guatemala.

Miguel manages to cross the border after a thousand hassles and
dangers. It is deepest night. He stretches out, exhausted, under a
tree. At daybreak, an enormous yellow cow wakens him by licking
his feet.

"*Good morning*," Miguel says, and the cow, frightened, runs off at full tilt, into the forest, lowing. From the forest promptly emerge five vengeful bulls. There is no escape. Behind Miguel is an abyss and the tree at his back has a smooth trunk. The bulls charge, then stop dead and stand staring, panting, breathing fire and smoke, tossing their horns and pawing the ground, tearing up undergrowth and raising the dust.

Miguel trembles in a cold sweat. Tongue-tied with panic, he stammers an explanation. The bulls stare at him, a little man half hunger and half fear, and look at each other. He commends himself to Marx and Saint Francis of Assisi as the bulls slowly turn their backs on him and wander off, heads shaking.

And so occurs the ninth birth of Miguel Mármol, at forty years of age.

(126)

1945: Hiroshima and Nagasaki

A Sun of Fire,

a violent light never before seen in the world, rises slowly, cracks the sky open, and collapses. Three days later, a second sun of suns bursts over Japan. Beneath remain the cinders of two cities, a desert of rubble, tens of thousands dead and more thousands condemned to die little by little for years to come.

The war was nearly over, Hitler and Mussolini gone, when President Harry Truman gave the order to drop atomic bombs on the populations of Hiroshima and Nagasaki. In the United States, it is the culmination of a national clamor for the prompt annihilation of the Yellow Peril. It is high time to finish off once and for all the imperial conceits of this arrogant Asian country, never colonized by anyone. The only good one is a dead one, says the press of these treacherous little monkeys.

Now all doubt is dispelled. There is one great conqueror among the conquerors. The United States emerges from the war intact and more powerful than ever. It acts as if the whole world were its trophy.

(140 and 276)

1945: Princeton

Einstein

Albert Einstein feels as if his own hand had pressed the button. Although he didn't make it, the atomic bomb would not have been possible without his discoveries about the liberation of energy. Now Einstein would like to have been someone else, to have devoted himself to some inoffensive task like fixing drains or building walls instead of investigating the secrets of life that others now use to destroy it.

When he was a boy, a professor said to him: *"You'll never amount to anything."*

Daydreaming, with the expression of someone on the moon, he wondered how light would look to a person able to ride on a beam. When he became a man, he found the answer in the theory of relativity, won a Nobel Prize, and deserved many more for his answers to other questions born in his mind of the mysterious link between Mozart's sonatas and the theorem of Pythagoras, or of the defiant arabesques that the smoke from his extra-long pipe drew in the air.

Einstein believed that science was a way of revealing the beauty of the universe. The most famous of sages has the saddest eyes in human history.

(150 and 228)

1945: Buenos Aires

Perón

General MacArthur takes charge of the Japanese, and Spruille Braden of the Argentines. To lead Argentina down the good road to Democracy, U.S. ambassador Braden brings together all the parties, Conservative to Communist, in a united front against Juan Domingo Perón. According to the State Department, Colonel Perón, the government's minister of labor, is the chief of a gang of Nazis. *Look* magazine calls him a pervert who keeps photos of nude Patagonian Indian women in his desk drawer along with pictures of Hitler and Mussolini.

Nonetheless, Perón flies swiftly along the road to the presidency with Evita, the radio actress with the feverish eyes and enticing voice;

and when he gets tired, or doubtful, or scared, it is she who takes
the bit in her teeth. Perón now attracts more people than all the
parties put together. When they call him "agitator," he accepts the
epithet as an honor. VIPs and the fashionably chic chant the name
of Ambassador Braden on the street corners of Buenos Aires, waving
hats and handkerchiefs; but in worker barrios, the shirtless shout the
name Perón. These laboring people, exiles in their own land, dumb
from so much shutting up, find both a fatherland and a voice in this
unusual minister who always takes their side.

Perón's popularity climbs and climbs as he shakes the dust off
forgotten social laws or creates new ones. His is the law that compels
respect for the rights of those who break their backs on estancias and
plantations. The law does not merely remain on paper; thus the country peon, almost a thing, becomes a rural worker complete with a
trade union.

(311 and 327)

1945: The Fields of Tucumán
The Familiar

flies into a rage over these novelties that disturb his dominions. Workers' unions infuriate and scare him more than the hilt of a knife.

On the sugarcane plantations of northern Argentina, the Familiar
is responsible for the obedience of the peons. If one answers back or
acts impertinently, the Familiar devours him in a single gulp. He
moves with a clank of chains and stinks of sulphur, but no one knows
if he is the devil in person or just an official. Only his victims have
seen him, and no one seems able to add up the accounts. It is rumored
that at night the Familiar turns into an enormous snake and patrols
the sheds where the peons sleep, or that he crouches in wait on the
roads in the form of a dog with flaming eyes, all black, with huge
teeth and claws.

(103 and 328)

A Wake for a Little Angel

In the northern provinces of Argentina, they don't weep for the death of small children. One less mouth on earth, one more angel in heaven. Death is drunk and dances from the first cock-crow, sucking in long draughts of carob-bean liquor and *chicha* to the rhythm of bass drum and guitar. While the dancers whirl and stomp their feet, the child is passed from arm to arm. Once the child has been well rocked and fully celebrated, everyone breaks into song to start it on its flight to Paradise. There goes the little traveler, clothed in its Sunday best, as the song swells; and they bid it farewell, setting off fireworks, taking great care not to burn its wings.

(104)

1945: The Fields of Tucumán
Yupanqui

He has the stony face of an Indian who stares impassively at the mountain that stares back at him, but he comes from the plains of the south, from the echoless pampa that hides nothing, this gaucho singer of the mysteries of the Argentine north. He comes on a horse, stopping anyplace, with anyone, at the whim of the road. To continue his journey he sings, singing what he has traveled, Atahualpa Yupanqui. And he sings to keep history going, because the history of the poor is either sung or lost as well he knows, he who is left-handed on the guitar and in his thinking about the world.

(202, 270, and 472)

1946: La Paz
The Rosca

At the summit there are three; at the foot of the mountain three million. The mountain is tin and is called Bolivia.

The three at the summit form the *rosca*: Simón Patiño in the center; on one side, Carlos Aramayo; on the other, Mauricio Hochschild. Half a century ago, Patiño was a down-and-out miner, but a fairy touched him with her magic wand and turned him into one of the world's richest men. Now he wears a vest with a gold chain, and kings and presidents sit at his table. Aramayo comes from the local aristocracy, Hochschild, from the airplane that brought him to Bolivia. Each of them has more money than the state.

All that the tin earns remains outside Bolivia. To avoid taxes, Patiño's headquarters are in the United States, Aramayo's in Switzerland, and Hochschild's in Chile. Patiño pays Bolivia fifty dollars a year in income tax, Aramayo twenty-two, Hochschild nothing. Of every two children born at the *rosca*'s mines, one doesn't survive.

Each member of the *rosca* has at his disposal a newspaper and various ministers and legislators. It is traditional for the foreign minister to receive a monthly salary from Patiño Mines. But now that President Gualberto Villarroel suggests the *rosca* pay taxes and salaries that are not merely symbolic, what is there to do but hatch a plot?

(97)

1946: La Paz
Villarroel

President Villarroel does not defend himself. He abandons himself to fate—as if it were a matter of fate.

He is attacked by paid gunmen followed by a great motley crowd of godly women and students. Brandishing torches, black flags, and bloody sheets, the insurgents invade the government palace, throw Villarroel off a balcony, then hang what's left of him, naked, from a lamppost.

Besides defying the *rosca*, Villarroel had wanted to give equal rights to whites and Indians, wives and lovers, legitimate and illegitimate children.

The world cheers the crime. The leaders of democracy commend the liquidation of a tyrant in the pay of Hitler, who with unpardonable insolence sought to raise the rock-bottom price of tin. And in Bolivia, a country that never stops toiling for its own misfortune, the fall of what is and the restoration of what was is wildly celebrated: happy days for the League of Morality, the Association of Mothers of Priests, the War Widows, the U.S. embassy, every complexion of rightist, nearly all of the left—left of the left of the moon!—and the *rosca*.

(97)

1946: Hollywood

Carmen Miranda

Sequined and dripping with necklaces, crowned by a tower of bananas, Carmen Miranda undulates against a cardboard tropical backdrop.

Born in Portugal, daughter of a penurious barber who crossed the ocean, Carmen is the chief export of Brazil. Next comes coffee.

This diminutive hussy has little voice, and what she has is out of tune, but she sings with her hands and with her gleaming eyes, and that is more than enough. She is one of the best-paid performers in Hollywood. She has ten houses and eight oil wells.

But Fox refuses to renew her contract. Senator Joseph McCarthy has called her obscene, because at the peak of one of her production numbers, a photographer revealed intolerable glimpses of bare flesh and who knows what else under her flying skirt. And the press has disclosed that in her tenderest infancy Carmen recited lines before King Albert of Belgium, accompanying them with wiggles and winks that scandalized the nuns and gave the king prolonged insomnia.

(401)

1948: Bogotá

On the Eve

In placid Bogotá, home of monks and jurists, General Marshall sits down with the foreign ministers of Latin America.

What gifts does he bring in his saddlebags, this Wise King of the Occident who irrigates with dollars the European lands devastated by the war? General Marshall, impassive, microphones stuck to his chest, resists the downpour of speeches. Without moving so much as an eyelid, he endures the protracted professions of democratic faith offered by many Latin American delegates anxious to sell themselves for the price of a dead rooster; while John McCloy, head of the World Bank, warns: *"I'm sorry, gentlemen, but I didn't bring my checkbook in my suitcase."*

Beyond the salons of the Ninth Pan-American Conference, even more florid speeches shower down throughout the length and breadth of the host country. Learned liberals announce that they will bring peace to Colombia *as the goddess Pallas Athena made the olive branch blossom on the hills of Athens*, and erudite conservatives promise *to draw unknown forces into the sunshine, and light up with the dark fire that is the entrails of the globe the timid votive light of the candelabra that is lit on the eve of treachery in the night of darkness*.

While foreign ministers clamor, proclaim, and declaim, reality persists. In the Colombian countryside the war between conservatives and liberals is fought with guns. Politicians provide the words, campesinos provide the corpses. And already the violence is filtering into Bogotá, knocking at the capital's doors and threatening its time-honored routines—always the same sins, always the same metaphors. At the bullfights last Sunday, the desperate crowd poured into the arena and tore to pieces a wretched bull that refused to fight.

(7)

1948: Bogotá
Gaitán

The political country, says Jorge Eliécer Gaitán, *has nothing to do with the national country*. Gaitán, head of the Liberal Party, is also its black sheep. Poor people of all persuasions adore him. *What is the difference between liberal hunger and conservative hunger? Malaria is neither conservative nor liberal!*

Gaitán's voice unbinds the poor who cry out through his mouth. He turns fear on its back. They come from everywhere to hear him— to hear themselves—the ragged ones, trekking through the jungle, spurring their horses down the roads. They say that when Gaitán speaks the fog splits in Bogotá; and that even in heaven Saint Peter listens and forbids the rain to fall on the gigantic crowds gathered by torchlight.

This dignified leader, with the austere face of a statue, does not hesitate to denounce the oligarchy and the imperial ventriloquist on whose knee the oligarchs sit without life of their own or words of their own. He calls for agrarian reform and articulates other truths to put an end to the long lie.

If they don't kill him, Gaitán will be Colombia's next president. He cannot be bought. To what temptation would he succumb, this man who scorns pleasure, sleeps alone, eats little, drinks nothing, and even refuses anesthesia when he has a tooth pulled?

(7)

1948: Bogotá
The *Bogotazo*

At 2:00 P.M. of this ninth of April, Gaitán has a date with one of the Latin American students who are gathering in Bogotá on the fringes of General Marshall's Pan-American ceremony.

At half past one, the student leaves his hotel, intending to stroll to Gaitán's office. But after a few steps a noise like an earthquake stops him, a human avalanche engulfs him. The people, pouring out of the barrios, streaming down from the hills, are rushing madly past him, a hurricane of pain and anger flooding the city, smashing store windows, overturning streetcars, setting buildings afire.

They've killed him! They've killed him!

It was done in the streets, with three bullets. Gaitán's watch stopped at 1:05 P.M.

The student, a corpulent Cuban named Fidel Castro, shoves his cap on his head and lets himself be blown along by the wind of people.

(7)

1948: Bogotá
Flames

Indian ponchos and workers' sandals invade the center of Bogotá, hands toughened by earth or stone, hands stained with machine oil or shoe polish, a tornado of porters, students, and waiters, washerwomen and market women, Jills of all beds and Jacks of all trades, ambulance chasers and fortune hunters. From the tornado a woman detaches herself, wearing four fur coats, clumsy and happy as a bear in love; running like a rabbit is a man with several pearl necklaces around his throat; walking like a tortoise, another with a refrigerator on his back.

At street corners, ragged kids direct traffic. Prisoners burst the bars of their cells. Someone cuts the fire hoses with a machete. Bogotá is an immense bonfire, the sky a vault of red; from the balconies of burning ministries typewriters plummet; from burning belltowers bullets rain. The police hide themselves or cross their arms before the fury.

At the presidential palace, a river of people is seen approaching. Machineguns have already repelled two of these attacks, although the crowd did succeed in hurling against the palace doors the disemboweled body of the puppet who killed Gaitán.

Doña Bertha, the first lady, sticks a revolver in her waistband and calls her confessor on the telephone: *"Father, be so good as to take my son to the American embassy."*

On another phone the president, Mariano Ospina Pérez, sees to the protection of General Marshall's house and dictates orders against the rebellious rabble. Then he sits and waits. The tumult grows in the streets.

Three tanks head the attack on the presidential palace. The tanks are swarming with people waving flags and yelling Gaitán's name, and behind them surges a multitude bristling with machetes, axes, and clubs. When they reach the palace the tanks halt. Their turrets turn slowly, aim to the rear, and commence mowing people down.

(7)

1948: Bogotá

Ashes

Someone wanders in search of a shoe. A woman howls, a dead child in her arms. The city smolders. Walk carefully or you'll step on bodies. A dismembered mannequin hangs on the streetcar cables. From the stairway of a burned monastery a naked, blackened Christ gazes skyward, arms outstretched. At the foot of that stairway, a beggar sits and drinks. The archbishop's mitre covers his head and a purple velvet curtain envelops his body. He further defends himself from the cold by sipping French cognac from a gold chalice, and offers drinks to passersby in a silver goblet. An army bullet ends the party.

The last shots ring out. The city, devastated by fire, regains order. After three days of vengeance and madness, a disarmed people returns to the old purgatory of work and woe.

General Marshall has no doubts. The *bogotazo* was the work of

Moscow. The government of Colombia breaks relations with the Soviet Union.

(7)

1948: Upar Valley
The *Vallenato*

"I want to let out a yell and they won't let me . . ."

The government of Colombia prohibits the "Vagabond Yell."
Whoever sings it risks jail or a bullet. Along the Magdalena River,
though, they keep singing.

The people of the Colombian coast defend themselves by making
music. The "Vagabond Yell" is a *vallenato* rhythm, one of the cowboy
songs that tell the story of the region and, incidentally, fill the air
with joy.

Accordion to breast, the troubadours prance and navigate. Accordion on thigh, they receive the first drinks at all parties and challenge each other to a duel of couplets.

The *vallenato* verses born of accordions thrust back and forth
like knives, like fusillades in daring musical battles that last for days
and nights in markets and cockfight rings. The singers' most fearsome
rival is Lucifer, that great musician, who gets bored in hell and comes
to America at the drop of a hat, disguised, looking for fun.

(359)

1948: Wroclaw
Picasso

This painter embodies the best painters of all times. They cohabit in
him, if rather uncomfortably. It is no easy task to assimilate such
intractable folk, ancient and modern, who spend so much time in
conflict with one another that the painter hasn't a free moment to
listen to speeches, much less make them.

But for the first and only time in his life, Pablo Picasso makes a
speech. This unheard-of event occurs in the Polish city of Wroclaw,
at a world congress of intellectuals for peace: *"I have a friend who
ought to be here . . ."*

Picasso pays homage to *the greatest poet of the Spanish language*

and one of the greatest poets on earth, who has always taken the side
of the unfortunate: Pablo Neruda, persecuted by the police in Chile,
cornered like a dog . . .

(442)

1948: Somewhere in Chile
Neruda

The main headline in the daily *El Imparcial* reads: *Neruda Sought*
Throughout the Country; and below: *Investigators locating his where-*
abouts will be rewarded.

The poet goes from hideout to hideout, traveling by night. Neruda is one of many suffering persecution for being red or for being
decent or for just being, and he doesn't complain of this fate, which
he has chosen. Nor does he regret the solitude: He enjoys and celebrates this fighting passion, whatever trouble it brings him, as he
enjoys and celebrates church bells, wine, eel broth, and flying comets
with wings spreads wide.

(313 and 442)

1948: San José de Costa Rica
Figueres

After six weeks of civil war, and two thousand dead, the rural middle
class comes to power in Costa Rica.

The head of the new government, José Figueres, outlaws the
Communist Party and promises *unconditional support to the struggle*
of the free world against Russian imperialism. But in an undertone
he also promises to continue to expand the social reforms the Communists have promoted in recent years.

Under the protection of President Rafael Calderón, friend of the
Communists, unions and cooperatives have multiplied in Costa Rica;
small landowners have won land from the great estates; health has
been improved and education extended.

The anticommunist Figueres does not touch the lands of the
United Fruit Company, that most powerful mistress, but nationalizes
the banks and dissolves the army, so that money will not speculate,

nor arms conspire. Costa Rica wants out of the ferocious turbulence of Central America.

(42, 243, 414, and 438)

1949: Washington
The Chinese Revolution

Between yesterday and tomorrow, an abyss. The Chinese revolution springs into the air and leaps the gap.

The news from Peking provokes anger and fear in Washington. After their long march of armed poverty, Mao's reds have triumphed. General Chiang Kai-shek flees. The United States enthrones him on the island of Formosa.

The parks in China had been forbidden to dogs and the poor, and beggars still froze to death in the early mornings, as in the old days of the mandarins; but it was not from Peking that the orders came. It was not the Chinese who named their ministers and generals, wrote their laws and decrees, and fixed their tariffs and salaries. By a geographical error, China was not in the Caribbean.

(156 and 291)

1949: Havana
Radio Theater

"Don't kill me," pleads the actor to the author.

Onelio Jorge Cardoso had had it in mind to polish off Captain Hook in the next episode; but if the character dies of a sword-thrust on the pirate ship, the actor dies of hunger in the street. The author, a good friend of the actor, promises him eternal life.

Onelio devises breathtaking adventures, but his radio plays enjoy little success.

He doesn't pour it on thick enough, he doesn't know how to wring hearts out like laundry—to the last drop. José Sánchez Arcilla, by contrast, touches the most intimate fibers. In his serial "The Necklace of Tears," the characters struggle against perverse destiny in nine hundred and sixty-five episodes that bathe the audience in tears.

But the greatest success of all time is "The Right to Be Born," by Felix B. Caignet. Nothing like it has ever been heard in Cuba or anywhere else. At the scheduled nighttime hour, it alone gets a hearing, a unanimous Mass. Movies are interrupted, streets empty, lovers suspend their dalliances, cocks quit fighting, and even flies alight for the duration.

For seventy-four episodes, all Cuba has been waiting for Don Rafael del Junco to speak. This character possesses The Secret. But not only is he totally paralyzed, he lost his voice in episode 197. We've now made it to episode 271 and Don Rafael still can only clear his throat. When will he manage to reveal The Truth to the good woman who sinned but once, succumbing to Mad Passion's call? When will he have the voice to tell her that Albertico Limonta, her doctor, is really the fruit of that same illicit love, the baby she abandoned soon after birth into the hands of a black woman with a white soul? When, oh, when?

The public, dying of suspense, does not know that Don Rafael is on a silence strike. This cruel silence will continue until the actor who plays Don Rafael del Junco gets the raise he has been demanding for two and a half months.

(266)

1950: Rio de Janeiro
Obdulio

Although the dice are loaded against him, Obdulio steps firmly and kicks. The captain of the Uruguayans, this commanding, muscular black man does not lose heart. The more the hostile multitude roars from the stands, the more Obdulio grows.

Surprise and sorrow in Maracaná Stadium: Brazil, the great, pulverizing, goal-scoring machine, the favorite all along, loses this last match at the last minute. Uruguay, playing for its life, wins the world football championship.

That night Obdulio Varela flees from his hotel, besieged by journalists, fans, and the curious. Preferring to celebrate alone, he goes looking for a drink in some remote dive or other, but everywhere meets weeping Brazilians.

"Obedulio is giving us the game," they were chanting in the stadium just hours ago, midway through the match. Now, bathed in tears, the same people cry, *"It was all Obedulio's fault."*

And Obdulio, having so recently disliked them, is stunned to see them individually. The victory begins to weigh on him. He has ruined the party of these good folk and begins to wonder if he shouldn't beg their pardon for the tremendous sin of winning. So he keeps on wandering the Rio streets, from bar to bar. Dawn finds him still drinking, embracing the vanquished.

(131 and 191)

1950: Hollywood
Rita

Changing her name, weight, age, voice, lips, and eyebrows, she conquered Hollywood. Her hair was transformed from dull black into flaming red. To broaden her brow, they removed hair after hair by painful electrolysis. Over her eyes they put lashes like petals.

Rita Hayworth disguised herself as a goddess, and perhaps was one—for the forties, anyway. Now, the fifties demand something new.

(249)

1950: Hollywood
Marilyn

Like Rita, this girl has been improved. She had thick eyelashes and a double chin, a nose round at the tip, and large teeth. Hollywood reduced the fat, suppressed the cartilage, filed the teeth, and turned the mousy chestnut hair into a cascade of gleaming gold. Then the technicians baptized her Marilyn Monroe and invented a pathetic childhood story for her to tell the journalists.

This new Venus manufactured in Hollywood no longer needs to climb into strange beds seeking contracts for second-rate roles in third-rate films. She no longer lives on hot dogs and coffee, or suffers the cold of winter. Now she is a star; or rather a small personage in a mask who would like to remember, but cannot, that moment when she simply wanted to be saved from loneliness.

(214 and 274)

1951: Mexico City
Buñuel

Stones rain upon Luis Buñuel. Most of the newspapers and press syndicates insist that Mexico expel this Spanish ingrate who repays favors with infamy. The film that arouses national indignation, *Los Olvidados*, depicts the slums of Mexico City. Adolescents who live hand to mouth in this horrendous underworld eat whatever they find, including each other, with garbage heaps for their playground. They peck each other to pieces, bit by bit, these baby vultures, and so fulfill the dark destiny their city has chosen for them.

A mysterious resonance, a strange force, echoes in Buñuel's films. Some long, deep roll of drums, perhaps the drums of his infancy in Calanda, make the earth tremble, even if the sound track registers no noise, and the world simulates silence and forgiveness.

(70 and 71)

1952: San Fernando Hill
Sick unto Death

is Colombia since Gaitán was murdered on that Bogotá street. In mountains and plains, frozen prairies and steamy valleys—everywhere—campesinos kill each other, poor against poor, all against all. A tornado of vendettas and vengeance allows Blackblood, the Claw, Tarzan, Tough Luck, the Roach, and other artists of butchery to excel at their chosen trade, but more ferocious crimes are committed by the forces of order. The Tolima Battalion kills fifteen hundred, not counting rapes or mutilations, in its sweep of the area from Pantamillo to San Fernando Hill. To leave no seed from which the future might grow, soldiers toss children aloft and run them through with bayonet or machete.

"Don't bring me stories," say those who give the orders, *"bring me ears."*

Campesinos who manage to escape seek protection deep in the mountains, leaving their smoking shacks in cinders behind them. Before leaving, in a sad ceremony they kill the dog, because he makes noise.

(217, 227, and 408)

1952: La Paz

El Illimani

Though you can't see him, he watches you. Hide where you like, he watches over you. No cranny escapes him. The capital of Bolivia belongs to him, although they don't know it, the gentlemen who till last night thought themselves masters of these houses, these people.

El Illimani, proud king, washes himself with mist. At his feet, the city begins its day. Campfires die out, the last machinegun volleys are heard. The yellow hats of miners overwhelm the military caps. An army that has never won against those outside nor lost against those within, collapses. People dance on any street corner. Handkerchiefs flutter, braids and multilayered skirts undulate to the beat of the *cueca*.

In the absolute blueness of the sky gleams El Illimani's crown of three peaks: From the snowy summits the gods contemplate the happiness of their children in arms, at the end of this endless foot-by-foot struggle through the back streets.

(17, 172, and 473)

1952: La Paz

Drum of the People

that beats and rolls and rolls again, vengeance of the Indian who sleeps in the yard like a dog and greets the master with bended knee: The army of the underdogs fought with homemade bombs and sticks of dynamite until, finally, the arsenal of the military fell into their hands.

Víctor Paz Estenssoro promises that from this day Bolivia will be for all Bolivians. By the mines the workers fly the national flag at half-mast, where it will stay until the new president fulfills his promise to nationalize tin. In London they see it coming: As if by magic, the price of tin falls by two-thirds.

On the Pairumani estate, Indians roast on a grill the prize bulls Patiño imported from Holland.

Aramayo's tennis courts, surfaced with brick dust from England, are turned into mule corrals.

(17, 172, and 473)

A Woman of the Bolivian Mines Gives the Recipe for a Homemade Bomb

Look for a little milk can. Put the dynamite right in the middle, a capsule. Then, bits of iron, slag, a little dirt. Add glass and small nails. Then cover it up good. Like this, see? You light it right there and—shsss!—throw it. If you have a sling you can throw it farther. My husband can throw from here to six blocks away. For that you put in a longer wick.

(268)

1952: *Cochabamba*
Cries of Mockery and Grievance

All over the Bolivian countryside times are changing: a vast insurgency against the large estates and against fear. In the Cochabamba valley, the women too hurl their defiance, singing and dancing.

At ceremonies of homage to the Christ of the Holy Cross, Quechua campesinos from the whole valley light candles, drink *chicha*, sing ballads, and cavort to the sound of accordions and charangos, around the Crucified One.

The young girls implore Christ for a husband who won't make them cry, for a mule loaded with corn, a white sheep and a black sheep, a sewing machine, or as many rings as their hands have fingers. Afterward they sing stridently, always in the Indian language, their protest. To Christ, to father, to boyfriend and to husband they promise love and service, at table as well as in bed, but they don't want to be battered beasts of burden anymore.

Singing, they shoot bullets of mockery at the bull's eye of the naked macho, well ravaged by years and insects, who sleeps or pretends to sleep on the cross.

(5)

Shameless Verses Sung by Indian Women
of Cochabamba to Jesus Christ

Little Father, to your flock,
"Daughter, daughter," you keep saying.
But how could you have fathered me
When you haven't got a cock?

"Lazy, lazy," you're reproving,
Little Father, Holy Cross,
But limp and lazy—look at you:
Standing up there, never moving.

Little fox with tail all curls,
Beady eyes on women spying,
Little old man with mousey face
And your nose so full of holes.

You won't put up with me unwed,
You condemn me to bear kids,
Dress and feed them while alive,
Bury them proper when they're dead.

Will you send to me a mate
Who would give me blows and kicks?
Why must every budding rose
Suffer the same wilted fate?

(5)

1952: Buenos Aires
The Argentine People Feel Naked
Without Her

Long live cancer! wrote some hand on a wall in Buenos Aires. They
hated her, they hate her, the well-fed—for being poor, a woman, and
presumptuous. She challenged them in talk and offended them in
life. Born to be a servant, or at best an actress in cheap melodramas,
Evita refused to memorize her part.

They loved her, they love her, the unloved—through her mouth they spoke their minds and their curses. Evita was the blonde fairy who embraced the leprous and ragged and gave peace to the despairing, a bottomless spring that gushed jobs and mattresses, shoes and sewing machines, false teeth and bridal trousseaux. The poor received these charities at a side door, while Evita wore stunning jewelry and mink coats in midsummer. Not that they begrudged her the luxury: They celebrated it. They felt not humiliated but avenged by her queenly attire.

Before the body of Evita, surrounded by white carnations, people file by, weeping. Day after day, night after night, the line of torches: a procession two weeks long.

Bankers, businessmen, and landowners sigh with relief. With Evita dead, President Perón is a knife without a cutting edge.

(311 and 417)

1952: On the High Seas
Wanted: Charlie the Tramp

Charles Chaplin sails for London. On the second day at sea, news reaches the ship that he won't be able to return to the United States. The attorney general applies to his case a law aimed at foreigners suspected of communism, depravity, or insanity.

Some years earlier Chaplin had been interrogated by officials of the FBI and the Immigration and Naturalization Service:

Are you of Jewish origin?

Are you a Communist?

Have you ever committed adultery?

Senator Richard Nixon and the gossip columnist Hedda Hopper agree: *Chaplin is a menace to our institutions.* Outside theaters showing his films, the Legion of Decency and the American Legion picket with signs demanding: *Chaplin, go to Russia.*

The FBI has for nearly thirty years been seeking proof that Chaplin is really a Jew named Israel Thonstein and that he works as a spy for Moscow. Their suspicions were aroused in 1923 when *Pravda* printed the comment: *Chaplin is an actor of undoubted talent.*

(121 and 383)

1952: London

An Admirable Ghost

named Buster Keaton has returned to the screen after long years of oblivion, thanks to Chaplin. *Limelight* opens in London, and in it for a few precious minutes Keaton teams up with Chaplin in an absurd double act that steals the show.

This is the first time Keaton and Chaplin have worked together. They appear gray-haired and wrinkled, though with the same charm as in those moments long ago, when they made silence wittier than words.

Chaplin and Keaton are still the best. They know that there is nothing more serious than laughter, an art demanding infinite work, and that as long as the world revolves, making others laugh is the most splendid of activities.

(382 and 383)

1953: Washington

Newsreel

The United States explodes the first H-bomb at Eniwetok.

President Eisenhower names Charles Wilson secretary of defense. Wilson, an executive of General Motors, has recently declared: *What's good for General Motors is good for America.*

After a long trial, Ethel and Julius Rosenberg are executed in the electric chair. The Rosenbergs, accused of spying for the Russians, deny guilt to the end.

The American city of Moscow exhorts its Russian namesake to change its name. The authorities of this small city in Idaho claim the exclusive right to call themselves Muscovites, and ask that the Soviet capital be rebaptized *to avoid any embarrassing associations.*

Half the citizens of the United States decisively support Senator McCarthy's campaign against the Communist infiltration of democracy, according to opinion polls.

One of the suspects McCarthy plans to interrogate, engineer Raymond Kaplan, commits suicide by throwing himself under a truck.

The scientist Albert Einstein appeals to intellectuals to refuse to testify before the House Un-American Activities Committee and to be prepared for jail or economic ruin. Failing this, believes Einstein, *the intellectuals deserve nothing better than the slavery which is intended for them.*

(45)

1953: Washington
The Witch Hunt

Incorrigible Albert Einstein, according to Senator McCarthy's list, is America's foremost *fellow traveler*. To get on the list, all you need to do is have black friends or oppose sending U.S. troops to Korea; but the case of Einstein is a much weightier one. McCarthy has proof to spare that this ungrateful Jew has a heart that tilts left and pumps red blood.

The hearing room, where the fires of this Inquisition burn, becomes a celebrity circus. Einstein's is not the only famous name that echoes here. For some time the Un-American Activities Committee has had its eye on Hollywood. The Committee demands names, and Hollywood names cause scandal. Those who won't talk lose their jobs and find their careers ruined; or go to jail, like Dashiell Hammett; or lose their passports, like Lillian Hellman and Paul Robeson; or are expelled from the country, like Cedric Belfrage. Ronald Reagan, a minor leading man, brands the reds and pinks who don't deserve to be saved from the furies of Armageddon. Another leading man, Robert Taylor, publicly repents having acted in a film in which Russians smile. Playwright Clifford Odets begs pardon for his ideas and betrays his old comrades. Actor José Ferrer and director Elia Kazan point their fingers at colleagues. To dissociate himself clearly from Communists, Kazan makes a film about the Mexican leader Emiliano Zapata in which Zapata is not the silent campesino who championed agrarian reform, but a charlatan who shoots off bullets and speeches in an unceasing diarrhea.

(41, 219, and 467)

1953: Washington

Portrait of a Witch Hunter

His raw material is collective fear. He rolls up his sleeves and goes to work. Skillful molder of this clay, Joseph McCarthy turns fear into panic and panic into hysteria.

Feverishly he exhorts them to betray. He swears not to shut his mouth as long as his country is infected by the Marxist plague. For him all ambiguity has the ring of cowardice. First he accuses, then he investigates. He sells certainties to the vacillating and lashes out, knee to groin or knife to belly, at anyone who questions the right of private property or opposes war and business as usual.

(395)

1953: Seattle

Robeson

They bar him from traveling to Canada, or anywhere else. When some Canadians invite him to perform, Paul Robeson sings to them by telephone from Seattle, and by telephone he swears that he will stand firm as long as there is breath in his body.

Robeson, grandson of slaves, believes that Africa is a source of pride and not a zoo run by Tarzan. A black with red ideas, friend of the yellows who are resisting the white invasion in Korea, he sings in the name of his insulted people and of all insulted peoples who by singing lift their heads; and he sings with a voice full of thundering heaven and quaking earth.

(381)

1953: Santiago de Cuba

Fidel

At dawn on July 26, a handful of youths attack the Moncada barracks. Armed with dignity and Cuban bravura and a few bird guns, they assault the dictatorship of Fulgencio Batista and half a century of colonization masquerading as a republic.

A few die in battle, but more than seventy are finished off by the army after a week of torture. The torturers tear out the eyes of Abel Santamaría, among others.

The rebel leader, taken prisoner, offers his defense plea. Fidel Castro has the look of a man who gives all of himself without asking anything in return. The judges listen to him in astonishment, missing not a word. His words are not, however, for the ones kissed by the gods; he speaks for the ones pissed on by the devils, and for them, and in their name, he explains what he has done.

Fidel Castro claims the ancient right of rebellion against despotism: *"This island will sink in the ocean before we will consent to be anybody's slaves . . ."*

He tosses his head like a tree, accuses Batista and his officers of exchanging their uniforms for butchers' aprons, and sets forth a program of revolution. In Cuba there could be food and work for all, and more to spare.

"No, that is not inconceivable."

(90, 392, and 422)

1953: Santiago de Cuba

The Accused Turns Prosecutor and Announces: "History Will Absolve Me"

What is inconceivable is that there should be men going to bed hungry while an inch of land remains unsown; what is inconceivable is that there should be children who die without medical care; that thirty percent of our campesinos cannot sign their names and ninety-nine percent don't know the history of Cuba; that most families in our countryside should be living in worse conditions than the Indians Columbus found when he discovered the most beautiful land human eyes had ever seen . . .

From such wretchedness it is only possible to free oneself by death; and in that the state does help them: to die. Ninety percent of rural children are devoured by parasites that enter from the soil through the toenails of their unshod feet.

More than half of the best cultivated production lands are in foreign hands. In Oriente, the largest province, the lands of the United Fruit Company and the West Indian Company extend from the north coast to the south coast . . .

Cuba continues to be a factory producing raw materials. Sugar

*is exported to import candies; leather exported to import shoes; iron
exported to import plows . . .*

(90)

1953: Boston
United Fruit

Throne of bananas, crown of bananas, a banana held like a scepter:
Sam Zemurray, master of the lands and seas of the banana kingdom,
did not believe it possible that his Guatemalan vassals could give him
a headache. *"The Indians are too ignorant for Marxism,"* he used to
say, and was applauded by his court at his royal palace in Boston,
Massachusetts.

Thanks to the successive decrees of Manuel Estrada Cabrera,
who governed surrounded by sycophants and spies, seas of slobber,
forests of familiars; and of Jorge Ubico, who thought he was Napoleon
but wasn't, Guatemala has remained part of United Fruit's vast dominion for half a century. In Guatemala United Fruit can seize whatever land it wants—enormous unused tracts—and owns the railroad,
the telephone, the telegraph, the ports, and the ships, not to speak
of soldiers, politicians, and journalists.

Sam Zemurray's troubles began when president Juan José Arévalo forced the company to respect the union and its right to strike.
From bad to worse: A new president, Jacobo Arbenz, introduces
agrarian reform, seizes United Fruit's uncultivated lands, begins
dividing them among a hundred thousand families, and acts as if
Guatemala were ruled by the landless, the letterless, the breadless,
the *less*.

(50 and 288)

1953: Guatemala City
Arbenz

President Truman howled when workers on Guatemala's banana plantations started to behave like people. Now President Eisenhower spits
lightning over the expropriation of United Fruit.

The government of the United States considers it an outrage that
the government of Guatemala should take United Fruit's account

books seriously. Arbenz proposes to pay as indemnity only the value that the company itself had placed on its lands to defraud the tax laws. John Foster Dulles, the secretary of state, demands twenty-five times that.

Jacobo Arbenz, accused of conspiring with Communists, draws his inspiration not from Lenin but from Abraham Lincoln. His agrarian reform, an attempt to modernize Guatemalan capitalism, is less radical than the North American rural laws of almost a century ago.

(81 and 416)

1953: San Salvador
Dictator Wanted

Guatemalan General Miguel Ydígoras Fuentes, distinguished killer of Indians, has lived in exile since the fall of dictator Ubico. Now, Walter Turnbull comes to San Salvador to offer him a deal. Turnbull, representative of both United Fruit and the CIA, proposes that Ydígoras take charge of Guatemala. There is money available for such a project, if he promises to destroy the unions, restore United Fruit's lands and privileges, and repay this loan to the last cent within a reasonable period. Ydígoras asks time to think it over, while making it clear he considers the conditions abusive.

In no time word gets around that a position is vacant. Guatemalan exiles, military and civilian, fly to Washington to offer their services; others knock at the doors of U.S. embassies. José Luis Arenas, "friend" of Vice-President Nixon, offers to overthrow President Arbenz for two hundred thousand dollars. General Federico Ponce says he has a ten-thousand-man army ready to attack the National Palace. His price would be quite modest, although he prefers not to talk figures yet. Just a small advance . . .

Throat cancer rules out United Fruit's preference, Juan Córdova Cerna. On his deathbed, however, Doctor Córdova rasps out the name of his own candidate: Colonel Carlos Castillo Armas, trained at Fort Leavenworth, Kansas, a cheap, obedient burro.

(416 and 471)

1954: Washington

The Deciding Machine, Piece by Piece

Dwight Eisenhower President of the United States. Overthrew the government of Mohammed Mossadegh in Iran because it nationalized oil. Has now given orders to overthrow the government of Jacobo Arbenz in Guatemala.

Sam Zemurray Principal stockholder in United Fruit. All his concerns automatically turn into U.S. government declarations, and ultimately into rifles, mortars, machineguns, and CIA airplanes.

John Foster Dulles U.S. Secretary of State. Former lawyer for United Fruit.

Allen Dulles Director of the CIA. Brother of John Foster Dulles. Like him, has done legal work for United Fruit. Together they organize "Operation Guatemala."

John Moors Cabot Secretary of State for Inter-American Affairs. Brother of Thomas Cabot, the president of United Fruit.

Walter Bedell Smith Under Secretary of State. Serves as liaison in Operation Guatemala. Future member of the board of United Fruit.

Henry Cabot Lodge Senator, U.S. representative to the United Nations. United Fruit shareholder. Has on various occasions received money from this company for speeches in the Senate.

Anne Whitman Personal secretary to President Eisenhower. Married to United Fruit public relations chief.

Spruille Braden Former U.S. ambassador to several Latin American countries. Has received a salary from United Fruit since 1948. Is widely reported in the press to have exhorted Eisenhower *to suppress communism by force in Guatemala*.

Robert Hill U.S. ambassador to Costa Rica. Collaborates on "Operation Guatemala." Future board member of United Fruit.

John Peurifoy U.S. ambassador to Guatemala. Known as *the butcher of Greece* for his past diplomatic service in Athens. Speaks no Spanish. Political background: the U.S. Senate, Washington, D.C., where he once worked as an elevator operator.

(416, 420, and 465)

1954: Boston

The Lie Machine, Piece by Piece

The Motor   The executioner becomes the victim; the victim, the executioner. Those who prepare the invasion of Guatemala from Honduras attribute to Guatemala the intention to invade Honduras and all Central America. *The tentacles of the Kremlin are plain to see*, says John Moors Cabot from the White House. Ambassador Peurifoy warns in Guatemala: *We cannot permit a Soviet republic to be established from Texas to the Panama Canal*. Behind this scandal lies a cargo of arms shipped from Czechoslovakia. The United States has forbidden the sale of arms to Guatemala.

Gear I   News and articles, declarations, pamphlets, photographs, films, and comic strips about Communist atrocities in Guatemala bombard the public. This educational material, whose origin is undisclosed, comes from the offices of United Fruit in Boston and from government offices in Washington.

Gear II   The Archbishop of Guatemala, Mariano Rossell Arellano, exhorts the populace to rise *against communism, enemy of God and the Fatherland*. Thirty CIA planes rain down his pastoral message over the whole country. The archbishop has the image of the popular Christ of Esquipulas, which will be named Captain General of the Liberating Brigade, brought to the capital.

Gear III   At the Pan-American Conference, John Foster Dulles pounds the table with his fist and gets the blessing of the Organization of American States for the projected invasion. At the United Nations, Henry Cabot Lodge blocks Jacobo Arbenz's demands for help. U.S. diplomacy is mobilized throughout the world. The complicity of England and France is obtained in exchange for a U.S. commitment to silence over the delicate matters of the Suez Canal, Cyprus, and Indochina.

Gear IV   The dictators of Nicaragua, Honduras, Venezuela, and the Dominican Republic not only lend training camps, radio transmitters, and airports to "Operation Guatemala," they also make a contribution to the propaganda campaign. Somoza I calls together the international press in Managua and displays some pistols with hammers and sickles stamped on them. They are, he says, from a Russian submarine intercepted en route to Guatemala.

(416, 420, and 447)

1954: Guatemala City
The Reconquest of Guatemala

Guatemala has neither planes nor antiaircraft installations, so U.S. pilots in U.S. planes bomb the country with the greatest of ease.

A powerful CIA transmitter, installed on the roof of the U.S. embassy, spreads confusion and panic: the Lie Machine informs the world that this is the rebel radio, the Voice of Liberation, transmitting the triumphal march of Colonel Castillo Armas from the jungles of Guatemala. Meanwhile, Castillo Armas, encamped on a United Fruit plantation in Honduras, awaits orders from the Deciding Machine.

Arbenz's government, paralyzed, attends the ceremony of its own collapse. The aerial bombings reach the capital and blow up the fuel deposits. The government confines itself to burying the dead. The mercenary army, *God, Fatherland, Liberty*, crosses the border. It meets no resistance. Is it money or fear that explains how Guatemala's military chiefs could surrender their troops without firing a shot? An Argentine doctor in his early twenties, Ernesto Guevara, tries in vain to organize popular defense of the capital: he doesn't know how or with what. Improvised militias wander the streets unarmed. When Arbenz finally orders the arsenals opened, army officers refuse to obey. On one of these dark ignoble days, Guevara has an attack of asthma and indignation; on another, one midnight after two weeks of bombings, President Arbenz slowly descends the steps of the National Palace, crosses the street, and seeks asylum in the Mexican embassy.

(81, 416, 420, and 447)

1954: Mazatenango
Miguel at Forty-Nine

As soon as the birds started singing, before first light, they sharpened their machetes, and now they reach Mazatenango at a gallop, in search of Miguel. The executioners are making crosses on a long list of those marked to die, while the army of Castillo Armas takes over Guatemala. Miguel is number five on the most-wanted list, condemned for being a red and a foreign troublemaker. Since his arrival on the run from El Salvador, he has not stopped for an instant his work of labor agitation.

They sic dogs on him. They aim to parade his body hanging from a horse along the roads, his throat slit by a machete. But Miguel, one very experienced and knowing animal, loses himself in the scrub.

And so occurs the tenth birth of Miguel Mármol, at forty-nine years of age.

(222)

1954: Guatemala City
Newsreel

The archbishop of Guatemala declares: *"I admire the sincere and ardent patriotism of President Castillo Armas."* Amid a formidable display of gibberish, Castillo Armas receives the blessing of the papal nuncio, Monsignor Genaro Verrolino.

President Eisenhower congratulates the CIA chiefs at the White House: *"Thanks to all of you. You've averted a Soviet beachhead in our hemisphere."*

The head of the CIA, Allen Dulles, assigns to a *Time* journalist the job of framing Guatemala's new constitution.

Time publishes a poem by the wife of the U.S. ambassador to Guatemala. The poem says that Mr. and Mrs. Peurifoy are *optimistic* because Guatemala is no longer *communistic*.

At his first meeting with the ambassador after the victory, President Castillo Armas expresses his concern at the insufficiency of local jails and the lack of necessary cells for all the Communists. According to lists sent from Washington by the State Department, Guatemala's Communists total seventy-two thousand.

The embassy throws a party. Four hundred Guatemalan guests sing in unison "The Star-Spangled Banner."

(416 and 420)

1954: Rio de Janeiro

Getulio

He wants to erase the memory of his own dictatorship, those bad old police-state days, and so in his final years governs Brazil as no one ever has before.

He takes the side of the wage earner. Immediately the profit-makers declare war.

To stop Brazil from being a colander, he corks up the hemorrhage of wealth. Immediately foreign capital takes to economic sabotage.

He recovers for Brazil its own oil and energy, which are as national a patrimony as anthem and flag. The offended monopolies immediately respond with a fierce counteroffensive.

He defends the price of coffee instead of burning half the crop, as was customary. The United States immediately cuts its purchases in half.

In Brazil, journalists and politicians of all colors and areas join the scandalized chorus.

Getulio Vargas has governed with dignity. When he is forced to bow down, he chooses the dignity of death. He raises the revolver, aims at his own heart, and fires.

(427, 429, and 432)

1955: Medellín

Nostalgia

It is almost twenty years since Carlos Gardel burned to death, and the Colombian city of Medellín, where the tragedy occurred, has become a place of pilgrimage and the focus of a cult.

The devotees of Gardel are known by their tilted hats, striped pants, and swaying walk. They slick down their hair, look out of the corners of their eyes, and have twisted smiles. They bow and sweep, as if in a constant dance, when shaking hands, lighting a cigarette, or chalking a billiard cue. They spend the night leaning against some suburban lamp-post, whistling or humming tangos which explain that all women are whores except mother, that sainted old lady whom God has taken to his glory.

Some local devotees, and certain visiting cultists from Buenos

Aires, sell relics of the idol. One offers genuine Gardel teeth, acquired on the spot when the plane blew up. He has sold more than thirteen hundred at an average of twelve dollars apiece. It was some years ago that he found his first buyer, a tourist from New York, a member of the Gardel Fan Club. On seeing the souvenir, how could the customer help but burst into tears?

(184)

1955: Asunción
Withdrawal Symptoms

When he commits the unforgivable sin of promulgating a divorce law, the Church makes the missing sign of the cross over him, and the military begin to conspire, in full daylight, to overthrow him.

The news is celebrated in drawing rooms and mourned in kitchens; Perón has fallen. Offering no resistance, he leaves Argentina, for Paraguay and exile.

In Asunción, his days are sad. He feels beaten, old, alone. He claims that by his act of renunciation a million deaths have been avoided. But he also says that the people didn't know how to defend what he gave them, that the ingrates deserve whatever misfortunes befall them, that they think with their bellies, not with their heads or hearts.

One morning Perón is confiding his bitterness to his host, Ricardo Gayol, when suddenly he half-closes his eyes and whispers: *"My smile used to drive them crazy. My smile . . ."*

He raises his arms and smiles as if he were on the palace balcony, greeting a plaza filled with cheering people. *"Would you like my smile?"*

His host looks at him, stupefied.

"Take it, it's yours," says Perón. He takes it out of his mouth and puts it in his host's hand—his false teeth.

(327)

1955: Guatemala City

One Year after the Reconquest of Guatemala,

Richard Nixon visits this occupied land. The union of United Fruit workers and five hundred and thirty-two other unions have been banned by the new government. The new penal code punishes with death anyone who calls a strike. Political parties are outlawed. The books of Dostoyevsky and other Soviet writers have been thrown onto the bonfire.

The banana kingdom has been saved from agrarian reform. The vice-president of the United States congratulates President Castillo Armas. For the first time in history, says Nixon, a Communist government has been replaced by a free one.

(416 and 420)

1956: Buenos Aires

The Government Decides That Peronism Doesn't Exist

While shooting workers on garbage dumps, the Argentine military decrees the nonexistence of Perón, Evita, and Peronism. It is forbidden to mention their names or their deeds. Possessing images of them is a crime. The presidential residence is demolished to the last stone, as though the disease were contagious.

But what about the embalmed body of Evita? She is the most dangerous symbol of the arrogance of the rabble who have sauntered the corridors of power as if in their own homes. The generals dump the body in a box labeled "Radio Equipment" and send it into exile. Just where is a secret. To Europe, rumor has it, or maybe to an island in mid-ocean. Evita becomes a wandering body traveling secretly through remote cemeteries, expelled from the country by generals who don't know—or don't want to know—that she lies within the people.

(311 and 327)

1956: León

Son of Somoza

Santa Marta, Santa Marta has a train, sing the musicmakers, dance the dancers, *Santa Marta has a train but has no tram;* and in the middle of the song and the fiesta, Rigoberto López Pérez, poet, owner of nothing, fells the owner of everything with four bullets.

A North American plane carries off the dying Anastasio Somoza to a North American hospital in the North American Panama Canal Zone, and he dies in a North American bed. They bury him in Nicaragua, with the honors of a prince of the Church.

Somoza I held power for twenty years. Every six years he lifted his state of siege for one day and held the elections that kept him on the throne. Luis, eldest son and heir, is now the richest and most powerful man in Central America. From Washington, President Eisenhower congratulates him.

Luis Somoza bows before the statue of his father, the bronze hero who gallops motionlessly in the very center of Managua. In the shadow of the horse's hoofs he seeks advice from the founder of the dynasty, guide to good government, proliferator of jails and businesses, then covers the monumental tomb with flowers.

Evading the vigilance of an honor guard, the hand of somebody, anybody, everybody, has hurriedly scrawled this epitaph on the marble tomb: *Here lies Somoza, a bit rottener than in life.*

(10, 102, and 460)

1956: Santo Domingo

In the Year Twenty-Six of the Trujillo Era

his likeness is sold in the markets, among the little engravings of the Virgin Mary, Saint George, and other miracle workers.

"Saints, cheap saints!"

Nothing Dominican is beyond his grasp. All belongs to him: the first night of the virgins, the last wish of the dying, the people and the cows, the air fleet and the chain of brothels, the sugar and wheat mills, the beer factory and the virility-potion bottling plant.

For twenty-six years Trujillo has occupied God's vice-presidency.

Every four years, this formula has been blessed by democratic elections: *God and Trujillo*, proclaim all walls.

In her work *Moral Meditations*, which earns her the title of First Lady of Caribbean Letters, Doña María de Trujillo compares her husband to El Cid and Napoleon Bonaparte. Plump Doña María, who practices usury during the week and mysticism on Sundays, has in turn been compared with Saint Teresa de Jesus by local critics.

With El Cid's sword or Napoleon's hat, Trujillo poses for statues. Statues multiply him in bronze and marble, with a chin he doesn't have and without the double chin he does. Thousands of statues: From high on their pedestals, Trujillo straddles the most remote corner of every city or village, watching. In this country not a fly shits without his permission.

(63 and 101)

1956: Havana
Newsreel

The Cuban army has thwarted an armed expedition from Mexico, surrounding the invaders, machinegunning and bombing them at a place called Alegría de Pío in Oriente province. Among the many dead are Fidel Castro, leader of the gang, and an Argentine Communist agitator, Ernesto Guevara.

After enjoying a long stay in the city of New York, Dr. Ernesto Sarrá and his very attractive and elegant wife, Loló, figures of the highest rank in this capital's social circles, have returned to Havana.

Also arriving from New York is Bing Crosby, the popular singer who, without removing his topcoat or beaver hat, declared at the airport: *"I have come to Cuba to play golf."*

A young Havanan, on the point of winning the grand prize in the "TV School Contest," fails to answer the next to last question. The final question, which remained unasked, was: *What is the name of the river that crosses Paris?*

An exceptional lineup will run tomorrow at the Marianao Racecourse.

(98)

1956: At the Foot of the Sierra Maestra

Twelve Lunatics

They go a week without sleep, huddled together like sardines in a can, vomiting, while the north wind toys playfully with the little boat *Granma*. After much seesawing in the Gulf of Mexico, they disembark in the wrong place, and a few steps ashore are swept by machinegun fire or burned alive by incendiary bombs, a slaughter in which almost all of them fall. The survivors consult the sky for directions but get the stars mixed up. The swamps swallow their backpacks and their arms. They have no food except sugarcane, and they leave its betraying refuse strewn along the trail. They lose their condensed milk by carrying the cans holes down. In a careless moment they mix their little remaining fresh water with sea water. They get lost and search aimlessly for one another. Finally, one small group discovers another small group on these slopes, by chance, and so the twelve saved from annihilation join together.

These men, or shadows of men, have a total of seven rifles, a little damp ammunition, and uncounted sores and wounds. Since the invasion began there is hardly a mistake they haven't made. But on this starless night they breathe fresher, cleaner air, and Fidel says, standing before the foothills of the Sierra Maestra: *"We've already won the war. Batista is fucked!"*

(98 and 209)

1957: Benidorm

Marked Cards

Between liberals and conservatives, a conjugal agreement. On a beach in the Mediterranean, Colombia's politicians sign the compromise that puts an end to ten years of mutual extermination. The two main parties offer each other an amnesty. From now on, they will alternate the presidency and divvy up the other jobs. Colombians will be able to vote, but not elect. Liberals and conservatives are to take turns in power, to guarantee the property and inheritance rights over the country that their families have brought or received as gifts.

In this pact among the wealthy there is no good news for the poor.

(8, 217, and 408)

1957: Majagual

Colombia's Sainted Egg

Burning towns and killing Indians, leveling forests and erecting wire fences, the masters of the land have pushed the campesinos right up against the river banks in this coastal region of Colombia. Many campesinos have nonetheless refused to serve as slaves on the haciendas and have instead become fishermen—artists at gritting their teeth and living on what they can find. Eating so much turtle, they learn from him: The turtle never lets go what he catches in his mouth and knows how to bury himself on the beaches in the dry season when the seagulls threaten. With that and God's help they get by.

Few monks remain in these hot regions. Here on the coast no one takes the Mass seriously. Whoever isn't paralyzed runs from marriage and work, and, the better to enjoy the seven deadly sins, indulges in endless siestas in endless hammocks. Here God is a good fellow, not a grouchy, carping police chief.

The boring Christ of Jegua is dead—a broken doll that neither sweats nor bleeds nor performs miracles. No one has even wiped the bat shit off him since the priest fled with all the silver. But very much alive, sweating and bleeding and miracle-working, is Our Little Black Lord, the dark Christ of San Benito Abad, giving counsel to anyone who will stroke him affectionately. Alive, too, and wagging their tails, are the frisky saints who appear on the Colombian coast at the drop of a hat and stick around.

One stormy night, some fishermen discover God's face, agleam in lightning flashes, on a stone the shape of an egg. Since then they celebrate the miracles of Saint Egg, dancing the *cumbia* and drinking to his health.

The parish priest of Majagual announces that he will go up river at the head of a battalion of crusaders, throw the sacrilegious stone to the bottom of the waters, and set fire to their little palm-frond chapel.

In the tiny chapel, where Masses are celebrated with lively mu-

sic, the fishermen stand guard around Saint Egg. Ax in hand, day
and night.

(159)

1957: Sucre
Saint Lucío

While the Majagual priest declares war on Saint Egg, the priest of
Sucre expels Saint Lucía from his church, because a female saint with
a penis is unheard of.

At first it looked like a cyst, or a bump on the neck; but it kept
moving lower and lower, and growing, bulging beneath the sacred
tunic that shortened every day. Everyone pretended not to notice,
until one day a child suddenly blurted out: "*Saint Lucía has a dick!*"

Exiled, Saint Lucío finds refuge in a hut not far from the little
temple of Saint Egg. In time, the fishermen put up an altar to him,
because Saint Lucío is a fun-loving, trustworthy guy who joins the
binges of his devotees, listens to their secrets, and is happy when
summer comes and the fish begin to rise.

This he, who used to be she, doesn't figure among the saints
listed in the Bristol Almanac, nor has Saint Egg been canonized by
the Pope of Rome. Neither has Saint Board, unhinged from the box
of soap in which a laundrywoman found the Virgin Mary; or Saint
Kidney, the humble kidney of a cow in which a slaughterer saw
Christ's crown of thorns. Nor Saint Domingo Vidal . . .

(159)

1957: The Sinú River Banks
Saint Domingo Vidal

He had been a dwarf and a paralytic. The people had named him a
saint, Saint Domingo Vidal, because with his prophetic hunches he
had known just where on this Colombian coast a lost horse had strayed,
and which cock would win the next fight, and because he had asked
nothing for teaching the poor how to read and defend themselves
from locusts and omnivorous landlords.

Son of Lucifer, the Church called him. A priest hauled him
out of his grave inside the chapel of Chimá and broke his bones with

an ax and hammer. His shattered remains ended up in a corner of the plaza, and another priest wanted to throw them in the garbage. The first priest died a writhing death, his hands turning into claws; the other suffocated, wallowing in his own excrement.

Like Saint Egg, Saint Lucío, and many of their local colleagues, Saint Domingo Vidal remains happily alive in the fervor of all those hereabouts who love—either in or out of wedlock—and in the noisy throng of people who share the grim battle for land and the joys of its fruits.

Saint Domingo Vidal protects the ancient custom of the Sinú River villagers, who visit each other bearing gifts of food. The people of one village bear litters to another loaded with flowers and delicacies from the river and its banks: dorado or shad stews, slices of catfish, iguana eggs, riced coconut, cheese, sweet *mongomongo*; and while the recipients eat, the donors sing and dance around them.

(160)

1957: Pino del Agua
Crucito

Batista offers three hundred pesos and a cow with calf to anyone who brings him Fidel Castro, alive or dead.

On the other side of the crests of the Sierra Maestra, the guerrillas sweat and multiply. They quickly learn the rules of war in the brush: to mistrust, to move by night, never to sleep twice in the same place, and above all, to make friends with the local people.

When the twelve bedraggled survivors arrived in this sierra, they knew not a single campesino, and the River Yara only through the song that mentions it. A few months later there are a few campesinos in the rebel ranks, the kind of men who cut cane for a while at harvest time and then are left to starve in unknown territory; and now the guerrillas know these areas as if they had been born in them. They know the names of the places, and when they don't, they baptize them after their own fashion. They have given the Arroyo of Death its name because there a guerrilla deserted who had sworn to fight to the death.

Others die fighting, without having sworn anything.

While smoking his pipe during the rest periods, José de la Cruz— "Crucito"—sierra troubadour, composes in ten-verse *guajira* stanzas the entire history of the Cuban revolution. For lack of paper he commits it to memory, but has it taken from him by a bullet, on the heights of Pino del Agua during an ambush of army trucks.

(209)

1957: El Uvero
Almeida

Juan Almeida claims he has a joy inside him that keeps tickling, making him laugh and jump. A very stubborn joy if one considers that Almeida was born poor and black on this island of private beaches which are closed to the poor because they are poor and to blacks because they stain the water; and that, to make matters worse, he decided to be a bricklayer's helper and a poet; and that, as if those were not complications enough, he rolled his life into this crap game of the Cuban revolution, and as one of the Moncada assailants was sentenced to jail and exile, and was navigator of the *Granma* before becoming the guerrilla that he is now; and that he has just stopped two bullets—not mortal, but motherfuckers—one in the left leg and one in the shoulder, during the three-hour attack on the Uvero barracks, down by the shore.

(209)

1957: Santiago de Cuba
Portrait of an Imperial Ambassador

Earl Smith, ambassador of the United States, receives the keys to the city of Santiago de Cuba. As the ceremony proceeds and the speeches pour forth, a commotion is heard through the curtains. Discreetly, the ambassador peers out the window and observes a number of women approaching, clad in black, chanting the national anthem and shouting *"Liberty!"* The police club them down.

The next day, the ambassador visits the U.S. military base at Guantánamo. Then he tours the iron and nickel mines of the Freeport Sulphur Company, which, thanks to his efforts, have just been exempted from taxes.

The ambassador publicly expresses his disgust with the police beatings, although he recognizes that the government has a right to defend itself from Communist aggression. Advisers have explained to the ambassador that Fidel has been abnormal since childhood, from having fallen off a moving motorcycle.

The ambassador, who was a champion boxer in his student days, believes General Batista must be defended at any cost. With Batista in power, tourists can pick from photos handed them on the airplane their pretty mulatta for the weekend. Havana is a North American city, full of one-armed bandits from Nevada and mafia bosses from Chicago, and with plenty of telephones to order a nice hot supper to be brought on the next flight out of Miami.

(431)

1957: El Hombrito
Che

In the Hombrito Valley, the rebels have installed an oven for baking bread, a printshop consisting of an old mimeograph machine, and a clinic that functions in a one-room hut. The doctor is Ernesto Guevara, known as Che, who apart from his nickname has retained certain Argentine customs, like maté and irony. American pilgrim, he joined Fidel's forces in Mexico, where he settled after the fall of Guatemala to earn a living as a photographer at one peso per photo, and as a peddler of little engravings of the Virgin of Guadalupe.

In the Hombrito clinic, Che attends a series of children with bloated bellies, almost dwarfs, and aged girls worn out from too many births and too little food, and men as dry and empty as gourds, because poverty turns everyone into a living mummy.

Last year, when machineguns mowed down the newly landed guerrillas, Che had to choose between a case of bullets and a case of medicines. He couldn't carry both and decided on the bullets. Now he strokes his old Thompson rifle, the only surgical instrument he really believes in.

(209)

Old Chana, Campesina of the
Sierra Maestra, Remembers:

Poor dear Che! I always saw him with that curse of his asthma and said, "Ay, Holy Virgin!" With the asthma he would get all quiet, breathing low. Some folks with asthma get hysterical, cough and open their eyes and open their mouth. But Che tried to soften up the asthma. He would throw himself in a corner to rest the asthma.

He didn't like sympathy. If you said, "Poor guy," he gave you a quick look that didn't mean anything, and meant a lot.

I used to warm him up a bit of water to rub on his chest for relief. He, the big flatterer, would say, "Oh, my girlfriend." But he was such a rascal.

(338)

1958: Stockholm
Pelé

Brazilian football glows. It dances and makes one dance. At the World Cup in Sweden, Pelé and Garrincha are the heroes, proving wrong those who say blacks can't play in a cold climate.

Pelé, thin as a rake, almost a boy, puffs out his chest and raises his chin to make an impression. He plays football as God would play it, if God decided to devote himself seriously to the game. Pelé makes a date with the ball anywhere, any time, and she never stands him up. He sends her high in the air. She makes a full curve and returns to his foot, obedient, grateful, or perhaps tied by an invisible elastic band. Pelé lifts her up, puffs out his chest, and she rolls smoothly down his body. Without letting her touch the ground he flips her to the other foot as he flings himself, running like a hare, toward the goal. No one can catch him, with lasso or bullet, until he leaves the ball, shining, white, tight against the back of the net.

On and off the field, he takes care of himself. He never wastes a minute of his time, nor lets a penny fall from his pocket. Until recently he was shining shoes down at the docks. Pelé was born to rise; and he knows it.

(279)

1958: Stockholm
Garrincha

Garrincha plays havoc with the other teams, always threatening to break through. Half turn, full turn, he looks like he's coming, but he's going! He acts like he's going, but he's coming. Flabbergasted opponents fall on their asses as if Garrincha were scattering banana peels along the field. At the goal line, when he has eluded them all, including the goalie, he sits on the ball. Then he backs up and starts again. The fans are amused, but the managers go crazy. Garrincha, carefree bird with bandy legs, plays for laughs, not to win, and forgets the results. He still thinks soccer's a party, not a job or a business. He likes to play for nothing, or a few beers, on beaches or ragged little fields.

He has many children, his own and other people's. He drinks and eats as if for the last time. Openhanded, he gives everything away, loses the works. Garrincha was born to fall; and he doesn't know it.

(22)

1958: Sierra Maestra
The Revolution Is an Unstoppable Centipede

As the war reaches its height, beneath the bullets Fidel introduces agrarian reform in the Sierra Maestra. Campesinos get their first land, not to speak of their first doctor, their first teacher, even their first judge—which is said to be a less dangerous way to settle a dispute than the machete.

Batista's more than ten thousand soldiers can't seem to do anything but lose. The rebel army is infinitely smaller and still poorly armed, but under it, above it, within it, ahead of and behind it, are the people.

The future is now. Fidel launches a final offensive: Cuba from end to end. In two columns, one under the command of Che Guevara, the other under Camilo Cienfuegos, a hundred and sixty guerrillas descend from the mountains to conquer the plain.

(98 and 209)

1958: Yaguajay
Camilo

Magically eluding bombardment and ambush, the invading columns
strike for the island's gut, slicing Cuba in two as Camilo Cienfuegos
takes the Yaguajay barracks after eleven days of fighting and Che
enters the city of Santa Clara. Suddenly, half of Batista's island has
disappeared.

Camilo Cienfuegos, brave and greedy, fights at such close quarters that, killing an enemy soldier, he catches his rifle in mid-air
without its touching the ground. Several times the fatal bullet that
should have been his just barely wasn't, and once he nearly died from
gobbling down a whole kid after two days of eating nothing at all.

Camilo has the beard and mane of a biblical prophet, but where
a worry-creased face should be, there's only an ear-to-ear grin. The
feat he is most proud of is that time up in the mountains when he
fooled a light military plane by painting himself red with iodine and
lying still with his arms crossed.

(179 and 210)

1959: Havana
Cuba Wakes Up Without Batista

on the first day of the year. The dictator lands in Santo Domingo and
seeks refuge with his colleague Trujillo; back in Havana, for the former
hangmen, it's *sauve qui peut*, a stampede.

U.S. Ambassador Earl Smith is appalled. The streets have been
taken over by rabble and by a few dirty, hairy, barefoot guerrillas,
just a Latin Dillinger gang who dance the *guaguancó*, marking time
with rifle shots.

(98 and 431)

The Rumba

The *guaguancó* is a kind of rumba, and every self-respecting Cuban
has the rumba under his belt, in peace, war, and anything between.
Even when picking a fight, the Cuban rumbas, so now he joins the

dance of the bullets without a second thought, and the crowds surge behind the drums that summon them.

"I'm enjoying it. And if they get me, too bad. At least I'm enjoying it."

On any street or field the music lets loose. There's no stopping it—that rumba rhythm on drums and crates, or, if there are no drums or crates, on bodies, or just in the air. Even ears dance.

(86, 198, and 324)

1959: Havana
Portrait of a Caribbean Casanova

Porfirio Rubirosa, the Dominican ambassador, looks with dread on this horrifying spectacle. He has nothing for breakfast but a cup of coffee. The news has taken away his appetite. While servants by the dozen nail down boxes and close trunks and suitcases, Rubirosa nervously lights a cigarette and puts his favorite song, "Taste of Me," on the phonograph.

The sun, they say, never sets on his bed. Trujillo's man in Cuba is a famous enchanter of princesses, heiresses, and movie stars. Rubirosa beguiles them with flattery and plays the ukulele to them before loving or beating them.

Some say his tremendous energy derives from the milk of his infancy, which came from sirens' tits. Dominican patriots insist that his secret is a virility elixir Trujillo concocts from the *pega-palo* plant and exports to the United States.

Rubirosa's career began when Trujillo made him his son-in-law; continued when, as Dominican ambassador to Paris, he sold visas to Jews persecuted by Hitler; and was perfected in his marriages to multi-millionairesses Doris Duke and Barbara Hutton. It is the smell of money that excites the tropical Casanova, as the smell of blood excites sharks.

(100)

1959: Havana

"We have only won the right to begin,"

says Fidel, who rides into town on top of a tank, direct from the Sierra Maestra. To a surging crowd he explains that all this, while it might look like a conclusion, is no more than a beginning.

Half of Cuba's land is uncultivated. According to the statistics, last year was the most prosperous in the island's history; but the campesinos, who can't read statistics or anything else, haven't noticed. From now on, a different cock will crow, with agrarian reform and a literacy campaign, as in the sierra, the most urgent tasks. But before that, the dismantling of an army of butchers. The worst torturers go up against a wall. The aptly named "Bonebreaker" faints each time the firing squad takes aim. They have to bind him to a post.

(91)

1960: Brasília

A City, or Delirium in the Midst of Nothing

Brazil lifts the curtain on its new capital. Suddenly, Brasília is born at the center of a cross traced on the red dust of the desert, very far from the coast, very far from everything, out at the end of the world— or perhaps its beginning.

The city has been built at a dizzying speed. For three years this was an anthill where workers and technicians labored shoulder to shoulder, night and day, sharing jobs, food, and shelter. But when Brasília is finished, the fleeting illusion of brotherhood is finished, too. Doors slam: This city is not for servants. Brasília locks out those who raised it with their own hands. Their place is piled together in shacks that blossom by God's grace on the outskirts of town.

This is the government's city, house of power. No people in its plazas, no paths to walk on. Brasília is on the moon: white, luminous, floating way up, high above Brazil, shielded from its dirt and its follies.

Oscar Niemeyer, architect of its palaces, did not dream of it that way. When the great inaugural fiesta occurs, Niemeyer does not appear on the podium.

(69 and 315)

1960: Rio de Janeiro
Niemeyer

He hates right angles and capitalism. Against capitalism there's not much he can do; but against the right angle, that oppressor, constrictor of space, his architecture triumphs. It's free and sensual and light as clouds.

Niemeyer imagines human habitations in the form of a woman's body, a sinuous shoreline, or a tropical fruit. Also in the form of a mountain, if the mountain breaks up into beautiful curves against the sky, as do the mountains of Rio de Janeiro, designed by God on that day when God thought he was Niemeyer.

(315)

1960: Rio de Janeiro
Guimaraes Rosa

Daring and undulating, too, is the language of Guimaraes Rosa, who builds houses with words.

Works warm with passion are created by this formal gentleman, metronomically punctual, incapable of crossing a street against the light. Tragedy blows ferociously through the stories and novels of the smiling career diplomat. When he writes he violates all literary rules, this bourgeois conservative who dreams of entering the Academy.

1960: Artemisa
Thousands and Thousands of Machetes

wave in the air, brushing, rubbing, colliding, clashing, providing a background of battle-music for Fidel's speech—or, rather, for the song he is singing from the platform. Here, on the eastern end of the island, he explains to sugar workers why his government has expropriated Texaco Oil.

Cuba reacts to each successive blow with neither trepidation nor deference. The State Department refuses to accept the agrarian reform: Cuba divides the U.S.-owned estates among campesinos. Eisenhower sends planes to set fire to canefields and threatens not to buy Cuban sugar: Cuba breaks the commercial monopoly and exchanges sugar for oil with the Soviet Union. U.S. oil companies refuse to refine Soviet oil: Cuba nationalizes them.

Every discourse is a course. For hours and hours Fidel reasons and asks, teaches and learns, defends and accuses, while Cuba gropes forward, each step a search for the way.

(91)

1961: Santo Domingo
In the Year Thirty-One of the Trujillo Era

The paperweight on his desk, lying amid gilt cupids and dancing girls, is a porcelain baseball glove. Surrounded by busts of Trujillo and photos of Trujillo, Trujillo scans the latest lists of conspirators submitted by his spies. With a disdainful flick of the wrist he crosses out names, men and women who will not wake up tomorrow, while his torturers wrench new names from prisoners who scream in the Ozama fortress.

The lists give Trujillo cause for sad reflection. Leading the conspirators arrayed against him are the U.S. ambassador and the archbishop primate of the Indies, who only yesterday shared his government. Now Empire and Church are repudiating their faithful son, who has become unpresentable in the eyes of the world, and whose prodigal hand they now reject. Such ingratitude from the authors of capitalist development in the Dominican Republic hurts him deeply. Nevertheless, among all the decorations that hang from his breast, his belly, and the walls, Trujillo still loves best the Grand Cross of the Order of Saint Gregory, which he received from the Vatican, and the little medal which, many years ago, recognized his services to the U.S. Marines.

Until death he will be the Sentinel of the West, despite all the grief, this man who has dubbed himself Benefactor of the Fatherland, Savior of the Fatherland, Father of the Fatherland, Restorer of Financial Independence, Champion of World Peace, Protector of Culture, First Anticommunist of the Americas, Outstanding and Most Illustrious Generalísimo.

(60, 63, and 101)

1961: Santo Domingo
The Defunctísimo

leaves as his bequest an entire country—in addition to nine thousand
six hundred neckties, two thousand suits, three hundred and fifty
uniforms, and six hundred pairs of shoes in his closets in Santo Domingo, and five hundred and thirty million dollars in his private Swiss
bank accounts.

Rafael Leónidas Trujillo has fallen in an ambush, bullets tattooing
his car. His son, Ramfis, flies in from Paris to take charge of the
legacy, the burial, and vengeance.

Colleague and buddy of Porfirio Rubirosa, Ramfis Trujillo has
acquired a certain notoriety since a recent cultural mission to Hollywood. There, he presented Mercedes Benzes and chinchilla coats
to Kim Novak and Zsa Zsa Gabor in the name of the hungry but
generous Dominican people.

(60, 63, and 101)

1961: Bay of Pigs
Against the Wind,

against death, moving ahead, never back, the Cuban revolution remains scandalously alive no more than eight minutes' flying time from
Miami.

To put an end to this effrontery, the CIA organizes an invasion
to be launched from the United States, Guatemala, and Nicaragua.
Somoza II sees the expeditionary force off at the pier. In the Cuban
Liberation Army, machine-tooled, oiled, and greased by the CIA,
soldiers and policemen from the Batista dictatorship cohabit with
displaced inheritors of sugar plantations, banks, newspapers, gambling casinos, brothels, and political parties.

"Bring me back some hairs from Castro's beard!" Somoza instructs them.

U.S. planes, camouflaged and decorated with the star of the
Cuban Air Force, enter Cuban skies. These planes, flying low, strafe
the people who greet them, then bomb the cities. After this softening-
up operation, the invaders land haplessly in the swamps of the Bay
of Pigs.

Meanwhile, President Kennedy golfs in Virginia. He has issued the invasion order, but it was Eisenhower who had set the plan in motion, Eisenhower who gave it the green light at the same desk where he approved the invasion of Guatemala. Allen Dulles, head of the CIA, assured him it would be as simple to do away with Fidel as it was with Arbenz. A matter of a couple of weeks, give or take a day or two; even the same CIA team to take charge of it. Same men, same bases. The landing of the liberators would unleash popular insurrection on this island under the boot of red tyranny. U.S. intelligence operatives report exactly that. The people of Cuba, fed up with forming queues, await the signal to rise.

(415 and 469)

1961: Playa Girón

The Second U.S. Military Defeat
in Latin America

It takes Cuba only three days to finish off the invaders. Among the dead are four U.S. pilots. The seven ships of the invasion fleet, escorted by the United States Navy, flee or sink in the Bay of Pigs.

President Kennedy assumes full responsibility for this CIA fiasco.

The Agency believed, as always, in the reports of its local spies, whom it paid to say what it was desperate to hear; and, as always, it confused geography with a military map unrelated to people or to history. The marshes the CIA chose for the landing had been the most miserable spot in all Cuba, a kingdom of crocodiles and mosquitos—that is, until the revolution. Then human enthusiasm had transformed these quagmires, peppering them with schools, hospitals, and roads.

The people here are the first to face the bullets of the invaders who have come to save them.

(88, 435, and 469)

1961: Havana

Portrait of the Past

The invaders—hangers-on and hangmen, young millionaires, veterans of a thousand crimes—answer the journalists' questions. No one assumes responsibility for Playa Girón; no one assumes responsibility for anything. They were all cooks.

Ramón Calvino, famous torturer of the Batista regime, suffers total amnesia when confronted by the women he had beaten, kicked and raped, who identify and revile him. Father Ismael de Lugo, chaplain of the assault brigade, seeks shelter beneath the Virgin's cloak. He had fought on Franco's side in the Spanish war—on the Virgin's advice, he says—and joined the invasion force to keep the Virgin from having to suffer any more the spectacle of communism. Father Lugo invokes the tycoon Virgin, owner of some bank or nationalized plantation, who thinks and feels like the other twelve hundred prisoners: that right is the right of property and inheritance; freedom, the freedom of enterprise; the model society, a business corporation; exemplary democracy, a shareholders' meeting.

All the invaders have been educated in the ethics of impunity. None admit to having killed anybody; but then, like them, poverty doesn't exactly sign its name to its crimes either. Some journalists question them about social injustice, but they wash their hands of it. the system washes its hands. After all, children in Cuba—in all of Latin America—who die soon after birth, die of gastroenteritis, not capitalism.

(397)

1961: Washington

Who Invaded Cuba? A Dialogue in the U.S. Senate

SENATOR CAPEHART: *How many [planes] did we have?*
ALLEN DULLES (director of the CIA): *How many did the Cubans have?*
SENATOR SPARKMAN: *No, the Americans had how many?*
DULLES: *Well, these are Cubans.*
SPARKMAN: *The rebels.*

DULLES: *We do not call them rebels.*

CAPEHART: *I mean, the revolutionary forces.*

SPARKMAN: *When he said how many did we have, that is what we are referring to, anti-Castro forces.*

RICHARD M. BISSELL (deputy director of the CIA): *We started out, sir, with sixteen B-26s . . .*

(108)

1961: Havana
María de la Cruz

Soon after the invasion, a vast crowd assembles in the plaza to hear Fidel announce that the prisoners will be exchanged for children's medicines. Then he gives out diplomas to forty thousand campesinos who have learned to read and write.

An old woman insists on mounting the platform, insists so energetically that finally they bring her up. She flaps vainly at the too-high microphone, until Fidel hands it down to her.

"I wanted to meet you, Fidel. I wanted to tell you . . ."

"Look, you'll make me blush."

But the old woman, all wrinkles and little bones, isn't about to be put off. She says she's finally learned to read and write at the age of a hundred and six. She introduces herself. Her Christian name is María de la Cruz, because she was born on the day that the Holy Cross was invented; her surname is Semanat, after the sugar plantation on which she was born a slave, the daughter of slaves, granddaughter of slaves. In those days the masters sent blacks who tried to get an education to the pillory, María de la Cruz explains, because blacks were supposed to be machines that went into action at the sound of a bell, to the rhythm of whips, and that was why she took so long to learn.

María de la Cruz takes over the platform. After speaking, she sings. After singing, she dances. It's been more than a century since María de la Cruz began dancing. Dancing she emerged from her mother's belly and dancing she journeyed through pain and horror until she arrived here, where she should have been long ago. Now no one can stop her.

(298)

1961: Punta del Este

Latrine Diplomacy

After the fiasco of the military landing in Cuba, the United States changes its tune, announcing a massive landing of dollars in Latin America.

To isolate Cuba's bearded ones, President Kennedy floods Latin America with a torrent of donations, loans, investments.

"Cuba is the hen that laid your golden eggs," Che Guevara tells the Pan-American Conference at Punta del Este, calling this proposed program of bribery an enormous joke on Latin America.

So that nothing should change, the rhetoric of change is unleashed. The conference's official reports run to half a million pages, not one of which neglects to mention "revolution," "agrarian reform," or "development." While the United States knocks down the prices of Latin American products, it promises latrines for the poor, for Indians, for blacks—no machinery, no equipment, just latrines.

"For the technical gentlemen," says Che, *"planning amounts to the planning of latrines. If we took them seriously, Cuba could be . . . a paradise of the latrine!"*

(213)

1961: Escuinapa

The Tale Spinner

Once he saddled and mounted a tiger, thinking it was a burro. Another time he belted his pants with a live snake—only noticing because it had no buckle. Everyone believes him when he explains that no plane can land unless grains of corn are thrown on the runway, or when he describes the terrible bloodbath the day the train went mad and started running sideways. *"I never lie,"* lies Wily Humbug.

Wily, a shrimp fisherman in the Escuinapa estuaries, is a typical loose tongue in this region. He is of that splendid Latin American breed of tale spinners, magicians of crackerbarrel talk that's always spoken, never written down.

At seventy, his eyes still dance. He even laughed at Death, who came one night to seek him out.

"Toc toc toc," Death knocked.

"Come in," Wily coaxed from his bed. *"I was expecting you."*
But when he tried to take her pants down, Death fled in panic.

(309)

1961: São Salvador de Bahia
Amado

While Wily Humbug scares off death in Mexico, in Brazil novelist
Jorge Amado invents a captain who scares off solitude. According to
Amado, this captain defies hurricanes and will-o'-the-wisps, bestrides
seaquakes and black whirlpools, while treating his barrio neighbors
to drinks prepared from the recipes of an old Hong Kong sea-wolf.

When the captain is shipwrecked off the coast of Peru, his neighbors are shipwrecked too. It wrings their hearts, timid retired officials
that they are, sick with boredom and rheumatism, to see a mountain
of ice advancing toward the ship, off the port bow, on the foggy North
Sea; or the monsoon blowing furiously on the Sea of Bengal. All shiver
with pleasure as the captain evokes once again the Arab beauty who
bit juicy grapes as she danced on the sands of Alexandria, wearing
nothing but a white flower in her navel.

The captain has never left Brazil, nor set foot on any kind of
boat, because the sea makes him sick. He sits in the living room
of his house and the house sails off, drifting farther than Marco Polo
or Columbus or the astronauts ever dreamed.

(19)

1962: Cosalá
One Plus One Is One

Hitched to the same post, overloaded with dry wood, they look at
each other. He, amorously; she, dizzily. As the male and the female
burro consider and reconsider each other, devout women cross the
plaza, heading toward church, wrapped up in prayer. Because it's
Good Friday they chant mournful Masses for Our Lord Jesus Christ
as they go by, all in black: black mantillas, black stockings, black
gloves. They become frantic when the two burros, breaking their
bonds, romp over to enjoy themselves right there, in the plaza, facing
the church, rumps to city hall.

Screams resound across Mexico. The mayor of Cosalá, José Antonio Ochoa, emerges onto the balcony, lets out a shriek, and covers his eyes. He promptly orders the rebellious burros shot. They fall dead, hooked together in love.

(308 and 329)

1962: Villa de Jesús María
One Plus One Is All

In another mountain village not far away, the Cora Indians don masks and paint their naked bodies. As on every Good Friday, they give things new names while the fiesta lasts—passion of Christ, magic deer-hunt, murder of the god Sun, that crime from which human life on earth began.

"Let him die, let him kill, let him beget."

At the foot of the cross, dancing lovers offer themselves, embrace, enter one another, while the clown dancers skip about imitating them. Everyone joins in love-play, caressing, tickling, teasing. Everyone eats as they play: Fruits become projectiles, eggs bombs, and this great banquet ends in a war of hurled tortillas and showering honey. The Cora Indians enjoy themselves like lunatics, dancing, loving, eating in homage to the first agonies of the dying Christ. From the cross he smiles his thanks.

(46)

1963: Bayamo
Hurricane Flora

pounds Cuba for more than a week. The longest hurricane in the nation's history attacks, retreats, then returns as if realizing it had forgotten to smash a few last things. Everything spins around this giant, furious snake which twists and strikes suddenly, where least expected.

Useless to nail up doors and windows. The hurricane rips everything off, playing with houses and trees, flipping them into the air. The sky empties of panicky birds, while the sea floods the whole east of the island. From a base at Bayamo, brigades venture forth in launches and helicopters; volunteers come and go rescuing people

and animals, vaccinating whatever they find alive and burying or
burning the rest.

(18)

1963: Havana

Everyone a Jack-of-All-Trades

On this hurricane-devastated island, blockaded and harassed by the
United States, getting through the day is a feat. Store windows display
Vietnam solidarity posters but not shoes or shirts, and to buy the
smallest thing, you wait hours in line. The occasional automobile runs
on piston rings made of ox horns, and in art schools pencil graphite
is ground up to approximate paint. In the factories, cobwebs cover
some new machines, because a particular spare part has not yet completed its six-thousand-mile journey to get here. From remote Baltic
ports come the oil and everything else Cuba needs, and a letter to
Venezuela has to circle the globe before reaching its nearby destination.

And it's not only things that are lacking. Many know-it-alls have
gone to Miami on the heels of the have-it-alls.

And now?

"Now we have to invent."

At eighteen, Ricardo Gutiérrez paraded into Havana, rifle held
high, amid a tide of rifles, machetes, and palm-frond sombreros celebrating the end of Batista's dictatorship. On the following day he
had to take charge of various enterprises abandoned by their owners.
A women's underwear factory, among others, fell to his lot. Immediately the raw-material problems began. There was no latex foam
for the brassieres. The workers discussed the matter at a meeting and
decided to rip up pillows. It was a disaster. The pillow stuffing couldn't
be washed because it never dried.

Ricardo was twenty when they put two pesos in his pocket and
sent him to administer a sugar mill. He had never seen a sugar mill
in his life, even from a distance. There he discovered that cane juice
has a dark color. The previous administrator, a faithful servant with
a half-century of experience, had disappeared over the horizon carrying under his arm the oil portrait of Julio Lobo, lord of these canefields which the revolution has expropriated.

Now the foreign minister sends for him. Raúl Roa sits on the floor before a big map of Spain spread over the carpet, and starts to draw little crosses. This is how Ricardo finds out, at twenty-two, that they have made him a consul.

"*But I type with only two fingers,*" he stammers.

"*I type with one and I'm a minister,*" says Roa, putting an end to the matter.

1963: Havana
Portrait of the Bureaucrat

A black time engenders a red time that will make possible a green time: Solidarity slowly replaces greed and fear. Because it is capable of invention, of creation and madness, the Cuban revolution is making out. But it has enemies to spare. Among those most to be feared is the bureaucrat, devastating as the hurricane, asphyxiating as imperialism. There is no revolution without this germ in its belly.

The bureaucrat is the wooden man, that bloodless error of the gods, neither decisive nor indecisive, an echo with no voice, a transmitter of orders, not ideas. He considers any doubt heresy, any contradiction treason; confuses unity with unanimity, and sees the people as an eternal child to be led by the ear.

It is highly improbable that the bureaucrat will put his life on the line. It is absolutely impossible that he'll put his job on the line.

1963: Havana
Bola de Nieve

"*This is Yoruba-Marxism-Leninism,*" says Bola de Nieve, singer of Guanabacoa, son of Domingo the cook and Mama Inés. He says it in a sort of murmur, in his enormous little hoarse, fleshy voice. *Yoruba-Marxism-Leninism* is the name Bola de Nieve gives to the ardor and jubilation of these people who dance the Internationale with swaying hips, in this revolution born of the fierce embrace of Europe and Africa on the sands of America. In this place, gods made by men are crossed with men made by gods, the former descending to earth, the latter launched to conquer heaven; and Bola de Nieve celebrates it all with his salty songs.

1963: Río Coco

On His Shoulders He Carries
the Embrace of Sandino,

which time has not obliterated. Thirty years later, Colonel Santos López returns to war in the northern forests, so that Nicaragua may *be*.

A few years ago, the Sandinista Front was born. Carlos Fonseca Amador and Tomás Borge gave it birth along with Santos López and others who'd never known Sandino but wanted to perpetuate him.

The job will cost them blood, and they know it: *"So much filth can't be washed with water, no matter how holy,"* says Carlos Fonseca.

Lost, weaponless, drenched by the eternal rain, with nothing to eat—but eaten up, fucked over, and frustrated—the guerrillas wander the forest. There is no worse moment than sunset. Day is day and night is night, but dusk is the hour of agony, of frightful loneliness, and the Sandinistas are nothing yet, or nearly nothing.

(58 and 267)

1963: San Salvador

Miguel at Fifty-Eight

Miguel is living, as usual, from hand to mouth, unionizing campesinos and making mischief, when the police catch him in some little town and haul him, hands and feet bound, into the city of San Salvador.

Here he gets a protracted beating. For eight days they beat him hung up, and for eight nights they beat him on the floor. His bones creak, his flesh cries out, but he utters no sound as they torture him for his secrets. Yet when the captain insults the people he loves, the defiant old man heaves up his bleeding remains; the plucked rooster lifts his crest and crows.

Miguel orders the captain to shut his swinish trap. The captain buries a revolver barrel in his neck. Miguel defies him to shoot. The two remain face to face, ferocious, both gasping as if blowing on embers: the soldier, finger on trigger, eyes fixed on Miguel's; Miguel unblinking, counting the seconds, the centuries, as they pass, listening to the pounding of his heart as it rises into his head. Miguel gives himself up for dead now, really dead, when suddenly a shadow dims the furious glitter of the torturer's eyes, a weariness, or who knows what, and Miguel takes those eyes by storm. The torturer blinks, as if surprised to be where he is. Slowly, he lowers the gun, and with it, his eyes.

And so occurs the eleventh birth of Miguel Mármol, in his fifty-eighth year.

(222)

1963: Dallas
The Government Decides That Truth Doesn't Exist

At noon, on a street in Dallas, the president of the United States is assassinated. He is hardly dead when the official version is broadcast. In that version, which will be the definitive one, Lee Harvey Oswald alone has killed John Kennedy.

The weapon does not coincide with the bullet, nor the bullet with the holes. The accused does not coincide with the accusation: Oswald is an exceptionally bad shot of mediocre physique, but according to the official version, his acts were those of a champion marksman and Olympic sprinter. He has fired an old rifle with impossible speed and his magic bullet, turning and twisting acrobatically to penetrate Kennedy and John Connally, the governor of Texas, remains miraculously intact.

Oswald strenuously denies it. But no one knows, no one will ever know what he has to say. Two days later he collapses before the television cameras, the whole world witness to the spectacle, his mouth shut by Jack Ruby, a two-bit gangster and minor trafficker in women and drugs. Ruby says he has avenged Kennedy out of patriotism and pity for the poor widow.

(232)

1963: Santo Domingo

A Chronicle of Latin American Customs

From the sands of Sosúa, he used to swim out to sea, with a band playing to scare off the sharks.

Now, General Toni Imbert, potbellied and slack, rarely goes into the water; but he still returns to the beach of his childhood. He likes to sit on the waterfront, take aim, and shoot sharks. In Sosúa, the sharks compete with the poor for the leftovers from the slaughter-house. General Imbert is sorry for the poor. From the beach, he throws ten-dollar bills at them.

General Imbert greatly resembles his bosom friend, General Wessin y Wessin. Even with a cold, both can smell a Communist a mile off; and both have won many medals for getting up early and killing shackled people. When they say *"el presidente,"* both refer to the president of the United States.

Dominican graduates of the U.S. School of the Americas in Panama, Generals Imbert and Wessin y Wessin both fattened up under Trujillo's protection. Then both betrayed him. When, after Trujillo's death, elections were held and the people voted *en masse* for Juan Bosch, they could not stand still. Bosch refused to buy planes for the Air Force, announced agrarian reform, supported a divorce law, and raised wages.

The red lasted seven months. Imbert, Wessin y Wessin, and other generals of the nation have recovered power, that rich honey-comb, in an easy barracks revolt at dawn.

The United States loses no time recognizing the new government.

(61 and 281)

1964: Panama

Twenty-Three Boys Are Pumped Full of Lead

when they try to hoist the flag of Panama on Panamanian soil.

"We only used bird-shot," the commander of the North American occupation forces says defensively.

Another flag flies over the strip that slits Panama from sea to sea. Another law prevails, another police keep watch, another language is spoken. Panamanians may not enter the Canal Zone without permission, even to pick up fallen fruit from a mango tree, and they work here at second-class pay, like blacks and women.

The Canal Zone, North American colony, is both a business and a military base. The School of the Americas' courses are financed with the tolls ships pay. In the Canal Zone barracks, Pentagon officers teach anticommunist surgery to Latin American military men who will soon, in their own countries, occupy presidencies, ministries, commands, and embassies.

"They are the leaders of the future," explains Robert McNamara, secretary of defense of the United States.

Wary of the cancer that lies in wait for them, these military men will cut off the hands of anyone who dares to commit agrarian reform or nationalization, and tear out the tongues of the impudent or the inquisitive.

(248)

1964: Rio de Janeiro
"There are dark clouds,"

says Lincoln Gordon:

"Dark clouds are closing in on our economic interests in Brazil . . ."

President João Goulart has just introduced agrarian reform, the nationalization of oil refineries, and an end to the flight of capital. The indignant ambassador of the United States loudly attacks him. From the embassy, rivers of money flow to pollute public opinion, and the military prepare to seize power. A shrill call for a coup d'état is publicized by the media. Even the Lions Club signs it.

Ten years after Vargas's suicide the same furor erupts again, several times stronger. Politicians and journalists call for a uniformed Messiah who can put some order into the chaos. The TV broadcasts a film showing Berlin walls cutting Brazilian cities in two. Newspapers and radios exalt the virtues of private capital, which turns deserts into oases, and the merits of the armed forces, who keep Communists from stealing the water. Down the avenues of the chief cities the March of the Family with God for Liberty pleads to heaven for mercy.

Ambassador Lincoln Gordon excoriates the Communist plot: Goulart, estancia owner, is betraying his class at the moment of choice between devourers and devoured, between the makers and the objects of opinions, between the freedom of money and the freedom of people.

(115 and 141)

1964: Juiz de Fora

The Reconquest of Brazil

Almost thirty years after Captain Olympio Mourão Filho fabricated a Communist plot at the orders of President Vargas, General Mourão Filho buys a Communist plot fabricated by Ambassador Lincoln Gordon. The modest general confesses that in political matters he is just a uniformed ox, but he does understand about Communist conspiracies.

In the Juiz de Fora barracks he raises his sword: *"I'll snatch Brazil from the abyss!"*

Mourão has been awake since before dawn. While shaving he recites the psalm of David, the one that declares that all verdure will perish. Then he eats breakfast, congratulates his wife on being married to a hero, and at the head of his troops sets out to march on Rio de Janeiro.

The rest of the generals fall into line, and from the United States, already heading for Brazil, come one aircraft carrier, numerous planes and warships, and four fuel-supply ships. It's "Operation Brother Sam," to assist the rising.

João Goulart, irresolute, watches it happen. His colleague Lyndon Johnson sends warmest approval to the authors of the coup, even though Goulart still occupies the presidency; the State Department immediately offers generous loans to the new government. From the south, Leonel Brizola's attempt at resistance produces no echo. At last, Goulart heads into exile.

Some anonymous hand writes on a wall in Rio de Janeiro: *"No more middlemen! Lincoln Gordon for president!"*

But the triumphant generals choose Marshall Castelo Branco, a solemn military man without a sense of humor or a neck.

(115, 141, and 307)

1964: La Paz

Without Shame or Glory,

like the president of Brazil, President Víctor Paz Estenssoro boards a plane that will take him into exile.

He leaves behind him René Barrientos, babbling aviator, as dictator of Bolivia. Now the U.S. ambassador participates in cabinet meetings, seated among the ministers, and the manager of Gulf Oil draws up economic decrees.

Paz Estenssoro had been left devastatingly alone, and along with him falls the national revolution after twelve years in power. Bit by bit the revolution had turned around until it had shown its back to the workers, the better to suckle the new rich and the bureaucrats who squeezed it dry. Now, a slight puff suffices to blow it over.

Meanwhile, the divided workers fight among themselves, as if they were Laime and Jucumani tribesmen.

(16, 17, 26, and 473)

1964: North of Potosí

With Savage Fury

the Laime Indians fight the Jucumanis. The poorest of poor Bolivia, pariahs among pariahs, they devote themselves to killing one another on the frozen steppe north of Potosí. Five hundred from both tribes have died in the past ten years; the burned huts are beyond counting. Battles continue for weeks, without letup or mercy. The Indians cut one another to pieces to avenge petty grievances or disputes over scraps of sterile land in these lofty solitudes to which they were banished long, long ago.

Laimes and Jucumanis live on potatoes and barley, all the steppe with great effort will yield them. They sleep on sheepskins, accompanied by lice that welcome the warmth of their bodies.

For the ceremonies of mutual extermination they cover their heads with rawhide caps in the exact shape of the conquistadors' helmets.

(180)

Hats

in today's Bolivia are descended from Europe, brought by conquistadors and merchants; but they have been adapted to belong to this land and this people. Originally they were like cattle brands, compulsory disguises that helped each Spanish master recognize the Indians he owned. As time passed, communities began to deck out their headgear with their own stamps of pride, symbols of joy: stars and little moons of silver, colored feathers, glass beads, paper flowers, crowns of corn . . . Later, the English flooded Bolivia with bowlers and top hats: the black stovepipe hat of the Potosí Indian women, the white one of those of Cochabamba. By some mistake, the borsalino hat arrived from Italy and settled down on the heads of La Paz's Indian women.

The Bolivian Indian, man or woman, boy or girl, may go barefoot, but never hatless. The hat prolongs the head it protects; and when the soul falls, the hat picks it up off the ground.

(161)

1965: San Juan, Puerto Rico
Bosch

People stream into the streets of Santo Domingo, armed with whatever they can find, and pitch themselves against the tanks. "Thieves, get out!" they yell. "Come back, Juan Bosch, our president!"

The United States holds Bosch prisoner in Puerto Rico, preventing his return to his country in flames. A man of strong fiber, all tendon and tension, Bosch, alone in his anger, bites his fists, and his blue eyes pierce walls.

A journalist asks him over the phone if he is an enemy of the United States. No, he is only an enemy of U.S. imperialism.

"No one who has read Mark Twain," says Bosch, *"can be an enemy of the United States."*

(62 and 269)

1965: Santo Domingo

Caamaño

Into the melee pour students, soldiers, women in hair curlers. With barricades of barrels and overturned trucks, the rumbling advance of the tanks is stopped. Stones and bottles fly, while from the wingtips of swooping planes machinegun fire sweeps the Ozama River bridge and the thronged streets. The tide of people rises, and rising, separates the soldiers who had formerly served Trujillo: on one side, those commanded by Imbert and Wessin y Wessin, who are shooting people; on the other, the followers of Francisco Caamaño, who break open the arsenals and begin distributing rifles.

This morning, Colonel Caamaño set off the uprising for Bosch's return, believing it would be a matter of minutes. By midday, he realized it was a long job, that he would have to confront his comrades-in-arms, that blood was flowing; and had a horrifying presentiment of national tragedy. At nightfall he sought asylum in the Salvadoran embassy.

Collapsed in an armchair, Caamaño tries to sleep. He takes sedatives, his usual dose and more, but nothing works. Insomnia, teeth-grinding, nail-biting: Trujillo's legacy to him from the time when he was an officer in the dictator's army and performed, or saw performed, dark, sometimes atrocious deeds. Tonight it's worse than ever. He no sooner closes his eyes than he starts to dream. Dreaming, he is honest with himself; awakening he trembles, weeps, rages with shame for his fear.

Morning comes and his exile ends: It has lasted just one night. Colonel Caamaño wets his face and leaves the embassy. He walks staring at the ground, through the smoke of the fires, thick smoke that casts a shadow, and emerges into the shimmering light of day to return to his post at the head of the rebellion.

(223)

1965: Santo Domingo
The Invasion

Not by air, not by land, not by sea. General Wessin y Wessin's planes and General Imbert's tanks cannot still the free-for-all in the burning city any more than the ships that fire on the Government Palace, occupied by Caamaño, but kill housewives.

The United States embassy, which calls the rebels *Communist scum* and *a gang of thugs*, reports that there is no way to stop the disturbance and requests urgent aid from Washington. The Marines land.

Next day, the first invader dies: a boy from the mountains of northern New York State, shot from a roof, in a narrow street of this city whose name he had never heard in all his life. The first Dominican victim is a child of five. He dies on a balcony from a grenade explosion. The invaders had mistaken him for a sniper.

President Lyndon Johnson warns that he will not tolerate another Cuba in the Caribbean. More troops land. And more. Twenty thousand, thirty-five thousand, forty-two thousand. As U.S. soldiers tear up Dominicans, North American volunteers stitch them together in hospitals. Johnson exhorts his allies to join this Western Crusade. The military dictatorship of Brazil, the military dictatorship of Paraguay, the military dictatorship of Honduras, and the military dictatorship of Nicaragua all send troops to the Dominican Republic to save the democracy threatened by its people.

Trapped between river and sea, in the old barrio of Santo Domingo, its people resist.

José Mora Otero, secretary general of the Organization of American States, meets privately with Colonel Caamaño. He offers him six million dollars to leave the country, and is told to go to hell.

(62, 269, and 421)

1965: Santo Domingo
One Hundred Thirty-Two Nights

and this war of sticks and knives and carbines against mortars and machineguns still goes on. The city smells of gunpowder, garbage, and death.

Unable to force a surrender, the invaders, all-powerful as they are, have no alternative but agreement. The nobodies, the nothings have not let themselves be beaten. They have fought fierce battles by night, every night, house to house, body to body, yard by yard, until the moment the sun raised his flaming flag from the bottom of the sea, when they lowered themselves into darkness until the next night. And after so many nights of horror and glory, the invading troops do not succeed in installing General Imbert in power, nor General Wessin y Wessin, nor any other general.

(269 and 421)

1965: Havana

This Multiplier of Revolutions,

Spartan *guerrillero*, sets out for other lands. Fidel makes public Che Guevara's letter of farewell. "*Now nothing legal ties me to Cuba,*" says Che, "*only the bonds that cannot be broken.*"

Che also writes to his parents and to his children. He asks his children to be able to feel in their deepest hearts any injustice committed against anyone in any part of the world.

Here in Cuba, asthma and all, Che has been the first to arrive and the last to go, in war and in peace, without the slightest weakening.

Everyone has fallen in love with him—the women, the men, the children, the dogs, and the plants.

(213)

Che Guevara Bids Farewell to His Parents

Once again I feel under my heels the ribs of Rocinante: I return to the road with shield on arm . . .

Many will call me an adventurer, and that I am; only of a different type—of those who risk their hides to demonstrate their truths. This may be the decisive one. I do not seek it but it is within the logical estimate of probabilities. If that's how it is, this is my last embrace.

I have loved you a lot, only haven't known how to express my affection; I am extremely rigid in my actions and I think you sometimes didn't understand me. It wasn't easy to understand me, but just believe me today.

Now the will that I have polished with the delight of an artist will sustain this flabby pair of legs and these weary lungs. I will do it. Think once in a while about this little twentieth-century condottiere.

(213)

1966: Patiocemento
"We know that hunger is mortal,"

said the priest Camilo Torres. *"And if we know that, does it make sense to waste time arguing whether the soul is immortal?"*

Camilo believed in Christianity as the practice of loving one's neighbor, and wanted that love to be effective. He had an obsession about effective love. That obsession made him take up arms, and because of it, he has died, in an unknown corner of Colombia, fighting with the guerrillas.

(448)

1967: Llallagua
The Feast of San Juan

Bolivian miners are sons of the Virgin and nephews of the Devil, but neither can save them from early death. They are buried in the bowels of the earth, an implacable rain of mine dust annihilating them: In just a moment, a few short years, their lungs turn to stone and their tracheas close. Even before the lungs forget to breathe, the nose forgets smells and the tongue forgets tastes, the legs become like lead and the mouth discharges nothing but insult and vengefulness.

When they emerge from the pit, the miners look for a party. While their short life lasts and their legs still move, they need to eat spicy stews and swallow strong drink and sing and dance by the light of the bonfires that warm the barren plain.

On this night of San Juan, as the greatest of all fiestas is in progress, the army crouches in the mountains. Almost nothing is known here about the guerrillas of the distant Ñancahuazú River, although the story goes that they are fighting for a revolution so beautiful that, like the ocean, it has never been seen. But General Barrientos believes that a sly terrorist is lurking within every miner.

Before dawn, just as the Feast of San Juan is ending, a hurricane of bullets slashes through the town of Llallagua.

(16, 17, and 458)

1967: Catavi
The Day After

The light of the new day is like a glitter of bones. Then the sun hides behind clouds as the outcasts of the earth count their dead and carry them off in little carts. The miners march down a narrow muddy road in Llallagua. The procession crosses the river, dirty saliva flowing among stones of ash, and threads onto the vast pampa heading toward Catavi cemetery.

The sky, immense roof of tin, has no sun, and the earth no bonfires to warm it. Never was this steppe so frozen.

Many graves have to be dug. Bodies of every size are lined up, stretched out, waiting.

From the top of the cemetery wall, a woman screams.

(458)

1967: Catavi
Domitila

cries out against the murderers from the top of the wall.

She lives in two rooms without latrine or running water with her miner husband and seven children. The eighth child is eager to be born. Every day Domitila cooks, washes, sweeps, weaves, sews, teaches what she knows, cures what she can, prepares a hundred meat pies, and roams the streets looking for buyers.

For insulting the Bolivian army, they arrest her. A soldier spits in her face.

(458)

The Interrogation of Domitila

He spat in my face. Then he kicked me. I wouldn't take it and I slapped him. He punched me again. I scratched his face. And he was hitting me, hitting me . . . He put his knee here on my belly. He squeezed my neck and I almost choked. It seemed like he wanted to make my belly burst. He tightened his hold more and more . . . Then, with my two hands, with all my two hands, with all my strength I pulled his hands down. And I don't remember how, but I had grabbed him with my fist and was biting him, biting . . . I was horribly disgusted tasting his blood in my mouth . . . Then, with all my fury— tchá—I spat his blood all over his face. A tremendous howling started. He grabbed me, kicked me, hollered at me . . . He called the soldiers and had me seized by four or more of them . . .

When I woke up as if from a dream, I'd been swallowing a piece of my tooth. I felt it here in my throat. Then I noticed that this monster had broken six of my teeth. The blood was pouring over me and I couldn't open my eyes or my nose . . .

Then, as if fate ordained it, I began to give birth. I started to feel pains, pains and pains, and sometimes the baby that was coming seemed too much for me . . . I couldn't stand it any more. And I went to kneel down in a corner. I supported myself and covered my face, because I couldn't muster even a bit of strength. My face felt as if it was going to burst. And in one of those moments it came. I saw that the baby's head was already out . . . And right there I fainted.

How long afterward I don't know: "Where am I? Where am I?"

I was completely wet. The blood and the liquid that comes when you give birth had soaked me all over. Then I made an effort and somehow I got hold of the baby's cord. And pulling up the cord, at the end of the cord I found my little baby, cold, frozen, there on the floor.

(458)

1967: Catavi

The God in the Stone

After the gale of bullets, a gale of wind sweeps through the mining town of Llallagua removing all the roofs. In the neighboring parish of Catavi, the same wind topples and breaks the statue of the Virgin.

Its stone pedestal, however, remains intact. The priest comes to pick off the floor the pieces of the Immaculate One.

Look, father, say the workers, and they show him how the pedestal has shrugged off the burdensome Virgin.

Inside this pedestal the conquered ancient gods still sleep, dream, breathe, care for petitioners, and remind the mine workers that the great day will come: *Our day, the one we're waiting for.*

From the day it was originally found and worshipped by the workers the priest had condemned the miracle-working stone. He had shut it up in a cement cage so that the workers couldn't parade it in processions; then he put the Virgin on top of it. The mason who caged the stone at the priest's order has been shaking with fever and squinting ever since that fateful day.

(268)

1967: On the Ñancahuazú River Banks
Seventeen Men March to Annihilation

Cardinal Maurer arrives in Bolivia. From Rome he brings the Pope's blessings and word that God unequivocally backs General Barrientos against the guerrillas.

Meanwhile, hungry and disoriented, the guerrillas twist and turn through the Ñancahuazú River scrub. There are few campesinos in these immense solitudes; and not one, not a single one, has joined the little troop of Che Guevara. His forces dwindle from ambush to ambush. Che does not weaken, won't let himself weaken, although he feels that his body is a stone among stones, a heavy stone he drags along at the head of the others; nor does he let himself be tempted by the idea of saving the group by abandoning the wounded. By Che's order they all move at the pace of those least able to move: Together they will all be saved or lost.

Lost. Eighteen hundred soldiers, led by U.S. Rangers, are treading on their shadow. A ring is drawing tighter and tighter. Finally, a couple of campesino informers and the radar of the U.S. National Security Agency reveal their exact location.

(212 and 455)

1967: Yuro Ravine

The Fall of Che

Machinegun bullets break his legs. Sitting, he fights until the rifle is blown from his hands.

The conquering soldiers fall to blows over his watch, his canteen, his belt, his pipe. Several officers interrogate him, one after another. Che keeps quiet as his blood flows. Vice Admiral Ugarteche, daring land-wolf, head of the navy in a country without an ocean, insults and threatens him. Che spits in his face.

From La Paz comes the order to finish off the prisoner. A burst of gunfire. Che dies from a treacherous bullet shortly before his fortieth birthday, the age at which Zapata and Sandino died, also from treacherous bullets.

In the little town of Higueras, General Barrientos exhibits his trophy to journalists. Che lies on a laundry sink. They shoot him a final time, with flashbulbs. This last face has accusing eyes and a melancholy smile.

(212 and 455)

1967: Higueras

Bells Toll for Him

Did he die in 1967 in Bolivia because he guessed wrong about the when and the where and the how? Or did he not die at all, not anywhere, because he wasn't wrong about what really matters despite all the whens and wheres and hows?

He believed that one must defend oneself from the traps of greed without ever letting down one's guard. When he was president of the National Bank of Cuba, he signed the banknotes "Che," in mockery of money. For love of people, he scorned things. Sick is the world, he thought, in which to have and to be mean the same thing. He never kept anything for himself, nor ever asked for anything.

Living is giving oneself, he thought; and he gave himself.

1967: *La Paz*
Portrait of a Supermacho

On the shoulders of Nene, his giant bodyguard, General Barrientos crosses the city of La Paz. From Nene's shoulders he greets those who applaud him. He enters the government palace. Seated at his desk, with Nene behind him, he signs decrees that sell at bargain prices the sky, the soil, and the subsoil of Bolivia.

Ten years ago, Barrientos was putting in time in a Washington, D.C., psychiatric clinic when the idea of being president of Bolivia entered his head. He'd already made a career for himself as an athlete. Disguising himself as a North American aviator, he laid siege to power; and now he exercises it, machinegunning workers and pulling down libraries and wages.

The killer of Che is a cock with a loud crow, a man with three balls, a hundred women, and a thousand children. No Bolivian has flown so high, made so many speeches, or stolen so much.

In Miami, the Cuban exiles elect him Man of the Year.

(16, 17, 337, and 474)

1967: *Estoril*
Society Notes

Pinned to the hostess's gleaming coiffure are some of the world's largest diamonds. The cross on her granddaughter's necklace displays one of the world's largest emeralds. The Patiños, inheritors of one of the world's largest fortunes, throw one of the world's largest parties.

To make a thousand people happy night and day for a week, the Patiños collect *all* the elegant flowers and fine drinks buyable in Portugal. The invitations have gone out well ahead, so that the fashion-designers and society reporters could do their jobs properly. Several times a day the ladies change their dresses, all exclusive designs, and when two similar gowns appear in one salon, someone observes that she will fry Yves Saint-Laurent in oil. The orchestras come by charter from New York. The guests come in yachts or private planes.

Europe's nobility is out in force. The late lamented Simón Patiño, the anthropophagous Bolivian, devourer of miners, bought top-quality alliances. He married his daughters to a count and a marquis, and his son to a king's first cousin.

(34)

1967: Houston
Ali

They called him Cassius Clay: He chooses to call himself Muhammad Ali.

They made him a Christian: He chooses to make himself a Muslim.

They made him defend himself: No one punches like Ali, so fierce and fast, light tank, bulldozing feather, indestructible possessor of the world crown.

They told him that a good boxer confines his fighting to the ring: He says the real ring is something else, where a triumphant black fights for defeated blacks, for those who eat leftovers in the kitchen.

They advised discretion: From then on he yells.

They tapped his phone: From then on he yells on the phone, too.

They put a uniform on him to send him to Vietnam: He pulls it off and yells that he isn't going, because he has nothing against the Vietnamese, who have done no harm to him or to any other black American.

They took away his world title, they stopped him from boxing, they sentenced him to jail and a fine: He yells his thanks for these compliments to his human dignity.

(14 and 149)

1968: Memphis
Portrait of a Dangerous Man

The Reverend Martin Luther King preaches against the Vietnam War. He protests that twice as many blacks as whites are dying there, cannon fodder for an imperial adventure comparable to the Nazi crimes. The poisoning of water and land, the destruction of people and harvests are part of a plan of extermination. Of the million Vietnamese dead, says the preacher, the majority are children. The United States, he claims, is suffering from an infection of the soul; and any autopsy would show that the name of that infection is Vietnam.

Six years ago the FBI put this man in Section A of the Reserved List, among those dangerous individuals who must be watched and jailed in case of emergency. Since then the police hound him, spying on him day and night, threatening and provoking him.

Martin Luther King collapses on the balcony of a Memphis hotel. A bullet full in the face puts an end to this nuisance.

(254)

1968: San Jose, California

The Chicanos

Judge Gerald Chargin passes sentence on a lad accused of incest, and while he's at it, advises the young man to commit suicide and tells him, *"You Chicanos are worse than animals, miserable, lousy, rotten people . . ."*

The Chicanos are the descendants of those who came across the border river from Mexico to harvest cotton, oranges, tomatoes, and potatoes at dirt-cheap wages, and who stayed on in these southwestern and western states, which until little more than a century ago were the north of Mexico. In these lands, no longer theirs, they are used and despised.

Of every ten North Americans killed in Vietnam, six are blacks or Hispanics. And to them they say:

If you're so tough and strong, you go to the front lines first.

(182, 282, 369, and 403)

1968: San Juan, Puerto Rico

Albizu

Puerto Ricans are also good at dying in Vietnam in the name of those who took away their country.

The island of Puerto Rico, North American colony, consumes what it doesn't produce and produces what it doesn't consume. On its abandoned lands not even the rice and beans of the national dish are grown. Washington teaches the Puerto Ricans to breathe refrigerated air, eat canned food, drive long, well-chromed cars, sink up to the neck in debt, and lose their souls watching television.

Pedro Albizu Campos died a while back after almost twenty years spent in U.S. jails for his unceasing activities as an agitator. To win back the fatherland, one should love it with one's soul and one's life, he thought, as if it were a woman; to make it breathe again, one should rescue it with bullets.

He always wore a black tie for the lost fatherland. He was more and more alone.

(87, 116, 199, and 275)

1968: Mexico City
The Students

invade the streets. Such demonstrations have never been seen before in Mexico, so huge, so joyous, everyone linked arm in arm, singing and laughing. The students cry out against President Díaz Ordaz and his ministerial mummies, and all the others who have taken over Zapata's and Pancho Villa's revolution.

In Tlatelolco, a plaza where Indians and conquistadors once fought to the death, a trap is sprung. The army blocks every exit with strategically placed tanks and machineguns. Inside the corral, readied for the sacrifice, the students are hopelessly jammed together. A continuous wall of rifles with fixed bayonets advances to seal the trap.

Flares, one green, one red, give the signal. Hours later, a woman searches for her child, her shoes leaving bloody tracks on the ground.

(299 and 347)

"There was much, much blood," says the mother of a student,

"so much that I felt it thick on my hands. There was also blood on the walls. I think the walls of Tlatelolco have their pores full of blood; all Tlatelolco breathes blood . . . The bodies lay on the concrete waiting to be removed. I counted many from the window, about sixty-eight. They were piling them up in the rain. I remembered that my

*son Carlitos was wearing a green corduroy jacket and I thought I
saw it on each body . . ."*

(347)

1968: Mexico City
Revueltas

He has been around for half a century, but repeats daily the crime
of being young. Always at the center of any uproar, José Revueltas
now denounces the owners of power in Mexico, who, out of incurable
hatred for all that pulses, grows, and changes, have murdered three
hundred students in Tlatelolco.

"*The gentlemen of the government are dead. For that they
kill us.*"

In Mexico, power assimilates or annihilates, shoots deadly lightning with a hug or a slug, consigns to grave or prison the impudent
ones who will not be bought off with a sinecure. The incorrigible
Revueltas rarely sleeps outside a cell; and when he does, he spends
the night stretched out on some bench in a park, or on a desk at the
university. Hated by the police for being a revolutionary and by
dogmatists of all types for being free, he is condemned by pious leftists
for his predilection for cheap bars. Not long ago, his comrades provided him with a guardian angel to save him from temptation, but
the angel had to pawn his wings to pay for the sprees they enjoyed
together.

(373)

1968: Banks of the River Yaqui
The Mexican Revolution Isn't There Anymore

The Yaqui Indians, warriors for centuries, call upon Lázaro Cárdenas.
They meet him on a bright sunny prairie in northern Mexico, near
their ancestral river.

Standing in the shade of a leafy breadfruit tree, the chiefs of the
eight Yaqui tribes welcome him. On their heads gleam the plumes
reserved for great occasions.

"*Remember, Tata?*" Thirty years have passed and this is a great occasion. The top chief speaks: *"Tata Lázaro, do you remember? You gave us back the lands. You gave us hospitals and schools."*

At the end of each sentence the chiefs beat the ground with their staves, and the dry echo reverberates across the prairie.

"You remember? We want you to know, the rich have taken back the lands. The hospitals have been turned into barracks. The schools are cantinas."

Cárdenas listens and says nothing.

(45)

1968: Mexico City
Rulfo

In the silence, the heartbeat of another Mexico. Juan Rulfo, teller of tales about the misadventures of the dead and the living, keeps silent. Fifteen years ago he said what he had to say, in a small novel and a few short stories, and since then he says nothing. Or rather, he made the deepest kind of love, and then went to sleep.

1969: Lima
Arguedas

splits his skull with a bullet. His story is the story of Peru: Sick with Peru, he kills himself.

The son of whites, José María Arguedas was raised by Indians and spoke Quechua throughout his childhood. At seventeen, he was torn away from the sierra and thrust into the coastal area—from the small communal towns to the proprietorial cities.

He learned the language of the victors and spoke and wrote it. He never wrote *about* the vanquished, rather *from* them. He knew how to express them; but his feat was his curse. He felt that everything about him was treachery or failure; he felt torn apart. He couldn't be Indian; he didn't want to be white. He couldn't endure both the scorning and the being scorned.

This lonely wayfarer walked at the edge of an abyss, between two enemy worlds that divided his soul. Many an avalanche of anguish

swept down on him, worse than any landslide of mud and rocks, until
finally he was overwhelmed.

(30 and 256)

1969: Sea of Tranquillity
The Discovery of the Earth

The space ship from Houston, Texas, puts down its long spider legs
on the Moon. Astronauts Armstrong and Aldrin see the Earth as no
one has seen it before, an Earth that is not the generous breast that
gives us milk and poison to suck, but a handsome frozen stone rotating
in the solitude of the universe. The Earth seems to be childless,
uninhabited, perhaps even indifferent, as if it didn't feel a single
tickle from the human passions that swarm on its soil.

Via television and radio, the astronauts send us preprogrammed
words about the great step that humanity is taking, while they stick
the flag of the United States of America into the stony Sea of Tran-
quillity.

1969: Bogotá
The Urchins

They have the street for a home. They are cats made for jumping and
slapping, sparrows for flying, little cocks for fighting. They go about
in packs, in gangs. They sleep in clusters, bunched together against
the freezing dawns. They eat what they steal or the leftovers they
beg or the garbage they find; they have grey teeth and faces burned
by the cold.

Arturo Dueñas, of the Twenty-second Street gang, leaves his
pack, fed up with offering his bottom to be spanked just because he's
the smallest, the bedbug, the tick. He decides he'll fare better on
his own.

One night, a night like any other, Arturo slips under a restaurant
table, grabs a chicken leg, and brandishing it like a flag, scoots off
down an alley. When he finds some obscure nook, he sits down to
have supper. A little dog watches him and licks its chops. Several
times Arturo pushes it away, but the dog returns. They examine each

other: The two are equals, sons of nobody, beaten, pure bone and grime. Arturo resigns himself and shares.

Since then they've gone together on winged feet, sharing the danger, the booty, and the lice. Arturo, who has never talked to anybody, opens up, and the little dog sleeps curled up at his feet.

One accursed day the police catch Arturo robbing buns and haul him to the Fifth Precinct for a tremendous beating. When, in time, Arturo returns to the street, all battered, the little dog is nowhere to be seen. Arturo runs back and forth, searching wildly everywhere, but it doesn't appear. A lot of questions, and nothing. A lot of calling, and nothing. No one in the world is so alone as this child of seven who is alone on the streets of the city of Bogotá, hoarse from so much screaming.

(68 and 342)

1969: Any City
Someone

On a corner, by a red light, someone swallows fire, someone washes windshields, someone sells Kleenex, chewing gum, little flags, and dolls that make pee-pee. Someone listens to the horoscope on the radio, pleased that the stars are concerned about him. Walking between the tall buildings, someone would like to buy silence or air, but doesn't have the cash. In a filthy barrio, amid swarms of flies above and armies of rats below, someone hires a woman for three minutes. In a whorehouse cell the raped becomes the rapist, better than making it with a donkey in the river. Someone talks to no one on the phone, after hanging up the receiver. Someone talks to no one in front of the TV set. Someone talks to no one in front of a one-armed bandit. Someone waters a pot of plastic flowers. Someone climbs on an empty bus, at dawn, and the bus stays empty.

1969: Rio de Janeiro
Expulsion from the Slums

They refuse to go. They have been the poorest of the poor in the countryside and now they're the poorest in the city, always the last in line, people with cheap hands and dancing feet. Here, at least, they live near the places where they earn their bread. The inhabitants of Praia do Pinto and the other slums covering Rio de Janeiro's mountains have turned stubborn. But the military has long eyed these tracts, highly salable and resalable and well-suited for speculation, and so the problem will be solved by means of an opportune fire. The firemen never turn up. Dawn is the hour of tears and cinders. After fire destroys the houses made of garbage, they sweep up the people like garbage and take them far away for dumping.

(340)

1969: Baixo Grande
A Castle of Garbage

Old man Gabriel dos Santos does what his dreams tell him to do. He dreams the same crazy dreams in Brazil that Antonio Gaudí dreamed decades ago in Catalonia, in far-off Barcelona, although old Gabriel has never heard of Gaudí or seen his works.

As soon as he awakes, old Gabriel starts modeling with his hands the marvels he sees in his dreams, before they get away from him. Thus he has built the House of the Flower. In it he lives, on the slope of a hill beaten by the ocean wind. From dream to dream, through the years, old Gabriel's home keeps growing, this strange castle or beast of bright colors and sinuous forms, all made of garbage.

Old Gabriel, worker in the salt mines, never went to school, never watched television, never had money. He knows no rules, has no models. He plays around, in his own free style, with whatever leftovers the nearby city of Cabo Frío throws his way: fenders, headlights, splintered windows and smashed bottles, broken dishes, bits of old iron, chair legs, wheels . . .

(171)

1969: Arque Pass
The Last Stunt of Aviator Barrientos

Cardinal Maurer says that President Barrientos is like Saint Paul, because he roams the Bolivian countryside handing out truths. Barrientos also hands out money and soccer balls. He comes and goes, raining banknotes by helicopter. Gulf Oil gave the helicopter to Barrientos in exchange for the two billion dollars' worth of gas and one billion of petroleum that Barrientos gave Gulf Oil.

On this same helicopter, Barrientos paraded with Che Guevara's body tied to its skids through the skies of Bolivia. On this helicopter Barrientos arrives at Arque Pass on one of his incessant junkets, and as usual tosses money down on the campesinos; but on taking off, he collides with a wire fence and crashes against some rocks, burning himself alive. After burning so many pictures and books, fiery Barrientos dies cooked to a crisp in his helicopter, filled to the brim with banknotes that burn with him.

(16, 17, and 474)

1969: San Salvador and Tegucigalpa
Two Turbulent Soccer Matches

are played between Honduras and El Salvador. Ambulances remove the dead and wounded from the stands, while fans continue the stadium uproar in the streets.

Immediately, the two countries break relations. In Tegucigalpa, automobile windshields carry stickers that say: *Honduran—grab a stick, be a man, kill a Sal-va-dor-e-an.* In San Salvador, the newspapers urge the army to invade Honduras *to teach those barbarians a lesson.* Honduras expels Salvadoran campesinos, who are mostly unaware they are foreigners, having never seen an identity document. The Honduran government forces the Salvadorans to leave with nothing but what they have on, and then burns their shacks, describing the expulsion as "agrarian reform." The government of San Salvador considers all Hondurans who live there to be spies.

War soon breaks out. The army of El Salvador crosses into Honduras and advances, machinegunning border villages.

(84, 125, and 396)

1969: San Salvador and Tegucigalpa
The Soccer War

pits as enemies two fragments of Central America, shreds of what was a single republic a century and a half ago.

Honduras, a small agrarian country, is dominated by big landlords.

El Salvador, a small agrarian country, is dominated by big land-lords.

The campesinos of Honduras have neither land nor work.

The campesinos of El Salvador have neither land nor work.

In Honduras there is a military dictatorship born of a coup d'état.

In El Salvador there is a military dictatorship born of a coup d'état.

The general who governs Honduras was trained at the School of the Americas in Panama.

The general who governs El Salvador was trained at the School of the Americas in Panama.

From the United States come the weapons and advisers of the dictator of Honduras.

From the United States come the weapons and advisers of the dictator of El Salvador.

The dictator of Honduras accuses the dictator of El Salvador of being a Communist in the pay of Fidel Castro.

The dictator of El Salvador accuses the dictator of Honduras of being a Communist in the pay of Fidel Castro.

The war lasts one week. While war continues, the people of Honduras think their enemy is the people of El Salvador and the people of El Salvador think their enemy is the people of Honduras. They leave four thousand dead on the battlefields.

(84 and 125)

1969: Port-au-Prince

A Law Condemns to Death Anyone Who Says or Writes Red Words in Haiti

Article One: Communist activities are declared to be crimes against the security of the state, in whatsoever form: any profession of Communist faith, verbal or written, public or private, any propagation of Communist or anarchist doctrines through lectures, speeches, conversations, readings, public or private meetings, by way of pamphlets, posters, newspapers, magazines, books, and pictures; any oral or written correspondence with local or foreign associations, or with persons dedicated to the diffusion of Communist or anarchist ideas; and furthermore, the act of receiving, collecting, or giving funds directly or indirectly destined for the propagation of said ideas.

Article Two: The authors and accomplices of these crimes shall be sentenced to death. Their movable and immovable property shall be confiscated and sold for the benefit of the state.

> *Dr. François Duvalier*
> *President-for-Life*
> *of the Republic of Haiti*
> (351)

1970: Montevideo
Portrait of a Torture Trainer

The Tupamaro guerrillas execute Dan Anthony Mitrione, one of the North American instructors of the Uruguayan police.

The dead man gave his courses to officers in a soundproof basement. For his practical lessons he used beggars and prostitutes pulled off the street. He showed his pupils the effects of various electric voltages on the most sensitive parts of the human body, and how to apply emetics and other chemical substances efficaciously. In recent months three men and a woman died during these classes in the Technique of Interrogation.

Mitrione despised disorder and dirt. A torture chamber should be as aseptic as an operating room. And he detested incorrect language: *"Not balls, commissioner. Testicles."*

He also abominated useless expense, unnecessary movement, avoidable damage.

"It's an art, more than a technique," he said. *"The precise pain in the precise place, in the precise amount."*

(225)

1970: Managua
Rugama

A distinguished poet, a little man in a surplice who received Holy Communion standing up, shoots his last bullet and dies resisting a whole battalion of Somoza's troops.

Leonel Rugama was twenty.

Of friends, he preferred chess players.

Of chess players, those who lose because of the girl passing by.

Of those who pass by, the one who stays.

Of those who stay, the one who has yet to come.

Of heroes, he preferred those who don't say they are dying for their country.

Of countries, the one born of his death.

(399)

1970: Santiago de Chile
Landscape after Elections

In a display of unpardonably bad conduct, the Chilean people elect Salvador Allende president. Another president, of the International Telephone and Telegraph Corporation, offers a million dollars to whoever can put an end to this disgrace, while the president of the United States earmarks ten million for the affair. Richard Nixon instructs the CIA to prevent Allende from sitting in the presidential chair; or, should he sit, to see that the chair doesn't stay under him long.

General René Schneider, head of the army, rejects the call for a coup d'état and is struck down in an ambush: *"Those bullets were for me,"* says Allende.

Loans from the World Bank and all other official and private banks are suspended, except those for the military. The price of copper plummets.

From Washington, Secretary of State Henry Kissinger explains: *"I don't see why we should have to stand by and let a country go Communist due to the irresponsibility of its own people."*

(138, 181, and 278)

1971: Santiago de Chile
Donald Duck

and his nephews spread the virtues of consumer civilization among the savages of an underdeveloped country with picture-postcard landscapes. Donald's nephews offer soap bubbles to the stupid natives in exchange for nuggets of pure gold, while Uncle Donald fights outlaw revolutionaries who disturb order.

From Chile, Walt Disney's comic strips are distributed throughout South America and enter the souls of millions of children. Donald Duck does not come out against Allende and his red friends; he doesn't need to. The world of Disney is already the lovable zoo of capitalism: Ducks, mice, dogs, wolves, and piglets do business, buy, sell, respond to advertising, get credit, pay dues, collect dividends, dream of bequests, and compete among themselves to have more and get more.

(139 and 287)

1971: Santiago de Chile
"Shoot at Fidel,"

the CIA has ordered two of its agents. Certain TV cameras that appear to be busy filming Fidel Castro's visit to Chile conceal automatic pistols. The agents zoom in on Fidel, they have him in their sights—but neither shoots.

For many years now, specialists of the CIA's technical services division have been dreaming up attacks on Fidel. They've spent fortunes trying out cyanide capsules in chocolate malteds, and pills that dissolve in beer and rum and are untraceable in an autopsy. They've tried bazookas and telescopic rifles, a thirty-kilo plastic bomb that an agent was to put in a drain beneath a speaker's platform. Even poisoned cigars: They fixed up a special Havana for Fidel—supposed to kill the moment it touched his lips. But it didn't work, so they tried another guaranteed to produce nausea and, worse yet, a high-pitched voice—if they couldn't kill *him*, they hoped at least to kill his prestige. To this end also they tried spraying the microphone with a powder guaranteed to provoke in mid-speech an irresistible tendency to talk nonsense, and then, as the coup de grâce, concocted a depilatory potion to make his beard fall out, leaving him naked before the crowd.

(109, 137, and 350)

1972: Managua
Nicaragua, Inc.

The tourist arrives in Somoza's plane or ship and lodges in one of Somoza's hotels in the capital. Tired, he falls asleep on a bed and mattress manufactured by Somoza. On awaking, he drinks Presto coffee, property of Somoza, with milk from Somoza's cows and sugar harvested on a Somoza plantation and refined in a Somoza mill. He lights a match produced by Somoza's firm, Momotombo, and tries a cigarette from the Nicaraguan Tobacco Company, which Somoza owns in association with the British-American Tobacco Company.

The tourist goes out to change money at a Somoza bank and buys the Somoza daily *Novedades* on the corner. Reading *Novedades* is an impossible feat, so he throws the paper into the garbage which, tomorrow morning, will be collected by a Mercedes truck imported by Somoza.

The tourist climbs on one of Somoza's Condor buses, which will take him to the mouth of the Masaya volcano. Rolling toward the fiery crest, he sees through the window the barrios of tin cans and mud where live the dirt-cheap hands used by Somoza.

The tourist returns at nightfall. He drinks a rum distilled by Somoza, with ice from the Somoza Polar company, eats meat from one of his calves, butchered in one of his slaughterhouses, with rice from one of his farms and salad dressed with Corona oil, which belongs jointly to Somoza and United Brands.

Half past midnight, the earthquake explodes. Perhaps the tourist is one of the twelve thousand dead. If he doesn't end in some common grave, he will rest in peace in a coffin from Somoza's mortuary concern, wrapped in a shroud from El Porvenir textile mill, property of . . .

(10 and 102)

1972: Managua
Somoza's Other Son

The cathedral clock stops forever at the hour the earthquake lifts the city into the air. The quake shakes Managua and destroys it.

In the face of this catastrophe Tachito Somoza proves his virtues both as statesman and as businessman. He decrees that bricklayers shall work sixty hours a week without a centavo more in pay and declares: *"This is the revolution of opportunities."*

Tachito, son of Tacho Somoza, has displaced his brother Luis from the throne of Nicaragua. A graduate of West Point, he has sharper claws. At the head of a voracious band of second cousins and third uncles, he swoops down on the ruins. He didn't invent the earthquake, but he gets his out of it.

The tragedy of half a million homeless people is a splendid gift for this Somoza, who traffics outrageously in debris and lands; and, as if that weren't enough, he sells in the United States the blood donated to victims of the quake by the International Red Cross. Later, he extends this profitable scam: Showing more initiative and enterprising spirit than Count Dracula, Tachito Somoza founds a limited company to buy blood cheap in Nicaragua and sell it dear on the North American market.

(10 and 102)

Tachito Somoza's Pearl of Wisdom

I don't show off my money as a symbol of power, but as a symbol of job opportunities for Nicaraguans.

(434)

1972: Santiago de Chile
Chile Trying to Be Born

A million people parade through the streets of Santiago in support of Salvador Allende and against the embalmed bourgeoisie who pretend to be alive and Chilean.

A people on fire, a people breaking the custom of suffering: In search of itself, Chile recovers its copper, iron, nitrates, banks, foreign trade, and industrial monopolies. It also nationalizes the ITT telephone system, paying for it the small amount that ITT said it was worth in its tax returns.

(278 and 449)

1972: Santiago de Chile
Portrait of a Multinational Company

ITT has invented a night scope to detect guerrillas in the dark, but doesn't need it to find them in the government of Chile—just money, of which the company is spending plenty against President Allende.

Recent experience shows how worthwhile it is: The generals who now rule Brazil have repaid ITT several times over the dollars invested to overthrow President Goulart.

ITT, with its four hundred thousand workers and officials in seventy countries, earns much more than Chile. On its board of directors sit men who were previously directors of the CIA and the World Bank. ITT conducts multiple businesses on all the continents: It produces electronic equipment and sophisticated weapons, organizes national and international communication systems, participates in space flights, lends money, works out insurance deals, exploits forests, provides tourists with automobiles and hotels, and manufactures telephones and dictators.

(138 and 407)

1973: Santiago de Chile
The Trap

By diplomatic pouch come the dollars that finance strikes, sabotage, and lies. Businessmen paralyze Chile and deny it food. There is no other market than the black market. People have to form long lines for a pack of cigarettes or a kilo of sugar. Getting meat or oil requires a miracle of the Most Sainted Virgin Mary. The Christian Democrats and the newspaper *El Mercurio* abuse the government and openly demand a redemptory coup d'état, since the time has come to finish with this red tyranny. Newspapers, magazines, and radio and TV stations echo the cry. For the government it is tough to make any move whatsoever: judges and parliamentarians dig in their heels, while in the barracks key military men whom Allende believes loyal conspire against him.

In these difficult times, workers are discovering the secrets of the economy. They're learning it isn't impossible to produce without bosses or supply themselves without merchants. But they march without weapons, empty-handed, down this freedom road.

Across the horizon sail U.S. warships preparing to exhibit themselves off the Chilean coast. The military coup, so much heralded, occurs.

(181, 278, and 449)

1973: Santiago de Chile
Allende

He likes the good life. He has said many times that he doesn't have what it takes to be an apostle or a martyr. But he has also said that it's worthwhile to die for that without which it's not worthwhile to live.

The rebel generals demand his resignation. They offer him a plane to take him out of Chile. They warn him that the presidential palace will be bombarded.

Together with a handful of men, Salvador Allende listens to the news. The generals have taken over the country. Allende dons a helmet and readies his rifle. The first bombs fall with a shuddering crash. The president speaks on the radio for the last time:

"*I am not going to resign . . .*"

(449 and 466)

1973: Santiago de Chile
Great Avenues Will Open Up, Announces Salvador Allende in His Final Message

I am not going to resign. Placed in a critical moment of history, I will pay with my life for the loyalty of the people. And let me tell you that I am sure the seed we sowed in the dignified conscience of Chileans will definitely not be destroyed. They have the force. They might be able to overcome us, but social processes cannot be stopped with crime or force. History is ours and the people make it . . .

Workers of my country: I have faith in Chile and its destiny. Other men will surmount this gray and bitter moment when treason seeks to impose itself. Rest assured that, much sooner than later, great avenues will once again open up through which free mankind shall pass to build a better society. Long live Chile, long live the people, long live the workers! These are my last words. I am certain that my sacrifice will not be in vain.

1973: Santiago de Chile
The Reconquest of Chile

A great black cloud rises from the flaming palace. President Allende dies at his post as the generals kill Chileans by the thousands. The Civil Registry does not record the deaths, because the books don't have room enough for them, but General Tomás Opazo Santander offers assurances that the victims do not exceed .01 percent of the population, which is not, after all, a high social cost, and CIA director William Colby explains in Washington that, thanks to the executions, Chile is avoiding a civil war. Señora Pinochet declares that the tears of mothers will redeem the country.

Power, all power, is assumed by a military junta of four members, formed in the School of the Americas in Panama. Heading it is General Augusto Pinochet, professor of geopolitics. Martial music resounds against a background of explosions and machinegun fire. Radios broadcast decrees and proclamations which promise more bloodshed, while the price of copper suddenly rises on the world market.

The poet Pablo Neruda, dying, asks for news of the terror. At moments he manages to sleep, and raves in his sleep. The vigil and the dream are one great nightmare. Since he heard Salvador Allende's proud farewell on the radio, the poet has begun his death-throes.

(278, 442, and 449)

1973: Santiago de Chile
The Home of Allende

Before attacking the presidential palace, they bombarded Allende's house.

Afterward, the soldiers wiped out whatever remained. With bayonets they ripped up paintings by Matta, Guayasamín, and Portocarrero; with axes they smashed furniture.

A week has passed. The house is a garbage heap. Arms and legs from the suits of armor that adorned the staircase are littered everywhere. In the bedroom a soldier snores, sleeping off a hangover, his legs flung apart, surrounded by empty bottles.

From the living room comes a moaning and panting. There, in a big yellow armchair, torn apart but still standing, the Allendes' bitch is giving birth. The puppies, still blind, grope for her warmth and milk. She licks them.

(345)

1973: Santiago de Chile
The Home of Neruda

Amid the devastation, in a home likewise chopped to bits, lies Neruda, dead from cancer, dead from sorrow. His death isn't enough, though, Neruda being a man so stubbornly alive, so the military must kill his things. They splinter his happy bed and happy table, they disembowel his mattress and burn his books, smash his lamps and his colored bottles, his pots, his paintings, his seashells. They tear the pendulum and the hands off his wall clock; and with a bayonet gouge out the eye of the portrait of his wife.

From his devastated home, flooded with water and mud, the poet leaves for the cemetery. A cortege of intimate friends escorts him, led by Matilde Urrutia. (He once said to her: *It was so beautiful to live when you were living.*)

Block by block, the cortege grows. On every street corner it is joined by people who fall into step despite the military trucks bristling with machineguns and the carabineros and soldiers who come and go on motorcycles and in armored cars, exuding noise and fear. Behind some window, a hand salutes. High on some balcony a handkerchief waves. This is the twelfth day since the coup, twelve days of shutting up and dying, and for the first time the Internationale is heard in Chile—the Internationale hummed, groaned, wept, but not sung until the cortege becomes a procession and the procession a demonstration, and the people, marching against fear, break into song in the streets of Santiago, at the top of their lungs, with all their voices, to accompany in a fitting way Neruda, the poet, their poet, on his last journey.

(314 and 442)

1973: Miami

Sacred Consumerism Against
the Dragon of Communism

The bloodbath in Chile inspires fear and disgust everywhere, but not in Miami: A jubilant demonstration of exiled Cubans celebrates the murder of Allende and all the others.

Miami now has the greatest concentration of Cubans in the world, Havana excepted. Eighth Street is the Cuba that was. The dreams of bringing down Fidel have faded, but walking down Eighth Street one returns to the good old lost days.

Bankers and mafiosi run the show here; anyone who thinks is crazy or a dangerous Communist, and blacks still know their place. Even the silence is strident. Plastic souls and flesh-and-blood automobiles are manufactured. In the supermarkets, things buy people.

(207)

1973: Recife

Eulogy of Humiliation

In the capital of northeast Brazil, Gilberto Freyre attends the opening of a restaurant named for his famous book, *Great House and Slave Quarters*. Here, the writer celebrates the fortieth anniversary of the book's first edition.

The waiters serving the tables are dressed as slaves. Atmosphere is created by whips, shackles, pillories, chains, and iron collars hanging from the walls. The guests feel they have returned to a superior age when black served white without any joking, as the son served the father, the woman her husband, the civilian the soldier, and the colony the motherland.

The dictatorship of Brazil is doing everything possible to further this end. Gilberto Freyre applauds it.

(170 and 306)

1974: Brasília
Ten Years after the Reconquest of Brazil

the economy is doing very well. The people, very badly. According to official statistics, the military dictatorship has made Brazil an economic power, with a high growth index for its gross national product. They also show that the number of undernourished Brazilians has risen from twenty-seven million to seventy-two million, of whom thirteen million are so weakened by hunger that they can no longer run.

(371, 377, and 378)

1974: Rio de Janeiro
Chico

This dictatorship hurts people and decomposes music. Chico Buarque, made of music and people, sings against it.

Of every three songs he writes, the censor bans or mutilates two. Almost daily, the political police make him undergo long interrogations. As he enters their offices, they search his clothing. As he leaves, Chico searches his innards to see if the police have put a censor in his soul or, in an unguarded moment, confiscated his joy.

1974: Guatemala City
Twenty Years after the Reconquest of Guatemala

In towns and cities chalk crosses appear on doors, and by the roadsides heads are stuck on stakes. As a lesson and a warning, crime is turned into a public spectacle. The victims are stripped of name and history, then thrown into the mouth of a volcano or to the bottom of the sea, or buried in a common grave under the inscription *NN*, which means *non nato*, which means not born. For the most part this state terrorism functions without uniform. It is called the Hand, the Shadow, the Lightning Flash, the Secret Anticommunist Army, the Order of Death, the Squadron of Death.

General Kjell Laugerud, newly come to the presidency after

faked elections, commits himself to a continued application in Guatemala of the techniques pioneered by the Pentagon in Vietnam. Guatemala is the first Latin American laboratory for dirty war.

(450)

1974: Forests of Guatemala
The Quetzal

was always the joy of the air in Guatemala. The most resplendent of birds continues to be the symbol of this country, although now rarely if ever seen in the high forests where it once flourished. The quetzal is dying out while vultures are multiplying. The vulture, who has a good nose for death from afar, completes the work of the army, following the executioners from village to village, circling anxiously.

Will the vulture, shame of the sky, replace the quetzal on banknotes, in the national anthem, on the flag?

1974: Ixcán
A Political Education Class in Guatemala

Full of worms and uncertainties, the guerrillas cross the forest. These famished shadows have been walking in the dark for many days beneath a roof of trees, shut off from the sun. For a clock, they use the voices of the thicket: The nightjar sings from the river announcing dawn; at dusk the parrots and macaws begin their scandalous chatter; when night falls the badgers scream and the coatis cough. On this occasion, for the first time in months, the guerrillas hear a cock crow. A village is close by.

In this village on this sierra, a landlord known as the Tiger of Ixcán is boss. Like the other masters of this land, he is exempted from the law and criminal responsibility. On his farms are gallows, whips, and pillories. When the local labor force is insufficient, the army sends him Indians by helicopter, to cut down trees or pick coffee for nothing.

Few have seen the Tiger of Ixcán. All fear him. He has killed many, has had many killed.

The guerrillas bring the Indians together and show them. The Tiger, dead, looks like an empty costume.

(336)

1974: Yoro
Rain

In Chile he has seen a lot of dying, his dearest friends shot, beaten, or kicked to death. Juan Bustos, one of President Allende's advisers, has saved himself by a hair.

Exiled in Honduras, Juan drags out his days. Of those who died in Chile, how many died instead of him? From whom is he stealing the air he breathes? He has been this way for months, dragging himself from sorrow to sorrow, ashamed of surviving, when one evening his feet take him to a town called Yoro, in the central depths of Honduras.

He arrives in Yoro for no particular reason, and in Yoro spends the night under any old roof. He gets up very early and starts walking half-heartedly through the dirt streets, fearing melancholy, staring without seeing.

Suddenly, the rain hits him, so violent that Juan covers his head, though noticing right away that this prodigious rain isn't water or hail. Crazy silver lights bounce off the ground and jump through the air.

"It's raining fish!" cries Juan, slapping at the live fish that dive down from the clouds and leap and sparkle around him. Never again will it occur to him to curse the miracle of being alive, never again will he forget that he had the luck to be born in America.

"That's right," says a neighbor, quietly, as if it were nothing. *"Here in Yoro it rains fish."*

1975: San Salvador
Miguel at Seventy

Each day of life is an unrepeatable chord of a music that laughs at death. With the dangerous Miguel still alive, El Salvador's masters decide to hire an assassin to send his life and his music somewhere else.

The assassin has a dagger hidden beneath his shirt. Miguel sits talking to students at the university. He is telling them that young people must take the place of their jaded elders, that they must act, risk their necks, and do what must be done without cackling like hens each time they lay an egg. The assassin slowly slips through the audience until he's right behind Miguel. But as he raises the blade, a woman screams and Miguel automatically flings himself to the ground, just avoiding the blow.

And thus occurs the twelfth birth of Miguel Mármol, at seventy years of age.

(222)

1975: San Salvador
Roque

Roque Dalton, Miguel Mármol's pupil in the art of resurrection, has twice escaped death up against the wall. Once he was saved because the government fell; the second time because the wall itself fell, thanks to an opportune earthquake. He also escaped from the torturers, who left him in bad shape but alive, and from the police, who chased him with blazing guns. He even escaped from stone-throwing soccer fans, from the fury of a woman scorned, and from numerous husbands thirsting for revenge.

Profound yet playful, the poet Roque preferred to laugh at himself than take life too seriously, and so saved himself from grandiloquence, solemnity, and other ailments so gravely afflicting Latin American political poetry.

Only from his comrades can he not save himself. It is they who condemn him, for the crime of Difference of Opinion. This bullet, the only one that could find Roque, had to come from right beside him.

(127)

1975: Amazon River
Tropical Landscape

The ship chugs slowly up the Amazon on this endless voyage from Belém to Manaos. Now and then, some shack masked by tangled lianas comes into view, and a naked child waves his hand at the crew.

On the jammed deck someone reads the Bible aloud, sonorous praises to God, but most people prefer to laugh and sing as bottles and cigarettes pass from mouth to mouth. A tame cobra entwines itself on iron crossbeams, brushing against the skins of dead brothers drying in the air. The owner of the cobra, seated on the deck, challenges the other passengers to a game of cards.

A Swiss journalist traveling on this ship has for hours been watching a poor, bony old man embracing a large carton he never unclutches, even in his sleep. Stung by curiosity, the Swiss offers cigarettes, cookies, and conversation, but the old fellow is one without vices who isn't hungry and has nothing to say.

In the middle of the voyage, in mid-jungle, the old man disembarks. The Swiss, helping him take the big carton ashore, peeks through the half-open lid and sees inside, wrapped in cellophane, a plastic palm tree.

(264)

1975: Amazon River
This Is the Father of All Rivers,

the mightiest river in the world, and the jungle sprouting from its breath is the last lung of this planet. The adventurous and the avaricious have flocked to Amazonia since the first Europeans who came this way discovered Indians with reversed feet, who walked backward instead of forward over these lands promising prodigious fortunes.

Since then, all business in Amazonia starts with a massacre. At an air-conditioned desk in São Paulo or New York, a corporate executive signs a check which amounts to an extermination order, for the initial job of clearing the jungle begins with Indians and other wild beasts.

They give the Indians sugar or salt mixed with rat poison, or bomb them from the air, or hang them by the feet to bleed to death without bothering to skin them, because who would buy the hides?

The job is finished off by Dow Chemical's defoliants, which devastated Vietnam's forests and now Brazil's. Blind tortoises stumble about where trees used to be.

(55, 65, 67, and 375)

1975: Ribeirão Bonito
A Day of Justice

Large as countries are the lands of the cattle companies, conquerors of Amazonia. The Brazilian generals exempt them from taxes, open up roads for them, give them credits and permission to kill.

The companies use tattered campesinos from the northeast transplanted here by rivers and poverty. The campesinos kill Indians, and are killed in turn; they steal the Indians' lands, and are stolen from in turn. They drive off the Indians' cattle, whose flesh they will never taste.

When the highway reaches the village of Ribeirão Bonito, the police begin the expulsion. Campesinos who resist are persuaded in jail. Pulverizing them with clubs or sticking needles under their fingernails prove useful techniques. The priest João Bosco Burnier arrives in the village, enters the jail, asks for the torturers. A cop replies by blowing his head off with a bullet.

The next day, furious women—Carmesinha, Naide, Margarida—erect an enormous cross. Behind them, six hundred campesinos brandish axes, picks, sticks. The whole village joins the attack, singing in chorus, a magnificent voice of voices; and now, where the jail stood, a small pile of rubble remains.

(65 and 375)

1975: Huayanay
Another Day of Justice

For some years the community of Huayanay in the Peruvian Andes has had a terrible affliction: Matías Escobar. This scoundrel, thief of goats and women, arsonist and murderer, does much harm before the community catches, judges, sentences, and executes him. Matías dies of two hundred and thirty blows in the village Plaza de Armas: Each member of the community contributes one blow, and afterward two hundred and thirty thumbprints sign the confession.

No one has paid the slightest attention to General Velasco Alvarado's decree that made Quechua an official language. Quechua is not taught in the schools or accepted in the courts. In the incomprehensible Castilian tongue a judge interrogates various Huayanay Indians, jailed in Lima. He asks them, as if it wasn't known, who killed Matías Escobar.

(203)

1975: Cuzco
Condori Measures Time by Bread

He works as a mule. At cockcrow the first cargo is already loaded on his back at the market or the station, and until nightfall he is on the streets of Cuzco transporting whatever he can get in exchange for whatever he can get. Crushed beneath the weight of bundles and years, his clothing in shreds, a man in shreds, Gregorio Condori works and remembers as long as his back and his memory hold out.

Since his bones hardened as a boy, he has been shepherd and pilgrim, laborer and soldier. In Urcos he was jailed for nine months for accepting a little broth made from a stolen cow. In Sicuani he saw his first train, a black snake snorting fire out of its head, and years later he fell on his knees as a plane crossed the sky like a condor announcing with hoarse screams the end of the world.

Condori remembers the history of Peru in terms of loaves: *"When five big loaves of pure wheat bread cost one real, and three cost half a real, Odría took the presidency from Bustamante."*

And then someone else came along who seized power from Odría, and then someone else, and another, and another, until finally Velasco threw out Belaúnde. And now who'll throw out Velasco? Condori has heard that Velasco sides with the poor.

(111)

1975: Lima
Velasco

A rooster crows out of tune. Hungry birds peck at dry grains. Blackbirds flap their wings over others' nests. Not exactly thrown out, he leaves anyway. Sick, pecked to pieces, discouraged, General Juan Velasco Alvarado quits the presidency of Peru.

The Peru he leaves is less unjust than the one he found; he took on the imperial monopolies and the feudal lords, and tried to enable Indians to be something more than exiles in their own land.

The Indians, tough as esparto grass, keep hoping their day will come. By Velasco's decree the Quechua language now has the same rights as Spanish, and is equally official, though no official cares. The Academy of the Quechua Language gets a subsidy from the state— the equivalent of six dollars and seventy-five cents a year.

1975: Lima

The Altarpieces of Huamanga

In Lima painters and scholars are indignant; even the avant-garde registers shock. The National Art Prize has been given to Joaquín López Antay, altarpiece-maker of Huamanga. A scandal. Artisanship is okay, say the Peruvian artists, as long as it knows its place.

The altarpieces of Huamanga, first created as portable altars, have been changing their casts of characters with the passage of time. Saints and apostles have given way to sheep suckling their lambs with the condor watching over the world, laborers and shepherds, punitive bosses, hatmakers in their workshops, and singers mournfully caressing their charangos.

López Antay, intruder into Art Heaven, learned from his Indian grandmother how to make altarpieces. More than half a century ago she taught him to do saints, and now she watches him at work, from the peace of her grave.

(31 and 258)

The Molas of San Blas

The Cuna Indians, on Panama's San Blas islands, make molas to be shown off from back or breast. With needle and thread, talent and patience, they combine scraps of colored cloth in unrepeatable patterns. Sometimes they imitate reality; sometimes they invent it. And sometimes, wanting to copy, just copy, some bird they have seen, they cut and sew, stitch by stitch, and end up discovering a new creature more colorful and melodious and fleet than any bird that's ever soared in the sky.

The Bark Paintings of the Balsas River

Before the rains, in the season of the new moon, they strip off the bark of the amate tree. The stripped tree dies. On its skin the Mexican Indians of the Balsas River region paint flowers and fantasies, radiant mountain birds and monsters lying in wait, or they paint the daily round of events in communities which greet the Virgin in devout procession and summon the rain in secret ceremonies.

Before the European conquest, other Indians had painted on amate bark the codices that told of people's lives and of the stars. When the conquistadors imposed their paper and their images, amates disappeared. For more than four centuries no one in the land of Mexico painted on this forbidden paper. Not long ago, in the middle of our century, amates returned: *"All the people are painters. All. Everyone."*

Ancient life breathes through these amates, which come from afar, from so very far away, but never arrive tired.

(57)

The Arpilleras of Santiago

The children, sleeping three to a bed, stretch out their arms toward a flying cow. Santa Claus has a bag of bread, not toys, slung over his shoulder. At the foot of a tree a woman begs. Under the red sun a skeleton drives a garbage cart. On endless roads go men without faces. An enormous eye watches. At the center of the silence and the fear steams the communal stewpot.

Chile is this world of colored rags against a background of flour sacks. With scraps of wool and old cloth, women from Santiago's wretched slums embroider arpilleras. The arpilleras are sold in churches. That anyone buys them is incredible. The women are amazed: *"We embroider our problems, and our problems are ugly."*

This was first done by the wives of prisoners. Then others took it up—for money, which is a help, but not just for money. Embroidering arpilleras brings the women together, eases their loneliness and sadness, and for a few short hours breaks the routine of obedience to husband, father, macho son, and General Pinochet.

The Little Devils of Ocumicho

Like the Chilean arpilleras, the little clay devils of the Mexican village of Ocumicho are the creations of women. These devils make love, in pairs or in groups, go to school, drive motorcycles or airplanes, sneak into Noah's Ark, hide among the rays of the moon-loving sun, and intrude into Christmas nativity scenes. They lie in wait under the table at the Last Supper, while Jesus Christ, nailed to the cross, shares a meal of Patzcuaro lakefish with his Indian disciples. Eating, Christ laughs from ear to ear as if he had suddenly discovered that this world is more easily redeemed by pleasure than by pain.

In dark, windowless houses the Ocumicho potters model these luminous figures. Women tied to an endless chain of children, prisoners of drunken husbands who beat them, practice a new free-style art. Condemned to submission, destined for sadness, they create each day a new rebellion.

On Private Property and the Right of Creation

Buyers want the Ocumicho potters to sign their works, so they use stamps to engrave their names at the foot of their little devils. But often they forget, or use a neighbor's stamp if their own isn't handy, so that María comes out as the artist of a work by Nicolasa, or vice versa.

They don't understand this business of solitary glory. In their Tarascan Indian community, all are one when it comes to this sort of thing. Outside the community, like the tooth that falls from a mouth, one is nobody.

(183)

1975: Cabimas
Vargas

Oil, passing along the banks of Lake Maracaibo, has taken away the colors. In this Venezuelan garbage dump of sordid streets, dirty air, and oily waters, Rafael Vargas lives and paints.

Grass does not grow in Cabimas, dead city, emptied land, nor do fish remain in its waters, nor birds in its air, nor roosters in its dawns; but in Vargas's paintings the world is in fiesta, the earth breathes at the top of its lungs, the greenest of trees burst with fruit and flowers, and prodigious fish, birds, and roosters jostle one another like people.

Vargas hardly knows how to read or write. He does know how to earn a living as a carpenter, and how as a painter to earn the clean light of his days: His is the revenge, the prophecy of one who paints not the reality he knows but the reality he needs.

1975: Salta

Happy Colors of Change

As in a painting by the Venezuelan Vargas, in the Argentine province of Salta police patrol cars were painted yellow and orange. Instead of sirens, they had music, and instead of prisoners, children: Patrol cars rolled along filled with children who came and went from remote shacks to the city's schools. Punishment cells and torture chambers were demolished. The police withdrew from soccer games and demonstrations. The tortured went free and the torturers, officers who specialized in breaking bones with hammers, disappeared behind bars. Police dogs, which once had terrorized the poor, began giving acrobatic performances in the slums.

This happened a couple of years ago, when Rubén Fortuny was Salta's chief of police. Fortuny didn't last long. While he did what he did, though, other men like him were committing similar insanities throughout Argentina, as if the whole country were clasped in some euphoric embrace.

Sad epilogue to this newest Peronist episode: Perón, having returned to power, has died, and the hangmen are once again free and busy.

They kill Fortuny with a bullet in the heart. Then they kidnap the governor who appointed him, Miguel Ragone. All they leave of Ragone is a bloodstain and a shoe.

1975: Buenos Aires

Against the Children of Evita and Marx

But for Argentines the dangerous wind of change refuses to die down. The military see the threat of social revolution peeking out of every door and prepare to save the nation. They have been saving the nation for nearly half a century; and more recently, in courses in Panama, have found support in the Doctrine of National Security, which confirms for them that the enemy is within. Certain finishing touches are added to the next coup d'état. The program of national purification will be applied *by every means*: This is a war, a war against the children of Evita and Marx, and in war the only sin is inefficiency.

(106, 107, and 134)

1976: Madrid

Onetti

He doesn't expect to find any messages in any bottles in any sea. But the despairing Juan Carlos Onetti refuses to be alone. He would be alone, of course, if it weren't for the inhabitants of the town of Santa María, sad like himself, invented by him to keep him company.

Onetti has lived in Madrid since he came out of prison. The military rulers of Uruguay had jailed him because a story to which he had given a prize in a competition he was judging was not to their liking.

Hands clasped behind his neck, the exile contemplates the damp stains on the ceiling of his room in Santa María or Madrid or Montevideo or who knows where. From time to time he picks himself up and writes shouts that only seem like whispers.

1976: San José

A Country Stripped of Words

President Aparicio Méndez declares that *the Democratic Party of the United States and the Kennedy family are sedition's best partners in Uruguay*. A journalist tapes this sensational revelation, in the presence of the bishop of the city of San José and other witnesses.

Aparicio Méndez was chosen president in an election in which twenty-two citizens voted: fourteen generals, five brigadiers, and three admirals. The military have forbidden their president to talk to journalists, to anyone, in fact, except his wife. For this particular indiscretion they punish the newspaper that publishes his declaration with two days' suspension; and the journalist is fired.

Before silencing their president, the military took the reasonable precaution of silencing the rest of Uruguay. Every word that is not a lie is subversive. No one may mention any of the thousands of politicians, trade unionists, artists, and scientists who have been placed outside the law. The word *guerrilla* is officially banned; instead, one must say *lowlife*, *criminal*, *delinquent*, or *evildoer*. Carnival musicians, typically cheeky and disrespectful, may not sing the words *agrarian reform*, *sovereignty*, *hunger*, *clandestine*, *dove*, *green*, *summer*, or *contracanto*. Nor may they sing the word *pueblo*, even when it means a small city.

In the kingdom of silence the chief jail for political prisoners is called Liberty. The prisoners, held in isolation, invent codes to speak without voices, knocking on the walls from cell to cell to form letters and words so they can continue liking and teasing each other.

(124 and 235)

A Uruguayan Political Prisoner, Mauricio Rosencof, Says His Piece

It is like the struggle of a man who resists being turned into a cow. Because they put us in a cow-making machine and told us that instead of talking we should moo. And that is the question: How a prisoner can resist being animalized in such a situation. It is a battle for dignity . . . There was one compañero who got hold of a bit of sugarcane, bored a hole in it with his fingernail, and made a flute. And this clumsy, rudimentary thing stammers a sort of music . . .

(394)

1976: Liberty
Forbidden Birds

The Uruguayan political prisoners may not talk without permission,
or whistle, smile, sing, walk fast, or greet other prisoners; nor may
they make or receive drawings of pregnant women, couples, butterflies, stars, or birds.

One Sunday, Didaskó Pérez, school teacher, tortured and jailed
for having ideological ideas, is visited by his daughter Milay, age
five. She brings him a drawing of birds. The guards destroy it at the
entrance to the jail.

On the following Sunday, Milay brings him a drawing of trees.
Trees are not forbidden, and the drawing gets through. Didaskó praises
her work and asks about the colored circles scattered in the treetops,
many small circles half-hidden among the branches: *"Are they oranges? What fruit is it?"*

The child puts a finger on his mouth. *"Ssssshhh."*

And she whispers in his ear: *"Silly. Don't you see they're eyes?
They're the eyes of the birds that I've smuggled in for you."*

(204 and 459)

1976: *Montevideo*
Seventy-Five Methods of Torture,

some copied, others invented thanks to the creativity of the Uruguayan military, punish solidarity. Anyone doubting property rights
or the law of obedience ends up in jail, grave, or exile. The danger-
meter classifies citizens in three categories, A, B, or C, according to
whether they are "dangerous," "potentially dangerous," or "not dangerous." Trade unions become police stations, and wages are cut in
half. Whoever thinks or has ever thought loses his or her job. In
primary schools, high schools, even the university, speaking of José
Artigas's agrarian reform program is prohibited. Who cares if it was
the first in America? Nothing is allowed to contradict this order of
the deaf and dumb. Obligatory new texts impose military pedagogy
on the students.

(235)

1976: Montevideo

"One Must Obey," the New Official Texts Teach Uruguayan Students

The existence of political parties is not essential for a democracy. We have the clear example of the Vatican, where political parties do not exist and nevertheless there is a real democracy . . .

The equality of women, badly interpreted, means stimulating her sex and her intellectuality, while postponing her mission as mother and wife. If from the juridical standpoint man and woman are evidently equal, such is not the case from the biological standpoint. The woman as such is subject to her husband and hence owes him obedience. It is necessary that in any society there be a head who serves as guide, and the family is a society . . .

It is necessary for some to obey in order that others may exercise command. If no one obeyed, it would be impossible to rule . . .

(76)

1976: Montevideo

The Head Shrinkers

Dedicated to the prohibition of reality and the arson of memory, the Uruguayan military have beaten the world record for newspaper closures.

The weekly *Marcha*, after a long life, has ceased to be. One of its editors, Julio Castro, has been tortured to death, then disappeared—a dead man without a corpse. The other editors have been sentenced to prison, exile, or silence.

One night Hugo Alfaro, a movie critic condemned to wordlessness, sees a film that excites him. As soon as it ends he runs home and types a few pages, in a big hurry because it's late and *Marcha* closes its entertainment pages in the early hours. As he pecks out the last period, Alfaro suddenly realizes that *Marcha* hasn't existed for two years. Ashamed, he drops his review in a desk drawer.

This review, written for no one, deals with a Joseph Losey film set during the Nazi occupation of France, a film which shows how the machinery of repression grinds up not just the persecuted but also those who think they are safe, those who know what is happening, and even those who prefer not to know.

Meanwhile, on the River Plata's other bank, the Argentine military make their own coup d'état. One of the heads of the new dictatorship, General Ibérico Saint-Jean, clarifies things: *"First we'll kill all the subversives. Then we'll kill the collaborators. Then the sympathizers. Then the undecided. And finally, we'll kill the indifferent."*

(13 and 106)

1976: La Perla
The Third World War

From the top of a hill, on a chestnut mount, an Argentine gaucho looks on. José Julián Solanille sees a long military caravan approaching. He recognizes General Menéndez dismounting from a Ford Falcon. Out of trucks, shoved by clubs, tumble men and women, hoods over their heads, hands tied behind their backs. The gaucho sees one of the hooded ones make a break for it. He hears the shots. The fugitive falls, gets up, and falls, several times before falling for the last time. When the fusillade begins, men and women collapse like rag dolls. The gaucho spurs his horse and takes off. Behind him black smoke rises.

This valley, in the first undulations of the Córdoba sierra, is one of the many dumps for corpses. When it rains, smoke drifts up from the pits because of the quicklime they throw on the bodies.

In this holy war, the victims *disappear*. Those not swallowed by the earth are devoured by fish at the bottoms of rivers or the sea. Many have committed no greater crimes than appearing on a list of phone numbers. They march into nothingness, into the fog, into death, after torture in the barracks. *No one is innocent*, says Monseñor Plaza, bishop of La Plata, and General Camps says it is right to liquidate a hundred suspects if only five of them turn out to be guilty. Guilty of terrorism.

Terrorists, explains General Videla, *are not only those who plant bombs, but also those who act with ideas contrary to our Western and Christian civilization*. This is vengeance for the defeat of the West in Vietnam:

"We are winning the Third World War," crows General Menéndez.

(100, 107, and 134)

1976: Buenos Aires
The Choice

One prisoner, pregnant, is offered the choice between rape or the electric prod. She chooses the prod, but after an hour can no longer endure the pain. They all rape her. As they rape her, they sing the Wedding March.

"Well, this is war," says Monseñor Gracelli.

The men who burn breasts with blowtorches in the barracks wear scapulars and take communion every Sunday.

"Above us all is God," says General Videla.

Monseñor Tortolo, president of the Episcopate, compares General Videla with Jesus Christ, and the military dictatorship with the Easter Resurrection. In the name of the Holy Father, nuncio Pío Laghi visits the extermination camps, exalts the military's love of God, Fatherland, and Family, and justifies state terrorism on the grounds that civilization has the right to defend itself.

(106, 107, and 134)

1976: La Plata
Bent over the Ruins, a Woman Looks

for something in her home that has not been destroyed. The forces of order have shattered María Isabel de Mariani's home, and she pokes through the remains in vain. What they have not stolen, they have pulverized. Only one record, Verdi's *Requiem*, is intact.

María Isabel would like to find in the litter some memento of her children and of her granddaughter, a photo or toy, book, ashtray, anything. Her children, suspected of running a clandestine press, have been gunned down. Her three-month-old granddaughter has been given away or sold as war booty by the officers.

It is summer, and the smell of gunpowder mixes with the aroma of flowering lindens. That aroma will forever be unbearable. María Isabel has no one to be with. She is the mother of subversives. Seeing her coming, her friends cross the street or avert their eyes. Her telephone is silent. No one tells her anything, even lies. Without help she proceeds to put the shreds of her destroyed home in boxes. Well after nightfall she pulls the boxes onto the sidewalk. Very early in the morning the garbage men collect the boxes, one by one, gently, without knocking them over. The garbage men treat the boxes with great care, as if aware they are full of the bits of a broken life. Silently peering through the remains of a venetian blind, María Isabel thanks them for this caress, the only one she has had since the sorrow began.

(317)

1976: *Forest of Zinica*
Carlos

He criticized you to your face, praised you behind your back.

He had the myopic, fanatical gaze of an angry rooster, sharp brown eyes from which he saw farther than others, a man of all or nothing; but moments of joy made him jump like a small child, and when he gave orders he seemed to be asking favors.

Carlos Fonseca Amador, leader of the Nicaraguan revolution, has died fighting in the jungle.

A colonel brings the news to the cell where Tomás Borge lies shattered.

Together they had traveled a long road, Carlos and Tomás, since the days when Carlos sold newspapers and candy in Matagalpa. Together they founded, in Tegucigalpa, the Sandinista Front.

"*He's dead,*" says the colonel.

"*You're wrong, colonel,*" says Tomás.

(58)

1977: *Managua*
Tomás

Bound to an iron ring, teeth chattering, drenched in shit, blood, and vomit, Tomás Borge is a pile of broken bones and stripped nerves, a scrap lying on the floor waiting for the next round of torture.

But this remnant of himself can still sail down secret rivers that take him beyond pain and madness. Letting himself go, he drifts into another Nicaragua. He sees it.

Through the hood that squeezes his face swollen by blows, he sees it: He counts the beds in each hospital, the windows in each school, the trees in each park, and sees the sleepers fluttering their eyelids, bewildered, those long dead from hunger and everything else that kills now being awakened by newly born suns.

(58)

1977: Solentiname Archipelago
Cardenal

The herons, looking at themselves in the shimmering mirror, lift their beaks. The fishermen's boats are already returning, and behind them swim the turtles that come here to give birth on the beach.

In a wooden cabin, Jesus is seated at the fishermen's table. He eats turtle eggs, fresh-caught *guapote*, and cassava. The forest, searching for him, slips its arms through the windows.

To the glory of this Jesus, Ernesto Cardenal, the poet-monk of Solentiname, writes. To his glory sings the trumpeter *zanate*, the homeless bird, always flying among the poor, that freshens its wings in the lake waters. And to his glory the fishermen paint. They paint brilliant pictures that announce Paradise—all brothers, no bosses, no peons—until one night the fishermen who paint Paradise decide to start making it, and cross the lake to attack the San Carlos barracks.

From the darkness, the owl promises trouble: *"Screwed . . . screwed . . ."*

The dictatorship kills many as these seekers of Paradise pass through the mountains and valleys and islands of Nicaragua. *The dough rises, the big loaf swells . . .*

(6 and 77)

Omar Cabezas Tells of the Mountain's Mourning for the Death of a Guerrilla in Nicaragua

I never forgave Tello for being killed with one bullet, just one bullet . . . I felt a great fear, and it was as if the mountain, too, felt fear. The wind dropped and the trees stopped swaying, not a leaf stirred, the birds stopped singing. Everything froze, awaiting that moment when they'd come and kill the lot of us.

And we set out. When we broke into a marching pace up the ravine, it was as if we were shaking the mountain, as if we were grabbing her and telling her: Who the hell does this bitch think she is?

Tello lived with the mountain. I'm convinced he had relations with her, she bore him sons; and when Tello died she felt that all was over, her commitment was gone, that all the rest was foolishness . . . But when she saw the will to fight of the men marching there over her, in her heart she realized that Tello was not the beginning and end of the world. Though Tello may have been her son, though he may have been her life, her secret lover, her brother, her creature, her stone, though Tello may have been her river . . . he was not the end of the world, and that after him came all of us who could still light a fire in her heart.

(73)

1977: Brasília
Scissors

Over a thousand Brazilian intellectuals sign a manifesto against censorship.

In July of last year, the military dictatorship stopped the weekly *Movimiento* from publishing the United States Declaration of Independence, because in it is said that the people have the right and the duty to abolish despotic governments. Since then the censorship has banned: the Bolshoi Ballet, because it is Russian; the erotic prints of Pablo Picasso, because they are erotic; and the *History of Surrealism*, because one of its chapters has the word *revolution* in its title ("Revolution in Poetry").

(371)

1977: Buenos Aires
Walsh

He mails a letter and several copies. The original letter, to the military junta that rules Argentina. The copies, to foreign press agencies. On the first anniversary of the coup d'état, he is sending a sort of statement of grievances, a record of the infamies committed by a regime that can only stagger in its dance of death. At the bottom he puts his signature and number (Rodolfo Walsh, I.D. 2845022). He is only steps from the post office when their bullets cut him down; and he is carried off wounded, not to be seen again.

His naked words were scandalous where such fear reigns, dangerous while the great masked ball continues.

(461)

1977: Río Cuarto
The Burned Books of Walsh and Other Authors Are Declared Nonexistent

IN VIEW OF *the measure taken by the ex–Military Intervention of this National University in fulfillment of express superior orders, with respect to withdrawing from the Library Area all reading material of an antisocial nature and whose contents exuded ideologies alien to the Argentine National Being, constituting a source of extreme Marxist and subversive indoctrination, and*
WHEREAS: *Said literature having been opportunely incinerated, it is fitting to strike it from the patrimony of this House of Advanced Studies, the Rector of the National University of Río Cuarto*
RESOLVES: *To strike from the patrimony of the National University of Río Cuarto (Library Area) all the bibliography listed below:* [Long list follows of books by Rodolfo Walsh, Bertrand Russell, Wilhelm Dilthey, Maurice Dobb, Karl Marx, Paulo Freire, and others].

(452)

1977: Buenos Aires

The Mothers of the Plaza de Mayo,

women born of their children, are the Greek chorus of this tragedy. Brandishing photos of their disappeared ones, they circle round and round the obelisk, before the Pink House of the government, as obstinately as they make pilgrimages to barracks, police stations, and sacristies, dried up from so much weeping, desperate from so much waiting for those who were and are no longer, or perhaps still are . . . who knows?

"I wake up believing he's alive," says one, say all. "I begin to disbelieve as the morning goes on. He dies on me again at noon. He revives in the evening, I begin to believe he'll come soon, and I set a place for him at the table, but he dies again and at night I fall asleep without hope. When I wake up, I feel he's alive . . ."

They call them *madwomen*. Normally no one speaks of them. With the situation normalized, the dollar is cheap and certain people, too. Mad poets go to their deaths, and normal poets kiss the sword while praising silence. With total normality the Minister of Finance hunts lions and giraffes in Africa and the generals hunt workers in the suburbs of Buenos Aires. New language rules make it compulsory to call the military dictatorship *Proceso de Reorganización Nacional*.

(106 and 107)

1977: Buenos Aires

Alicia Moreau

Sometimes she goes overboard in her faith, anticipating social revolution in a none too realistic way, or explodes publicly in tirades against military power and the Pope of Rome. But what would become of the Plaza de Mayo mothers without the enthusiasm of this sprite woman? She never lets them grow discouraged or feel defeated by so much indifference and jeering: *"One can always do something,"* she tells them. *"Together. Each one on her own, no. Let's—we have to—"*

She grasps her cane and is the first to move.

Alicia Moreau is nearly a hundred years old. She has been in the struggle since the days when socialists drank only water and sang only the Internationale. She has witnessed many marvels and betrayals, births and deaths, and whatever her momentary troubles, she keeps believing that it's worthwhile to believe. Alicia Moreau is as lively now as she was when the century began and she made speeches from soapboxes between red flags in the worker barrios of Buenos Aires, or crossed the Andes on muleback, hurrying the animal so as not to arrive late at a feminist congress.

(221)

1977: Buenos Aires
Portrait of a Croupier

The Minister of Finance of the Argentine dictatorship is a pious devotee of private enterprise. He thinks about it on Sundays, when he kneels at the Mass, and also on weekdays, when he gives courses at the Military School. Nevertheless, the minister correctly withdraws from the company he directs, generously ceding it to the state for ten times its worth.

The generals turn the country into a barracks. The minister turns it into a casino. Argentina is deluged with dollars and consumer goods. It is the time of the hangman, but also of the conman and the conjurer. The generals order the country to shut up and obey, while the minister orders it to speculate and consume. Anyone who works is a sucker, anyone who protests, a corpse. To cut wages in half and reduce rebellious workers to nothing, the minister slips sweet silver bribes to the middle class, who fly to Miami and return loaded with mountains of gadgets and gimmickry. In the face of the daily massacre, people shrug their shoulders: *"They must have done something. It's for a good reason."*

Or they whistle and look the other way: *"Don't get involved."*

(143)

1977: Caracas

The Exodus of the Intruders

The prophet spoke in a café on Caracas's Calle Real de Sabana Grande. An extraterrestrial with flaming eyes appeared for a moment and announced that on a certain August Sunday a furious ocean would split the mountains and wipe out the city.

Bishops, witches, astronomers, and astrologers repeatedly issued reassurances that there was nothing to worry about, but they couldn't stop the panic from growing, from rolling like a ball through the barrios of Caracas.

Yesterday was the Sunday in question. The president of the republic ordered the police to take charge of the city. More than a million Caracans stampeded, fled with their belongings on their backs. More automobiles than people remained in the city.

Today, Monday, the fugitives begin to return. The ocean is where it always was, the mountains too. In the valley, Caracas continues to exist. And so the oil capital recovers its terrified citizens. They reenter as if begging pardon, because they know now that they are superfluous, that this is a world of wheels, not legs. Caracas belongs to its prepotent automobiles, not to whoever dares cross its streets to the annoyance of the machines. What would become of these people, condemned to live in a city that doesn't belong to them, if María Lionza didn't protect them and José Gregorio didn't cure them?

(135)

María Lionza

Her breasts rise above the center of Caracas and reign, nakedly, over the frenzy. In Caracas, in all Venezuela, María Lionza is a goddess.

Her invisible palace is far from the capital on a mountain in the Sorte chain. The rocks scattered over this mountain were once María Lionza's lovers, men who paid for a night of embraces by being converted into breathing stones.

Simón Bolívar and Jesus of Nazareth work for her in the sanctuary. Also helping her are three secretaries: one black, one Indian, one white. They attend to the faithful, who come loaded with offerings of fruit, perfumes, and undergarments.

María Lionza, untamed woman, feared and desired by God and Satan, has the powers of heaven and hell. She can inspire happiness or unhappiness; she saves if she feels like saving, and thunders if she feels like thundering.

(190 and 346)

José Gregorio

He is chastest of the chaste, María Lionza's white secretary. Doctor José Gregorio Hernández has never yielded to the temptations of the flesh. All the insinuating women who approached him ended up in convents, repenting, bathed in tears. This virtuous Physician of the Poor, this Apostle of Medicine, ended his days in 1919, undefeated. His immaculate body was pitilessly crushed by one of the two or three automobiles that circulated in Caracas at a snail's pace in those happy days. After death, the miraculous hands of José Gregorio have continued prescribing remedies and operating on the sick.

In the sanctuary of María Lionza, José Gregorio busies himself with public health problems. He has never failed to turn up from the Great Beyond at the call of sufferers, the only saint ever in a necktie and hat.

(363)

1977: Graceland
Elvis

Once, his way of shaking his left leg evoked screams. His lips, his eyes, his sideburns were sexual organs.

Now a soft ball of flab, Elvis Presley, dethroned king of rock 'n' roll, lies in bed, his glance floating between six television screens. The TVs, suspended from the ceiling, are each tuned to a different channel. Between sleep and dreams, always more asleep than awake, Elvis fires unloaded pistols, click, click, at the images he doesn't like. The suet ball of his body covers a soul made of Codeine, Morphine, Valium, Seconal, Placidyl, Quaalude, Nembutal, Valmid, Demerol, Elavil, Aventyl, Carbrital, Sinutab, and Amytal.

(197 and 409)

1978: San Salvador
Romero

The archbishop offers her a chair. Marianela prefers to talk standing up. She always comes for others; but this time Marianela comes for herself. Marianela García Vilas, attorney for the tortured and disappeared of El Salvador, does not come this time to ask the archbishop's solidarity with one of the victims of D'Aubuisson, Captain Torch, who burns your body with a blowtorch, or of some other military horror specialist. Marianela doesn't come to ask help for anyone else's investigation or denunciation. This time she has something personal to say to him. As mildly as she can she tells him that the police have kidnapped her, bound, beaten, humiliated, stripped her—and that they raped her. She tells it without tears or agitation, with her usual calm, but Archbishop Arnulfo Romero has never before heard in Marianela's voice these vibrations of hatred, echoes of disgust, calls for vengeance. When Marianela finishes, the archbishop, astounded, falls silent too.

After a long silence, he begins to tell her that the Church does not hate or have enemies, that every infamy and every action against God forms part of a divine order, that criminals are also our brothers and must be prayed for, that one must forgive one's persecutors, one must accept pain, one must . . . Suddenly, Archbishop Romero stops.

He lowers his glance, buries his head in his hands. He shakes his head, denying it all, and says: *"No, I don't want to know."*

"I don't want to know," he says, and his voice cracks.

Archbishop Romero, who always gives advice and comfort, is weeping like a child without mother or home. Archbishop Romero, who always gives assurance, the tranquillizing assurance of a neutral God who knows all and embraces all—Archbishop Romero doubts.

Romero weeps and doubts and Marianela strokes his head.

(259 and 301)

1978: La Paz

Five Women

"What is the main enemy? The military dictatorship? The Bolivian bourgeoisie? Imperialism? No, compañeros. I want to tell you just this: Our main enemy is fear. We have it inside us."

This is what Domitila said at the Catavi tin mine, and then she came to the capital with four other women and more than twenty kids. On Christmas Day they started their hunger strike. No one believed in them. Some thought it a ridiculous joke: *"So five women are going to overthrow the dictatorship?"*

The priest Luis Espinal is the first to join them. In no time there are fifteen hundred people starving themselves all over Bolivia. The five women, accustomed to hunger since they were born, call water *chicken* or *turkey* and salt *pork chop*, and feed on laughter. Meanwhile the hunger strikers multiply—three thousand, ten thousand—until the Bolivians who have stopped eating and working can no longer be counted, and twenty-three days after the start of the hunger strike the people invade the streets, and now nothing can be done to stop them.

The five women have overthrown the military dictatorship.

(1)

1978: Managua

"The Pigsty"

is what Nicaraguans call the National Palace. On the first floor of this pretentious Parthenon senators spout off. On the second, deputies.

One midday in August, a handful of guerrillas led by Edén Pastora and Dora María Téllez attack the Pigsty and in three minutes capture all of Somoza's legislators. To get them released, Somoza has but to free Sandinista prisoners. People line the airport road to cheer them.

This is turning out to be a year of continuous war. Somoza started it with the murder of the journalist Pedro Joaquín Chamorro. Infuriated people promptly incinerate several of the dictator's businesses. Flames consume the prosperous Plasmaféresis, Inc., which exports Nicaraguan blood to the United States. The people swear that they won't rest until the vampire himself is buried in some place darker than the night, with a stake impaling his heart.

(10 and 460)

Tachito Somoza's Pearl of Wisdom

I am a businessman, but humble.

(434)

1978: Panama City
Torrijos

General Omar Torrijos says he does not want to enter history. He only wants to enter the Canal Zone, stolen by the United States at the turn of the century. Thus he wanders the world from country to country, government to government, platform to platform. When accused of serving Moscow or Havana, Torrijos laughs. Every people, he says, swallows its own aspirins for its own headache. If it comes to that, he says, he gets along better with the Castristas than with the castrati.

Finally the canal's fences fall. The United States, pressured by the world, signs a treaty that restores to Panama, by degrees, the canal and the prohibited zone that encloses it.

"*It's better this way,*" says Torrijos, relieved. They've saved him the disagreeable task of blowing up the canal and all its installations.

(154)

1979: Madrid
Intruders Disturb the Quiet Ingestion of the Body of God

In a big church in Madrid, a special Mass celebrates the anniversary of Argentine independence. Diplomats, business executives, and military men have been invited by General Leandro Anaya, ambassador of the dictatorship which is so busy across the sea protecting the Argentine heritage of fatherland, faith, and other proprieties.

Through the stained-glass windows rich lights illumine the faces and fashions of the ladies and gentlemen. On Sundays like this, God is worthy of confidence. Very occasionally a timid cough decorates the silence, as the priest performs the rite: imperturbable silence of eternity, eternity of the Lord's elect.

The moment of communion comes. Ringed by bodyguards, the Argentine ambassador approaches the altar. He kneels, closes his eyes, opens his mouth. Instantly the flutter of white handkerchiefs unfurling, covering the heads of the women who walk up the aisles, all the aisles. The mothers of the Plaza de Mayo advance softly, cottony rustle, until they surround the bodyguards who surround the ambassador. Then they stare at him. Simply stare. The ambassador opens his eyes, looks at all these women looking at him without blinking, and swallows his saliva, while the priest's hand remains paralyzed in midair, the Host between his fingers.

The whole church is filled with these women. Suddenly there are no longer saints or merchants in this temple, nothing more than a multitude of uninvited women: black dresses, white handkerchiefs, all silent, all on their feet.

(173)

1979: New York
Banker Rockefeller Congratulates Dictator Videla

His Excellency Jorge Rafael Videla
President of Argentina
Buenos Aires, Argentina

Dear Mr. President,
I am very grateful to you for taking time to receive me during my recent visit to Argentina. Not having been there for seven years, it was encouraging to see what progress your government has made during the past three years, both in controlling terrorism and strengthening the economy. I congratulate you on what you have achieved and wish you every success for the future . . .
With warm good wishes,

Sincerely,

David Rockefeller

(384)

1979: Siuna

Portrait of a Nicaraguan Worker

José Villarreina, married, three children. Works for the North American company Rosario Mines, which seventy years ago overthrew President Zelaya. Since 1952, Villarreina has been scraping gold from the excavations at Siuna; even so, his lungs are not yet entirely rotted out.

At 1:30 P.M. on July 3, 1979, Villarreina looks out from one of the mineshafts and a mineral-loaded cart tears off his head. Thirty-five minutes later, the company notifies the dead man that in accordance with articles 18, 115, and 119 of the Labor Code, he is discharged for nonfulfillment of his contract.

(362)

1979: In All Nicaragua

The Earth Buckles

and shakes worse than in all the earthquakes put together. Airplanes fly over immense stretches of jungle dropping napalm, and bomb cities crisscrossed with barricades and trenches. The Sandinistas take over León, Masaya, Jinotega, Chinandega, Estelí, Carazo, Jinotepe . . .

While Somoza awaits a sixty-five-million-dollar loan, approved by the International Monetary Fund, in Nicaragua they fight tree by tree, house by house. With masks or handkerchiefs covering their faces, the youths attack with rifles or machetes, sticks or stones; even a toy gun serves to make an impression.

In Masaya, which in the language of the Indians means *city that burns*, the fighters, adept in pyrotechnics, turn drainpipes into mortars and invent a fuseless contact bomb which explodes on striking. Old women weave between the bullets carrying large bags full of bombs, which they hand around like loaves of bread.

(10, 238, 239, and 320)

1979: In All Nicaragua
Get It Together, Everyone,

don't lose it, the big one is here, the shit has hit the fan, hell has broken loose, we're at fever heat, fighting with nothing but a home-made arsenal against tanks, armored cars, and planes, so everyone get into it, from here on no one ducks out, it's our war, the real thing, if you don't die killing you'll die dying, shoulder to shoulder makes us bolder, all together now, the people is us.

(10, 238, and 239)

From the Datebook of Tachito Somoza

1979
Thursday, July 12,
Love

1979: Managua
"Tourism must be stimulated,"

orders the dictator while Managua's eastern barrios burn, set ablaze by the air force.

From his bunker, great steel and cement uterus, Somoza rules. Here nothing penetrates, not the thunder of bombs, not the screams of people, nothing to ruffle the perfect silence. Here one sees nothing, smells nothing. In this bunker Somoza has lived for some time, right in the center of Managua but about as far from Nicaragua as you can get; and in this bunker, he now sits down with Fausto Amador.

Fausto Amador is the father of Carlos Fonseca Amador. The son, founder of the Sandinista Front, understood patriotism; the father, administrator general for the richest man in Central America, understands patrimony.

Surrounded by mirrors and plastic flowers, seated before a computer, Somoza, with Fausto Amador's help, organizes the liquidation of his businesses, which means the total pillage of Nicaragua.

Afterward, Somoza says on the telephone: *"I'm not going and they're not throwing me out."*

(10, 320, and 460)

1979: *Managua*
Somoza's Grandson

They're throwing him out and he's going. At dawn, Somoza boards a plane for Miami. In these final days the United States abandons him, but he does not abandon the United States: *"In my heart, I will always be part of this great nation."*

Somoza takes with him the gold ingots of the Central Bank, eight brightly colored parrots, and the coffins of his father and brother. He also takes the living body of the crown prince.

Anastasio Somoza Portocarrero, grandson of the founder of the dynasty, is a corpulent military man who has learned the arts of command and good government in the United States. In Nicaragua, he founded, and until today directed, the Basic Infantry Training School, a juvenile army group specializing in interrogations of prisoners—and famous for its skill. Armed with pincers and spoons, these lads can tear out fingernails without breaking the roots and eyes without injuring the lids.

The Somoza clan goes into exile as Augusto César Sandino strolls through Nicaragua beneath a rain of flowers, a half century after they shot him. This country has gone mad; lead floats, cork sinks, the dead escape from the cemetery, and women from the kitchen.

(10, 322, and 460)

1979: *Granada*
The Comandantes

Behind them, an abyss. Ahead and to either side, an armed people on the attack. La Pólvora barracks in the city of Granada, last stronghold of the dictatorship, is falling.

When the colonel in command hears of Somoza's flight, he orders the machineguns silenced. The Sandinistas also stop firing.

Soon the iron gate of the barracks opens and the colonel appears, waving a white rag. *"Don't fire."*

The colonel crosses the street. *"I want to talk to the comandante."*

A kerchief covering one of the faces drops. *"I'm the comandante,"* says Mónica Baltodano, one of the Sandinista women who lead troops. *"What?"*

Through the mouth of the colonel, this haughty macho, speaks the military institution, defeated but dignified. Virility of the pants, honor of the uniform. *"I don't surrender to a woman!"* roars the colonel.

And he surrenders.

1979: In All Nicaragua
Birth

The Nicaragua newly born in the rubble is only a few hours old, fresh new greenery among the looted ruins of war; and the singing light of the first day of Creation fills the air that smells of fire.

1979: Paris
Darcy

The Sorbonne confers the title of Doctor Honoris Causa on Darcy Ribeiro. He accepts, he says, on the merit of his failures.

Darcy has failed as an anthropologist, because the Indians of Brazil are still being annihilated. He has failed as rector of the university because the reality he wanted it to transform proved obdurate. He has failed as Minister of Education in a country where illiteracy never stops multiplying. He has failed as a member of a government that tried and failed either to make agrarian reform or to control the cannibalistic habits of foreign capital. He has failed as a writer who dreamed of forbidding history to repeat itself.

These are his failures. These are his dignities.

(376)

1979: Santiago de Chile
Stubborn Faith

General Pinochet stamps his signature on a decree that imposes private property on the Mapuche Indians. The government offers funds, fencing, and seeds to those who agree to parcel out their communities with good grace. If not, the government warns, they'll accept without any grace.

Pinochet is not the first to believe that greed is part of human nature and that God wants it that way. Long ago, the conquistador Pedro de Valdivia had tried to break up the indigenous communities of Chile. Since then, by fire and sword everything has been seized from the Indians, everything: land, language, religion, customs. But the Indians, hemmed in, trapped in poverty, exhausted by so much war and so much swindling, persist in believing that the world is a shared home.

1979: Chajul
Another Kind of Political Education in Guatemala

Patrocinio Menchú, Maya-Quiché Indian, born in the village of Chimel, had, along with his parents, defended the lands of his harassed community. From his parents he learned to walk the heights without slipping, to greet the sun according to ancient custom, to clear and fertilize the ground, and to stake his life on it.

Now, he is one of the prisoners that the army trucks have brought to the village of Chajul for the people to see. Rigoberta, his sister, recognizes him, although his face is swollen from beatings and he bleeds from his eyes, his tongueless mouth, and his nail-less fingers.

Five hundred soldiers—Indians too, Indians of other regions—stand guard over the ceremony. Herded into a circle, the whole population of Chajul is forced to watch. Rigoberta has to watch, while within her, as in everyone, a silent, moist curse blooms. The captain displays the nude bodies, flayed, mutilated, still alive, and says that these are Cubans who have come to stir up trouble in Guatemala. Showing off the details of the punishments that each one earned, the captain yells:

"Have a good look at what's in store for guerrillas!"
Then he soaks the prisoners with gasoline and sets fire to them.
Patrocinio Menchú was still tender corn. It was only sixteen years
ago that he was planted.

(72)

The Mayas Plant Each Child That Is Born

High up in the mountains, the Indians of Guatemala bury the umbilical cord while presenting the child to Grandpa Volcano, Mother
Earth, Father Sun, Grandma Moon, all the powerful grandparents,
and asking them to protect the newly born from danger and error.

*Before the rain that irrigates us and before the wind that bears
us witness, we, who are part of you, plant this new child, this new
compañero, in this place . . .*

1980: La Paz
The Cococracy

General Luis García Meza, author of the 189th coup d'état in a century
and a half of Bolivia's history, announces that he will establish a free
economy, as in Chile, and make sure all extremists disappear, as in
Argentina.

With García Meza, the cocaine traffickers take over the state.
His brand-new Interior Minister, Colonel Luis Arce Gómez, divides
his time and energy between drug smuggling and heading up the
Bolivian Section of the World Anticommunist League. He will not
rest, he says, never rest, *until the cancer of Marxism is extirpated*.

The military government raises the curtain by assassinating Marcelo Quiroga Santa Cruz, enemy of Gulf Oil and its forty thieves,
implacable foe of hidden filth.

(157 and 257)

1980: Santa Ana de Yacuma

Portrait of a Modern Businessman

He fires from the hip, both bullets and bribes. At his waist he carries a golden pistol, in his mouth a golden smile. His bodyguards use machineguns with telescopic sights. He has twelve missile-armed combat planes and thirty cargo planes that take off early each morning from the Bolivian jungle loaded with cocaine paste. Roberto Suárez, cousin and colleague of the new Interior Minister, exports a ton a month.

"My philosophy," he says, *"is to do good."*

He claims that the money he has given to the Bolivian military would suffice to pay the country's external debt.

Like a good Latin American businessman, Suárez sends his winnings to Switzerland, where they find refuge in banking secrecy. But in Santa Ana de Yacuma, the town where he was born, he has paved the main street, restored the church, and given sewing machines to widows and orphans; and when he turns up there he bets thousands of dollars on a roll of the dice or a cockfight.

Suárez is the most important Bolivian capitalist in a huge multinational enterprise. In his hands, the price of a coca leaf is multiplied by ten as it changes into paste and leaves the country. Later, as it becomes powder and reaches the nose that inhales it, its price soars two hundred times. Like any raw material from a poor country, coca lines the pockets of intermediaries, and above all intermediaries in the rich country that consumes it transformed into cocaine, the white goddess.

(157, 257, and 439)

The White Goddess

is the most expensive of the divinities. She costs five times as much as gold. In the United States, ten million devotees yearn and burn, ready to kill, and kill themselves for her. Every year they throw thirty billion dollars at the foot of her shining altar of pure snow. In the long run she will annihilate them; from the start she steals their souls; but in exchange she offers to make them, by her good grace, supermen for a moment.

(257 and 372)

1980: Santa Marta

Marijuana

Out of each dollar of dreams that a U.S. marijuana smoker buys, barely one cent reaches the hands of the Colombian campesinos who grow it. The other ninety-nine cents go to the traffickers, who in Colombia have fifteen hundred airports, five hundred airplanes, and a hundred ships.

On the outskirts of Medellín or Santa Marta, the drug mafiosi live in ostentatious mansions. In front they like to display on granite pedestals the small planes they used in their first operation. They rock their children in gold cradles, give golden fingernails to their lovers, and on ring finger or necktie wear diamonds as discreet as headlights.

The mafiosi habitually fumigate their forces. Four years ago they machinegunned Lucho Barranquilla, most popular of the traffickers, on a street corner in the city of Santa Marta. The murderers sent to the funeral a floral wreath in the form of a heart and took up a collection to erect a statue of the departed in the main plaza.

(95 and 406)

1980: Santa Marta

Saint Agatón

Lucho Barranquilla was widely mourned. The children who played in his amusement park wept for him, as did the widows and orphans he protected, and the cops who ate from his hand. In fact, the whole city of Santa Marta, which lived thanks to his loans and donations, wept. And Saint Agatón wept for him, too.

Saint Agatón is the patron saint of drunkards. On Carnival Sunday, drunks from the whole Colombian coast descend on the village of Mamatoco, on Santa Marta's outskirts. There they take Saint Agatón out of his church and parade him, singing dirty songs and spraying him with firewater, just the way he likes.

But what the drunks are parading is only a white-bearded impostor brought from Spain. The true Saint Agatón, who had an Indian face and a straw hat, was kidnapped half a century ago by a temperance priest who fled with the saint under his surplice. God punished that priest with leprosy and crossed the eyes of the sacristan who accompanied him, but left the real Saint Agatón hidden in the remote village of Sucre.

A committee has gone to Sucre in recent days to plead with him to return: *"Since you left,"* they tell him, *"there's no more miracles or fun."*

Saint Agatón refuses. He says he won't go back to Santa Marta, because there they killed his friend Lucho Barranquilla.

1980: Guatemala City

Newsreel

It was General Romeo Lucas García, president of Guatemala, who gave the order to set fire to the Spanish embassy with its occupants inside. This statement comes from Elías Barahona, official spokesman for the Ministry of the Interior, who calls a press conference after seeking asylum in Panama.

According to Barahona, General Lucas García is personally responsible for the deaths of the thirty-nine persons roasted alive by the police bombs. Among the victims were twenty-seven Indian leaders who had peacefully occupied the embassy to denounce the massacres in the Quiché region.

Barahona also states that General Lucas García commands the paramilitary and parapolice bands known as the Squadrons of Death, and helps draw up the lists of opponents condemned to disappear.

The former press secretary of the Interior Ministry claims that in Guatemala a "Program of Pacification and Eradication of Communism" is being carried out, based on a four-hundred-and-twenty-page document drawn up by specialists in the United States on the basis of their experience in the Vietnam war.

In the first half of 1980 in Guatemala, twenty-seven university professors, thirteen journalists, and seventy campesino leaders, mainly Indians, have been murdered. The repression has had a special intensity for Indian communities in the Quiché region, where large oil deposits have recently been discovered.

(450)

1980: Uspantán
Rigoberta

She is a Maya-Quiché Indian, born in the village of Chimel, who has been picking coffee and cotton on the coastal plantations since she learned to walk. In the cotton fields she saw two of her brothers die— Nicolás and Felipe, the youngest—and also her best friend, still only half grown. All fell victim to pesticide spraying.

Last year in the village of Chajul, Rigoberta Menchú saw how the army burned alive her brother Patrocinio. Soon afterward, her father suffered the same fate in the Spanish embassy. Now, in Uspantán, the soldiers have killed her mother, very gradually, cutting her to pieces bit by bit after dressing her up in guerrilla's clothing.

Of the community of Chimel, where Rigoberta was born, no one remains alive.

Rigoberta, who is a Christian, has been taught that true Christians forgive their persecutors and pray for the souls of their executioners. When they strike you on one cheek, she was taught, the true Christian offers the other.

"I no longer have a cheek to offer," says Rigoberta.

(72)

1980: San Salvador
The Offering

Until a couple of years ago, he only got along well with God. Now he speaks with and for everyone. Each child of the people tormented by the powerful is a child of God crucified; and in the people God is renewed after each crime the powerful commit. Now Monseñor Romero, archbishop of El Salvador, world-breaker, world-revealer, bears no resemblance to the babbling shepherd of souls whom the powerful used to applaud. Now ordinary people interrupt with ovations his sermons denouncing state terrorism.

Yesterday, Sunday, the archbishop exhorted the police and soldiers to disobey the order to kill their campesino brothers. In the name of Christ, Romero told the Salvadoran people: *Arise and go.*

Today, Monday, the murderer arrives at the church escorted by two police patrols. He enters and waits, hidden behind a pillar. Romero is celebrating Mass. When he opens his arms and offers the bread and the wine, body and blood of the people, the murderer pulls the trigger.

(259 and 301)

1980: Montevideo
A People Who Say No

The dictatorship of Uruguay calls a plebiscite and loses.

This people forced into silence seemed dumb; but when it opens its mouth, it says no. The silence of these years has been so deafening that the military mistook it for resignation. They never expected such a response. They asked only for the sake of asking, like a chef who orders his chickens to say with what sauce they prefer to be eaten.

1980: In All Nicaragua
On Its Way

The Sandinista revolution doesn't shoot anybody; but of Somoza's army not a brass band remains. The rifles pass into everybody's hands, while the banner of agrarian reform is unfurled over desolate fields.

An army of volunteers, whose weapons are pencils and vaccines, invades its own country. Revolution, revelation, of those who believe and create; not infallible gods of majestic stride, but ordinary people, for centuries forced into obedience and trained for impotence. Now, even when they trip, they keep on walking. They go in search of bread and the word: This land, which opened its mouth, is eager to eat and speak.

1980: Asunción
Stroessner

Tachito Somoza, dethroned, exiled, is blown to pieces on a street corner in Asunción.

"Who did it?" ask the journalists in Managua.

*"Fuenteovejuna,"** replies comandante Tomás Borge.

Tachito had found refuge in the capital of Paraguay, the only city in the world where there was still a bronze bust of his father, Tacho Somoza, and where a street was still named "Generalisimo Franco."

Paraguay, or the little that is left of Paraguay after so much war and plunder, belongs to General Alfredo Stroessner. Every five years this veteran colleague of Somoza and Franco holds elections to confirm his power. So that people can vote, he suspends for twenty-four hours Paraguay's eternal state of siege.

Stroessner believes himself invulnerable because he loves no one. The State is him. Every day, at precisely 6:00 P.M., he phones the president of the Central Bank and asks him:

"How much did we make today?"

1980: In All Nicaragua

Discovering

Riding horseback, rowing, walking, the brigadistas of the literacy campaigns penetrate the most hidden corners of Nicaragua. By lamplight they teach the handling of a pencil to those who don't know, so that they'll never again be fooled by people who think they're so smart.

While they teach, the brigadistas share what little food they have, stoop down to weed and harvest crops, skin their hands chopping wood, and spend the night on the floor slapping at mosquitos. They discover wild honey in the trees, and in the people legends, verses, lost wisdom; bit by bit they get to know the secret languages of the herbs that enliven flavors, cure pains, and heal snake bites. Teaching, the brigadistas learn the marvel and malevolence of this country, their country, inhabited by survivors; in Nicaragua, anyone who doesn't die of hunger, disease, or a bullet, dies of laughter.

(11)

* The allusion is to the play *Fuenteovejuna* by the Spanish playwright Lope de Vega (1562–1635), in which all the people of the town of that name claim collective responsibility for the death of a tyrant. The most famous passage in the play reads: "Who killed the Comendador? Fuenteovejuna, señor."

1980: New York

The Statue of Liberty Seems
Pitted with Smallpox

because of the poisonous gases so many factories throw into the sky, and which rain and snow bring back to earth. One hundred and seventy lakes have been murdered by this acid rain in New York State alone, but the director of the Federal Office of Management and Budget says it's not worth bothering about. After all, those lakes are only four percent of the state total.

The world is a racetrack. Nature, an obstacle. The deadly breath of the smokestacks has left four thousand lakes without fish or plants in Ontario, Canada.

"We'd better ask God to start over," says a fisherman.

1980: New York

Lennon

A shirt hung out on a roof flaps its arms. The wind complains. The roaring and screaming of city life is joined by the shriek of a siren rushing through the streets. On this dirty day in Manhattan, John Lennon, musical innovator, has been murdered.

He didn't want to win or kill. He didn't agree that the world should be a stock market or a barracks. Lennon was on the sidelines of the track. Singing or whistling with a distracted look, he watched the wheels of others turn in the perpetual vertigo that comes and goes between madhouse and slaughterhouse.

1981: Surahammar

Exile

What is the distance that separates a Bolivian mining camp from a city in Sweden? How many miles, how many centuries, how many worlds?

Domitila, one of the five women who overthrew a military dictatorship, has been sentenced to exile by another military dictatorship and has ended up, with her miner husband and her many children, in the snows of northern Europe.

From where there's too little anything to where there's too much everything, from lowest poverty to highest opulence. Eyes full of wonder in these faces of clay: Here in Sweden they throw in the garbage nearly new TVs, hardly used clothing and furniture, and refrigerators and dishwashers that work perfectly. To the junkyard goes last year's automobile.

Domitila is grateful for the support of the Swedes and admires them for their liberty, but the waste offends her and the loneliness troubles her. These poor rich folk live all alone before the television, drinking alone, eating alone, talking to themselves:

"Over there in Bolivia," says—recommends—Domitila, *"even if it's for a fight, we get together."*

(1)

1981: Celica Canton
"Bad Luck, Human Error, Bad Weather"

A plane crashes at the end of May, and so ends the life of Jaime Roldós, president of Ecuador. Some campesinos hear the explosion and see the plane in flames before it crashes.

Doctors are not permitted to examine the body. No autopsy is attempted. The black box never turns up; they say the plane had none. Tractors smooth over the scene of the disaster. Tapes from the Quito, Guayaquil, and Loja control towers are erased. Various witnesses die in accidents. The Air Force's report discounts in advance any crime.

Bad luck, human error, bad weather. But President Roldós was defending Ecuador's coveted oil, had restored relations with prohibited Cuba, and backed accursed revolutions in Nicaragua, El Salvador, Palestine.

Two months later another plane crashes, in Panama. *Bad luck, human error, bad weather.* Two campesinos who heard the plane explode in the air disappear. Omar Torrijos, guilty of rescuing the Panama Canal, knew he wasn't going to die in bed of old age.

Almost simultaneously, a helicopter crashes in Peru. *Bad luck, human error, bad weather.* This time the victim is the head of the

Peruvian army, General Rafael Hoyos Rubio, an old enemy of Standard Oil and other benevolent multinational corporations.

(154 and 175)

1982: South Georgia Islands
Portrait of a Brave Fellow

The mothers of the Plaza de Mayo called him *the Angel*, because of his pink baby face. He had spent some months working with them, always smiling, always ready to lend a hand, when, one evening, the soldiers pick up several of the movement's most active militants as they leave a meeting. These mothers disappear, like their sons and daughters, and nothing more is heard of them.

The kidnapped mothers have been fingered by *the Angel*; that is, Frigate Lieutenant Alfredo Astiz, member of Task Force 3-3-2 of the Navy's Mechanics School, who has a long and brilliant record in the torture chambers.

This spy and torturer, now a lieutenant on a warship, is the first to surrender to the English in the Malvinas war. He surrenders without firing a shot.

(107, 134, 143, and 388)

1982: Malvinas Islands
The Malvinas War,

patriotic war that for a moment united trampled and tramplers, ends with the victory of Great Britain's colonial army.

The Argentine generals and colonels who promised to shed their last drops of blood have not so much as cut a finger. Those who declared war haven't even put in a guest appearance. So that the Argentine flag might fly over these ice cubes, a just cause in unjust hands, the high command sent to the slaughterhouse youngsters roped into compulsory service, who died more of cold than of bullets.

Their pulses do not flicker. With firm hands, these rapers of bound women, hangmen of disarmed workers, sign the surrender.

(185)

1982: *The Roads of La Mancha*
Master Globetrotter

completes his first half century of life far from where he was born. In a Castilian village, in front of one of the windmills that challenged Don Quixote, Javier Villafañe, patriarch of America's puppeteers, celebrates the birthday of his favorite son. To be worthy of this great date, Javier decides to marry a pretty gypsy he has just met; and Master Globetrotter presides over the ceremony and banquet with his characteristic melancholy dignity.

They've gone through life together, these two, puppeteering along the roads of the world, sweetness and mischief, Master Globetrotter and the pilgrim Javier. Whenever Master Globetrotter gets sick, a victim of worms or moths, Javier heals his wounds with infinite patience and afterward watches over his sleep.

At the start of each performance, before an expectant crowd of children, the two tremble as if at their first show.

1982: *Stockholm*
Novelist García Márquez Receives the Nobel Prize and Speaks of our Lands Condemned to One Hundred Years of Solitude

I dare to think that it is this outsized reality, and not just its literary expression, that has deserved the attention of the Swedish Academy of Letters. A reality not of paper, but one that lives within us and determines each instant of our countless daily deaths, and that nourishes a source of insatiable creativity full of sorrow and beauty, of which this roving and nostalgic Colombian is but one cipher more, singled out by fortune. Poets and beggars, musicians and prophets, warriors and scoundrels, all creatures of that unbridled reality, we have had to ask but little of our imagination, for our crucial problem has been a lack of conventional means to render our lives believable. This, my friends, is the crux of our solitude . . .

The interpretation of our reality through patterns not our own serves only to make us ever more unknown, ever less free, ever more solitary . . .

No: the immeasurable violence and pain of our history are the result of age-old inequities and untold bitterness, and not a conspiracy plotted three thousand leagues from our homes. But many European leaders and thinkers have thought so, this with the childishness of old-timers who have forgotten the fruitful excesses of their youth, as if it were impossible to find another destiny than to live at the mercy of the two great masters of the world. This, friends, is the very scale of our solitude . . .

(189)

1983: Saint George's
The Reconquest of the Island of Grenada

Tiny Grenada, hardly visible speck of green in the immensity of the Caribbean, suffers a spectacular invasion of Marines. President Ronald Reagan sends them to murder socialism, but the Marines kill a corpse. Some days earlier, certain native military men, greedy for power, had already assassinated socialism, in the name of socialism.

Behind the Marines lands North American secretary of state George Shultz. At a press conference he says: *"At first sight I realized that this island could be a splendid real estate prospect."*

1983: La Bermuda
Marianela

Every morning at dawn, they lined up, these relatives, friends, and lovers of the disappeared of El Salvador. They came looking for or offering news; they had no other place to ask about the lost or bear witness. The door of the Human Rights Commission was always open; or one could simply step through the hole the last bomb had opened in its wall.

Since the guerrilla movement started growing in the countryside, the army has no longer bothered to use prisons. The Commission denounced them before the world: *July: fifteen children under fourteen who had been detained charged with terrorism are found decapitated. August: thirteen thousand five hundred civilians murdered or disappeared so far this year . . .*

Of the Commission's workers, Magdalena Enríquez, the one who laughed most, was the first to fall. Soldiers dumped her flayed body on the beach. Then came the turn of Ramón Valladares, found riddled with bullets in the roadside mud. Only Marianela García Vilas remained: *"The bad weed never dies,"* she said.

They kill her near the village of La Bermuda in the burned lands of Cuscatlán. She was walking with her camera and tape recorder collecting proof that the army fires white phosphorus at rebellious campesinos.

(259)

1983: Santiago de Chile
Ten Years after the Reconquest of Chile

"You have the right to import a camel," says the Minister of Finance. From the TV screen the minister exhorts Chileans to make use of free trade. In Chile anyone can decorate his home with an authentic African crocodile, and democracy consists of choosing between Chivas Regal and Johnnie Walker Black Label.

Everything is imported: brooms, birdcage swings, corn, water for the whiskey. Baguette loaves come by air from Paris. The economic system, imported from the United States, obliges Chileans to scratch at the entrails of their mountains for copper, and nothing more. Not a pin can they manufacture, because South Korean pins come cheaper. Any creative act is a crime against the laws of the market—that is, the laws of fate.

From the United States come television programs, cars, machineguns, and plastic flowers. In the upper-class neighborhoods of Santiago, one cannot move without bumping into Japanese computers, German videocassettes, Dutch TVs, Swiss chocolates, English marmalade, Danish hams, clothing from Taiwan, French perfumes, Spanish tuna, Italian oil . . .

He who does not consume does not exist. Everyone else is simply used and discarded, although they pay the bills for this credit-card fiesta.

The unemployed scavenge through refuse. Everywhere one sees signs that say: *No openings. Do not insist.*

The foreign debt and the suicide rate have increased six-fold.

(169 and 231)

1983: A Ravine Between Cabildo and Petorca
Television

The Escárates had nothing—until Armando brought that box on his mule.

Armando Escárate had been away a whole year, working at sea as a cook for fishermen, and also in the town of La Ligua, doing odd jobs and eating leftovers, toiling night and day until he could put together enough money to pay for it.

When Armando got off his mule and opened the box, the family was struck dumb with fright. No one had ever seen the like of it in these regions of the Chilean cordillera. From afar people came, as if on pilgrimage, to examine the full-color Sony that ran off a truck battery.

The Escárates had nothing. They still have nothing, and continue to sleep huddled together, barely getting by on the cheese they make, the wool they spin, and the flocks of goats they graze for the boss of the hacienda. But the television rises like a totem in the middle of their mud shanty roofed with reeds. From the screen Coca-Cola offers them the sparkle of life, and Sprite, bubbles of youth; Marlboro cigarettes give them virility; Cadbury candies, human communication; Visa credit cards, wealth; Dior perfumes and Cardin shirts, distinction; Cinzano vermouth, social status; the Martini, passionate love. Nestlé powdered milk provides them with eternal vigor, and the Renault automobile with a new way to live.

(230)

1983: Buenos Aires
The Granny Detectives

While the military dictatorship disintegrates in Argentina, the Plaza de Mayo grandmothers go looking for their lost grandchildren. These children, imprisoned with their parents or born in concentration camps, have been distributed as war booty, and more than one has for parents his own parents' murderers. The grannies investigate on the basis of whatever they can dig up—photos, stray data, a birthmark, someone who saw something—and so, beating out a path with native shrewdness and umbrella blows, they have recovered a few children.

Tamara Arze, who disappeared at one-and-a-half, did not end up in military hands. She is in a suburban barrio, in the home of the good folk who picked her up where she was dumped. At the mother's appeal, the grannies undertook the search for her. They had only a few leads, but after a long, complicated sweep, they have located her. Every morning Tamara sells kerosene from a horse-drawn cart, but she doesn't complain of her fate. At first she doesn't even want to hear about her real mother. Very gradually the grannies explain to her that she is the daughter of Rosa, a Bolivian worker who never abandoned her. That one night her mother was seized at the factory gate, in Buenos Aires . . .

(317)

1983: Lima

Tamara Flies Twice

Rosa was tortured—under the supervision of a doctor who indicated when to stop—and raped, and shot at with blank cartridges. She spent eight years in prison, without trial or explanation, and only last year was expelled from Argentina. Now, in Lima airport, she waits while her daughter Tamara flies over the Andes toward her.

Accompanying Tamara on the flight are two of the grannies who found her.

She devours every bit of food she is served on the plane, not leaving a crumb of bread or a grain of sugar.

In Lima, Rosa and Tamara discover each other. They look in the mirror together. They are identical: same eyes, same mouth, same marks in the same places.

When night comes, Rosa bathes her daughter. Putting her to bed, she smells a milky, sweetish smell on her; and so she bathes her again. And again. But however much soap she uses, there is no way to wash off the smell. It's an odd smell . . . And suddenly Rosa remembers. This is the smell of little babies when they finish nursing: Tamara is ten, and tonight she smells like a newly born infant.

(317)

1983: Buenos Aires
What If the Desert Were Ocean and the Earth Were Sky?

The mothers and grandmothers of the Plaza de Mayo are frightening. For what would happen if they tired of circling in front of the Pink House and began signing government decrees? And if the beggars on the cathedral steps grabbed the archbishop's tunic and biretta and began preaching sermons from the pulpit? And if honest circus clowns began giving orders in the barracks and courses in the universities? And if they did? And if?

(317)

1983: Plateau of Petitions
The Mexican Theater of Dreams

As they do every year, the Zapotec Indians come to the Plateau of Petitions.

On one side is the sea, on the other, peaks and precipices.

Here dreams are turned loose. A kneeling man gets up and goes into the wood, an invisible bride on his arm. Someone moves like a languid jellyfish, navigating in an aerial ship. One makes drawings in the wind and another rides by with slow majesty, astride a tree branch. Pebbles become grains of corn, and acorns, hen's eggs. Old people become children, and children, giants; the leaf of a tree becomes a mirror that imparts a handsome face to anyone looking at it.

The spell is broken should anyone dare not be serious about this dress rehearsal of life.

(418)

1983: Tuma River
Realization

In Nicaragua, bullets whiz back and forth between dignity and scorn; and the war extinguishes many lives.

This is one of the battalions fighting the invaders. These volunteers have come from the poorest barrios of Managua to the far plains of the Tuma River.

Whenever there is a quiet moment, Beto, *the prof*, spreads the contagion of letters. The contagion occurs when some militiaman asks him to write a letter for him. Beto does it, and then: *"This is the last one I'll write for you. I'm offering you something better."*

Sebastián Fuertes, iron soldier from El Maldito barrio, a middle-aged man of many wars and women, is one of those who came up and was sentenced to alphabetization. For some days he has been breaking pencils and tearing up sheets of paper in the respites from shooting, and standing up to a lot of heavy teasing. And when May First arrives, his comrades elect him to make the speech.

The meeting is held in a paddock full of dung and ticks. Sebastián gets up on a box, takes from his pocket a folded paper, and reads the first words ever born from his hands. He reads from a distance, stretching out his arm, because his sight is little help and he has no glasses.

"Brothers of Battalion 8221! . . ."

1983: Managua

Defiance

Plumes of smoke rise from the mouths of volcanos and the barrels of guns. The campesino goes to war on a burro, with a parrot on his shoulder. God must have been a primitive painter the day he dreamed up this land of gentle speech, condemned to die and to kill by the United States, which trains and pays the contras. From Honduras, the Somocistas attack it; from Costa Rica, Edén Pastora betrays it.

And now, here comes the Pope of Rome. The Pope scolds those priests who love Nicaragua more than heaven, and abruptly silences those who ask him to pray for the souls of murdered patriots. After quarreling with the Catholic multitude gathered in the plaza, he takes off in a fury from this bedeviled land.

1983: Mérida

The People Set God on His Feet,

and the people know that to stand up in the world, God needs their help.

Every year, the child Jesus is born in Mérida and elsewhere in Venezuela. Choristers sing to the strains of violins, mandolins, and guitars, while the godparents gather up in a big cloth the child lying in the manger—delicate task, serious business—and take him for a walk.

The godparents walk the child through the streets. The kings and shepherds follow, and the crowd throws flowers and kisses. After such a warm welcome into the world, the godparents put Jesus back in the manger where Mary and Joseph are waiting for him.

Then, in the name of the community, the godparents stand him up for the first time, and make sure he remains upright between his parents. Finally the rosary is sung and all present get a little cake of the old-fashioned kind with twelve egg yolks, and some sweet mistela wine.

(463)

1983: Managua

Newsreel

In a Managua barrio, a woman has given birth to a hen, according to the Nicaraguan daily *La Prensa*. Sources close to the ecclesiastical hierarchy do not deny that this extraordinary event may be a sign of God's anger. The behavior of the crowd before the Pope may have exhausted the Divine Patience, these sources believe.

Back in 1981, two miracles with equally broad repercussions occurred in Nicaragua. The Virgin of Cuapa made a spectacular appearance that year in the fields of Chontales. Barefoot, crowned with stars, and enveloped in a glowing aura that blinded witnesses, the Virgin made declarations to a sacristan named Bernardo. The Mother of God expressed her support for President Reagan's policies against atheistic, Communist-inspired Sandinismo.

Shortly afterward, the Virgin of the Conception sweated and wept copiously for several days in a Managua house. The archbishop, Monseñor Obando, appeared before his altar and exhorted the faithful to pray for the forgiveness of the Most Pure. The Virgin of the Conception's emanations stopped only when the police discovered that the owners of the plaster image were submerging it in water and shutting it in a refrigerator at night so that it would perspire when exposed to the intense local heat, before the crowd of pilgrims.

1984: The Vatican
The Holy Office of the Inquisition

now bears the more discreet name of the Congregation for the Doctrine of the Faith. It no longer burns heretics alive, although it might like to. Its chief headache these days comes from America. In the name of the Holy Father, the inquisitors summon Latin American theologians Leonardo Boff and Gustavo Gutiérrez, and the Vatican sharply reprimands them for lacking respect for the Church of Fear.

The Church of Fear, opulent multinational enterprise, devotee of pain and death, is anxious to nail on a cross any son of a carpenter of the breed that now circulates within America's coasts inciting fishermen and defying empires.

1984: London
Gold and Frankincense

Top officials of the United States, Japan, West Germany, England, France, Italy, and Canada, forgather at Lancaster House to congratulate the organization that guarantees the freedom of money. The seven powers of the capitalist world unanimously applaud *the work of the International Monetary Fund in the developing countries*.

The congratulations do not mention the executioners, torturers, inquisitors, jailers, and informers who are the functionaries of the Fund in these *developing countries*.

A Circular Symphony for Poor Countries, in
Six Successive Movements

So that labor may be increasingly obedient and cheap, the poor countries need legions of executioners, torturers, inquisitors, jailers, and informers.

To feed and arm these legions, the poor countries need loans from the rich countries.

To pay the interest on these loans, the poor countries need more loans.

To pay the interest on the loans on top of loans, the poor countries need to increase their exports.

To increase their exports, products condemned to perpetually collapsing prices, the poor countries need to lower production costs.

To lower production costs, the poor countries need increasingly obedient and cheap labor.

To make labor increasingly obedient and cheap, the poor countries need legions of executioners, torturers, inquisitors . . .

1984: Washington
1984

The U.S. State Department decides to suppress the word *murder* in its reports on violations of human rights in Latin America and other regions. Instead of *murder*, one must say: *illegal or arbitrary deprivation of life*.

For some time now, the CIA has avoided the word *murder* in its manuals on practical terrorism. When the CIA murders an enemy or has him murdered, it *neutralizes* him.

The State Department calls any war forces it lands south of its borders *peace-keeping forces*; and the killers who fight to restore its business interests in Nicaragua *freedom fighters*.

(94)

1984: Washington

We Are All Hostages

Nicaragua and other insolent countries still act as if unaware that history has been ordered not to budge, under pain of total destruction of the world.

"*We will not tolerate . . .*" warns President Reagan.

Above the clouds hover the nuclear bombers. Farther up, the military satellites. Beneath the earth and beneath the sea, the missiles. The Earth still rotates because the great powers permit it to do so. A plutonium bomb the size of an orange would suffice to explode the entire planet, and a good-size discharge of radiation could turn it into a desert populated by cockroaches.

President Reagan says Saint Luke (14:31) advises increasing military funding to confront the Communist hordes. The economy is militarized; weapons shoot money to buy weapons to shoot money. They manufacture arms, hamburgers, and fear. There is no better business than the sale of fear. The president announces, jubilantly, the militarization of the stars.

(430)

1984: São Paulo

Twenty Years after the Reconquest of Brazil

The last president of the military dictatorship, General Figueiredo, leaves the government to civilians.

When they ask him what he would do if he were a worker earning the minimum wage, General Figueiredo replies: "*I would put a bullet through my head.*"

Brazil suffers a famished prosperity. Among countries selling food to the world, it stands in fourth place; among countries suffering hunger in the world, sixth place. Now Brazil exports arms and automobiles as well as coffee, and produces more steel than France; but Brazilians are shorter and weigh less than they did twenty years ago.

Millions of homeless children wander the streets of cities like São Paulo, hunting for food. Buildings are turning into fortresses, doormen into armed guards. Every citizen is either an assailant or assailed.

(371)

1984: Guatemala City
Thirty Years after the Reconquest of Guatemala,

the Bank of the Army is the country's most important, after the Bank of America. Generals take turns in power, overthrowing each other, transforming dictatorship into dictatorship; but all apply the same policy of land seizure against the Indians guilty of inhabiting areas rich in oil, nickel, or whatever else turns out to be of value.

These are no longer the days of United Fruit, but rather of Getty Oil, Texaco, and the International Nickel Company. The generals wipe out many Indian communities wholesale and expel even more from their lands. Multitudes of hungry Indians, stripped of everything, wander the mountains. They come from horror, but they are not going to horror. They walk slowly, guided by the ancient certainty that someday greed and arrogance will be punished. That's what the old people of corn assure the children of corn in the stories they tell them when night falls.

(367 and 450)

1984: Rio de Janeiro
Mishaps of Collective Memory in Latin America

Public accountant João David dos Santos jumped for joy when he managed to collect his many overdue accounts. Only payment in kind, but something. For lack of funds, a social science research center paid him its whole library of nine thousand books and over five thousand magazines and pamphlets devoted to contemporary Brazilian history. It contained very valuable material on the peasant leagues of the Northeast and the Getulio Vargas administration, among other subjects.

Then accountant dos Santos put the library up for sale. He offered it to cultural organizations, historical institutes, and various ministries. No one had the money. He tried universities, state and private, one after another. No takers. He left the library on loan at one university for a few months, until they started demanding rent. Then he tried private citizens. No one showed the slightest interest. The nation's history is an enigma, a lie, or a yawn.

The unhappy accountant dos Santos feels great relief when he finally succeeds in selling his library to the Tijuca Paper Factory, which turns all these books, magazines, and pamphlets into tinted toilet paper.

(371)

1984: Mexico City
Against Forgetting,

the only death that really kills, Carlos Quijano wrote what he wrote. This grouch and troublemaker was born in Montevideo as the century was born, and dies in exile, as Uruguay's military dictatorship is falling. He dies at work, preparing a new Mexican edition of his magazine *Marcha*.

Quijano celebrated contradictions. Heresy for others to him was a sign of life. He condemned imperialism, humiliator of nations and multitudes, and proclaimed that Latin America is destined to create a socialism worthy of the hopes of its prophets.

(356)

1984: Mexico City
The Resurrection of the Living

The Mexicans make a custom of eating death, a sugar or chocolate skeleton dripping with colored caramel. In addition to eating it, they sing it, dance it, drink it, and sleep it. Sometimes, to mock power and money, the people dress death in a monocle and frock coat, epaulettes and medals, but they prefer it stripped naked, racy, a bit drunk, their companion on festive outings.

Day of the Living, this Day of the Dead should be called, although on reflection it's all the same, because whatever comes goes and whatever goes comes, and in the last analysis the beginning of what begins is always the end of what ends.

"*My grandfather is so tiny because he was born after me,*" says a child who knows what he's talking about.

1984: Estelí
Believing

They preside over childbirth. Giving life and light is their profession. With practiced hands they straighten the child if it's coming out wrong, and communicate strength and peace to the mother.

Today, the midwives of the Estelí villages and mountains close to Nicaragua's border are having a party to celebrate something that truly deserves joy: For a year now not one new baby in this region has died of tetanus. The midwives no longer cut umbilical cords with a machete, or burn them with tallow, or tie them off without disinfectant; and pregnant women get vaccines that protect the child living inside. Now no one here believes that vaccines are Russian witches' brews meant to turn Christians into Communists; and no one, or almost no one, believes that a newborn can die from the fixed stare of a drunken man or a menstruating woman.

This region, this war zone, suffers continuous harassment by the invaders.

"*Here, we are in the alligator's mouth.*"

Many mothers go off to fight. The ones who stay share their breasts.

1984: Havana
Miguel at Seventy-Nine

Since the dawn of the century, this man has gone through hell and died several times over. Now, from exile, he still energetically accompanies his people in their war.

The dawn light always finds him up, shaved and conspiring. He could just as easily keep turning in the revolving door of memory;

but he doesn't know how to be deaf when the voices of these new times and the roads he still hasn't traveled call out to him.

And so at seventy-nine every day is a new birth for Miguel Mármol, old master of the art of constant rebirth.

1984: Paris
The Echoes Go Searching for the Voice

While writing words that loved people, Julio Cortázar was making his own journey, a journey backward through the tunnel of time. He was traveling from the end to the beginning, from discouragement to enthusiasm, from indifference to passion, from solitariness to solidarity. At almost seventy, he was a child of all ages at once.

A bird that flew toward the egg, Cortázar went forward by going back, year after year, day after day, toward the embrace of lovers who make the love that makes them. And now he dies, now he enters the earth, like a man who, entering a woman, returns to the place he comes from.

1984: Punta Santa Elena
The Eternal Embrace

They were found only recently in the wasteland that once was Zumpa beach in Ecuador. And here they are, in full sunlight, for anyone who wants to see: a man and a woman lying in embrace, sleeping lovers, out of eternity.

Excavating an Indian cemetery, an archaeologist came upon this pair of skeletons bound together by love. It was eight thousand years ago that the lovers of Zumpa committed the irreverence of dying without separating themselves, and anyone who approaches can see that death does not cause them the slightest concern.

Their splendid beauty is surprising, considering that they are such ugly bones in such an ugly desert, pure dryness and grayness; and more surprising is their modesty. These lovers, sleeping in the wind, seem not to have grasped that they have more mystery and grandeur than the pyramids of Teotihuacán or the sanctuary of Machu Picchu or the waterfalls of Iguazú.

1984: Violeta Parra Community
The Stolen Name

The dictatorship of General Pinochet changes the names of twenty bone-poor communities, tin and cardboard houses, on the outskirts of Santiago de Chile. In the rebaptism, the Violeta Parra community gets the name of some military hero. But its inhabitants refuse to bear this unchosen name. They are Violeta Parra or nothing.

A while back they had decided in unanimous assembly to name themselves after the campesina singer with the raspy voice who in her songs of struggle knew how to celebrate Chile's mysteries.

Violeta was sinful and saucy, given to guitar-strumming and long talks and falling in love, and with all her dancing and clowning around she kept burning the empanadas. *Thanks to life, which has given me so much,* she sang in her last song; and a turbulent love affair sent her off to her death.

(334 and 440)

1984: Tepic
The Found Name

In the mountains of Nayarit in Mexico, there was a community that had no name. For centuries this community of Huichol Indians had been looking for a name. Carlos González found one by sheer accident.

This Huichol had come to the city of Tepic to buy seeds and visit relatives. Crossing a garbage dump, he picked up a book thrown into the rubbish. It was years ago that Carlos had learned to read the Castilian language, and he could still just about manage it. Sitting in the shade of a projecting roof, he began to decipher the pages. The book spoke of a country with a strange name, which Carlos couldn't place but which had to be far from Mexico, and told a story of recent occurrence.

On the way home, walking up the mountain, Carlos continued reading. He couldn't tear himself away from this story of horror and bravery. The central character of the book was a man who had kept his word. Arriving at the village, Carlos announced euphorically: *"At last we have a name!"*

And he read the book aloud to everyone. This halting recital took him almost a week. Afterward, the hundred and fifty families voted. All in favor. Dancing and singing they performed the baptism.

So finally they have a name for themselves. This community bears the name of a worthy man who did not doubt at the moment of choice between treachery and death.

"I'm going to Salvador Allende," the wayfarers say now.

(466)

1984: Bluefields
Flying

Deep root, lofty trunk, dense foliage: from the center of the world rises a thornless tree, one of those trees that know how to give themselves to the birds. Around the tree whirl dancing couples, navel to navel, undulating to a music that wakens stones and sets fire to ice. As they dance, they dress and undress the tree with streaming ribbons of every color. On this tormented, continuously invaded, continuously bombarded coast of Nicaragua, the Maypole fiesta is celebrated as usual.

The tree of life knows that, whatever happens, the warm music spinning around it will never stop. However much death may come, however much blood may flow, the music will dance men and women as long as the air breathes them and the land plows and loves them.

1986: Montevideo
A Letter

Cedric Belfrage
Apartado Postal 630
Cuernavaca, Morelos
Mexico

My Dear Cedric:
Here goes the last volume of Memory of Fire. *As you'll see, it ends in 1984. Why not before, or after, I don't know. Perhaps because that was the last year of my exile, the end of a cycle, the end of a century;*

or perhaps because the book and I know that the last page is also the first.

Forgive me if it came out too long. Writing it was a joy for my hand; and now I feel more than ever proud of having been born in America, in this shit, in this marvel, during the century of the wind.

No more now, because I don't want to bury the sacred in palaver. Abrazos,

Eduardo

(End of the third volume of
Memory of Fire.)

The Sources

1. Acebey, David. *Aquí también Domitila*. La Paz: n.p., 1984.
2. Adams, Willi Paul. *Los Estados Unidos de América*. Madrid: Siglo XXI, 1979.
3. Aguiar, Cláudio. *Caldeirão*. Rio de Janeiro: José Olympio, 1982.
4. Aguilar Camín, Héctor. *Saldos de la revolución. Cultura y política de México, 1910–1980*. Mexico City: Nueva Imagen, 1982.
5. Aguiló, Federico. *Significado socio-antropológico de las coplas al Cristo de Santa Vera Cruz*. Paper presented at the second Conference of Bolivian Studies, Cochabamba, 1984.
6. Agudelo, William. *El asalto a San Carlos. Testimonios de Solentiname*. Managua: Asoc. para el Desarrollo de Solentiname, 1982.
7. Alape, Arturo. *El bogotazo. Memorias del olvido*. Bogotá: Pluma, 1983.
8. ———. *La Paz, la violencia: testigos de excepción*. Bogotá: Planeta, 1985.
9. Alegría, Claribel, and D. J. Flakoll. *Cenizas de Izalco*. Barcelona; Seix Barral, 1966.
10. ———. *Nicaragua: la revolución sandinista. Una crónica política, 1855–1979*. Mexico: Era, 1982.
11. Alemán Ocampo, Carlos. *Y también enséñenles a leer*. Managua: Nueva Nicaragua, 1984.
12. Alfaro, Eloy, *Narraciones históricas*. (Preface by Malcolm D. Deas.) Quito: Editora Nacional, 1983.
13. Alfaro, Hugo. *Navegar es necesario*. Montevideo: Banda Oriental, 1985.
14. Ali, Muhammad. *The Greatest: My Own Story*. New York: Random House, 1975.
15. Allen, Frederick Lewis. *Apenas ayer. Historia informal de la decada del 20*. Buenos Aires: EUDEBA, 1964.
16. Almaraz Paz, Sergio. *Requiem para una república*. La Paz: Universidad, 1969.
17. ———. *El poder y la caída*. La Paz and Cochabamba: Amigos del Libro, 1969.
18. Almeida Bosque, Juan. *Contra el agua y el viento*. Havana: Casa de las Américas, 1985.
19. Amado, Jorge. *Los viejos marineros*. Barcelona: Seix Barral, 1983.
20. Amorim, Enrique. *El Quiroga que yo conocí*. Montevideo: Arca, 1983.
21. Anderson, Thomas. *El Salvador. Los sucesos políticos de 1932*. San José de Costa Rica: EDUCA, 1982.
22. Andrade, Joaquim Pedro de. *Garrincha, alegria do povo*. (Film produced by Barreto, Nogueira, and Richers.) Rio de Janeiro, 1963.

23. Andrade, Mário de. *Macunaíma, o herói sem nenhum caráter*. Belo Horizonte and Brasília: Itatiaia, 1984.

24. Andrade, Roberto. *Vida y muerte de Eloy Alfaro*. Quito: El Conejo, 1985.

25. Andreu, Jean. "Borges, escritor comprometido," in *Texto crítico*, No. 13, Veracruz, April–June 1979.

26. Antezana, Luis E. *Proceso y sentencia de la reforma agraria en Bolivia*. La Paz: Puerta del Sol, 1979.

27. Arenales, Angélica. *Siqueiros*. Mexico City: Bellas Artes, 1947.

28. Arévalo Martínez, Rafael. *Ecce Pericles. La tiranía de Manuel Estrada Cabrera en Guatemala*. San José de Costa Rica: EDUCA, 1983.

29. Arguedas, Alcides. *Pueblo enfermo*. La Paz: Juventud, 1985.

30. Arguedas, José María. *El zorro de arriba y el zorro de abajo*. Buenos Aires: Losada, 1971.

31. ———. *Formación de una cultura nacional indoamericana*. Mexico City: Siglo XXI, 1975.

32. Aricó, José (ed.). *Mariátegui y los orígenes del marxismo latinoamericano*. Mexico City: Pasado y Presente, 1980.

33. Azuela, Mariano. *Los de abajo*. Mexico City: FCE, 1960.

34. Baptista Gumucio, Mariano. *Historia contemporánea de Bolivia, 1930–1978*. La Paz: Gisbert, 1978.

35. Barrán, José P., and Benjamín Nahum. *Batlle, los estancieros y el Imperio Británico. Las primeras reformas, 1911–1913*. Montevideo: Banda Oriental, 1983.

36. Barreto, Lima. *Os bruzundangas*. São Paulo: Ática, 1985.

37. Barrett, Rafael. *El dolor paraguayo*. (Preface by Augusto Roa Bastos.) Caracas: Ayacucho, 1978.

38. Bayer, Osvaldo. *Los vengadores de la Patagonia trágica*. Buenos Aires: Galerna, 1972, 1974; and Wuppertal: Hammer, 1977.

39. Beals, Carleton. *Banana Gold*. Managua: Nueva Nicaragua, 1983.

40. ———. *Porfirio Díaz*. Mexico City: Domés, 1982.

41. Belfrage, Cedric. *The American Inquisition, 1945–1960*. Indianapolis: Bobbs-Merrill, 1973.

42. Bell, John Patrick. *Guerra civil en Costa Rica. Los sucesos políticos de 1948*. San José de Costa Rica: EDUCA, 1981.

43. Beloch, Israel, and Alzira Alves de Abreu. *Dicionário histórico-biográfico brasileiro, 1930–1983*. Rio de Janeiro: Fundação Getúlio Vargas, 1984.

44. Benítez, Fernando. *Lázaro Cárdenas y la revolución mexicana. El porfirismo*. Mexico City: FCE, 1977.

45. ———. *Lázaro Cárdenas y la revolución mexicana. El cardenismo*. Mexico City: FCE, 1980.

46. ———. *Los indios de México* (Vol. 3). Mexico City: Era, 1979.

47. ———. *La ciudad de México, 1325–1982*. Barcelona and Mexico City: Salvat, 1981, 1982.

48. Benítez, Fernando, *et al. Juan Rulfo, homenaje nacional*. Mexico City: Bellas Artes/SEP, 1980.

49. Benvenuto, Ofelia Machado de. *Delmira Agustini*. Montevideo: Ministerio de Instrucción Pública, 1944.

50. Bernays, Edward. *Biography of an Idea*. New York: Simon and Schuster, 1965.

51. Berry, Mary Frances, and John W. Blassingame. *Long Memory: The Black Experience in America*. New York and Oxford: Oxford University Press, 1982.

52. Bezerra, João. *Como dei cabo de Lampião*. Recife: Massangana, 1983.

53. Bingham, Hiram. *Machu Picchu, la ciudad perdida de los incas*. Madrid: Rodas, 1972.

54. Bliss, Michael. *The Discovery of Insulin*. Toronto: McClelland and Stewart, 1982.

55. Bodard, Lucien. *Masacre de indios en el Amazonas*. Caracas: Tiempo Nuevo, 1970.

56. Bolaños, Pío. *Génesis de la intervención norteamericana en Nicaragua*. Managua: Nueva Nicaragua, 1984.

57. Bonfil Batalla, Guillermo. *El universo del amate*. Mexico City: Museo de Culturas Populares, 1982.

58. Borge, Tomás. *Carlos, el amanecer ya no es una tentación*. Havana: Casa de las Américas, 1980.

59. Borges, Jorge Luis. *Obras completas, 1923–1972*. Buenos Aires: Emecé, 1974.

60. Bosch, Juan. *Trujillo: causas de una tiranía sin ejemplo*. Caracas: Las Novedades, 1959.

61. ———. "Crisis de la democracia de América en la República Dominicana," in *Panoramas*, No. 14, supplement, Mexico City, 1964.

62. ———. *La revolución de abril*. Santo Domingo: Alfa y Omega, 1981.

63. ———. *Clases sociales en la República Dominicana*. Santo Domingo: PLD, 1982.

64. Bravo-Elizondo, Pedro. "La gran huelga del salitre en 1907," in *Araucaria*, No. 33, Madrid, 1986.

65. Branford, Sue, and Oriel Glock. *The Last Frontier, Fighting Over Land in the Amazon*. London: Zed, 1985.

66. Brecht, Bertolt. *Diario de trabajo*. Buenos Aires: Nueva Visión, 1977.

67. Buarque de Holanda, Sérgio. *Visão do paraíso*. São Paulo: Universidad, 1969.

68. Buitrago, Alejandra. *Conversando con los gamines*. (Unpublished.)

69. Bullrich, Francisco, *et al. América Latina en su arquitectura*. Mexico City: Siglo XXI, 1983.

70. Buñuel, Luis. *Mi último suspiro (memorias).* Barcelona: Plaza y Janés, 1982.

71. ———. *Los olvidados.* Mexico City: Era, 1980.

72. Burgos, Elisabeth. *Me llamo Rigoberta Menchú y así me nació la conciencia.* Barcelona: Argos-Vergara, 1983.

73. Cabezas, Omar. *La montaña es algo más que una inmensa estepa verde.* Managua: Nueva Nicaragua, 1982.

74. Cabral, Sergio. *As escolas de samba: o quê, quem, como, quando e porquê.* Rio de Janeiro: Fontana, 1974.

75. ———. *Pixinguinha. Vida e obra.* Rio de Janeiro: Lidador, 1980.

76. Caputo, Alfredo. *Educación moral y cívica.* Montevideo: Casa del Estudiante, 1978. See also textbooks by Dora Noblía and Graciela Márquez, and by Sofía Corchs and Alex Pereyra Formoso.

77. Cardenal, Ernesto. *Antología.* Managua: Nueva Nicaragua, 1984.

78. Cárdenas, Lázaro. *Ideario político.* Mexico City: Era, 1976.

79. Cardona Pena, Alfredo. *El monstruo en el laberinto. Conversaciones con Diego Rivera.* Mexico City: Diana, 1980.

80. Cardoza y Aragón, Luis. *La nube y el reloj. Pintura mexicana contemporánea.* Mexico City, UNAM, 1940.

81. ———. *La revolución guatemalteca.* Mexico City: Cuadernos Americanos, 1955.

82. ———. *Diego Rivera. Los frescos en la Secretaría de Educación Pública.* Mexico City: SEP, 1980.

83. ———. *Orozco.* Mexico City: FCE, 1983.

84. Carías, Marco Virgilio, and Daniel Slutzky. *La guerra inútil. Análisis socio-económico del conflicto entre Honduras y El Salvador.* San José de Costa Rica: EDUCA, 1971.

85. Carpentier, Alejo. *Tientos y diferencias.* Montevideo: Arca, 1967.

86. ———. *La música en Cuba.* Havana: Letras Cubanas, 1979.

87. Carr, Raymond. *Puerto Rico: A Colonial Experiment.* New York: Vintage, 1984.

88. Casaus, Víctor. *Girón en la memoria.* Havana: Casa de las Américas. 1970.

89. Cassá, Roberto. *Capitalismo y dictadura.* Santo Domingo: Universidad, 1982.

90. Castro, Fidel. *La revolución cubana, 1953–1962.* Mexico City: Era, 1972.

91. ———. *Hoy somos un pueblo entero.* Mexico City: Siglo XXI, 1973.

92. Castro, Josué de. *Geografia da fome.* Rio de Janeiro: O Cruzeiro, 1946.

93. Cepeda Samudio, Álvaro. *La casa grande.* Buenos Aires: Jorge Álvarez, 1967.

94. Central Intelligence Agency. *Manuales de sabotaje y guerra psicológica*

para derrocar al gobierno sandinista. (Preface by Philip Agee.) Madrid: Fundamentos, 1985.

95. Cervantes Angulo, José. *La noche de las luciérnagas.* Bogotá: Plaza y Janés, 1980.

96. Céspedes, Augusto. *Sangre de mestizos. Relatos de la guerra del Chaco.* La Paz: Juventud, 1983.

97. ———. *El presidente colgado.* La Paz: Juventud, 1985.

98. "Cien años de lucha." Various authors, special edition of *Cuba*, Havana, October 1968.

99. Clark, Ronald William. *Edison: The Man Who Made the Future.* New York: Putnam, 1977.

100. Clase, Pablo. *Rubi. La vida de Porfirio Rubirosa.* Santo Domingo: Cosmos, 1979.

101. Crassweller, Robert D. *Trujillo. La tragica aventura del poder personal.* Barcelona: Bruguera, 1968.

102. Crawley, Eduardo. *Dictators Never Die: A Portrait of Nicaragua and the Somozas.* London: Hurst, 1979.

103. Colombres, Adolfo. *Seres sobrenaturales de la cultura popular argentina.* Buenos Aires: Del Sol, 1984.

104. Coluccio, Félix. *Diccionario folklórico argentino.* Buenos Aires: n.p., 1948.

105. Collier, James Lincoln. *Louis Armstrong: An American Genius.* New York: Oxford University Press, 1983.

106. Comisión Argentina por los Derechos Humanos. *Argentina: proceso al genocidio.* Madrid: Querejeta, 1977.

107. Comisión Nacional sobre la Desaparición de Personas. *Nunca más.* Buenos Aires: EUDEBA, 1984.

108. Committee on Foreign Relations, U.S. Senate. *Briefing on the Cuban Situation.* Washington, D.C., May 2, 1961.

109. Committee to Study Governmental Operations with Respect to Intelligence Activities, U.S. Senate. *Alleged Assassination Plots Involving Foreign Leaders: An Interim Report.* Washington, D.C., November 20, 1975.

110. Condarco Morales, Ramiro. *Zárate, el temible Willka. Historia de la rebelión indígena de 1899.* La Paz: n.p., 1982.

111. Condori Mamani, Gregorio. *De nosotros, los runas.* (Testimonies collected by Ricardo Valderrama and Carmen Escalante.) Madrid: Alfaguara, 1983.

112. Constantine, Mildred. *Tina Modotti. Una vida frágil.* Mexico City: FCE, 1979.

113. Cooke, Alistair. *America.* New York: Knopf, 1977.

114. Cordero Velásquez, Luis. *Gómez y las fuerzas vivas.* Caracas: Lumego, 1985.

115. Corrêa, Marcos Sá. *1964 visto e comentado pela Casa Branca*. Porto Alegre: L y PM, 1977.

116. Corretger, Juan Antonio. *Albizu Campos*. Montevideo: El Siglo Ilustrado, 1969.

117. Cueva, Gabriela de la. *Memorias de una caraqueña de antes del diluvio*. San Sebastián: n.p., 1982.

118. Cummins, Lejeune. *Don Quijote en burro*. Managua: Nueva Nicaragua, 1983.

119. Cunha, Euclides da. "A margem da história," in *Obra completa*. Rio de Janeiro: Aguilar, 1966.

120. Chandler, Billy Jaynes. *Lampião, o rei dos cangaceiros*. Rio de Janeiro: Paz e Terra, 1980.

121. Chaplin, Charles. *My Autobiography*. New York: Simon and Schuster, 1964.

122. Christensen, Eleanor Ingalls. *The Art of Haiti*. Philadelphia: Art Alliance, 1975.

123. Chumbita, Hugo. *Bairoletto. Prontuario y leyenda*. Buenos Aires: Marlona, 1974.

124. Daher, José Miguel. "Méndez: el Partido Demócrata de EE. UU. es socio de la sedición," in *La Mañana*, Montevideo, October 9, 1976.

125. Dalton, Roque. *Las historias prohibidas del Pulgarcito*. Mexico City: Siglo XXI, 1974.

126. ———. *Miguel Mármol. Los sucesos de 1932 en El Salvador*. Havana: Casa de las Américas, 1983.

127. ———. *Poesía*. (Mario Benedetti, ed.) Havana: Casa de las Américas, 1980.

128. Dardis, Tom. *Keaton: The Man Who Wouldn't Lie Down*. New York: Scribners, 1979.

129. Darío, Rubén. *Poesía*. (Preface by Angel Rama.) Caracas: Ayacucho, 1977.

130. Davies, Marion. *The Times We Had: Life With William Randolph Hearst*. Indianapolis and New York: Bobbs–Merrill, 1975.

131. Delgado Aparaín, Mario. "Mire que sos loco, Obdulio," in *Jaque*, Montevideo, January 25, 1985.

132. Deutscher, Isaac. *The Prophet Outcast: Trotsky, 1929–1940*. London: Oxford University Press, 1963.

133. Della Cava, Ralph. *Milagre em Joaseiro*. Rio de Janeiro: Paz e Terra, 1977.

134. *Diario de Juicio, El*. (Court record of trial of heads of Argentine dictatorship.) Buenos Aires: Perfil, 1985.

135. *El Nacional* and *Ultimas Noticias*, Caracas, August 28–29, 1977.

136. Dias, José Humberto. "Benjamin Abrahão, o mascate que filmou Lam-

pião," in *Cadernos de Pesquisa*, No. 1, Rio de Janeiro, Embrafilme, September 1984.

137. *Documentos de la CIA. Cuba acusa.* Havana: Ministerio de Cultura, 1981.

138. *Documentos secretos de la I.T.T.* Santiago de Chile: Quimantú, 1972.

139. Dorfman, Ariel, and Armand Mattelart. *Para leer al Pato Donald.* Mexico City: Siglo XXI, 1978.

140. Dower, John. *War Without Mercy: Race and Power in the Pacific War.* New York: Pantheon, 1986.

141. Dreifuss, René Armand. *1964: A conquista do Estado. Ação politica, poder e golpe de classe.* Petrópolis: Vozes, 1981.

142. Drot, Jean-Marie. *Journal de voyage chez les peintres de la Fête et du vaudou en Haiti.* Geneva: Skira, 1974.

143. Duhalde, Eduardo Luis. *El estado terrorista argentino.* Buenos Aires: El Caballito, 1983.

144. Dumont, Alberto Santos. *O que eu vi, o que nós veremos.* Rio de Janeiro: Tribunal de Contas, 1983.

145. Duncan, Isadora. *My Life.* New York: Liveright, 1955.

146. Durst, Rogério. *Madame Satã: com o diabo no corpo.* São Paulo: Brasiliense, 1985.

147. Eco, Umberto. *Apocalíptis e integrados ante la cultura de masas.* Barcelona: Lumen, 1968.

148. Edison, Thomas Alva. *Diary.* Old Greenwich: Chatham, 1971.

149. Edwards, Audrey, and Gary Wohl. *Muhammad Ali. The People's Champ.* Boston and Toronto: Little Brown, 1977.

150. Einstein, Albert. *Notas autobiográficas.* Madrid: Alianza, 1984.

151. Eisenstein, S. M. *¡Que viva México!.* (Preface by José de la Colina.) Mexico City: Era, 1971.

152. Elgrably, Jordan. "A través del fuego. Entrevista con James Baldwin," in *Quimera*, No. 41, Barcelona, 1984.

153. Enzensberger, Hans Magnus. *Política y delito.* Barcelona: Seix Barral, 1968.

154. Escobar Bethancourt, Rómulo. *Torrijos: ¡colonia americana, no!* Bogotá: Valencia, 1981.

155. Faingold, Raquel Zimerman de. *Memorias de una familia inmigrante.* (Unpublished.)

156. Fairbank, John K. *The United States and China.* Cambridge: Harvard University Press, 1958.

157. Fajardo Sainz, Humberto. *La herencia de la coca. Pasado y presente de la cocaína.* La Paz: Universo, 1984.

158. Falcão, Edgard de Cerqueira. *A incompreensão de uma época.* São Paulo: Tribunais, 1971.

159. Fals Borda, Orlando. *Historia doble de la Costa. Resistencia en el San Jorge*. Bogotá: Valencia, 1984.

160. ————. *Historia doble de la Costa. Retorno a la tierra*. Bogotá: Valencia, 1986.

161. Faría Castro, Haroldo and Flavia de. "Los mil y un sombreros de la cultura boliviana," in *Geomundo*, Vol. 8, No. 6, Santiago de Chile, June 1984.

162. Fast, Howard. *The Passion of Sacco and Vanzetti: A New England Legend*. Westport, Conn.: Greenwood, 1972.

163. Faulkner, William. *Absalom, Absalom*. New York: Modern Library, 1951.

164. Federación Universitaria de Córdoba. *La reforma universitaria*. Buenos Aires: FUBA, 1959.

165. Feinstein, Elaine. *Bessie Smith, Empress of the Blues*. New York: Viking, 1985.

166. Folino, Norberto. *Barceló, Ruggierito y el populismo oligárquico*. Buenos Aires: Falbo, 1966.

167. Foner, Philip S. *The Case of Joe Hill*. New York: International Publications, 1965.

168. Ford, Henry (with Samuel Crowther). *My Life and Work*. New York: Doubleday, 1926.

169. Foxley, A. *Experimentos neoliberales en América Latina*. Santiago de Chile: CIEPLAN, 1982.

170. Freyre, Gilberto. *Casa grande e senzala*. Rio de Janeiro: José Olympio, 1966.

171. Fróes, Leonardo. *A casa de flor*. Rio de Janeiro: Funarte, 1978.

172. Frontaura Argandoña, Manuel. *La revolución boliviana*. La Paz and Cochabama: Amigos del Libro, 1974.

173. Gabetta, Carlos. *Todos somos subversivos*. Buenos Aires: Bruguera, 1983.

174. Gaitán, Jorge Eliécer. *1928. La masacre de las bananeras*. Bogotá: Los Comuneros, n.d.

175. Galarza Zavala, Jaime. *Quiénes mataron a Roldós*. Quito: Solitierra, 1982.

176. Galasso, Norberto, *et al. La década infame*. Buenos Aires: Carlos Pérez, 1969.

177. Galíndez, Jesús. *La era de Trujillo*. Buenos Aires: Sudamericana, 1962.

178. Gálvez, Manuel. *Vida de Hipólito Yrigoyen*. Buenos Aires: Tor, 1951.

179. Gálvez, William. *Camilo, señor de la vanguardia*. Havana: Ciencias Sociales, 1979.

180. Gandarillas, Arturo G. "Detrás de linderos del odio: laimes y jucumanis," in *Hoy*, La Paz, October 16, 1973.

181. Garcés, Joan. *El estado y los problemas tácticos en el gobierno de Allende*. Mexico City: Siglo XXI, 1974.

182. García, F. Chris. *Chicano Politics: Readings*. New York: n.p., 1973.

183. García Canclini, Néstor. *Las culturas populares en el capitalismo*. Havana: Casa de las Américas, 1982.

184. García Lupo, Rogelio. "Mil trescientos dientes de Gardel," in *Marcha*, No. 1004, Montevideo, April 8, 1960.

185. ———. *Diplomacia secreta y rendición incondicional*. Buenos Aires: Legasa, 1983.

186. García Márquez, Gabriel. *La hojarasca*. Buenos Aires: Sudamericana, 1969.

187. ———. *Cien años de soledad*. Buenos Aires: Sudamericana, 1967.

188. ———. "Algo más sobre literatura y realidad," in *El País*, Madrid, July 1, 1981.

189. ———. "La soledad de la América Latina" (Nobel Prize acceptance speech), in *Casa*, No. 137, Havana, March–April 1983.

190. Garmendia, Hermann. *María Lionza, ángel y demonio*. Caracas: Seleven, 1980.

191. Garrido, Atilio. "Obdulio Varela. Su vida, su gloria y su leyenda," in *El Diario*, "Estrellas deportivas" supplement, Montevideo, September 20, 1977.

192. Gallegos Lara, Joaquín. *Las cruces sobre el agua*. Quito: El Conejo, 1985.

193. Gil, Pío. *El Cabito*. Caracas: Biblioteca de autores y temas tachirenses, 1971.

194. Gilly, Adolfo. *La revolución interrumpida*. Mexico City: El Caballito, 1971.

195. Gilman, Charlotte Perkins. *Herland*. (Preface by Ann J. Lane.) New York: Pantheon, 1979.

196. ———. *The Yellow Wallpaper*. New York: Feminist Press, 1973.

197. Goldman, Albert. *Elvis*. New York: McGraw-Hill, 1981.

198. Gómez Yera, Sara. "La rumba," in *Cuba*, Havana, December 1964.

199. González, José Luis. *El país de cuatro pisos y otros ensayos*. San Juan de Puerto Rico: Huracán, 1980.

200. González, Luis. *Pueblos en vilo*. Mexico City: FCE, 1984.

201. ———. *Historia de la Revolución Mexicana, 1934–1940: Los días del presidente Cárdenas*. Mexico City: Colegio de México, 1981.

202. González Bermejo, Ernesto. "Interview with Atahualpa Yupanqui," in *Crisis*, No. 29, Buenos Aires, September 1975.

203. ———. "¿Qué pasa hoy en el Perú?," in *Crisis*, No. 36, Buenos Aires, April 1976.

204. ———. *Las manos en el fuego*. Montevideo: Banda Oriental, 1985.

205. Granados, Pedro. *Carpas de México. Leyendas, anécdotas e historia del teatro popular.* Mexico City: Universo, 1984.

206. Grigulevich, José. *Pancho Villa.* Havana: Casa de las Américas, n.d.

207. Grupo, Areíto. *Contra viento y marea.* Havana: Casa de las Américas, 1978.

208. Guerra, Ramiro. *La expansión territorial de los Estados Unidos.* Havana: Ciencias Sociales, 1975.

209. Guevara, Ernesto Che. *Pasajes de la guerra revolucionaria.* Havana: Arte y Literatura, 1975.

210. ———. "Camilo, imagen del pueblo," in *Granma*, Havana, October 25, 1967.

211. ———. *El socialismo y el hombre nuevo.* Mexico City: Siglo XXI, 1977.

212. ———. *El diario del Che en Bolivia.* Bilbao: Zalla, 1968.

213. ———. *Escritos y discursos.* Havana: Ciencias Sociales, 1977.

214. Guiles, Fred Lawrence. *Norma Jean.* New York: McGaw-Hill, 1969.

215. Guillén, Nicolás. "Un olivo en la colina," in *Hoy*, Havana, April 24, 1960.

216. Guzmán, Martín Luis. *El águila y la serpiente.* Mexico City: Cía. General de Ediciones, 1977.

217. Guzmán Campos, Germán (with Orlando Fals Borda and Eduardo Umaña Luna). *La violencia en Colombia.* Bogotá: Valencia, 1980.

218. Hardwick, Richard. *Charles Richard Drew: Pioneer in Blood Research.* New York: Scribners, 1967.

219. Hellman, Lillian. *Scoundrel Time.* Boston: Little Brown, 1976.

220. Hemingway, Ernest. *Enviado especial.* Barcelona, Planeta, 1968.

221. Henault, Mirta. *Alicia Moreau de Justo.* Buenos Aires: Centro Editor, 1983.

222. Heras León, Eduardo. Interview with Miguel Mármol. (Unpublished.)

223. Hermann, Hamlet. *Francis Caamāno.* Santo Domingo: Alfa y Omega, 1983.

224. Herrera, Hayden. *Frida. A Biography of Frida Kahlo.* New York: Harper and Row, 1983.

225. Hervia Cosculluela, Manuel. *Pasaporte 11.333. Ocho años con la CIA.* Havana: Ciencias Sociales, 1978.

226. Hidrovo Velasquez, Horacio. *Un hombre y un río.* Portoviejo: Gregorio: 1982.

227. Hobsbawm, Eric J. *Primitive Rebels.* New York: Norton, 1965.

228. Hoffman, Banesh. *Einstein.* Barcelona: Salvat, 1984.

229. Huezo, Francisco. *Últimos días de Rubén Darío.* Managua: Renacimiento, 1925.

230. Huneeus, Pablo. *La cultura huachaca o el aporte de la televisión.* Santiago de Chile: Nueva Generación, 1981.

231. ———. *Lo comido y lo bailado*. . . . Santiago de Chile: Nueva Generación, 1984.

232. Hurt, Henry. *Reasonable Doubt: An Investigation into the Assassination of John F. Kennedy*. New York: Holt, Rinehart, and Winston, 1986.

233. Huxley, Francis. *The Invisibiles*. London: Hart-Davis, 1966.

234. Ianni, Octavio. *El Estado capitalista en la época de Cárdenas*. Mexico City: Era, 1985.

235. Informes sobre la violación de derechos humanos en el Uruguay, realizados por Amnesty International, la Comisión de Derechos Humanos y el Comité de Derechos Humanos de las Naciones Unidas y La Comisión Interamericana de Derechos Humanos de la OEA. [Accounts of the violation of human rights in Uruguay. Collected by Amnesty International; the Committee on Human Rights of the United Nations; and the Inter-American Commission on Human Rights of the OAS.]

236. Instituto de Edustios del Sandinismo. *Ni vamos a poder caminar de tantas flores*. (Testimonies of Sandino's soldiers; unpublished).

237. ———. *El sandinismo. Documentos básicos*. Managua: Nueva Nicaragua, 1983.

238. ———. *La insurrección popular sandinista en Masaya*. Managua: Nueva Nicaragua, 1982.

239. ———. *¡Y se armó la runga!* Managua: Nueva Nicaragua, 1982.

240. Jaramillo-Levi, Enrique, *et al. Una explosión en América: el canal de Panamá*. Mexico City: Siglo XXI, 1976.

241. Jenks, Leland H. *Nuestra colonia de Cuba*. Buenos Aires: Palestra, 1961.

242. Johnson, James Weldon. *Along This Way*. New York: Viking, 1933.

243. Jonas Bodenheimer, Susanne. *La ideología socialdemócrata en Costa Rica*. San José de Costa Rica: EDUCA, 1984.

244. Julião, Francisco, and Angélica Rodríguez. Testimony of Gregoria Zúñiga in "Los últimos soldados de Zapata," in *Crisis*, No. 21, Buenos Aires, January 1975.

245. Katz, Friedrich. *La servidumbre agraria en México en la época porfiriana*. Mexico City: Era, 1982.

246. ———. *La guerra secreta en México*. Mexico City: Era, 1983.

247. Kerr, Elizabeth M. *William Faulkner's Gothic Domain*. Port Washington, New York: Kennikat, 1979.

248. Klare, Michael T., and Nancy Stein. *Armas y poder en América Latina*. Mexico City: Era, 1978.

249. Kobal, John. *Rita Hayworth: The Time, the Place, and the Woman*. Norton, 1978.

250. Krehm, William. *Democracia y tiranías en el Caribe*. Buenos Aires: Palestra, 1959.

251. Labourt, José. *Sana, sana, culito de rana.* . . . Santo Domingo: Taller, 1979.
252. Landaburu, Jon, and Roberto Pineda. "Cuentos del diluvio de fuego," in *Maguaré*, No. 1, Bogotá, Universidad Nacional, June 1981.
253. Landes, Ruth. *A cidade das mulheres.* Rio de Janeiro: Civilização Brasileira, 1967.
254. Lane, Mark, and Dick Gregory. *Code Name Zorro: The Murder of Martin Luther King.* Englewood Cliffs, N.J.: Prentice-Hall, 1977.
255. Lapassade, Georges, and Marco Aurélio Luz. *O segredo da macumba.* Rio de Janeiro: Paz e Terra, 1972.
256. Larco, Juan. *et al. Recopilación de textos sobre José María Arguedas.* Havana: Casa de las Américas, 1976.
257. Latin America Bureau. *Narcotráfico y política.* Madrid: IEPALA, 1982.
258. Lauer, Mirko. *Crítica de la artesanía. Plástica y sociedad en los Andes peruanos.* Lima: DESCO, 1982.
259. La Valle, Raniero, and Linda Bimbi. *Marianella e i suoi fratelli. Una storia latinoamericana.* Milan: Feltrinelli, 1983.
260. Lavretski, I., and Adolfo Gilly. *Francisco Villa.* Mexico City: Macehual, 1978.
261. Levy, Alan. *Ezra Pound: The Voice of Silence.* Sag Harbor, N.Y.: Permanent, 1983.
262. Lichello, Robert. *Pioneer in Blood Plasma: Dr. Charles R. Drew.* New York: Messner, 1968.
263. Lima, Lourenço Moreira. *A coluna Prestes (marchas e combates).* São Paulo: Alfa-Omega, 1979.
264. Loetscher, Hugo. *El descubrimiento de Suiza por los indios.* Cochabamba: Amigos del Libro, 1983.
265. Loor, Wilfrido. *Eloy Alfaro.* Quito: n.p., 1982.
266. López, Oscar Luis. *La radio en Cuba.* Havana: Letras Cubanas, 1981.
267. López, Santos. *Memorias de un soldado.* Managua: FER, 1974.
268. López Virgil, José Ignacio. *Radio Pío XII: una mina de coraje.* Quito: Aler/Pío XII, 1984.
269. Lowenthal, Abraham F. *The Dominican Intervention.* Cambridge: Harvard University Press, 1972.
270. Luna, Félix. *Atahualpa Yupanqui.* Madrid: Júcar, 1974.
271. Machado, Carlos. *Historia de los orientales.* Montevideo: Banda Oriental, 1985.
272. Magalhães Júnior, R. *Rui. O homem e o mito.* Rio de Janeiro: Civilização Brasileira, 1964.
273. Maggiolo, Oscar J. "Política de desarrollo científico y tecnológico de América Latina," in *Gaceta de la Universidad*, Montevideo, March–April 1968.
274. Mailer, Norman. *Marilyn.* New York: Grossett and Dunlap, 1973.

275. Maldonado-Denis, Manuel. *Puerto Rico: mito y realidad*. San Juan de Puerto Rico: Antillana, 1969.
276. Manchester, William. *The Glory and the Dream: A Narrative History of America*. Boston: Little Brown, 1972.
277. Mariátegui, José Carlos. *Obras*. Havana: Casa de las Américas, 1982.
278. Marín, Germán. *Una historia fantástica y calculada: la CIA en el país de los chilenos*. Mexico City: Siglo XXI, 1976.
279. Mário Filho. *O negro no futebol brasileiro*. Rio de Janeiro: Civilização Brasileira, 1964.
280. Mariz, Vasco. *Heitor Villa-Lobos, compositor brasileiro*. Rio de Janeiro: Zahar, 1983.
281. Martin, John Bartlow. *El destino dominicano. La crisis dominicana desde la caída de Trujillo hasta la guerra civil*. Santo Domingo: Editora Santo Domingo, 1975.
282. Martínez, Thomas M. "Advertising and Racism: The Case of the Mexican-American," in *El Grito*, Summer 1969.
283. Martínez Assad, Carlos. *El laboratorio de la revolución: el Tabasco garridista*. Mexico City: Siglo XXI, 1979.
284. Martínez Moreno, Carlos. "Color del 900," in *Capítulo oriental*. Montevideo: CEDAL, 1968.
285. Matos, Cláudia. *Acertei no milhar. Samba e malandragem no tempo de Getúlio*. Rio de Janeiro: Paz e Terra, 1982.
286. Matos Díaz, Eduardo. *Anecdotario de una tiranía*. Santo Domingo: Taller, 1976.
287. Mattelart, Armand. *La cultura como empresa multinacional*. Mexico City: Era, 1974.
288. May, Stacy, and Galo Plaza. *United States Business Performance Abroad: The Case Study of United Fruit Company in Latin America*. Washington, D.C.: National Planning, 1958.
289. Medina Castro, Manuel. *Estados Unidos y América Latina, siglo XIX*. Havana: Casa de las Américas, 1968.
290. Mella, Julio Antonio. *Escritos revolucionarios*. Mexico City: Siglo XXI, 1978.
291. Mende, Tibor. *La Chine et son ombre*. Paris: Seuil, 1960.
292. Méndez Capote, Renée. *Memorias de una cubanita que nació con el siglo*. Santa Clara (de Cuba): Universidad, 1963.
293. Mendoza, Vincente T. *El corrido mexicano*. Mexico City: FCE, 1976.
294. Mera, Juan León. *Cantares del pueblo ecuatoriano*. Quito: Banco Central, n.d.
295. Métraux, Alfred. *Haiti. La terre, les hommes et les dieux*. Neuchâtel: La Baconnière, 1957.
296. Meyer, Eugenia. Interview with Juan Olivera López. (Unpublished.)

297. Meyer, Jean. *La cristiada. La guerra de los cristeros.* Mexico City: Siglo XXI, 1973.

298. Molina, Gabriel. *Diario de Girón.* Havana: Política, 1983.

299. Monsiváis, Carlos. *Días de guardar.* Mexico City: Era, 1970.

300. ———. *Amor perdido.* Mexico City: Era, 1977.

301. Mora, Arnoldo. *Monseñor Romero.* San José de Costa Rica: EDUCA, 1981.

302. Morais, Fernando. *Olga.* São Paulo: Alfa-Omega, 1985.

303. Morel, Edmar. *A revolta da chibata.* Rio de Janeiro: Graal, 1979.

304. Morison, Samuel E., and Henry S. Commager. *A Concise History of the American Republic.* New York: Oxford University Press, 1977.

305. Moussinac, Léon. *Sergei Michailovitch Eisenstein.* Paris: Seghers, 1964.

306. Mota, Carlos Guilherme. *Ideologia da cultura brasileira, 1933–1974.* São Paulo: Ática, 1980.

307. Maurão Filho, Olympio. *Memórias: a verdade de um revolucionário.* Porto Alegre: L y PM, 1978.

308. Murúa, Dámaso. *En Brasil crece un almendro.* Mexico City: El Caballito, 1984.

309. ———. *40 cuentos del Güilo Mentiras.* Mexico City: Crea, 1984.

310. Nalé Roxlo, Conrado, and Mabel Mármol. *Genio y figura de Alfonsina Storni.* Buenos Aires: EUDEBA, 1966.

311. Navarro, Marysa. *Evita.* Buenos Aires: Corregidor, 1981.

312. Nepomuceno, Eric. *Hemingway: Madrid no era una fiesta.* Madrid: Altalena, 1978.

313. Neruda, Pablo. *Confieso que he vivido.* Barcelona: Seix Barral, 1974.

314. ———. *Obras completas.* Buenos Aires: Losada, 1973.

315. Niemeyer, Oscar. Texts, drawings, and photos in a special edition of *Módulo,* Rio de Janeiro, June 1983.

316. Nimuendajú, Curt. *Mapa etno-histórico.* Rio de Janeiro: Fundaçao Nacional Pró-Memória, 1981.

317. Nosiglia, Julio E. *Botín de guerra.* Buenos Aires: Tierra Fértil, 1985.

318. Novo, Salvador. *Cocina mexicana. Historia gastronómica de la ciudad de México.* Mexico City: Porrúa, 1979.

319. Núñez Jiménez, Antonio. *Wifredo Lam.* Havana: Letras Cubanas, 1982.

320. Núñez Téllez, Carlos. *Un pueblo en armas.* Managua: FSLN, 1980.

321. O'Connor, Harvey. *La crisis mundial del petróleo.* Buenos Aires: Platina, 1963.

322. Olmo, Rosa del. *Los chigüines de Somoza.* Caracas: Ateneo, 1980.

323. Orozco, José Clemente. *Autobiografía.* Mexico: Era, 1979.

324. Ortiz, Fernando. *Los bailes y el teatro de los negros en el folklore de Cuba.* Havana: Letras Cubanas, 1981.

325. Ortiz Echagüe, Fernando. "Sobre la importancia de la vaca argentina

en París." Originally published in 1930; republished by Rogelio García Lupo in *Crisis*," No. 29, Buenos Aires, September 1975.

326. Ortiz Letelier, Fernando. *El movimiento obrero en Chile. Antecedentes 1891–1919*. Madrid: Michay, 1985.

327. Page, Joseph A. *Perón*. Buenos Aires: Vergara, 1984.

328. Paleari, Antonio. *Diccionario mágico jujeño*. San Salvador de Jujuy: Pachamama, 1982.

329. Paliza, Héctor. "Los burros fusilados," in *Presagio*, Culiacán, Sinaloa, No. 10, April 1978.

330. Paoli, Francisco J., and Enrique Montalvo. *El socialismo olvidado de Yucatán*. Mexico City: Siglo XXI, 1980.

331. Paramio, Ludolfo. *Mito e ideología*. Madrid: Corazón, 1971.

332. Pareja Diezcanseco, Alfredo. *Ecuador. La república de 1830 a nuestros días*. Quito: Universidad, 1979.

333. Pareja y Paz Soldán, José. *Juan Vicente Gómez. Un fenómeno telúrico*. Caracas: Ávila Gráfica, 1951.

334. Parra, Violeta. *Violeta del pueblo*. (Javier Martínez Reverte, ed.) Madrid: Visor, 1983.

335. Pasley, F. D. *Al Capone*. (Preface by Andrew Sinclair.) Madrid: Alianza, 1970.

336. Payeras, Mario. *Los días de la selva*. Havana: Casa de las Américas, 1981.

337. Peña Bravo, Raúl. *Hecos y dichos del general Barrientos*. La Paz: n.p., 1982.

338. Pérez, Ponciana (known as Chana la Vieja). Public testimony in *Cuba*, Havana, May–June 1970.

339. Pérez Valle, Eduardo. *El martirio del héroe. La muerte de Sandino*. Managua: Banco Central, 1980.

340. Perlman, Janice, E. *O mito da marginalidade. Favelas e política no Rio de Janeiro*. Rio de Janeiro: Paz e Terra, 1981.

341. Perón, Juan Domingo. *Tres revoluciones militares*. Buenos Aires: Síntesis, 1974.

342. Pineda, Virginia Gutiérriz de, *et al. El gamín*. Bogotá: UNICEF/Instituto Colombiano de Bienestar Familiar, 1978.

343. Pinto, L. A. Costa. *Lutas de famílias no Brasil*. São Paulo: Editora Nacional, 1949.

344. Pocaterra, José Rafael. *Memorias de un venezolano de la decadencia*. Caracas: Monte Ávila, 1979.

345. Politzer, Patricia. *Miedo en Chile*. (Testimonies of Moy de Tohá and others.) Santiago de Chile: CESOC, 1985.

346. Pollak-Eltz, Angelina. "María Lionza, mito y culto venezolano," in *Montalbán*, No. 2, Caracas, UCAB, 1973.

347. Poniatowska, Elena. *La noche de Tlatelolco*. Mexico City: Era, 1984.

348. Portela, Fernando, and Cláudio Bojunga. *Lampião. O cangaceiro e o outro*. São Paulo: Traço, 1982.

349. Pound, Ezra, *Selected Cantos*. New York: New Directions, 1970.

350. Powers, Thomas. *The Man Who Kept the Secrets: Richard Helms and the CIA*. New York: Knopf, 1979.

351. Presidency of the Republic of Haiti. Law of April 29, 1969. Palais National, Port-au-Prince.

352. Queiroz, María Isaura Pereira de. *Os cangaceiros*. São Paulo: Duas Cidades, 1977.

353. ———. *História do cangaço*. São Paulo: Global, 1982.

354. Querejazu Calvo, Roberto, *Masamaclay. Historia política, diplomática y militar de la guerra del Chaco*. Cochabamba and La Paz: Amigos del Libro, 1981.

355. Quijano, Aníbal. *Introducción a Mariátegui*. Mexico City: Era, 1982.

356. Quijano, Carlos. Various articles from *Cuadernos de Marcha*, Mexico City and Montevideo: CEUAL, 1984–85.

357. Quiroga, Horacio. *Selección de cuentos*. (Preface by Emir Rodríguez Monegal.) Montevideo: Ministerio de Instrucción Pública, 1966.

358. ———. *Sobre literatura*. (Preface by Roberto Ibáñez.) Montevideo: Arca, 1970.

359. Quiroz Otero, Ciro. *Vallenato. Hombre y canto*. Bogotá: Icaro, 1983.

360. Rama, Ángel. *Las máscaras democráticas del modernismo*. Montevideo: Fundación Ángel Rama, 1985.

361. Ramírez, Sergio, ed. *Augusto C. Sandino. El pensamiento vivo*. Managua: Nueva Nicaragua, 1984.

362. ———. *Estás en Nicaragua*. Barcelona: Muchnik, 1985.

363. Ramírez, Pedro Felipe. *La vida maravillosa del Siervo de Dios*. Caracas: n.p., 1985.

364. Ramos, Graciliano. *Memórias do cárcere*. Rio de Janeiro: José Olympio, 1954.

365. Ramos, Jorge Abelardo. *Revolución y contrarevolución en la Argentina*. Buenos Aires: Plus Ultra, 1976.

366. Rangel, Domingo Alberto. *Gómez, el amo del poder*. Caracas: Vadell, 1980.

367. Recinos, Adrián, trans. *Popol Vuh. Las antiguas historias del Quiché*. Mexico City: FCE, 1976.

368. Reed, John. *Insurgent Mexico*. New York: Simon and Schuster, 1969.

369. Rendón, Armando B. *Chicano manifesto*. New York: Macmillan, 1971.

370. Rengifo, Antonio. "Esbozo biográfico de Ezequiel Urviola y Rivero," in *Los movimientos campesinos en el Perú, 1879–1965*. Lima: Delva, 1977.

371. *Retrato do Brasil*. (Various authors.) São Paulo: Tres, 1984.

372. See 445a.

373. Revueltas, José. *México 68: Juventud y revolución*. Mexico City, Era, 1978.

374. Ribeiro, Berta G. "O mapa etno-histórico de Curt Nimuendajú," in *Revista de Antropologia*, Vol. XXV, São Paulo: Universidad, 1982.

375. Ribeiro, Darcy. *Os índios e a civilização*. Petrópolis: Vozes, 1982.

376. ———. Reception Speech on the Occasion of Receiving Doctorate honoris causa at the University of Paris VII, May 3, 1979; in *Módulo*, Rio de Janeiro, 1979.

377. ———. *Ensaios insólitos*. Porto Alegre: L y PM, 1979.

378. ———. *Aos trancos e barrancos. Como o Brasil deu no que deu*. Rio de Janeiro: Guanabara, 1986.

379. Rivera, Jorge B. "Discépolo," in *Cuadernos de Crisis*, No. 3, Buenos Aires, December 1973.

380. Roa Bastos, Augusto. *Hijo de hombre*. Buenos Aires: Losada, 1960.

381. Robeson, Paul. *Paul Robeson Speaks*. (Edited and with preface by Philip S. Foner.) Secaucus: Citadel, 1978.

382. Robinson, David. *Buster Keaton*. Bloomington: University of Indiana Press, 1970.

383. ———. *Chaplin: His Life and Art*. London: Collins, 1985.

384. Rockefeller, David. Letter to Gen. Jorge Rafael Videla, in *El Periodista*, No. 71, Buenos Aires, January 17–23, 1986.

385. Rodman, Selden. *Renaissance in Haiti: Popular Painters in the Black Republic*. New York: Pellegrini and Cudahy, 1948.

386. Rodó, José Enrique. *Ariel*. Madrid: Espasa-Calpe, 1971.

387. Rodríguez, Antonio. *A History of Mexican Mural Painting*. London: Thames and Hudson, 1969.

388. Rodríguez, Carlos. "Astiz el ángel exterminador," in *Madres de Plaza de Mayo*, No. 2, Buenos Aires, January 1985.

389. Rodríguez Monegal, Emir. *Sexo y poesía en el 900*. Montevideo: Alfa, 1969.

390. ———. *El desterrado. Vida y obra de Horacio Quiroga*. Buenos Aires: Losada, 1968.

391. Roeder, Ralph. *Hacia el México moderno: Porfirio Díaz*. Mexico City: FCE, 1973.

392. Rojas, Marta. *El que debe vivir*. Havana: Casa de las Américas, 1978.

393. Román, José. *Maldito país*. Managua: El pez y la serpiente, 1983.

394. Rosencof, Mauricio. Statement to Mercedes Ramírez and Laura Oreggioni, in *Asamblea*, No. 38, Montevideo, April 1985.

395. Rovere, Richard H. *Senator Joe McCarthy*. New York: Harcourt Brace Jovanovich, 1959.

396. Rowles, James. *El conflicto Honduras–El Salvador y el orden jurídico internacional*. San José de Costa Rica: EDUCA, 1980.

397. Rozitchner, León. *Moral burguesa y revolución*. Buenos Aires: Procyón, 1963.

398. Ruffinelli, Jorge. *El otro México. México en la obra de Traven, Lawrence y Lowry*. Mexico City: Nueva Imagen, 1978.

399. Rugama, Leonel. *La tierra es un satélite de la luna*. Managua: Nueva Nicaragua, 1983.

400. Rulfo, Juan. *Pedro Páramo* and *El llano en llamas*. Barcelona: Planeta, 1982.

401. Saia, Luiz Henrique. *Carmen Miranda*. São Paulo: Brasiliense, 1984.

402. Salamanca, Daniel. *Documentos para una historia de la guerra del Chaco*. La Paz: Don Bosco, 1951.

403. Salazar, Ruben. Articles in *Los Angeles Times*, February–August 1970.

404. Salazar Valiente, Mario. "El Salvador: crisis, dictadura, lucha, 1920–1980," in *América Latina: historia de medio siglo*. Mexico City: Siglo XXI, 1981.

405. Salvatierra, Sofonías. *Sandino o la tragedia de un pueblo*. Madrid: Talleres Europa, 1934.

406. Samper Pizano, Ernesto, *et al. Legalización de la marihuana*. Bogotá: Tercer Mundo, 1980.

407. Sampson, Anthony. *The Sovereign State of ITT*. Greenwich, Conn., Fawcett, 1974.

408. Sánchez, Gonzalo, and Donny Meertens. *Bandoleros, gamonales y campesinos. El caso de la violencia en Colombia*. Bogotá: El Áncora, 1983.

409. Sante, Luc. "Relic," in *The New York Review of Books*, Vol. 28, No. 20, New York, December 17, 1981.

410. Saume Barrios, Jesús. *Silleta de cuero*. Caracas: n.p., 1985.

411. Schaden, Egon. "Curt Nimuendajú. Quarenta anos a serviço do índio brasileiro e ao estudo de suas culturas," in *Problemas brasileiros*, São Paulo, December 1973.

412. Scalabrini Ortiz, Raúl. *El hombre que está solo y espera*. Buenos Aires: Plus Ultra, 1964.

413. Schinca, Milton. *Boulevard Sarandí. Anécdotas, gentes, sucesos, del pasado montevideano*. Montevideo: Banda Oriental, 1979.

414. Schifter, Jacobo. *La fase oculta de la guerra civil en Costa Rica*. San José de Costa Rica: EDUCA, 1981.

415. Schlesinger, Arthur M. *The Thousand Days: John F. Kennedy in the White House*. Boston: Houghton Mifflin, 1965.

416. Schlesinger, Stephen, and Stephen Kinzer. *Bitter Fruit: The Untold Story of the American Coup in Guatemala*. New York: Anchor, 1983.

417. Sebreli, Juan José. *Eva Perón: ¿aventurera o militante?*. Buenos Aires: Siglo Veinte, 1966.

418. Séjourné, Laurette. *Supervivencias de un mundo mágico*. Mexico: FCE, 1953.

419. Selser, Gregorio. *El pequeño ejército loco*. Managua: Nueva Nicaragua, 1983.

420. ———. *El guatemalazo*. Buenos Aires: Iguazú, 1961.

421. ———. *¡Aquí, Santo Domingo! La tercera guerra sucia*. Buenos Aires: Palestra, 1966.

422. ———. "A veinte años del Moncada," in *Cuadernos de Marcha*, No. 72, Montevideo, July 1973.

423. ———. *El rapto de Panamá*. San José de Costa Rica: EDUCA, 1982.

424. Senna, Orlando. *Alberto Santos Dumont*. São Paulo: Brasiliense, 1984.

425. Serpa, Phoción. *Oswaldo Cruz. El Pasteur del Brasil, vencedor de la fiebre amarilla*. Buenos Aires: Claridad, 1945.

426. Silva, Clara. *Genio y figura de Delmira Agustini*. Buenos Aires: EUDEBA, 1968.

427. Silva, José Dias da. *Brasil, país ocupado*. Rio de Janeiro: Record, 1963.

428. Silva, Marília T. Barboza da, and Arthur L. de Oliveira Filho. *Cartola. Os tempos idos*. Rio de Janeiro: Funarte, 1983.

429. Silveira, Cid. *Café: um drama na economia nacional*. Rio de Janeiro: Civilização Brasileira, 1962.

430. Slosser, Bob. *Reagan Inside Out*. New York: World Books, 1984.

431. Smith, Earl E. T. *El cuarto piso. Relato sobre la revolución comunista de Castro*. Mexico City: Diana, 1963.

432. Sodré, Nelson Werneck. *Oscar Niemeyer*. Rio de Janeiro: Graal, 1978.

433. ———. *História militar do Brasil*. Rio de Janeiro: Civilização Brasileira, 1965.

434. Somoza Debayle, Anastasio. *Filosofía social*. (Armando Luna Sulva, ed.) Managua: Presidencia de la República, 1976.

435. Sorensen, Theodore C. *Kennedy*. New York: Harper and Row, 1965.

436. Souza, Tárik de. *O som nosso de cada dia*. Porto Alegre: L y PM, 1983.

437. Stock, Noel. *Poet in Exile: Ezra Pound*. New York: Barnes and Noble, 1964.

438. Stone, Samuel. *La dinastía de los conquistadores. La crisis del poder en la Costa Rica contemporánea*. San José de Costa Rica: EDUCA, 1982.

439. Suárez, Roberto. Statements to *El Diario* and *Hoy*, La Paz, July 3, 1983.

440. Subercaseau, Bernardo (with Patricia Stambuk and Jaime Londoño). *Violeta Parra: Gracias a la vida. Testimonios*. Buenos Aires: Galerna, 1985.

441. Taibo, Paco Ignacio II, and Roberto Vizcaíno. *El socialismo en un solo puerto, Acapulco, 1919–1923*. Mexico City: Extemporáneos, 1983.

442. Teitelboim, Volodia. *Neruda*. Madrid: Michay, 1984.

443. Tello, Antonio, and Gonzalo Otero Pizarro. *Valentino, La seducción manipulada*. Barcelona: Bruguera, 1978.
444. Tibol, Raquel. *Frida Kahlo. Crónica, testimonio y aproximaciones*. Mexico City: Cultura Popular, 1977.
445. *Time Capsule, 1927: A History of the Year Condensed from the Pages of Time*. New York: Time-Life, 1928.
445a. *Time*. "High on Cocaine: A $30 Billion U.S. Habit," July 6, 1981.
446. Toqo. *Indiomanual*. Humahuaca: Instituto de Cultura Indígena, 1985.
447. Toriello, Guillermo. *La batalla de Guatemala*. Mexico City: Cuadernos Americanos, 1955.
448. Torres, Camilo. *Cristianismo y revolución*. Mexico City: Era, 1970.
449. Touraine, Alain. *Vida y muerte del Chile popular*. Mexico City: Siglo XXI, 1974.
450. Tribunal Permanente de los Pueblos. *El caso Guatemala*. Madrid: IEP-ALA, 1984.
451. Turner, John Kenneth. *Barbarous Mexico*. Austin: Univesity of Texas Press, 1969.
452. Universidad Nacional de Río Cuarto, Córdoba, Argentina. Resolution No. 0092 of February 22, 1977, signed by rector Eduardo José Pesoa; in *Soco Soco*, No. 2, Río Cuarto, April 1986.
453. Valcárcel, Luis E. *Machu Picchu*. Buenos Aires: EUDEBA, 1964.
454. Valle-Castillo, Julio. Introduction to Rubén Darío, *Prosas políticas*. Managua: Ministerio de Cultura, 1983.
455. Vásquez Díaz, Rubén. *Bolivia a la hora del Che*. Mexico City: Siglo XXI, 1968.
456. Vásquez Lucio, Oscar E. (Siulnas). *Historia del humor gráfico y escrito en la Argentina, 1801–1939*. Buenos Aires: EUDEBA, 1985.
457. Vélez, Julio, and A. Merino. *España en César Vallejo*. Madrid: Fundamentos, 1984.
458. Viezzer, Moema. *Si me permiten hablar: testimonio de Domitila, una mujer de las minas de Bolivia*. Mexico City: Siglo XXI, 1978.
459. Vignar, Maren. "Los ojos de los pájaros." In Maren and Marcelo Vignar, *Exilio y tortura*. (Unpublished.)
460. Waksman Schinca, Daniel, *et al. La batalla de Nicaragua*. Mexico City: Bruguera, 1980.
461. Walsh, Rodolfo. Letter to the Military Junta, in *Operación masacre*. Buenos Aires: De la Flor, 1984.
462. Weinstein, Barbara. *The Amazon Rubber Boom, 1850–1920*. Stanford: Stanford University Press, 1983.
463. Wettstein, Germán. "La tradición de la Paradura del Niño," in *Geomundo* (special edition on Venezuela), Panama City: 1983.
464. White, Judith. *Historia de una ignominia: La United Fruit Company en Colombia*. Bogotá: Presencia, 1978.

465. Wise, David, and Thomas B. Ross. *The Invisible Government.* New York: Random House, 1964.
466. Witker, Alejandro. *Salvador Allende, 1908–1973. Prócer de la liberación nacional.* Mexico City: UNAM, 1980.
467. Woll, Allen L. *The Latin Image in American Film.* Los Angeles: UCLA Press, 1977.
468. Womack, John, Jr. *Zapata and the Mexican Revolution.* New York: Knopf, 1968.
469. Wyden, Peter. *Bay of Pigs: The Untold Story.* New York: Simon and Schuster, 1980.
470. Ycaza, Patricio. *Historia del movimiento obrero ecuatoriano.* Quito: Cedime, 1984.
471. Ydígoras Fuentes, Miguel (with Mario Rosenthal). *My War with Communism.* Englewood Cliffs, N.J.: Prentice-Hall, 1963.
472. Yupanqui, Atahualpa. *Aires indios.* Buenos Aires: Siglo Veinte, 1985.
473. Zavaleta Mercado, René. *El desarrollo de la conciencia nacional.* Montevideo: Diálogo, 1967.
474. ———. "Consideraciones generales sobre la historia de Bolivia, 1932–1971." In *América Latina: historia de medio siglo,* (various authors). Mexico City: Siglo XXI, 1982.
475. ———. "El estupor de los siglos," in *Quimera* No. 1, Cochabamba, September 1985.